CREDITS

Creators of the Iron Kingdoms
Brian Snoddy
Matthew D. Wilson

Project Director
Bryan Cutler

Creative Director
Ed Bourelle

Game Design
Jason Soles
Matthew D. Wilson

Additional Development
Simon Berman
Ed Bourelle
David Carl
William Schoonover
William Shick
Brent Waldher

Continuity
Jason Soles
Douglas Seacat

Writers
Simon Berman
Douglas Seacat
Jason Soles

Additional Writing
Ed Bourelle
Aeryn Rudel
William Schoonover
William Shick
Brent Waldher

Editors
Bryan Cutler
Darla Kennerud
Michele Carter

Graphic Design Director
Josh Manderville

Graphic Design
Matt Ferbrache
Laine Garret
Josh Manderville

Art Director
Chris Walton

Cover Art
Néstor Ossandón

Illustrators
Chris Bourassa
Carlos Cabrera
Chippy
Alberto Dal Lago
Brian Despain
Mariusz Gandzel
Sean Murray
Marek Okon
Néstor Ossandón
Mateusz Ozminski
Miro Petrov
Karl Richardson
Greg Smith
Brian Snoddy
Florian Stitz
Kieth Thompson
Andrea Uderzo
Chris Walton
White Moon Dreams
Matthew D. Wilson

Firearms Consultant
Erik-Jason Yaple

Language Consultant
William Movish

Internal Playtesters
Oren Ashkenazi
Leo Carson
Phil Chinzi
Jack Coleman
Bryan Cutler
Cody Ellis
Matt Ferbrache
Dianne Ferrer
Bill French
Laine Garrett
William Hungerford
Jen Ikuta
Adam Johnson
Tony Konichek
Lyle Lowery
Josh Manderville
Meg Maples
Jason Martin
Aeryn Rudel
Ben Sanders
Nate Scott
Douglas Seacat
Chris Walton
Matt Warren

External Playtesters
Ray Bailey
Chris Bodan
Dan Brandt
Erik Breidenstein
Todd Crow
Brad Casey

Lane Daughtry
Mike Fehlauer
Logan Fisher
Stephen Forston
Peter Gaublomme
William Hayes
Jerry Holkins
Mike Krahulik
Stu Liming
Jeff Long
Rob Miles
James Moreland
Craig Poche
Josh Saulter
Derek Scott, Jr.
Tim Simpson
Jennifer Smith
Kiko Villaseñor
Jason Wolf
Anthony Woods

Print Management
Shona Fahland

Proofreaders
Simon Berman
Ed Bourelle
David Carl
Alex Chobot
Lauren Cutler
Shona Fahland
Lyle Lowery
William Schoonover
Douglas Seacat
William Shick
Brent Waldher

Visit: www.privateerpress.com

Privateer Press, Inc. 13434 NE 16th St. Suite 120 • Bellevue, WA 98005
Tel (425) 643-5900 • Fax (425) 643-5902

For online customer service, email frontdesk@privateerpress.com

Second printing: October 2012. Printed in China.

Iron Kingdoms Full Metal Fantasy Roleplaying Game Core Rules . . . . ISBN: 978-1-933362-89-2 . . . . PIP 405

TABLE OF CONTENTS

FULL METAL FANTASY ROLEPLAYING

A NOTE TO OUR FANS, OLD AND NEW

Soon after our humble beginnings over a decade ago, Privateer Press introduced the roleplaying community to the Iron Kingdoms through the *Witchfire Trilogy.* This epic three-part adventure thrust players into a world where steam and sorcery are found alongside blades and blasting powder in what we affectionately called Full Metal Fantasy. The Iron Kingdoms RPG was born in that grand adventure, and with it we created a lasting legacy we later expanded with our flagship miniatures games WARMACHINE and HORDES. While those games have continued to expand and explore the vast setting of the Iron Kingdoms, we never stopped wanting to return to the personal and individual exploration the original RPG offered adventurers.

This book is the culmination of over ten years of developing the rich cultures, diverse peoples, and vivid world that make up the Iron Kingdoms. Just as WARMACHINE and HORDES owe much of their foundation to the Iron Kingdoms RPG, so now does the new edition of the RPG owe its foundation to the huge amount of effort we have lovingly poured into the miniatures games. Not only has our journey through the Iron Kingdoms in WARMACHINE and HORDES increased the scope and understanding of the setting, the award-winning game mechanics of those systems also provided a strong foundation for how the new Iron Kingdoms RPG plays. Veterans of WARMACHINE and HORDES will recognize many of the core concepts of combat and challenge resolution, while new players will find these ideas easy to grasp yet full of strategic possibility.

At its core, the Iron Kingdoms RPG is about heroic individuals doing suitably heroic deeds. The feat point system gives players the chance to perform feats of strength and skill worthy of song and story. Players earn feat points by being heroic, so everyone is encouraged to play to his character's utmost potential. The Iron Kingdoms is home to a wealth of interesting heroes and villains. While designing the character creation portion of this book, we quickly realized a single class choice could never represent the myriad character possibilities that fill the pages of our books. The innovative career system introduced here allows players to mix and match various careers and archetypes to capture their character perfectly. From Warcaster Pirate to Gun Mage Aristocrat, the dual career system provides the flexibility to cover a huge range of possible characters.

Whether you cut your teeth on the *Witchfire Trilogy,* took up arms in the battles of WARMACHINE and HORDES, or are a new recruit, welcome to a new era of adventure in the Iron Kingdoms!

WHAT IS A ROLEPLAYING GAME?

A roleplaying game is a collaborative storytelling experience that is not only fun and rewarding but also memorable and enjoyable again upon future reflection. It takes place in the imagination of the players, where a set of rules provides the framework for resolving conflict. Players take on the roles of characters in the game, with one player acting as the Game Master. The Game Master crafts a story for the other players to experience. He narrates the action, plays all the characters not controlled by another player, and describes what players see as the game unfolds. As the story unfolds, the players act in unexpected ways to create a fun, engaging, and memorable experience for everyone involved.

The characters the players control are not merely inhabitants of the Iron Kingdoms. They are also heroes and adventurers with the skills to survive—and possibly to help shape the world around them. They are exceptional people who do remarkable things.

The character is a player's alter ego in the game. Players create their own characters and decide how they will develop through play. Players react to the events of the game by directing the actions of their characters. When determining if a character's actions are successful, they roll dice and refer to the stats and abilities of the character.

Though the game chiefly takes place in the minds of its participants, there are times (most often combat encounters) when the action of the game moves to the table top, where characters and their adversaries are represented by 32 mm scale models. The rules for combat in this book are written to utilize miniatures for combat in this way, and a large variety of miniatures are available from Privateer Press for this purpose.

Unlike board or card games, there is no winner or loser at the end of a roleplaying game. Instead, the purpose of the game is to enjoy the experience and tell a great story. Whether they succeed or fail, prosper or perish, your characters will play a central role in multiple adventures.

WHAT YOU NEED TO PLAY

You only need a few things before you can begin adventuring in the Iron Kingdoms. In addition to this book, you need a small group of people. One person needs to take on the Game Master duties, and then you need players to control the heroes of the story. A typical game will include one Game Master and between two and six players, with the ideal group size being four or five players.

Each player needs a character sheet for tracking the abilities, skills, and advancement of his character. You can track this information any way you prefer, but we've included a character sheet at the end of this book (p. 349) for you to photocopy and use. To maximize your enjoyment of combat encounters, you will want a 32 mm scale model to represent each character, a tape measure or ruler marked in inches to measure movement and attack ranges, and a few six-sided dice. Six will be plenty to cover all your needs.

The Game Master will need a table or playing surface where he can set up or draw the playing field, and it's a good idea to have a handful of tokens to help you keep track of things during the game.

HOW LONG THE GAME WILL LAST

The beauty of a roleplaying game is that it lasts as long as you want it to. It all depends on the story the Game Master wishes to tell. A typical game session usually lasts two to four hours, and most gaming groups meet regularly (usually once a week). Campaigns can be as short as one or two game sessions, but it is not uncommon for a larger, more complex, campaigns to last a year or more! The game is limited only by the imagination of its players and Game Master.

THIS BOOK AND OTHERS TO COME

This book is the core rulebook of the game. It serves as an introduction to the Iron Kingdoms and presents all the rules necessary to play the game. Chapter One details the history of the setting, from ancient history and cosmology to the more recent political events shaping the central nations. Chapter Two describes modern life in the Iron Kingdoms and what it is like to live there. Chapter Three covers all the rules for characters: how to create them, what they can do, and how they advance over time. Chapter Four presents the core rules of the game. This is where you will find directions for resolving combat and determining the success or failure of skills. Chapter Five dives into the arcane arts and lists the spells available to all spellcasting careers. Chapter Six offers descriptions and prices for weapons, armor, and equipment, and details rules on how to build and use mechanika (the fusion of magic and technology) as well as how to prepare and utilize alchemy. Finally, Chapter Eight provides guidance to the Game Master on how to develop and run a game of *Full Metal Fantasy Roleplaying*. At the end of the book you will find player resources like character sheets, templates, and an index.

This book is just the beginning of your adventure in the Iron Kingdoms. More books and supplements will come in the future that will delve deeper into the major kingdoms of western Immoren, present new rules for warlocks and warbeasts, explore the non-human civilizations inhabiting the forests and mountains, and describe the ancient civilizations that predate mankind. All along the way the rules will expand with new equipment, careers, and abilities to help you vary your playing experience.

GAME TERMS

The following game terms appear throughout this book. Become familiar with them now for ease of reference.

- **Game session** – A game session is when you sit down with your friends to play the *Iron Kingdoms Full Metal Fantasy Roleplaying Game*. It is a real world event, not an in-game duration of time. For example, getting together with friends for a night of play is a single game session.

- **Game Master**– The Game Master is the individual running the game, narrating the story, and setting the scenes. Before playing the *Iron Kingdoms Full Metal Fantasy Roleplaying Game*, a potential Game Master should familiarize himself with the setting by reading through this book, paying particular attention to the chapter "Full Metal Fantasy Game Mastering" (p. 327).

- **Player character (PC)** – A player character is a character controlled by a player. Contrast with non-player character.

- **Non-player character (NPC)** – Non-player characters are the background cast of the game and are controlled by the Game Master. NPCs include all monsters, antagonists, and allies with which the player characters interact. Contrast with player character (previous).

- **Enemy** – An enemy is any character (PC and/or NPC) doing something in opposition to the acting character.

WELCOME TO THE IRON KINGDOMS

Welcome to a land where magic and machinery intermingle and nations engage in conflict rooted in ancient grudges while exploiting innovations from an ongoing industrial revolution. The Iron Kingdoms lie in the heart of western Immoren, with thriving cities separated by dark wilderness regions that are home to feral beasts, savage tribes, and dangerous cults. To survive you'll need brains, brawn, and perhaps a loaded pistol or two.

Divided by culture and geography, the people of these nations are diverse, with attitudes and beliefs shaped by thousands of years of rich and bloody history. Not so long ago the region was subjugated by the Orgoth, terrible invaders from across the seas who plunged Immoren into a dark age of servitude. Gaining freedom required making use of arcane might and technological invention. The Iron Kingdoms now fight each other to control their own destinies.

The extensive cities grow by the year as people in rural regions abandon the toil of their ancestors to better themselves in soot-choked urban centers. The advent of steam power has revolutionized every walk of life. Smoke-belching factories pollute the air and dump alchemical waste into gutters, and many make their living under harsh and cramped conditions. Violence often seems the easiest solution to many problems. Yet within these cities exist endless possibilities for the clever or courageous. New trades and crafts have emerged, offering steam engines, clockwork machines, factory-forged goods, and fiendish weapons for those with the coin to afford them.

Mechanika, the combination of arcane power with engineering, has resulted in sweeping changes. One of the first and most dramatic mechanikal innovations were the mighty engines of war called colossals by which the people of western Immoren defeated the Orgoth. Those machines were replaced by smaller but more intelligent and agile automatons called steamjacks, used extensively for labor. Steamjacks haul goods from ships and trains, lift impossible loads for construction, and are employed on the fringes of civilization to chop wood or till fields. When armed for war, these machines are called warjacks, and some carry the most advanced weapons ever created.

The supernatural is a tangible and usually hostile thing in western Immoren. The dead rise from graveyards at the behest of necromancers to beset the living. The gods are real and to be feared as much as praised, and their priests can invoke both curses and blessings. Some say the Gift of Magic is more of a curse than a blessing. It arises spontaneously in children or young adults who become sorcerers and who cannot always control the forces they instinctively channel. They have at times been persecuted as witches, condemned by priests of both the Menite and Morrowan religions that hold sway over spiritual matters. Yet arcanists who master their talents and belong to respected orders become vital members of their communities. The militaries of every nation are eager to utilize such talents, especially those rare few with the warcaster ability allowing them to commune with the artificial minds of warjacks.

Though the Iron Kingdoms are dominated by humanity, other races also live within their borders. Trollkin, ogrun, and gobbers have adapted to urban life and can become well-respected bodyguards, soldiers, alchemists, and mechaniks. The dwarves of Rhul maintain their own nation but freely trade with the human kingdoms and are a common sight in the human lands. The occasional Iosan or Nyss elf may be encountered as an exotic rarity, their agendas an enigma.

The southernmost of the Iron Kingdoms is Cygnar, which emerged from the Corvis Treaties as the wealthiest nation, noted for its industrious cities and lands rich in resources yet also beset by enemies on all sides. Cygnar boasts some of the greatest minds in the history of the region. While famed for technological innovation, this nation is also a bastion for the dominant Church of Morrow.

Occupying a huge expanse of frozen northern land is the Empire of Khador. Its citizens are tough, weathered, and proud of their mutual solidarity. Khador has embraced industry as heartily as warfare, and its people work to exploit what resources they can scrape from these difficult lands. Khadorans have their own great inventors, and it is from this region that Immoren gained the steam engine and the railroad.

The western kingdom of Ord has its own distinct culture and has earned the respect of its neighbors for its strong navy and stalwart soldiers, but it has also endured great poverty. It is a realm of foggy bogs, wet marshes, and rocky farmland. The Ordic people find diversion in song, gambling, and ale rather than dwelling on life's inequities. Ord occupies a unique niche as a neutral nation that has become a haven to all manner of mercenaries and privateers.

Centrally located, the former nation of Llael is now occupied by Khador and contested by Menite zealots. A beleaguered Llaelese Resistance fights on, but many Llaelese see this cause as futile. The chaos of this region has made life difficult while creating lucrative opportunities for mercenaries, spies, missionaries, and anyone skilled at arms, engineering, or smuggling.

The Protectorate of Menoth is the newest Iron Kingdom. This theocracy emerged from the Cygnaran Civil War over a century ago as a result of a religious schism. While once beholden to Cygnaran law, the Protectorate declared independence and committed to a violent crusade against those refusing to pray to Menoth, the Creator of Man. Its priests enforce a strict interpretation of their religion to keep the population in line.

The nonhuman nations of Rhul and Ios lie adjacent to the lands of men, while to the west across the Meredius is the Nightmare Empire of Cryx, an island realm ruled by the Dragonfather, Toruk. Extensive wilds like the Gnarls, the Thornwood, the Bloodstone Marches, and the Wyrmwall Mountains present myriad savage hazards.

Those who would prosper in the Iron Kingdoms must be well armed and band together with others possessing the grit and fortitude to strike out in search of adventure. There are countless paths to fame and fortune—but just as many to death and ruin. Which fate is in store for you?

THE WINDLESS
WASTE

Uldenfrost

KHARDIC
SEA

Skrovenberg

Port Vladovar

Ohk

Tverkutsk

Scarsfell Forest

KHADOR

Skirov

Cherov-on-Dron

Porsk

New Vroggen

Khardov

KORSK

Rorschik

Volningrad

Midfast

MERIN

Corbhen

Fellig

Armandor

ORD

Berck

Carre Dova

Five Fingers

*Bay of
Stone*

*Dragon's Tongue
River*

Pt. Bourne

Gnarls

Ceryl

SEA OF A
THOUSAND
SOULS

MEREDIUS

New Larkholm

Orven

*Garlghast
Island*

Ramarck

Skirata Islands

*Giant's
Head*

SKELL

Blackwater

CRYX

Dreggsmouth

THE WAILING
SEA

Griddenguard

GHORD

Drotuhn

Hellspass

Laedry

Rynyr

LLAEL

MERYWYN

*Bloodsmeath
Marsh*

*Thornwood
Forest*

Groddenguard

Farhollow

Ulgar

Brunder

RHUL

Leryn

Rhydden

Iryss

IOS

SHYRR

Lynshynal

Armodeep

Gnarnwood

Black River

Corvis

Ternon Crag

Bainsmarket

Crael Valley

CYGNAR

Fharin

King's Vine

Ironhead Station

Steelwater Flats

CASPIA

Sul

Clockers Cove

Highgate

The Broken Coast

Mercir

*Raelthorne
Island*

Bloodbore Island

BLOODSTONE
MARCHES

IMER

PROTECTORATE
OF MENOTH

GULF OF
CYGNAR

Ancient Icthier

WESTERN IMMOREN

☆ CAPITALS   ✦ CITIES

7

Far more of history has been forgotten and turned to dust than was ever recorded, but we must delve into the past to comprehend the present.

—*The Writings of Asc. Angellia*

PREHISTORY AND COSMOLOGY

The cultures of western Immoren have deeply rooted histories stretching back into prehistory. The oldest histories and legends derive from tales passed by word of mouth for untold millennia before the written word. Even once the region's various cultures began to document history, records did not always survive intervening centuries and so much of the ancient past remains obscured.

This is doubly true for the legends from the times before the oldest civilizations. This includes myths passed down through the generations about the creation of the world, the origins of the gods, and the cosmology within which these unfathomable entities exist and perform their functions. Over time theologians have attempted to add to these ancient myths with understanding gained from trusted prophets or others who claim to have had special communion with divinities.

Despite these efforts, the gods remain elusive and enigmatic beings, only rarely communicating their will and preferring to do so through signs and portents or cryptic dreams. No one denies the existence of divine beings; rather, even those who dedicate their lives to studying such matters confront the fact that their understanding will forever be incomplete.

CREATION AND THE PRIMAL GODS
MENOTH AND THE DEVOURER WURM

Across the lands of western Immoren dominated by humanity, the most widely believed story about the origins of the world is that Menoth the Lawgiver arose from the formless chaos that predated Creation. He shaped Caen and its sun as an extension of his imperative to bring lasting order.

Having arisen self-made, Menoth adopted a form that pleased him, one that was later echoed among his greatest creation: mankind. In art and sculpture Menoth is depicted as a towering masked figure, his sublime visage concealed from mortal eyes to protect them from his naked wrath. This god strode Caen in the primal days, and mankind arose from Menoth's shadow as it fell upon the still-forming waters of the world as they withdrew from the land. Menoth imposed his rigid order upon the turning of the seasons and the cycles of life and death. In his wake, humanity arose and began to gather into tribes.

Menoth was not the only powerful entity to emerge from the unformed chaos, as from this darkness came the Devourer Wurm, also called the Beast of All Shapes, a bestial and forever changing monstrosity that would quickly become Menoth's greatest foe. Where Menoth gave rise to humanity, a race capable of higher thought, the Devourer Wurm spawned an endless variety of ravenous beasts and the horrors of the wilderness. All predators and dangerous beasts are thought to have arisen from and be connected to the Wurm, and since the dawn of time they have beset the offspring of Menoth and the works of civilization. The Wurm was filled with an endless hunger and sought only to eat and kill, to destroy and rend what had been created. Menoth knew the Wurm at once for his enemy and they would clash again and again in an unending hunt, a battle that has occupied both of these primal powers since the dawn of creation.

THE WURM AND THE NIGHT SKY

In ancient myths it was from the night sky that the Wurm first emerged, and this bestial god is strongly associated with certain celestial objects. This includes the Eye of the Wurm, now thought to be a remote planet also circling the sun, and Caen's three moons. Calder, the largest, is sometimes referred to as the "lord moon," while Laris, the second largest, is often called the "baleful moon." The third and smallest is Artis, which is described as a timid and shy maiden forever running from the Beast of All Shapes. Each of these moons has other associations, some of them more romantic, but through much of human history they have been seen as ominous figures connected to omens of natural disaster and ruin, particularly during key conjunctions. Followers of the Wurm have long revered the moons and conduct ritual feasts at times tied to Calder's cycle in particular, celebrating when it was both full and empty.

The first brutal and titanic clashes between Menoth and the Wurm took place across the surface of Caen, shattering the land and tearing great trenches in the deep oceans. Where one was thrown by the other, great chasms opened to divert the course of rivers, while the earth puckered with wounds that became volcanic eruptions of lava. The hammered and broken land gave rise to jagged mountains and deep valleys.

Eventually this chase led Menoth and the Wurm away from the physical world to Urcaen, a spiritual mirror of Caen. This would become the afterlife realm where the souls of those born and eventually slain on Caen would travel. In Urcaen the power of the gods was magnified, as this place proved to be the wellspring of the formless energy the divinities draw upon to shape reality. Urcaen is a region between the world and the formless chaos from which Menoth and the Wurm arose, given a semblance of form by proximity to and in reflection of the material world. Like Caen, Urcaen would be shaped by the clash between Menoth and the Wurm and this battle continues there still, with no sign of ever ending.

Thus occupied by these battles, Menoth had no time to shelter or guide humanity, and the scattered tribes were left to their own devices in the wild places. Some say mankind was cruelly neglected for a long era, left to live short and brutal lives while trying to survive countless horrors. Menites believe this time was a necessary crucible that strengthened mankind and allowed its tribes to find inner strength.

PERVASIVE EVIDENCE OF MENOTH

Contact between the inhabitants of western Immoren with other far-flung cultures has strengthened the belief that Menoth is indeed a primal god and Creator of Man, even among the scientific-minded. The first contact with foreign humans occurred with the arrival of hostile invaders called the Orgoth, who landed on Immorese shores having originated from a previously unknown continent to the west of Immoren. More recently, Immorese ships have made contact with a different culture thriving on the closer and more accessible southern continent of Zu. In both cases, anecdotal evidence suggests these vastly different human societies describe their creator as a towering masked figure, even if referring to him by a different name. Even the Orgoth are thought to have abandoned worship of the Creator in favor of more insidious powers.

Much of humanity forgot their Creator and many turned to worship the Wurm. All great predatory beasts and animals are seen as incarnations of the Wurm's primal hunger, and the tribes serving the Wurm glorified these intermediaries. They worshiped the wolf, the bear, the eagle, the serpent, and carved totems in their gathering places and gave them offerings. Some went so far as to profane the Creator's work by feasting upon the flesh of their own kind.

DHUNIA

Trollkin, ogrun, and gobbers have their own creation myths passed down through the generations. These races do not dispute that Menoth once walked Caen, gave rise to humanity, and is involved in an eternal clash with the Devourer Wurm. However, Dhunians insist their goddess is the first and most primal of the gods and is not simply the creator of the Dhunian races, but mother of all life. In these legends, Dhunia and Caen are synonymous, with the world described as the physical body of the goddess. The feminine forms carved of stone to represent Dhunia are abstractions of her aspect as a goddess of fertility and do not represent her actual being. Dhunia is inextricably bound up in the cycles of the seasons, which represent the natural process of death and rebirth.

These faiths believe that in the primeval days Dhunia and the Wurm were the only divine powers. To Dhunia was credited the rise of plants, nurturing rains, species that feed upon leaf and branch, the turning of the seasons, and the cycle whereby fresh births renewed life by replacing those slain by age, disease, or violence. The Wurm was credited with the predatory species that preyed on other creatures to survive, as well as the storms, earthquakes, floods, volcanic eruptions, and anything in nature that was abrupt and catastrophic.

The Dhunian races trace their origins to the often violent mingling of these two primal powers. The Wurm is said to be engaged in ongoing and repeated ravaging of Dhunia, the proof of which exists in the aftermath of every destructive storm and flood. In the earliest days, the Dhunian species were born of this coupling and it is for this reason that these races have qualities of both their divine mother and father—able to be savage and violent yet noble and honorable. In various times these races have been closer to one or the other of their divine parents, devoting their worship to either the Wurm or Dhunia.

The conflict between Dhunia and the Wurm is the basis for Dhunian legends about the origins of Menoth, whom they do not believe was self-created. In these legends, Dhunia wished a reprieve from the Wurm and so fostered a great hunter from the greatest of her children, which became Menoth, who was set upon the task of hunting the Devourer. The goddess bestowed on him the power, virility, and strength to fight the Wurm. As he hunted across Caen, humanity arose where he passed and proved to be a race consumed by the same desire to subjugate the wilderness. Menoth eventually chased the Wurm off Caen and into a shadowy realm born of the Wurm's nightmarish dreams, a place humans call Urcaen.

Menites consider this tale heretical and this has exacerbated violent confrontations between these faiths. Yet whatever the differences of opinions between these myths, Menoth, Dhunia and the Devourer Wurm are widely acknowledged as the first and primal gods. In this long dark era, tribes of these early races employed primitive weapons, clothing, and shelter and endured a variety of perils from the wilds, including ravenous beasts, natural disasters, and warfare from other tribes.

Neither Menite nor Dhunian myths give explanations for other gods, such as the pantheons worshiped by the elves of Ios or the dwarves of Rhul. The origins of these deities seem rooted in

ORBOROS, THE WORLD SERPENT

While most of humanity has long had an uncomfortable and hostile relationship with the entity called the Devourer Wurm and ignored Dhunia, a single ancient secret society has spent time and effort to understand the natural world's cosmology. The blackclads of the Circle Orboros draw supernatural power from the chaos embodied by the Devourer Wurm. They describe the natural world in a way not entirely dissimilar from Dhunian shamans, but together with a complex philosophy and systematic approach of their own. The blackclads believe both the Wurm and Dhunia are simply manifestations of a single primal and all-pervasive entity they call Orboros. By the philosophy of this group, Caen and therefore Dhunia represents the tangible physicality of Orboros, while the conscious will and the most violent impulses of Orboros are embodied in the Devourer Wurm. The Circle does not worship Orboros but are often mistaken as priests or prophets of the Devourer. The druids make use of this misconception to manipulate Devourer worshipers. By dint of their powers and esoteric mysticism, the blackclads exist outside society and are hated by Menites and mistrusted by most other religions.

Urcaen. Dhunians insist all life on Caen is connected to Dhunia and the Wurm, so the species created by other gods must be connected to these primal gods.

URCAEN, REINCARNATION, AND THE AFTERLIFE

From even the most ancient times, priests and shamans of the primal gods recognized that living flesh is connected to more ineffable spirit. Everything that lives has spiritual essence, although the simplest plants and creatures have similarly simple spirits. Intelligent races, those capable of complex thoughts, language, self-awareness, and the ability to craft tools, have more potent essence called souls. Souls are nearly indestructible and immortal, although they can suffer and change. After death, the spirit separates from flesh and passes into another state of existence. The mystery of the afterlife is inextricably tied to religion and the affairs of the gods.

Holy men have long been aware of the spiritual realm existing paradoxically both near and far removed from Caen, which they named Urcaen. It is here that most humans believe their souls travel after death. The consensus is that most of Urcaen is dangerous and foreboding, a spiritual mirror to the wilderness between cities on Caen. The only hope for an afterlife beyond wandering lost amid this spiritual wilderness is to spend one's life in pious devotion. After death, those who were pious are guided to the sheltered domain of their god.

The wilds beyond a god's domain is Hell. This is an unpredictable and terrifying expanse where souls are harried by monstrous beasts before being scooped into the maw of the Wurm and digested for an interminable era before being expelled as withered husks. Fear of death is entirely natural, and so is the desire to find religion as death nears. Whether hasty prayers at the final hour are enough for salvation is unknown; priests say the only sure course is a life better spent.

GODS OF THE DIVINE COURT

Lacyr   Ossyris   Scyrah   Lurynsar

Ayisla   Nyrro   Lyliss   Nyssor

DHUNIAN REINCARNATION

Dhunians do not depict their afterlife in similarly bleak terms as humanity, believing in a cycle of reincarnation. They do not deny Urcaen exists or that many souls travel there after death, but their souls are instead embraced by Dhunia. Rather than crossing over into the afterlife, their spiritual essence rejoins the Mother and can arise again as new life. It is from this vast collective reservoir that all life is reincarnated. The most refined and strongest spiritual essence becomes the souls of intelligent races like trollkin, ogrun, and gobbers. Most Dhunians expect to live multiple lifetimes, their souls strengthened by past experiences even if they are forgotten.

Not all Dhunian races or the greater natural beasts reincarnate in this way, as some follow the Wurm into Urcaen. Certain predatory creatures as well as worshipers of the Wurm or any foolish enough to spend their lives blinded by senseless violence and gluttony share this fate. In Urcaen these spirits are maddened by the ravenous howls of the Wurm to join the bestial god in mindless hunts on an endless cycle of turmoil. Those who worship the Devourer are glad to join the Wurm after death, seeing these hunts as a reward rather than a punishment.

BEGINNING OF THE WAR OF SOULS

Amid Menoth's battle with the Wurm, the god became aware of the influx of souls to Urcaen from the humans he had created in the dawn of the world. Those of the fallen who remembered their Creator joined Menoth in his battles, strengthening his efforts by what small degree they were able. In the aggregate their souls strengthened his cause and were seen as worthy of protection. So too did Menoth realize those who had forsaken him and turned to the Wurm would be joined to his ancient enemy. This is seen as the beginning of the War of Souls, a great cosmological conflict that continues to occupy the gods and the immortal souls of all who have walked Caen.

On learning that much of humanity had forgotten their Creator, Menoth became wrathful and returned his attention to Caen to reprimand the neglectful mortals. In the face of this fearsome manifestation, many human tribes abandoned their false gods and hastily sought to regain Menoth's, while others fled deeper into the wilderness and refused to give up their flawed beliefs. Menoth promised to shelter his followers after death in a domain called the City of Man where the Wurm could not reach them—nothing but endless torment would await those who turned from him. The War of Souls would eventually be joined by other faiths, but began amid the struggle between Menoth and the Wurm.

CREATION MYTHS OF OTHER DIVINE PANTHEONS
THE DIVINE COURT AND THE VELD

The elves that now reside in the reclusive kingdom of Ios had their origins in eastern Immoren, where these people had a particularly close relationship with their gods. Elven legends do not contradict the creation myths of Menites or Dhunians but instead stand apart. The close relationship between the elves and their creators allowed elven civilization to quickly flourish. While elves did not predate humanity, elven civilization spread across eastern Immoren and reached great heights before humans had mastered basic agriculture or masonry.

The oldest legends of the elves do not speak of the world's creation but rather of the Divine Court of Lyoss which came into being in a spiritual realm called the Veld, believed by human theologians to be an isolated area of Urcaen. Amid the Veld, the palace Lyoss was erected to house these gods and their created servants. Eight in number, these gods are associated with cycles of the passage of time. The origin of these gods has been attributed to a mingling between the sun and other celestial bodies like the moons. The elven gods worked together to ensure the security of their realm and to build a lasting domain amid the wilds. They arrived at a hierarchy based on their respective powers and capabilities.

First among them and leader of the gods was Lacyr, the Narcissar of Ages. At her side was the Incissar of Hours, Ossyris—described as both consort and co-ruler. That these gods waged war on the primal beasts beyond their domain is demonstrated by the titles taken by the gods. Ossyris was also the Sovereign of Conflict and the General of Lyoss. Next in the divine hierarchy were Ayisla and Nyrro, she the Nis-Arsyr of Night as well as the Watcher of the Gates of Lyoss, he the Arsyr of Day, Seneschal, and Lorekeeper. Vigilance was their charge, alternating day and night. Last were the four gods of the seasons: Scyrah, Nis-Issyr of Spring and Healer of the Divine Court; Lurynsar, Issyr of Summer, Arms Master of Lyoss and Chief of Scouts; Lyliss, Nis-Scyir of Autumn, Court Assassin, and Mistress of Poisons; and Nyssor, the Scyir of Winter and Grand Crafter.

It was Lurynsar, whose responsibility it was to scout far afield from the Veld, who observed mortal souls spilling into the remote wilds. Reporting this discovery to Lacyr, the Narcissar

ELVEN REINCARNATION AND AFTERLIFE

Even as Lacyr sought to improve upon the mortals she discovered crawling the face of Caen, so too she implemented a different cycle for the souls of her race to experience after death. The elves believe their fate in the afterlife to have been a complex arrangement involving reincarnation followed by a final rest in Lyoss.

Every elven soul that came to the gates of Lyoss in the Veld would be confronted by Ayisla, the Nis-Arsyr of Night, who would weigh their worth. Souls thought not yet ready to dwell among the gods were sent back to Caen and reborn. Others deemed sufficiently rich with experiences would pass the gates and enter the palace city of the gods, there to spend eternity experiencing spiritual refinement.

When an elven child is born, he or she might give rise to a new soul by the miracle of life, or alternately receive a reincarnated soul sent by Ayisla. Some claimed to be able to perceive these "older souls" looking into the eyes of a child and seeing the weight of his past. Such old souls were thought to be particularly wise, intelligent, and charismatic. These children have not been born since the Rivening. Instead, some elves have been born without souls, perhaps empty receptacles for old souls that have been lost.

of Ages followed the origins of these souls back to Caen. There she witnessed the barbarity of mortal existence. Seeing the trials and tribulations undertaken by these short-lived creatures she was amazed at how their difficulties strengthened their ineffable spiritual essence, which in turn strengthened the gods to whom they were linked. She became aware of the ecology of souls and saw how her court could benefit from the creation of a race bound to their worship.

Elven legends insist that their creation was a refinement whereby the crude and bestial shapes of other mortals were exceeded by their own forms as Lacyr committed to the exhausting birth of the elven race. Scyrah was midwife to this genesis, and so too did each of the gods play their part, linking the lives of their creation to the cycles of the seasons and the passage of night and day by the sequence of hours.

The elves that were birthed of Lacyr's labor would possess greater longevity, enlightenment, and other gifts that previous races lacked. The elves spread quickly across eastern Immoren and proved their superiority to the other creatures that sought to thrive there. When Lacyr was assured her creation was of the quality she sought, she made herself known to them and provided the wisdom of the Divine Court, offering arcane secrets necessary so they could surpass all rivals.

KHARG DROGUN AND THE GREAT FATHERS

The dwarves of Rhul have their own creation myth. The dwarves believe their flesh is descended directly of their gods, who are their actual and literal progenitors, the Great Fathers. They came into being in a place called *Kharg Drogun*, which translates as "The Land Beneath." Human theologians consider this simply another way to describe Urcaen, similar to the Veld.

The origins of the Great Fathers rests with a living mountain and god named Ghor, the greatest and tallest mountain of Kharg Drogun, which towered higher than any peak on Caen. This god-mountain was of tremendous power and deep-rooted malevolence. By his size and scope he was impervious to everything that walked or flew or swam. Yet Ghor was alone and sought distraction from those who could marvel at and appreciate his majesty. He searched within his bulk and drew forth thirteen of the finest crystals of his essence and carved these into shapes that pleased him, intended as useful slaves. Ghor bound them in shackles and taught the stone-born creatures that they must obey or be swallowed and ground into shapelessness.

The thirteen slaves created by Ghor had been created with clever hands, sharp eyes, and knew all that could be known of the shaping of stone and metal. Ghor desired they should build a great monument to his immortal glory. What Ghor did not realize was that they were not mindless slaves, but each had within him a spark of divinity. Almost at once the thirteen began to dream of freedom.

The names of the thirteen slaves that would become the Great Fathers are: Dhurg, Dohl, Dovur, Ghrd, Godor, Hrord, Jhord, Lodhul, Odom, Orm, Sigmur, Udo, and Uldar. Each would in time prove mastery over certain tasks and establish his own destiny. In the earliest days they were defined only by the oppression of Ghor and the shackles that bound them.

While tasked to construct the great monument, the thirteen discovered a true love for working stone and metal and a perfectionism that would allow nothing less than their best work, despite the hatred they bore their master. They toiled for years crafting the most glorious tribute they could imagine to immortalize the mountain-god. But when they presented it to Ghor, the cruel mountain mocked their achievement and unleashed a heaving earthquake to crack the earth and swallow their work. Ghor demanded that they commence again, and do better.

Knowing Ghor's complaints were baseless, the thirteen cleared the foundation and began to build anew, toiling this time for decades to create a work which was unquestionably superior. By the end of their labors they had come to love their new creation. Even this was not good enough for the tyrant Ghor, who pulverized their work to sand and dust and demanded they build again. The thirteen despaired. More than enslavement, they could not bear watching their work destroyed.

It was Orm, who would one day become patron of masonry and building, who called his brothers together and devised the plan to destroy Ghor and thereby set themselves free. They would appeal to the mountain-god's vanity and find a way to build something he could not bear to destroy. Godor, who would become patron of orators, was enlisted to propose to Ghor a tower so high it would touch the sky of the Land Beneath—the only difficulty being such an engineering feat would require materials extracted from Ghor's own body.

Ghor was enthralled with the idea and consented to contribute to the work. Dohl, who would become patron of mining, led the efforts of the thirteen, proving his talent with pick and shovel and his deep knowledge of stone. Ghrd, who would become patron of wealth, showed an affinity for following veins of precious ore and discovering pockets of crystals. The thirteen set about the task with all their pride and ingenuity, performing feats of engineering far advanced of anything witnessed before.

Meanwhile the thirteen mined a labyrinth of caves within Ghor, extracting the best stone and the richest veins of metal. Lodhul, who would become patron of feasts, distracted Ghor by hosting great gatherings of supplicants while his brothers weakened the mountain-god from within, preparing the mountain to collapse. As Ghor became hollow and weaker, the tower grew taller.

Countless seasons passed as the thirteen committed to this task, and the tower became the promised marvel, climbing to scrape the sky. The mountain-god was transfixed and basked in the adoration of petitioners who came to lavish praise on its construction, which he accepted as his due. Jhord and Odom, patrons of espionage and secrets, listened and learned all they could of Ghor's deepest secrets, as well as the world beyond their prison.

At last the thirteen reached the end of their work. As soon as they laid the last stone on the last spire, they set their plan in motion. They shattered the columns beneath the mountain beginning the rumbling collapse of Ghor. The thunderous din could be heard across Kharg Drogun as Ghor's immortal life was extinguished in an ever-widening cloud of dust and stone as the cave-riddled mountain fell inward. When the rumbling finished, the greatest mountain of Kharg Drogun collapsed to become gentle hills, near which stood the monument that would outlast it. This was the Tower Ghorfel, symbol of the Great Fathers and heart of the domain of the Rhulic gods.

As soon as Ghor fell, great monsters from the periphery of Kharg Drogun intruded, seeking to seize the lands for themselves. Great Father Dovur forged weapons with which to confront them, while Uldar forged armor to protect his brothers. After girding themselves, Dhurg, Hrord, and Udo respectively took up axes, blades, and hammers to wage war and secure their borders.

After having fought to earn an era of peace, Great Father Dohl—who had been mining below the ruins of Ghor—discovered an endless chasm. Making his brothers aware of this, and feeling overcome by curiosity, the Great Fathers travelled through and emerged on Caen, the land of the living. On witnessing the proliferation of life they were inspired to leave their mark on the world as well as to find companionship to end their lonely fraternal existence.

Even as they had been birthed from stone, they sought to find their equals in the earth, and so gathered the rich and fertile clay along the Ayers River where it flowed into what would become Lake Armsdeep among the Glass Peaks and from this loam they shaped the Claywives. These would become the matriarchs of the Rhulic people, as from the Great Fathers and the Claywives were sired the first dwarves in the ancient legendary days of the world's beginning.

For a time the Great Fathers and Claywives lived among the first dwarven clans, which took their names from their divine progenitors. The Great Fathers passed down the knowledge and lore they had acquired both during their enslavement and after. Most importantly the Great Fathers delivered the Edicts by which their lives should be governed. This includes the following core aspects of dwarven culture:

- The Edict of Authority, which outlines the family hierarchy around the clan

- The Edict of Building, establishing the importance of crafting and construction

- The Edict of Duels, describing the right to resolve disputes through physical confrontation

- The Edict of Feuds, with laws for larger conflicts between entire clans

- The Edict of Oaths, which defines the importance of sworn promises

- The Edict of Ownership, giving each dwarf the right to own that which he has created, traded for, been freely given, or won by lawful duel or feud

- The Edict of Unity, binding the dwarves to unite against external threats

From these first fundamental Edicts grew the Codex, which would become the written record and body of law for the Rhulic people, and the only unbroken record that has persisted from these ancient times into the modern day. The Codex and its Edicts would become not only the foundation for Rhulic society, but also the holy text by which the wisdom of the Great Fathers was preserved.

The Great Fathers knew they must return to Kharg Drogun, which they had left unprotected. The Claywives left with them and so the progenitors of the dwarves descended into the caverns below the earth to return to the Land Beneath, never again stepping foot on Caen. Their legacy was assured by the thriving and prospering dwarven clans, beginning with the thirteen most directly associated with each of the Great Fathers, as well as a proliferation of lesser clans that broke away from these first families to establish dynasties among the Glass Peaks.

The Great Fathers were remembered by the people they had sired, in services and prayers. Every soul was promised a place in Kharg Drogun after death, where they would join the Great Fathers at Tower Ghorfel and eternally refine themselves and their avocations.

TRIBAL ERA

With the exception of Rhul, all of the peoples of Immoren, west and east, include in their legends a period of tribal existence before the onset of true civilization. This period includes many myths and legends depicting direct interaction with the gods. It is believed the tribal period of the elves was quite different than that experienced by either humanity or trollkin. Elves organized into small city-states that periodically warred upon one another but possessed many advantages and an advanced understanding of mathematics, philosophy, and the arcane. The elves also had a short tribal period before the intervention leading to the rise of their civilization. Theirs was the first great civilization built on Immoren, and also the first to fall.

Rhulic priests of the Great Fathers insist their massive Codex—itself a vast library including both ancient tomes as well as modern legal decisions—includes written record tracing back to the origins of the first clans and the words of the Great Fathers. No outsider has been given access to the most ancient sacred texts to confirm this boast. The information contained in these tomes is narrowly focused on events within the Glass Peaks and is of limited use to the more far-flung neighboring cultures sharing the continent.

THE GIFTS OF MENOTH

Menites believe humanity may have continued in barbarity indefinitely if not for the Gifts of Menoth. How long humanity existed in perpetual turmoil before Menoth put aside his battle with the Wurm is unknowable, but is thought to be many thousands of years. While Menoth's wrath at having been forgotten was fierce, his rage diminished on witnessing the harsh indignities of life among the human tribes. Those who begged his forgiveness he treated with mercy and benevolence. He consented to bestow on them gifts forming the foundation for Menite civilization: the Flame, the Wall, the Sheaf, and the Law.

The Flame embodies many principles in the Menite faith, including faith and the legacy of the temple to preserve and teach religious doctrine, but it also represents the use of fire to drive back the darkness as well as to forge weapons and survive harsh winters. The Wall represents knowledge of masonry and engineering whereby the first permanent townships and fortifications were erected as shelter and also to divide settled lands from the wilderness. The Sheaf is knowledge of agriculture, whereby settled tribes began to till the earth, sow

seeds, irrigate, and harvest grain to support larger populations. It also represents the use of herds of cattle animals which would in time give rise to horses used as steeds and oxen to pull heavy loads, allowing Menite civilizations to prosper against rivals.

The Law is deemed the greatest of Menoth's gifts, representing the compact between Menoth and humanity as well as the agreements by which mankind settled into castes and combined settled tribes to create the first cities. Legends that predate writing do not define specific laws employed by the earliest and now forgotten civilizations. The eldest compact between Menoth and mankind defined how righteous rulers were to be legitimized and sanctified by the priest caste. To the priests fell the responsibility of conducting burial rites to speed souls of the dead to Menoth's side in Urcaen, there to join the Creator in his War of Souls.

ANCIENT HISTORY

The elves were the first to possess the written word and have the longest-reaching records, although their history is now a broken and shattered legacy with many gaps related to the collapse of their first empire into ruin and devastation. The dwarves of Rhul boast the only unbroken and continuous civilization—the establishment of Ghord as a home for their Codex took place more than two thousand years before the time of Cinot, who would begin the era of recorded history among the human Menites.

ONSET OF CIVILIZATION
THE EMPIRE OF LYOSS

For virtually all of human recorded history, eastern and western Immoren have been divided. Little was known by humanity of eastern Immoren. All that remains are the partially preserved records carried to Ios by the surviving refugees of Lyoss, the first great civilization of the age. They have rarely shared tales of their ancient past with outsiders.

In those ancient times, after the elves spread and multiplied for generations across northeastern Immoren, the Divine Court made themselves known and set them on the path of unification. The gods took an active hand in shaping their ways. Among the first task required of the leaders of the tribes was the construction of numerous great fanes—the temples of the elves—to facilitate communion with the gods. Connecting these gave rise to the Empire of Lyoss.

While the unification of the scattered tribes was a time of war and strife, it taught the Lyossans the arts of battle that served them well against external threats in the centuries to follow. Surrounded on all sides by aggressive and more primitive tribes of various species, including ruthless and vicious savages called skorne, Lyoss committed to expanding, patrolling its borders, and building vast cities. The continent itself was different in that age, without the vast sweeping desert that fills its center today. This region was crossed by myriad rivers dividing fertile farmlands.

The golden era of this empire would rise and pass into memory before the first great cities of mankind. The oldest towers of Nyshyl, its capital, were already old and starting to crumble before the first stones were laid for the Rhulic city of Ghord. The empire might well have encompassed all of Immoren in time, if not for a disaster of its own devising.

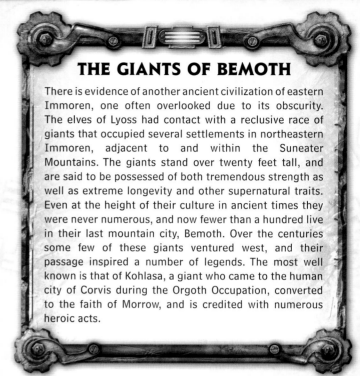

THE GIANTS OF BEMOTH

There is evidence of another ancient civilization of eastern Immoren, one often overlooked due to its obscurity. The elves of Lyoss had contact with a reclusive race of giants that occupied several settlements in northeastern Immoren, adjacent to and within the Suneater Mountains. The giants stand over twenty feet tall, and are said to be possessed of both tremendous strength as well as extreme longevity and other supernatural traits. Even at the height of their culture in ancient times they were never numerous, and now fewer than a hundred live in their last mountain city, Bemoth. Over the centuries some few of these giants ventured west, and their passage inspired a number of legends. The most well known is that of Kohlasa, a giant who came to the human city of Corvis during the Orgoth Occupation, converted to the faith of Morrow, and is credited with numerous heroic acts.

THE FEUD OF AGES AND THE FOUNDING OF GHORD

In the Glass Peaks of western Immoren, the dwarven clans descended from the Great Fathers fell into a conflict that escalated into a terrible conflagration. The words of the Great Fathers had not been forgotten, yet the Edicts of the Codex became twisted and used to justify feuds of a scope beyond all reason as clans beset clans and sought one another's extinction. Young clans felt oppressed by elder and more powerful ones and banded together to seize prestigious holdings. These then fought one another over dividing the spoils. This war was the Feud of Ages, the only major internal war in Rhulic history, a period viewed with shame.

Starting in 8500 BR, The Feud of Ages is believed to have lasted three hundred years, although the conflicts during this time were intermittent and irregular, occupying both small and larger battles as clans switched sides, allegiances, and both seized and abandoned significant claims. Control of the mountain passes and other routes of trade and travel such as the great rivers of the Glass Peaks and access to the inland sea of Lake Armsdeep were primary sources of contention.

The end of the Feud of Ages is closely tied to the founding of the great city of Ghord in 8200 BR, now capital of Rhul, the most ancient of great cities in western Immoren. Several of the foundational buildings of Ghord were already sacred, connected to the Great Fathers and Claywives. The thirteen clans that still bore the names of the Great Fathers and deemed most closely descended from them came to Ghord in the spirit of their progenitors to unite and join their estates and holdings. The most violent and vindictive of the younger warring clans who would not bow were cast out. The fate of these exiled clans is not well documented; some likely settled on the fringes of the

TIMELINE OF HISTORICAL ERAS

PREHISTORIC ERA

c. 10000 BR	Elven tribes unite as Empire of Lyoss in eastern Immoren
c. 8500–8200 BR	Feud of Ages among dwarves, Ghord settled
c. 7500 BR	Rhul established, led by the Stone Lords and Moot of Hundred Houses
c. 6500-6000 BR	Canon of the True Law found in Icthier, Cinot leads first Menite civilization
c. 4250 BR	Construction begins on Bridge of Worlds in Lyoss
c. 4000 BR	Cataclysm as Bridge of Worlds explodes: Lyoss destroyed and Icthier abandoned
c. 3900 BR	Ios established by refugees of Lyoss led by the hallytyr

WARLORD ERA

c. 3500 BR	Morrdh founded
c. 2800 BR	Valent Thrace establishes Calacia
c. 2200 BR	Priest-King Golivant drives the Molgur from the Wyrmwall
c. 2170 BR	Priest-King Khardovic founds Khard
c. 2050 BR	Calacia becomes Caspia

THOUSAND CITIES ERA

1930–1894 BR	Lives of the Twins, Morrow and Thamar, who ascend as divinities
1850–1612 BR	Midar and Thuria established
1500–1421 BR	Morrdh disintegrates and Khardic Empire established
1370–1073 BR	Tordor and Rynyr established
c. 1000 BR	Toruk driven from the mainland by his dragon brood; Cryx founded
840 BR	Divine Court leaves Ios to return to the Veld

ORGOTH OCCUPATION ERA

c. 600 BR	Orgoth blackships begin landing in western Immoren to begin conquest
433 BR	Orgoth exercise absolute power over human kingdoms in western Immoren
c. 150 BR	Thamar imparts the Gift of Magic to humanity
140 BR	The Rivening drives most Iosan priests insane
137–67 BR	Human sorcery begins; Sebastian Kerwin joins Circle of the Oath
34 BR	Scyrah returns to Shyrr alone of the gods

1 AR	Iron Fellowship declares Rebellion against the Orgoth
26 AR	Firearms invented by Order of the Golden Crucible
86–160 AR	Leryn, Rorschik, and Korsk liberated and join Caspia in Iron Alliance
191–201 AR	First colossals built; Orgoth initiate the Scourge; Orgoth defeated

IRON KINGDOMS ERA

202 AR	Corvis Treaties define borders of Cygnar, Khador, Llael, and Ord
241 AR	Invention of steamjacks
247–267 AR	First and Second Trollkin Wars; Colossal War; invention of warjacks
283 AR	Discovery of Cyriss
293–313 AR	Church of Morrow becomes state religion of Cygnar; Border Wars
390 AR	Destruction of Issyrah by Everblight; Everblight defeated
482–484 AR	Cygnaran Civil War gives rise to Protectorate of Menoth
510–511 AR	First Thornwood War between Khador and Cygnar

MODERN ERA

546 AR	Serfdom abolished in Khador
579 AR	Cygnar's King Vinter Raelthorne IV creates the Inquisition
581 AR	Ios closes borders to outsiders
584–588 AR	Scharde Invasions between Cryx and Cygnar
594 AR	Lion's Coup in Cygnar: Vinter IV overthrown and replaced by King Leto
603 AR	Vinter IV attacks Corvis leading a skorne army
604–605 AR	Llaelese War, ends with Khador in control of western Llael
606–607 AR	Caspia-Sul War; death of Hierarch Voyle
608 AR	Present year

region and eventually rejoined Rhul, but others went elsewhere either to establish communities as yet undiscovered, or to perish in obscurity.

The thirteen Stone Clans restored the Codex and created the government of what would become Rhul, with Ghord as its center. The leaders of each of these clans became the Stone Lords, and together governed and arbitrated disputes among the clans until 7500 BR when the Stone Lords consented to the founding of the Moot of the Hundred Houses, whereby the hundred greatest clans of Rhul would together oversee the laws and arbitration of Rhul, recording all disputes and their resolutions in the growing Codex. While duels and clan feuds on a smaller scale were an ordinary aspect of Rhulic politics, all such strife was carefully governed by the laws of the Moot and its stern judges, and never again was the general welfare of Rhul placed at risk.

Unlike some races, the dwarves did not multiply in great numbers or seek to spread beyond the Glass Peaks, and so while their civilization slowly expanded, it remained isolated from the barbaric tribes beyond the mountains. The passes providing entrance to Rhul were heavily fortified and garrisoned, giving Rhul uniquely formidable borders and allowing them to easily repel smaller and less ordered groups that might threaten them. While contact and trade was established between the Rhulic Moot and delegates of the Empire of Lyoss, interaction between them was limited and wary. As Lyoss continued to expand, the Rhulfolk prepared for the inevitability of war.

ICTHIER AND CINOT

There are scholars who believe that Menoth's chosen tribes established now forgotten civilizations, but there has been little evidence. If any such empires existed, they were swallowed by the sands to the east of the area now recognized as western Immoren. What is known is that the largest tribe of Menites undertook a pilgrimage west, following their priests on a journey where their passage was challenged by the godless until at last they reached the shores of Meredius. Here they founded the first great city of mankind, Icthier. At this holy site the words of the sacred Canon of the True Law were made manifest on stone as the first writings, inscribed by the hand of Menoth.

It was the study of these words that brought the knowledge of reading and writing to humanity, one of Menoth's greatest gifts. While first inscribed in stone, the words of the True Law would eventually be copied and translated countless times. It remains the sacred text of the Menite faith, although there are conflicting iterations and many of the original stone inscriptions have crumbled to dust over the passage of time. Historians that have carefully examined these and other copies of ancient writings from these early days believe Icthier was settled around 6500 BR, which marks the first recorded Menite civilization.

Passages in the True Law speak of kings that will arise chosen by the will of Menoth and whose holiness allow them to serve as conduits for the divine. These priest-kings are the most revered leaders in the Menite faith, each capable of manifesting awe-inspiring miracles in the name of the Creator of Man. Cinot was the first great priest-king of Icthier. He was said to be able to turn ash to grain and salt into nectar. It was through him that Menoth delivered the gift of the Sheaf to his people, and by his teachings Icthier flourished and allowed its growing numbers to be fed. He implemented aqueducts and irrigation, and organized the laborers of the city into quarrying stone with which to build both homes and walls. By his guiding hand the Menites were exalted above the warring tribes surrounding them.

As early civilization grew, so did the needs of the priesthood to organize. Cinot set the first hierarchy of the Menite faith and its clergy in place. His priests led the warriors of the faith in battle against both the godless savages that surrounded Icthier but also against the beasts of the wild. Cinot lived for four centuries guiding his people, his longevity another of the Creator's miracles. After he was gone the region continued to serve as a cradle of civilization. By 5500 BR a warrior of the faith named Belcor and a sage-priest named Geth led an exodus northward, seeking to spread civilization.

THE DRAGONFATHER

Dragons exist in the old legends as fiendishly powerful monsters once thought to be embodiments of the Devourer Wurm. They were imperishable terrors that passed overhead on shadowy wings and breathed fire on any that offended them. As scholars learn more of dragons they have become less certain of their nature, for they have little in common with anything else that walks or flies or swims.

All dragons originate from one progenitor: Toruk, called the Dragonfather. For the last sixteen centuries this creature has been worshiped as a god by those dwelling in the island empire west of Immoren. Those who worship the Dragonfather claim he has always been a part of the world, although he never participated in the frenzy of fertility and generation that gave rise to life on Caen. Toruk and the other dragons may not be alive, by ordinary reckoning—they do not breed or propagate as other species do, but possess immortality rooted in a heartstone, an indestructible crystal called an athanc. Toruk's worshipers believe that at some point in ages past Toruk became tired of his solitary existence and created a brood to serve him. He divided his athanc and from each splinter a new dragon came into being, each uniquely terrible.

This act did not proceed as intended, for the dragons were too similar to their maker. Each possessed inhuman pride and thought itself superior to all others. They refused to bow to their father and rebelled. Toruk was mightier than them individually, but together they were formidable. After a titanic struggle amid the skies of Caen, the dragons scattered. From that point forward, Toruk sought to hunt them down and gather the pieces of his essence, to undo his mistake.

The other dragons in their scattered lairs kept watch for their father and remained ready to flee from him. In the meanwhile they took out their aggression on lesser creatures that crawled upon the world. Many dragons earned their own sagas and legends as they laired atop inaccessible mountain peaks or other remote locations. Names such as Ashnephos, Blighterghast, Charsaug, Everblight, Halfaug, and Scaefang

prompt nearly as much fear and dread in their legends as that of Toruk the Dragonfather. On the few occasions a dragon has been defeated, often at great cost by vast armies, they have shown the ability to reform flesh and scale from their athanc and rise again. The only permanent extinction of dragons has been when one has fallen to the claws of Toruk or another of their kind. Gaulvang, Nektor, Pyromalfic, and Shazkz are names of dragons that are no more.

THE MOLGUR

Beyond the fields of civilization spreading from Icthier, struggles for dominance and survival occupied bands of trollkin, ogrun, goblins, and the tribes of humanity that had forsaken their Creator. The one uniting aspect shared by the wild tribes was a reverence for the Devourer Wurm, embodied in countless totemic forms. Shamans of these barbaric tribes supplicated the Wurm through bloody sacrifices, invoking their own miracles, deemed unholy by the Menites.

The rites of these groups involved cannibalism, self-mutilation, and bloodletting, conducted either upon one another or outsiders when they could gather in strength and raid fringe settlements. By and large the Menite communities had the greater discipline and the capacity to organize armed defense but the menace of the Molgur steadily grew, particularly as the barbarians began to gather in numbers. Though the Molgur possessed little organization, and battles between competing tribes was common, they shared an identity drawn from the shamans and their rites.

Bands of raiders would prey on even well defended rival villages or isolated townships. The Molgur learned to communicate with one another, creating a mongrel tongue unique to themselves, drawn from disparate dialects of a thousand tribes. They emulated the writings of the Menites, carving into stone a crude runic alphabet. Shamans discovered that these inscriptions empowered their mystical rites. Barter and news were spread from one Molgur tribe to another, with runners sent to challenge rivals or call a gathering for battle.

Records from the Menites of these early days speak of attacks by the Molgur in terrified language, describing them as "half man, half beast." Certain humans who have embraced the Wurm demonstrate the ability to transform, growing in size and strength while filled with a murderous madness. In modern times such savages still exist, in a tribe called the Tharn, which are most certainly direct descendants of the Molgur. The sight and sound of these blood-maddened warriors with their pounding drums and great howls was horrifying and blasphemous to the settled peoples. The Molgur poured from the wilderness and delighted in murder, feasting on the fallen, willing to destroy anything in their path.

THE CATACLYSM IN THE EAST

While the Menites spread their civilization and the Molgur began to band together, a great work was underway in the east which would forever change Immoren. Within the Empire of Lyoss, a message spread from the great fanes that the gods sought to walk among them. The greatest priests communed with the Divine Court and discerned their desire to create the Bridge of Worlds, a great structure which would facilitate crossing between the Veld and Caen.

The gods had discovered that in the passing of millennia there had been a thickening of the barriers between the afterlife and the world of the living. While mortal souls were light and insubstantial enough to pass through the membrane separating the worlds, the gods could only do so by exerting tremendous energies, making it very difficult for them to bestow blessings on their mortal followers. The Bridge of Worlds would allow the gods to pass to Caen whenever they wished. Its construction would be shared between mortal and divine, with half of the bridge built in the Veld, and the other half extending into the sky from Nyshyl, the capital of the empire.

Directed by the gods, the people of Lyoss began this undertaking circa 4250 BR. Arcane secrets were passed to them through the priesthood, including techniques by which force of will could be directed and magnified to lift and manipulate massive pieces of stone and metal. Through miracles of both engineering and the arcane, construction of the Bridge of Worlds began. It was not required that the Lyossans understand every principle of the work, but only that they follow the instructions of the gods. Great arcane generators were erected beneath the superstructure of the towering bridge, which would be the largest and most impressive engineering accomplishment ever attempted by mortal hands. While the bridge was being erected, a lattice of metal sigils was inlaid across the streets of the capital, extending for miles into the surrounding lines, an arcane foundation that distributed energy from the cyclopean structure.

Bolstered by their tremendous longevity and inspired by divine visions, multiple generations came to maturity and joined their parents and grandparents in contributing to the ongoing labor. Iosan records recovered from Lyoss suggest the bridge reached completion by 4000 BR. As the date of completion neared, the people of Lyoss were filled with eager anticipation and

CALENDAR USE

In the present era a single widely adopted calendar exists across the human and dwarven settled regions, having originated in Rhul before being adopted by the Morrowan and Menite faiths and kingdoms. Ios maintains a different calendar but any Iosan spending time outside that nation's borders learns to use the commonly employed one. The names of the months are different among each of these cultures, with Morrowan month names being the most widely employed throughout the Iron Kingdoms. Menite names are used in the Protectorate of Menoth and all-Menite communities, and the Rhulic month names are only used in Rhul and other all-Rhulic communities.

The standard calendar is comprised of thirteen months, each month broken into four weeks of seven days. This results in every month having 28 days, and a 364-day, 52-week year with a seasonal transition every ninety-one days (13 weeks). A slight astronomical flaw in the calendar requires a periodic adjustment every three years, addressed by adding an extra unmarked day after the last day of one year and before the first day of the new year, which also corresponds with the winter solstice. Called Odomsday by Rhulfolk, this adjustment is more commonly known in human lands as "The Longest Night," in reference to a celebratory festival thrown during this period. Since this day exists outside the calendar, some hold that the consequences for choices made during this festival do not matter and should not be judged.

The following thirteen months of the year are listed with names used by Morrowans (Menites, and Rhulfolk):

1st Month	Glaceus (Glaceus, Dovern)
2nd Month	Casteus (Casteus, Uldern)
3rd Month	Trineus (Trineus, Dolern)
4th Month	Tempen (Tempes, Ormul) — Vernal Equinox after 1st week
5th Month	Cinten (Cinoten, Odul)
6th Month	Rowen (Prautes, Gordu)
7th Month	Solesh (Septesh, Lodar) — Summer Solstice after 2nd week
8th Month	Octesh (Octesh, Durgar)
9th Month	Katesh (Sulesh, Odomar)
10th Month	Goloven (Golovus, Godesh) — Autumnal Equinox after 3rd week
11th Month	Doloven (Martus, Sigmon)
12th Month	Khadoven (Khadovus, Rordon)
13th Month	Ashtoven (Ashtovus, Jhoron) — Winter Solstice after last week

In western Immoren the days of the week are not named, but traditionally the weeks of the month have a name. The Morrowan week names are Vendarl (1st week), Malleus (2nd week), Donard (3rd week), and Gorim (4th week). The Menite week names are Ozeall, Luctine, Donard, and Vilmon. Documents using older formal notation specify dates by listing the day of the week within a month, although this has fallen out of favor in preference for simply denoting the day of the month. For example, the antiquated format: "Malleus 5th, Cinten" is equivalent to the more modern: "the 12th of Cinten" or "Cinten the 12th;" Malleus is the 2nd week of the month, so the 5th day of that week falls on the 12th day of the month. Modern scholars have determined this system is unnecessarily convoluted. Three letter abbreviations for month and week names are commonly employed.

prepared for a great festival to celebrate the arrival of the gods. The streets of Nyshyl were filled with pilgrims, the already crowded city filled to twice its normal capacity, with teeming throngs concentrated near the base of the bridge, where the hopeful intended to greet the gods.

Unfortunately the hopes of the Lyossan people could not forestall the Cataclysm. What went wrong is a mystery as much to the ancients as the scholars in the present, and even the gods themselves must not know, since otherwise it seems unfathomable they would have gone forward with their plans. The fact that the Divine Court was neither omniscient nor omnipotent was proven in the time to come. Not knowing the doom awaiting them, the Lyossans activated the great mechanisms of the Bridge of Worlds. For a moment all seemed well, as the eight gods of the Divine Court entered the world of Caen. At just that moment, the bridge exploded in a torrent of vast and sweeping power.

The explosive force was so great Immoren itself cracked and sundered. Along what was once the vibrant Hyless River opened the Abyss, a chasm so deep it reached the hot arteries of the world where molten stone flows like blood. Nyshyl, once a glorious capital, was instantly obliterated, together with the millions of Lyossans who had gathered. Where it stood was nothing but a gaping chasm, a wound in the world. The gods endured, but they found the world consumed by devastation.

Unnatural blue-white fires spread in the wake of this explosion, flames that burned indefinitely without apparent fuel and could not be extinguished. The very stones burned like cordwood. Weather patterns across Immoren changed irrevocably, and what was once a small desert far to the southwest of Nyshyl became a vast waste. Along the Abyss, freakish energies combined with seismic upheaval to birth the Stormlands, a region of unrelenting lightning and rain that still persists thousands of years later.

The Empire of Lyoss ceased to exist, delivered into annihilation. The destruction went far beyond the capital, causing death and carnage across all the major cities of the empire. Those inhabiting the fringes starved or were set upon by predators and beasts, including fresh horrors arisen in the wake of the arcane devastation. The empire might have been erased without a single survivor if not for the intervention of the weakened but still puissant gods of the Divine Court. The eight gods used their powers to shelter as many thousands of refugees as they could. Together they fled into the west where they would find shelter amid the isolated vale they named Ios.

Records pointing to the Cataclysm can be found in ancient human legends. In the annals of the ancient sage Angrund it was called the "Time of the Burning Sky." A tremendous bright light in the east presaged the destruction, when the night sky become like day, but with a baleful intensity that soon faded and was replaced by howling winds and storms. The earth opened to swallow entire towns on the eastern fringes while a rain of fire lasting sixty days and sixty nights blasted the region, creating what would subsequently be known as the Bloodstone Marches. Lakes dried up, livestock became barren, and dangerous creatures fled before the wild weather, wreaking havoc wherever they passed. The Menites scattered and most moved up the coast to the fertile region near the Black River that would soon be named Calacia. The city of Ancient Icthier, first city of men, was abandoned and would not be reclaimed for thousands of years.

THE RISE OF MORRDH

Sometime around 4800 BR, eight centuries before the Time of the Burning Sky, a strong civilization began to take root in a valley amid the heavily forested region now called the Thornwood. It is thought the first leaders of Morrdh were an offshoot sect of the Menite exodus led by Geth seven centuries earlier. There are fragmentary passages that hint of a schism that led to the founders of Morrdh turning from their Menite teachings, although inheriting many of the gifts of civilization provided by Cinot.

Little is known of the culture and religious beliefs of Morrdh, although in legends it is a kingdom associated with darkness and corruption. Whether the taint of Morrdh existed from its founding or festered later, the warriors of the Valley of Morrdh managed to drive back the Molgur tribes and secure their own legacy.

The people of Morrdh explored occult rituals that would never have been condoned by the Menite priesthood. Warfare with the Molgur gave rise to an aggressive and violent civilization, one with convoluted and brutal internal politics based on the competition between rival warlords. The Kingdom of Morrdh was not united until 3500 BR, after the warlords of ten smaller fiefdoms came to an uneasy accord. This allowed the fledgling kingdom to prosper against neighboring tribes.

Unearthed records suggest dark pacts and conspiracies at the heart of Morrdhic domination. Long before humanity mastered the arcane, the Lords of Morrdh were rumored to possess terrible powers, including the ability to make corpses rise from their graves and take up weapons to become tireless guardians.

Descriptions of battles by the neighboring Midar describe serpentine monsters descending from the sky on bat-like wings in answer to the call of Morrdhic generals. Other monsters erupted from below the earth to swallow enemies whole. Some of this has been dismissed as superstition, but all stories imply that the leaders of Morrdh had access to lore mankind was not meant to know. The tainted gains made by Morrdh as a civilization would foster evils within the Thornwood that still plague the present.

THE WARLORD ERA

The Warlord Era was the time when the Menite warrior-priests and priest-kings had their greatest and most sweeping battles against barbarism. It was a time of savagery and bloodshed which marked the founding of new city-states and paved the way for the proliferation of fiefdoms and pockets of armed settlements which would define life in western Immoren for thousands of years.

Even the smallest village needed to erect walls against the horrors that came from beyond the torch light, and prayers to Menoth were seen as providing the only clear path between life and death. In this era, the priest-kings of Calacia and Khard tamed the wild with the rule of law and the judgment of steel. By their example, the True Law of civilization became a weapon wielded against the barbaric throngs in service to the Devourer Wurm.

CALACIA, GOLIVANT, AND THE SHIELD OF THRACE

Between the Molgur who dominated the wild mountains to the west and the inhospitable wastes of the Bloodstone Marches to the east arose a thriving Menite community. Following the example of Cinot and those who came after, they quickly set to tilling the fertile land and created dozens of settlements, outposts, and temples.

These communities were united under the warrior-priest Valent of Thrace around 2800 BR. Drawing workers by the hundreds and hauling lumber from the nearby forests and stones from freshly dug quarries, they created the Hold of Calacia, a great fortress that would in time become a thriving city. A great line of walls and fortifications was erected at his behest to stand against the Molgur—the Shield of Thrace. The protected people of Calacia thrived and multiplied.

The Calacians demonstrated as much ingenuity as faith, as they had mastered the forging of iron and, in small quantities, the precious steel by which the blades of the priests' chosen warriors carried the Creator's strength. The Calacians innovated the recurved longbow, a far deadlier weapon than the short hunting bows used until this time. So armed, encased in metal armor, they proved their superiority against the spears, short blades, axes, and hides of the Molgur tribes. Even more important was their discipline and tactics, as well as the support of leading Menite priests who spoke prayers to set the followers of the Wurm ablaze.

In 2230 BR, the man who would eventually become Priest-King Golivant was born. On his maturity he rose to prominence,

proving blessed of the Lawgiver and by his rule the kingdom of Calacia began to repay the Molgur for a thousand years of bloody conflict. The effectiveness of his forays west of the Shield of Thrace to track down Molgur tribes and burn their villages did not go unnoticed, and in time the Molgur stirred to retaliate.

A champion rose among the Molgur tribes, a great trollkin chieftain named Horfar Grimmr, who gathered a vast horde with the cause of breaking through the Menite walls to burn Calacia to the ground. Grimmr was determined to show the valley-fed and teeming humans the might of the Molgur, and brought together the strength of their varied tribes. Bringing dozens of kriels of his own people, Grimmr also marched alongside ogrun, bogrin, and barbaric humans. Each of these races brought their own skills in combat as well as their courage, united by their worship of the Wurm and the desire to see Calacia destroyed.

A great battle took place at the Shield of Thrace with the fate of western Immoren in the balance. The Molgur crashed into the walls in waves, heedless of their losses, while archers on the walls rained arrows into their ranks and poured hot oil down upon them. The Molgur ignored their losses and threw carved logs up against the walls to climb them as ladders to fight on the battlements, and for a time succeeded in overwhelming the defenders.

Golivant led the army of Calacia to confront the foe and brought with him the very fire of Menoth and an imperishable will. Golivant and Grimmr fought several times, and in these battles the Menites eventually gained the upper hand. Golivant led his people in pushing the Molgur back and regained the battlements. Horfar Grimmr was captured and presented to the remaining barbarians in a grisly spectacle as he was tortured and executed. While Grimmr continued to shout defiance until his dying breath, the Molgur lost their will to fight and scattered into the mountains. Golivant was not inclined to allow them to lick their wounds and so set forth with his armies on a ten year campaign to end the Molgur.

Remnants of the savage tribes scattered, most going north to settle in the far frozen mountains, while others went west to hide among the Scharde Islands. The barbaric peoples who worshiped the Wurm would continue to plague civilized settlements for thousands of years, but never again as a unified people.

After Golivant's death, his son was slain by rivals and Calacia fragmented as factions sought control of the river valleys. However, in 2051 BR Golivant's grandson succeeded in uniting the region once more. He renamed the capital Caspia, and under his direction massive fortifications and walls were erected, all consecrated to Menoth. In subsequent generations it became known as the City of Walls.

THE FALL OF THE MOLGUR AND THE DHUNIAN RACES

The shattering of the Molgur was necessary for the rise of human civilization, but it had an impact on the other races that had joined in that tribal alliance. While humans could convert to Menoth, the ogrun, trollkin, gobbers, and bogrin were not given that choice. Members of these races were often slaughtered indiscriminately or driven out. In the wake of extensive persecution by Menite crusades, these races dwindled and turned inward to their surviving communities in remote and inhospitable places.

One of the largest impacts of the fall of the Molgur was the widespread abandonment of worship of the Wurm among these races. Though they knew the Wurm to be their divine father, this entity had become tainted by death and destruction. This led to the increase of Dhunian worship as these persecuted races turned to their divine mother, who offered fertility to replace the slain.

KHARDOVIC AND THE NORTH

Even as Golivant lay dying, a fierce warrior-priest named Khardovic was attempting to unite his people in the north. Geth's successors had come into this region to spread the word of Menoth, and their lessons took root among the mighty horselords who warred with one another across the plains south of the three great lakes. They adopted a written alphabet to suit the local tongues that would become known as Khurzic, which would in time give rise to the most prominent of the northern languages. A warrior-sect of northern Menites fiercely guarded the knowledge they had inherited, having translated the text of the True Law into Khurzic. Khardovic was the most prominent warlord of these people.

Khardovic is described as a giant of a man, fierce and proud and fanatically pious. Khardovic felt the calling to unite this region by blood and iron—it is said the crossroads in those days were decorated with pikes suspending the heads of countless of his enemies, those deemed too wild or irredeemable to convert. Like Golivant in the south, Khardovic was filled with the pious compulsion to rid his homelands of Wurm-worshiping savages.

Khardovic's campaign against those he saw to be in league with the Wurm was brutal and efficient, going directly to their shamans and confronting them. Slaughtering shamans of the Wurm proved highly effective, as many of the survivors immediately converted to the Menite faith. Priests followed behind Khardovic to bring the gentler teachings of the True Law to the remnants of the defeated tribes. By the time of his death, Khardovic had converted over a million savages to the Lawgiver, spreading Menite worship across the great north of what would one day be Khador. Some mountain tribes remained beyond his reach, but he ensured the Menite faith took root across the lowlands.

The people who inherited the legacy of Khardovic persist to this day, and all who call themselves Khards believe they have some connection to the chosen people who had gathered around Khardovic. Nearly every noble family in modern Khador claims descent from the vast family tree of Khardovic. These crusades also spread the Khurzic language and gave rise to lasting settlements. While the north would be caught up in turmoil and warfare throughout the next era, its leaders built walls around their towns, with impressive Menite temples at their centers.

Some claim these wild northern lands never fully embraced Menite teachings, adopting them from fear instead of belief. It is true that the totems endured, as did many superstitions in the remote reaches. The far northern Rustov, Vindol, and Vorgoi peoples never abandoned their beliefs, albeit in some cases old rites were changed and disguised. Elsewhere the fruits of civilization were enjoyed by brutal tyrants who sought to protect the holdings they seized through conquest. Little regard was given to the suffering of the peasants who toiled the fields, labored in mines and quarries, and who worked like slaves to erect temples and fortresses.

THE THOUSAND CITIES ERA

The spread of the Menite faith and the defeat of the Molgur allowed for the rapid spread of civilization across the plains, hills, forests, and coasts of western Immoren. Every fertile plot of ground or marginally defensible hillock was seized by ambitious lords. This ushered in an era no less torn by strife, but bringing many advancements. The settled peoples of this era had the luxury of ample food and shelter, as well as trade with neighbors, at least when they weren't at war. The battles of this era were not those between civilization and the wilderness but instead between rival city-states.

The spread of shipping and commerce also gave rise to new professions as well as dangers, with influential merchants as well as pirates and bandits preying on the citizens of the day. In the growing towns and cities, varied strata of society emerged, giving rise to those who could dedicate their lives to crafts other than farming or war. Across western Immoren a thousand petty fiefdoms and strongholds sprung up, each a fortified township led by a ruler who sought to unite the surrounding settlements and both protect and exploit them. By tradition, these rulers sought the blessings of Menite priests to legitimize their claims.

Soon conquest and diplomacy saw the weaker fiefdoms crushed or uniting paving the way for fewer but stronger kingdoms, each vying for domination. By the end of this era less than a dozen strong nations had cowed and consolidated most of the rest.

For all the changes that marked this era, it is remembered most for the rise of the Twins: a brother and sister from Caspia who would exceed mortal limits and carve very different paths to enlightenment before ascending to divinity.

ASCENDANCY OF THE TWINS

Morrow and Thamar were born in 1930 BR. The exact events of their early lives are shrouded in uncertainty. The little that is known comes from their combined writings, which were assembled into the Enkheiridion, the holy text of the Morrowan faith, and from accounts of their followers. Whatever their upbringing, Morrow and Thamar were brilliant and radical thinkers whose teachings would redefine the world for those who came after.

By the end of the Warlord Era, the Menite faith was unquestionably dominant. Chains of unbreakable spiritual fealty connected every human being to their Creator, and the True Law governed all aspects of life. Menite priests advised kings and sometimes governed their townships, and it fell to the scrutator caste to enforce the rule of law. After death the souls of the faithful would be governed by priests in the City of Man. Though civilization had come to Immoren, for the majority this meant servitude at the hands of spiritual tyrants.

Morrow was raised as a Menite and respected the Lawbringer for the gifts that fostered civilization. Yet he questioned how the True Law was interpreted, and in particular he challenged the tyranny of the priesthood. Thamar was even more extreme in her hatred of the Menite priesthood. Historians have surmised that the Twins' parents had been executed by scrutators, giving rise to this shared sentiment.

Their respective teachings proved to be tremendously subversive. From as early as 1905 BR the influence of their writings could be seen across the intellectual community of Caspia and beyond. Morrow served as a soldier for a decade of his early life, and he wrote about the horrors of war and the challenges of finding honor in the darkest moments. He was an orator beyond compare as well as a charismatic leader and spoke wherever he traveled, first in the streets of Caspia and later on pilgrimages abroad. He took time to lend aid to the less fortunate, particularly those suffering from lasting injuries, disease, or famine, and gained a reputation as a healer and worker of miracles.

Morrow's path to enlightenment—and the questions he would leave for later generations—emphasized the pursuit of a greater good. He believed living a good life required more than obeying the True Law, such as benevolence, mercy, compassion, and self-sacrifice. He postulated that through reflection and a deep understanding of the world a person could transcend the flesh, unlocking the limitless potential of the immortal soul. This power could then be wielded to the betterment of all.

Although at the outset Morrow and Thamar shared certain beliefs, their paths divided and became opposed. Both believed in questioning Menite authority and seeking enlightenment, but Thamar did not agree this required self-sacrifice. Rather, she asserted unlocking the potential of the human soul required absolute freedom—physical, mental, and spiritual. For her, the betterment of mankind required each person to find his individual strength and to rise above those who lacked the will. Thamar had a hunger for knowledge and came to believe the human mind could perceive the very fabric of reality and shape it. In her quest for enlightenment she immersed herself in the occult, seeking mastery of the supernatural and the ineffable, including unholy and forbidden lore. She learned to speak every tongue and consumed tomes and scrolls with a voracious appetite. While Morrow's teachings would take root and eventually be embraced by established society, Thamar was looked to by radical thinkers and outcasts as well as those seeking freedom from tyranny.

The Twins' respective cults and writings came to the attention of the scrutators across the south, who initiated a campaign to eradicate their influence. Their followers were seized, tortured, and then executed by being wracked or burned alive. Hearing of this persecution, Morrow and Thamar reconciled and put out a call to all who had suffered under Menite rule. Thousands saw this as their chance to repay the priesthood for countless excesses.

The gathering throngs became an army that marched on Caspia in 1900 BR. The priest-king of that city, Hierarch Heletius, met them with his own zealous soldiers, confident the Creator was on his side. Amid a great battle, Morrow fought the priest-king personally, eventually disarming him and demanding his surrender. Thamar intervened to impale the unarmed priest with her spear before he could answer. Morrow vowed she would answer for this act after the battle was won. This was the beginning of an irreconcilable divide. Soon the remaining Menite army was swept aside, and the Twins had their victory.

The pair were welcomed into Caspia as heroes. Morrow was urged to rule the city and guide its people, a responsibility he reluctantly accepted, hoping to put his principles into practice. The Enkheiridion speaks of this time as a difficult ordeal, when Morrow faced dilemmas for which there were no easy solutions. His writings admit to mistakes made in these years and warn that achieving the greater good is never simple for those in authority. His first travail involved cementing a peace with the remaining Menite priesthood. Morrow had no desire to drive them from the city or deprive them of their religion. Seeking harmony, he reached an accord: he promised to protect Menite temples and pay homage to the Creator of Man—and lastly, that Thamar would answer for the crime of murdering Hierarch Heletius.

Morrow brought his sister before him and told her what had been agreed. Displaying unusual humility, she begged forgiveness for her rash actions. Morrow thought her repentance insincere and exiled her from Caspia, promising death should she return. Thus Thamar endured being cast from the city she had fought to free, further embittering her to all who sat in authority, including her brother.

As master of the city, Morrow felt driven to expunge evil from its streets and ordered Thamar's followers imprisoned. He sought to eliminate all crime and corruption, a task that proved impossible and prompted increasingly stern measures. While life for the Caspian citizens was improved tremendously under Morrow's wise guidance, many freedoms were curtailed.

Living in exile, Thamar spent the next several years pursuing occult studies on the fringes of civilization. She mastered the fundamentals of alchemy, sought shamans of the Wurm in the wilderness, and tracked down sages of the black kingdom of Morrdh. She invented her own alphabet and a language called Telgesh, thought to be a key element of her eventual ascension. She also waged her own private war against the Menite priests and sowed the seeds of dissent in Caspia from afar by contacting those embittered by Morrow's rule.

There would be a climactic reunion between the Twins in 1894 BR. Thamar returned to Caspia and took charge of an army that rose up from within, and those who had governed the city in Morrow's name were murdered in their homes or set upon in the streets. Thamar carved a path of destruction through the city as she made her way to Morrow's palace displaying terrifying powers over the elements. Those who tried to stop her died, torn apart by fierce winds, set ablaze with dark fire, or pierced by her spear. Buildings around her crumbled to ruin, while behind her the dead arose and set upon the living. Morrow realized the only way he could prevent more harm to his city was to confront her personally. At the outer gate of what would eventually become the Sancteum, the Twins fought a fierce duel.

As Morrow sought to protect the innocent from his sister's unholy powers Thamar taunted him, accusing him of turning into what they had both despised. She pointed out how weak the city had become under his rule, with its people deprived of liberty and too meek to defend themselves from the hostile world beyond Caspia's walls. In a frenzy of destructive power, she caused the sky to blacken and summoned a storm of smoke and fire that threatened to consume the city. Morrow saw in these final moments how his own choices had led to this, how his unwillingness to forgive had sent her down a darker path. As Thamar prepared to destroy all he had built, he saw the only way to stop her was to sacrifice himself. He stepped forward and accepted the brunt of her wrath.

Thamar struck him down in full sight of the gathered throngs. All witnessed as Morrow's flesh became spirit and he ascended into the sky as the unnatural storm was dispersed by a light brighter than the sun. The power of Morrow's apotheosis stilled the wild air, crumbled the walking dead to dust, and protected those gathered from Thamar's hatred. Empowered by his example and no longer fearing Thamar, the masses overwhelmed her. Rather than using her power to escape, she remained true to her own path, unwilling to submit, and was torn apart by the mob. In death Thamar, too, ascended, become black smoke that dispersed as she passed to Urcaen. All that remained of her were the black pages of her writings.

One of Morrow's foremost disciples, a man named Laertes Prado, collected Thamar's written works, intent on destroying them, but an apparition of Morrow manifested and bade him stop. Morrow told Prado to bind his own writings with Thamar's. He insisted his sister's words should be preserved alongside his own to illustrate the Volition, encompassing both of their choices—in her writings were lessons as important to those who would come after as his own were. The figure then faded, but his followers did not mourn, knowing Morrow would continue to watch over them from Urcaen as a god.

THE PURGING

Morrow and Thamar became symbols of two distinct paths of enlightenment. Word of their respective ascensions spread despite efforts by the Menite scrutators to repress it. The Menites broadened their hunts and this became the Purging, a terrible time of religious strife pursued as vigorously as once the Menites had contested with the Molgur. Entire communities were declared anathema and eradicated as the fledgling Morrowans were driven into exile.

While Morrow's teachings were never entirely expunged from Caspia, the Menite Temple reclaimed leadership of the city in 1882 BR. This was the year that Keeper Laertes Prado was captured, then publically tortured and executed by the city's scrutators. The original Enkheiridion was lost and thought to have been destroyed, although copies had been transcribed by hand and were preserved by priests fleeing the city. Prado became a hero of the early church as he refused to name any Morrowans. In later centuries it came to light he had hidden the Enkheiridion and taken knowledge of its location to his grave.

In 1866 BR, a priest named Nolland Orellius heeded portents he claimed came from Morrow himself to found a fortified monastery deep in the Wyrmwall Mountains, and dedicated it to the preservation of the writings and teachings of the Twins. This was the Divinium, with Orellius becoming the first primarch of the Church of Morrow. Under his direction the church hierarchy took shape while its clergy organized efforts to hide the faithful from Menite scrutators.

Even as Orellius was chosen by Morrow, in death the god appeared to usher his soul to the afterlife. Orellius became the first Archon of Morrow, an angelic spirit who would assist the god in Urcaen. A week later, this archon manifested before Orellius' successor as a sign of Morrow's favor. From that point forward, every primarch after death has become an archon to join a growing host working to fulfill the will of Morrow. After the passing of the old, each new primarch has been signified by a manifestation of one or more archons as an unequivocal sign of Morrow's guiding hand. Morrow was named the Prophet, as through the archons he passed down prophecies to the faithful, as well as other momentous portents.

While the very survival of their faiths was tenuous in these early days, the teachings of the Twins proved to be enduring. Thamar's cult spread slowly even as Morrow's rose to prominence. The relationships between these faiths would prove to be complex and ever-changing, perhaps reflecting the relationships between the gods themselves.

THE FIRST ASCENDANTS AND SCIONS

Morrow and Thamar were followed by others heeding their teachings who rose to greatness and eventually achieved enlightenment, generally at the moment of death. Those who followed Morrow's path have joined him as ascendants, saint-like figures thought to embody the noblest aspects of the human soul. Those who followed Thamar are scions, deemed holy by her cult but vilified by the majority. The ascendants and scions became essential aspects of the faiths of the Twins—the faithful look to these holy beings as patrons and pray to them as intermediaries for Morrow or Thamar.

Morrow's first ascendant was a warrior woman of the frozen north named Katrena, a shield-maiden of noble birth from the Skirov tribes who heard Morrow's message and felt the calling to join the fledgling church at the Divinium. In this time of the Purging her martial skill was sorely needed and she inspired others to take up arms to defend the faith. Katrena protected the church's priests, including those brave enough to spread its teachings despite the Menite scrutators hunting them. She ultimately died and ascended in 1810 BR protecting the third primarch, Orestus I, from assassination. At the sight of her ascension, the would-be killers dropped their weapons and begged the primarch's forgiveness, converting to the faith. In subsequent centuries many who took up arms in the defense of others adopted Katrena's sigil. She would eventually be esteemed by those of noble birth who heeded Morrow's message and sought to honorably fulfill their responsibilities.

In life, Thamar had been joined in her occult investigations by Ekris, a man with a brilliant mind and an appetite for lore who was also her consort and disciple. On word of her ascension he vowed once to follow her path and rejoin her in Urcaen. Ekris spent decades retracing her steps and delving into the Telgesh glyphs, confirming their connection to the old writings and rituals of Morrdh. Ekris is said to have used forbidden lore to bargain with infernal powers to greatly extend his mortal life. For more than a hundred years he delved into occult mysteries and achieved his vow. He ascended after his death in 1780 BR to become Thamar's first scion. Ekris is prayed to by those seeking enlightenment through forbidden lore.

Other exceptional individuals would rise to ascension, not always predictably. The next scion was a witch named Delesle who spent her lifetime terrorizing Menite temples through the necromantic arts. While widely reviled, Delesle's attacks served to protect the early Morrowan faith. Her dark ascension was in 1610 BR, her death self-inflicted by falling upon a black sword. Scion Delesle became patron of necromancers as well as those rebelling against tyranny.

In 1590 BR a woman named Ellena ascended to join Morrow after spending decades traveling spreading the Morrowan faith

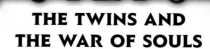

THE TWINS AND THE WAR OF SOULS

According to Morrowan Church doctrine, the Twins established their respective domains in Urcaen after their ascensions and joined the War of Souls against each other as well as Menoth and the Devourer Wurm. The exact nature of these conflicts is little understood by mortals except that periodic battles are thought to transpire between these divinities and their followers, with the Wurm being a constant threat to the domains of all gods in Urcaen. The afterlife of each of these faiths is described differently, but both Thamarites and Morrowans believe their souls continue to experience refinement in the hereafter. One's degree of piety is thought to affect the likelihood of arriving safely at the domain of one's patron, as well as being welcomed into its community. Thamar's domain is described as relatively welcoming but also possessing the least secure borders. Menoth's domain is the most heavily fortified but also the most discriminating, while Morrow's domain is between these extremes. Mortal souls periodically contribute to the defense of the realm of their divinity.

across western Immoren. Another selfless Morrowan paragon named Doleth sought enlightenment negotiating the Meredius. He is remembered for rescuing those caught amid the storms of these dangerous waters. He ascended in 1411 BR and gained a strong following among fishermen, sailors, and river boatmen, who pray to him in the hopes of safe journeys.

Demonstrating that not all followers of the goddess were as openly sinister as Ekris or Delesle was the unexpected ascension of Scion Drayce in 1400 BR, a prestigious and influential noble of early Thuria who had elevated his township to a regional power through ruthless politics and fostering trade. While openly condemned for his corruption, many subsequent sovereigns looked to Drayce's example and treated his writings as the guide to pragmatic rulership.

Over the centuries, more ascendants and scions would arise to strengthen their respective faiths. These holy emissaries are thought to manifest periodically on Caen to guide mortals. Ascendants work primarily through dreams and visions, while scions prefer to possess mortals and control their bodies to further their schemes on Caen.

WARS OF THE NORTH AND THE FALL OF MORRDH

While in the south the rise of the Twins led to religious purges, the Khards were at war in the north. The teachings of the Twins would eventually reach the northern lands as well, but spread more gradually over the centuries, facilitating accords between old and new religions.

By 1690 BR the lands just south of the Nychatha Mountains saw sporadic outbreaks of armed conflict between warlords of the Kossites, the Skirov, and the southern Khardic horselords. Kos never managed to unify as a kingdom, although its people were fierce in battle and especially dangerous in their native Scarsfell Forest. The Skirov had turned as zealously to the Menite faith as they had once howled at the moon in praise of the Wurm, and were mountain fighters without peer. Yet when the Skirov armies marched onto the plains to meet their Khardic foes they were ridden down by heavy horse. These battles may have continued interminably if a terrible plague had not swept through both the Skirov and Kossites, mysteriously leaving the Khards untouched. The Khards were able to use this advantage to seize huge stretches of lands. Among the cities conquered by the Khards was Molga, that they called Khardov in veneration of Khardovic.

The kingdom of Morrdh, now in decline, was torn by internal strife and wars abroad. An internal power struggle left the kingdom weak and ruled by madmen who antagonized their neighbors at a time when the people were desperate to rebuild. Lacking the funds to pay for their wars, the lords of Morrdh committed an unforgivable blasphemy by ordering the plunder of several burial sites in northern Midar to bolster their failing treasury.

This galvanized the Midar against them, and soon these two kingdoms became locked in a bitter struggle. Morrdh had become diminished within the dark forests and valleys of its interior, its military strength a shadow of what it once had been. While its lords possessed dread powers, these did not suffice to allow it to endure a lengthy war of attrition against the Midar with their fertile farmlands and abundant population. The Midar would eventually become a bastion of the Morrowan faith, and so the fall of Morrdh by 1500 BR was seen by most as a Morrowan triumph over an ancient evil that had plagued these lands for two thousand years. The scattered descendants of Morrdh became the Morridane, who have ever since been scorned and treated with suspicion.

The destruction of Morrdh gave other neighboring kingdoms the opportunity to consolidate under strong lords. Slowly but inexorably the Thousand Cities became apportioned off and divided by the borders of growing kingdoms. The kingdom of Thuria rose to dominance in the west, initially banding together for mutual protection against the trollkin of the Gnarls. While the Midar remained only loosely confederated and never formalized central rulership, their communities made pacts of mutual solidarity, eventually coming to be known as the Midlunds. North of Thuria and south of the Khardic plains rose the Kingdom of Tordor.

By 1443 BR Khardov was the largest city in the north and began to exercise its dominance over neighboring territories. Gains seized from Kos and the Skirov led the young but charismatic Sveynod Skelvoro to declare himself emperor, founding the Khardic Empire. The Kos were the first to fall to them. The last of the Kos nobles finally surrendered to the emperor in 1382 BR.

A number of other proud horselords dwelling east of Khardov refused to bow to the emperor, claiming their own lineage descending directly from Priest King Khardovic. In his last years, the now elderly Emperor Skelvoro proved his political acumen by persuading the horse lords they could join and serve the empire without bowing to his rule, accrediting them as princes in their own right. Thus assuaged and with the Khardic horselords united, the empire waged a long war against Skirov.

Skelvoro's successor eventually forced the Skirov from their mountain strongholds and the Skirov joined the Khardic Empire in 1263 BR, bringing the Menite faith to the mountain communities. The emperor wisely allowed the region to be governed by Menite priests, freeing his own vassals to engage in battles elsewhere. Eventually the Morrowan faith gained a foothold; the people of this region have long shown a predilection toward faith and zealotry, whichever god they embraced.

Mirroring the wars of the north, Tordor fought with Thuria in 1322 BR and annexed that rival kingdom by 1313 BR. Thuria remained largely intact and her citizens continued proudly to call themselves Thurian even as their leaders swore oaths of fealty to Tordoran castellans. With Thuria's strength behind her, Tordor became a rising power, particularly notable for a formidable fleet of Dirgenmast ships that dominated Immoren's western coasts.

One of the last of the northern peoples to defy the Khardic Empire were the eastern horselords, who in 1169 BR united under the Tzepescis, Umbreykos, and Chardovosks to create the kingdom of Umbrey, which declared itself independent of the empire. Korska became their capital and began to arm and fortify in anticipation of war. Their position was strengthened through ties of commerce and trade to the lowland peoples settling a fertile region northeast of the Thornwood, which became the kingdom of Rynyr in 1073 BR.

RECONCILIATION OF FAITHS

The Purging conducted by the Menites against the Morrowans was at its most brutal in the early centuries of the Thousand Cities Era. Early Morrowans knew they must worship in secret anywhere the scrutators held sway. Morrowan shrines and churches were hidden or disguised. Menite temples were filled with secret worshipers of the Twins. The rise of other ascendants and scions continued to draw converts. Morrowan numbers in some regions made it difficult for the scrutators to actively repress the Prophet's followers from a fear of widespread unrest. This was particularly true where the Morrowan faith took root among the sons and daughters of ruling families.

Amid this time of religious strife lived a Morrowan soldier and chaplain named Solovin, a healer versed in alchemy and battlefield surgery who felt the calling to walk the war-torn city-states of Thuria. He earned such a reputation for his dedication to saving lives that that even the Menite priests refrained from interfering with his work. In 1253 BR, after years spent tending to the wounded of myriad conflicts, his help was beseeched by the steward of a small fiefdom south of Thuria. This steward's master, King Eldrin, had apparently fallen prey to a strange illness.

Solovin discovered King Eldrin had unwittingly given himself over to Scion Remel, one of Thamar's most malicious servants. The king's possessed body was serving to incubate a terrible plague that would soon be unleashed on the region. Solovin attempted to sanctify the body to free the king's soul, but failed. He realized his only chance of success would be to lure Scion Remel into his own flesh and held him there, suffering horribly as disease wracked his body but containing it in the process. At his death, Scion Remel and his plague were destroyed, while Solovin ascended to join Morrow. Solovin became the patron of Morrowan healers, while the Thamarites in subsequent years excised all records of Remel, claiming no true scion could have been destroyed in this fashion.

Despite these and other miracles, the Menite Temple still refused to acknowledge the divinity of the Twins. The first inroads toward an accord between these embattled religions was to take place shortly after Solovin's ascension when a Menite delegation was invited to meet with Morrowan leaders at the Divinium. Though they accepted this invitation, the Menites were not disposed toward an accord, and in fact harbored among them those plotting to kill the Morrowan primarch. This included the infamous assassin Khorva. A devout Thamarite, she had accepted a contract to murder the primarch after seeing visions from the dark twin. Taking the place of the masked scrutator Sicarius, she joined the delegation. Amid these negotiations, Khorva was able to get close enough to Primarch Loriachas to strike him down.

While she succeeded in murdering the Morrowan primarch on holy ground, this set in motion an unprecedented chain of divine manifestations. Ascendant Katrena appeared in a blaze of silver light to avenge the primarch's death and killed Khorva. As the shocked and amazed delegates looked on, Thamar appeared to claim Khorva's soul as she in turn ascended. Katrena and Thamar seemed poised to do battle when Morrow manifested to gather the soul of his primarch, now become an archon. These divinities clashed briefly before both sides vanished in a blinding flash.

In the aftermath, councils of visgoths were assembled and doctrine was written in 1247 BR to explain these events to the satisfaction of the Menite temples. These measures allowed the Menites to reach a grudging accord with the Morrowan faith. They determined that Menoth had allowed Morrow's divinity by way of an accommodation whereby Morrow knelt to Menoth as his Creator. Morrow is said to have been given sanction to shepherd those who worshiped him, so long as he stood as guardian against the perfidy of his sister. Further, his followers were required to acknowledge the Creator, attend Menite services, and pay tithes to the temple. This theological accommodation allowed Morrowans to worship openly and to build churches of their faith.

THE AGE OF REASON: THE CLOCKWORK RENAISSANCE

The consolidation of strong kingdoms, while responsible for many bloody wars, also allowed advances in culture and science. The reconciliation between the dominant Menite temples and the Morrowans allowed for the dissemination of ideas and contact between thinkers across great distances. This was facilitated by safer roads and river traffic across western Immoren.

By 1100 BR a number of alchemists had begun to exchange correspondence on methods and formulae, making great steps toward codifying their art. By 1000 BR, the Khards had devised a railed road upon which a horse-drawn carriage could be moved with greater speed, used initially for hauling ore. In a number of major cities, intellectual advancement came with the establishment of universities and organized efforts to find bright minds and educate them.

Early in this era amid the kingdom of Rynyr was born a prodigious scholar, historian, and linguist named Angellia. A woman of singular piety as well as intelligence, Angellia worked tirelessly to preserve the ancient history of the region before turning her attention to the lives of the Twins. It was through her efforts that the original Enkheiridion was recovered from a forgotten vault in Caspia, together with the writings of Keeper Prado which described the ascension of the Twins. This restoration is counted the greatest act of scholarship of the age. Angellia penned the definitive translation of the Enkheiridion into the Caspian of the day, as well as writing dozens of highly influential theological works that would guide the Morrowan Church for centuries. Angellia ascended in 1027 BR.

Soon thereafter, in the southern city of Mercir, a renowned Morrowan rector turned clockmaker named Janus Gilder used his expertise to create the first printing press. He was able to run ink across the carved blocks and then feed vellum sheets into the mechanism, quickly producing multiple prints. The Janus block press was soon evolved into the Janus type press, and when moveable type was innovated and metal plates put in use, the mechanism became extremely useful. Initially employed to copy religious catechisms for wider dispersal, the press helped the Church of Morrow disseminate its doctrines far abroad. This invention led to the wider spread of reading and general education, allowing a variety of books to be duplicated and distributed.

During the next two hundred years, clockwork and other precision-crafted inventions found new ways to address familiar problems. This included lenses crafted to fine specifications, allowing for high powered telescopes, as well as applying engineering to the arts of war, such as the first geared repeating crossbow. The use of better telescopes and the sextant for measuring stars and distance became a boon to navigation, which in turn led to advances in cartography, with efforts undertaken to update maps.

The advances of this era were almost undone by the Time of the Long Sun starting in 822 BR, one of the worst droughts in history. This caused crop failures across western Immoren. It is thought that hundreds of thousands may have died, with the tribal Idrians being hit the hardest. As far west as Ord and southern Khador, temperatures were unseasonably hot and rains few and far between, causing starvation and privation. This period might have been much worse if not for the actions of a Morrowan monk named Gordenn. He devoted his life to alleviating hunger and overseeing food distribution, taking

FOUNDING OF A NIGHTMARE EMPIRE

Before 1000 BR, the largest of the Scharde Islands had become a haven for pirates and raiders preying on the shipping sent along the Broken Coast. This large island became home to thirteen self-proclaimed pirate kings who had divided the region among them. Each possessed a formidable fleet manned by pirates and smugglers. Their strength in numbers combined with the treacherous nature of the channels between these poorly charted islands made it difficult for mainland fleets to retaliate.

These pirate kings did not know that Toruk the Dragonfather loomed in their destiny. For centuries Toruk had patiently stalked his progeny across Immoren and beyond, cornering them in their lairs before consuming their athancs. Those that were left were the greatest and most intelligent of his brood, and they gathered to create an alliance for mutual protection. Together they attacked the Dragonfather above the skies of Immoren. In the greatest clash since the dawn of time, Toruk and the dragons fought with claw and fang, while the skies boiled with the heat of their fire. Blighted blood and flame rained down upon the desert wastes.

For the first time the Dragonfather was forced to flee, driven from Immoren. Blighterghast, the greatest of Toruk's children, landed amid the highest peaks of the Wyrmwall Mountains there to take up a tireless vigil watching to the west against the Dragonfather's return.

The lord of all dragons landed amid the Scharde Islands, there to make his new lair and home. Toruk did not waste time recovering from his wounds, but immediately set about subjugating the island inhabitants to forge a new empire that would worship him as a god.

First Toruk sent an emissary to the pirate kings, bidding them gather to hear his demands. They were too proud to listen, too arrogant, underestimating the creature that had come among them. Toruk knew he must make an example to convince them. His blighted breath consumed the largest and greatest vessel of the pirate fleets, the *Atramentous*, transforming it and its crew into deathless servants of indomitable will. Seeing the scope of the power set against them, all but one prostrated themselves and begged mercy. Lord Moorcraig alone remained stubbornly defiant behind the walls of his castle, but they did not avail him against Toruk's all-consuming fire.

Swearing fealty to their master, the remaining pirate kings Toruk transformed into twelve lich lords of Cryx and were sent rule over his dominion. This was the origin of the Nightmare Empire, which has existed since as a blight upon western Immoren, a brooding presence west of the Broken Coast. Toruk would raise armies, plunder the island of its resources, and consume the very souls of its people. Eventually he would unleash his armies upon his progeny.

The drought did not deter the Khardic Empire from pressing its claims against the Umbreans, and the Horselord Wars began in 821 BR. This would initiate nearly a century of intermittent battles and conflict between these two northern powers. Ultimately the Khards proved they had the numbers and the will to subjugate their enemies no matter the cost in blood. The Umbrean princes of the Black Ring were forced to surrender to the Khardic emperor in 716 BR, bringing these wars to an end. Korska became the eastern capital of the Khardic Empire while Khardov remained the primary seat of power in the west.

In the south, Caspia continued to prosper, particularly as several of its most fertile farmlands survived the drought relatively intact. The Midlunds came to rely on Caspia, becoming a protectorate in all but name. The City of Walls continued to grow and soon was acknowledged as a wonder of the age, a city unrivaled anywhere in western Immoren and once again a center of education, invention, and lively intellectual debate.

In 712 BR the Church of Morrow decided there was no need for its administrative and spiritual center to be so isolated. While the Divinium would remain a fortress monastery to guard sacred relics, the primarch and the Exordeum, his advising council, moved to the Sancteum within Caspia. Soon construction began on the Archcourt Cathedral, the greatest work of architecture of the era.

The cathedral was designed by a genius named Sambert. A true man of his age, Sambert was an unsurpassed sculptor, painter, architect, engineer, and mason, who devoted his work to paying homage to the divine. While remembered for countless works of sacred art and architecture, his greatest achievement was the Archcourt Cathedral, a building like no others with flying buttresses and spires admired even by the city's Menites as a testament to the unassailable hold of civilization. Sambert ascended in 605 BR upon completion of his great statue of Morrow, the light of his transfiguration taking place on the very location where the Prophet had his apotheosis thirteen centuries before.

advantage of then recent advances in agriculture and irrigation. Gordenn is credited with countless miracles in this era, such as transforming barren farmlands into fertile soil and calling down rain through prayer. By the time of his ascension in 812 BR, Gordenn was credited for saving the lives of tens of thousands who otherwise would have died of starvation.

Technology and innovation continued to advance on other fronts—Copolius penned *Crucibilus Synthetatus* in 753 BR, the most detailed work on alchemy in its time. Taking advantage of printing presses, this book was widely distributed, providing a shared foundation for this field. Of even greater significance was the work of the engineer Drago Salvoro, who built the first steam engine in 743 BR. Advances in piston-driven engines eventually followed. By 698 BR steam engines powered most of the heavy equipment in Khardic mines. Ore haulers, sifters, drills, and other machines were converted to run from steam power instead of water driven mills.

These technologies would in time be duplicated in neighboring kingdoms and applied to many industrial uses. 620 BR brought forth the first construction of steam-powered vessels built by Tordoran shipwrights. Soon these vessels were being built in Caspia as well. Around the same time, the first steam-powered locomotive was built in Korsk. The Khards were amid the beginnings of constructing a rail line between Korsk and the mines in the Skirov region when all such works were put on hold by the momentous landing of hostile invaders from across the western sea. In one of the greatest tragedies of Immoren's long history, just as the region was experiencing a golden era of advancement, sleek shadows crossed the Meredius—black ships sailed by invaders bent on conquest.

EXODUS OF THE DIVINE COURT

Even as the Age of Reason proceeded in human lands, the inheritors of an older and more advanced civilization were experiencing considerable hardship. In the secluded kingdom of Ios, the elves and their gods had become aware of a deep cosmological imbalance that was causing their people to atrophy. Fertility rates were down, average life spans had shortened noticeably, and disease was on the rise. The gods that walked among them had been endeavoring to fight this decay for long centuries, to no avail. Eventually they decided that their absence from the Veld was the problem, and that they must return. In 840 BR, to much sadness among the Iosan people, the Divine Court left their fanes and departed, seeking to find passage to the Veld.

In the aftermath of this, several of the Iosan cities that had tended to their respective gods fell into decay. Most notably, the inhabitants of the city of Darsael, which had been home to Nyssor, the god of Winter, decided to leave Ios on a holy pilgrimage. Led by a priest and prophet named Aeric, who claimed to have received instructions from Nyssor himself, these elves moved to the northern mountains of Khador. Over time they became the Nyss, a distinct people who reverted to a more primitive and nomadic tribal existence among the frozen peaks of the Shard Mountains.

ORGOTH OCCUPATION ERA

The invasion of the Orgoth from across the Meredius and the long period of their occupation forever changed this region and had a drastic impact on its history. This dark era lasted for eight centuries but is divided into three distinct periods: the first two hundred years of the invasion and bloody subjugation, four hundred years of occupation, and the tumultuous two hundred year rebellion which eventually served to drive the Orgoth out.

ORGOTH INVASION

The earliest surviving accounts of the invasion were written by Caspian sailors who witnessed the arrival of blackships landing on western shores. By that time the western Khardic Empire had already been beset by the Orgoth. The empire was by this point the greatest power in western Immoren but could not slow the advance of this foreign threat. Rumors of chaos and bloodshed along the empire's western coasts began to filter south.

Many of the early accounts written by neighboring kingdoms were less than sympathetic, as the Khardic Empire had many enemies. The gravity of the situation became clearer when the invaders fell on Tordor next, but still no cohesive plan of shared defense was considered. Many thought the foreigners must have outreached their grasp with Tordor, whose naval might was the envy of western Immoren, yet the blackships of the invaders were rowed by men with inhuman stamina, and supported by sails that gathered a wind that seemed to blow only for them. The great Dirgenmast Fleet of Tordor sailed out against the enemy and never returned, its proud vessels fighting to the last man before sinking into the depths.

The Orgoth broadened their attacks and blackships by the dozens landed on other shores, pouring forth bloodthirsty and ruthlessly efficient warriors. The rulers of each kingdom and freehold looked to their own defenses and watched the fall of their neighbors, hoping to avoid the same fate. All attempts to negotiate with the invaders met with the return of the decapitated heads of emissaries.

Fierce in demeanor and merciless in war, the Orgoth were attired in armor and wielded weapons adorned with countless howling forms. That the Orgoth had martial prowess was proven and confirmed early in these battles, but it was their darker powers that added to the terror of their attacks in the accounts of survivors. They proved skilled at exploiting the fear of their enemies.

In a time when the people of western Immoren had little exposure to the arcane beyond the miracles invoked by priests, the Orgoth wielded dread powers that had not been seen since the time of Morrdh. Among the Orgoth were warwitches, sirens that invoked green fire and caused the sky to rain blood that melted flesh. Alongside their soldiers marched twisted undead abominations called dreads, disfigured corpses with limbs of iron. On the battlefields where Orgoth warlords fought, they carried spiked cages that collected the howling and tormented souls of the slain, used to fuel other unholy weaponry. It was suggested that the Orgoth sought slaughter and the capture of souls to offer sacrifices to the dark gods they worshiped. In return, the Orgoth seemed blessed with invincibility, or so it seemed as army after army was swept aside.

By 589 BR steam powered river vessels sent by Thuria and Caspia began making raids against Orgoth outposts but achieved little. In the next three years, Caspia would lose most of her western holdings, and the Orgoth would conquer both Thuria and the Midlunds. The Khards continued to fight a desperate and losing struggle, steadily pushed east, but both Tordor and Thuria were enslaved and put to work erecting the first of what would be many Orgoth fortresses. From these the fearsome governors of this foreign empire would oversee their subjugated territories, accumulating resources and slaves to ship across the ocean. The Khardic Empire fell by 569 BR, and Rynyr surrendered by 542 BR, although its outlying regions continued to resist.

The subjugation of the Thousand Cities was long and bloody and required. two centuries of strife. Some kingdoms were able to hold out for decades and preserve the integrity of their lands, only to eventually be overwhelmed. What the Orgoth seized, they kept, and set their slaves to work in labor camps, mining iron or quarrying stone to erect massive fortifications. These would serve as impenetrable symbols of Orgoth domination and as centers of their administration.

In the end, the only kingdom of mankind able to defy the Orgoth and remain free was Caspia, although none felt victorious

as the decades lengthened and the Orgoth strengthened their stranglehold on the region. Caspia was forced to pull back from its periphery territories and by 433 BR only the City of Walls escaped Orgoth dominion. So great was the sense of peril that by this time both Menite and Morrowan faiths had put aside their differences, with the armed protectors of both faiths fighting against the foe. Indeed, after Caspia's last king was killed in battle, the heads of both churches stepped forward as leaders and worked to rally the people of Caspia.

It was amid these desperate straits that the Orgoth warlord Kolegzein IV sent a messenger to Caspia, asking for these religious leaders to meet him to negotiate terms. It was thought that the Orgoth, who had never faced fortifications on a scale of the City of Walls, might be overextended. It seems likely the Caspians consented to meet the Orgoth in the interest of buying

time for her beleaguered armies. Not understanding this enemy possessed no shared concepts of honor, the Morrowan Primarch Gallumus and the Menite Hierarch Sadron IV went forth in their full splendor to speak with the Orgoth warlord.

The spiritual leaders of Caspia were taken captive despite flag of truce and hauled within sight of Caspia's walls, where its defenders watched on. The Menite cleric Garven Dratheus, who stood atop the walls and gave witness, wrote of the words spoken by Kolegzein:

You are ours. Your women, your children, they are no longer yours. You belong to us, your every breath, every drop of blood, every inch of skin. Every tear, every laugh, every broken bone, every drop of sweat is ours. You are the chattel of this land made fat by your own weakness. That I deign to speak to you this once is a warning. Your bodies in life are ours; in death, your souls shall also belong to us.

LIMITS OF THE ORGOTH INVASION

Though the Orgoth were formidable, they were not omnipotent. Even as they held most of western Immoren under their iron lash, they confined their exploits to the inheritors of the Thousand Cities. Attempts against other neighboring powers were less successful.

Rhul has been criticized for its neutrality during most of the Occupation, but to the dwarven perspective there was little to differentiate this era from previous human wars of unification, such as the rise of the Khardic Empire. Battle came to Rhul unbidden in 542 BR, just after the capitulation of Rynyr. The Orgoth sent an invasion force up the Black River to besiege Horgenhold, one of the great fortress cities of Rhul. Records in Rhul depict this as a grim and difficult struggle, one that tested the limits of the defenders and nearly depleted the local garrisons. Eventually Rhulic warriors rallied to drive the Orgoth back, and the tyrants never again besieged Rhulic fortresses.

Perhaps contributing to the Orgoth decision to abandon subsequent attacks on Rhul was the loss of a sizable fleet four years later. The first and greatest of the Orgoth cities built on Immorese soil was Drer Drakkerrung on Garlghast Island. It was from this fortress that the Orgoth launched ships sent to expand their holdings by seizing the other Scharde Islands. This set the Orgoth against the Cryxian Empire, which had previously ignored them. After a Satyxis fleet sent to intercept the Orgoth ships was annihilated, Toruk took to wing for the first time in centuries to deal with this threat personally. By fire and fang Toruk demonstrated the folly of intruding on his domain, sending the entire Orgoth fleet into the depths. This would be the last time the Orgoth challenged Cryx.

No similar incursion was launched against Ios. The reasons for this are unknown, but it added to the mystique of this nation in the eyes of the human kingdoms.

After this speech Kolegzein cut the throats of the primarch and hierarch and drank their still warm and flowing blood. Their corpses were bled dry and dangled on gallows by ropes made from the hair of their own escorting priests within sight of Caspia's walls until their bones were picked clean by carrion birds and fell untouched to the earth. The deaths of these spiritual leaders prompted no holy manifestation, no wrathful smiting by either Menoth or Morrow, and the defenders quailed behind the walls thinking their gods had forsaken them or were powerless against the vast evil embodied in the Orgoth.

While the Orgoth had proven their supremacy over the faiths of western Immoren, Caspia would not fall in this siege or subsequent ones. Its great walls and the ingenuity of its people proved too difficult to overcome by force of arms, even combined with their tactics of terror. Its unsurpassed walls could shield its entire navy while at dock, and its garrison was formidable. Starving Caspia proved to be impractical, with its access to the river and the gulf, and its navy proved able to defend its fishing fleet from the blackships. Caspia even managed to protect its immediate farmlands, those in closest proximity to the towering walls. Rather than invest in an extensive campaign to break this city, the Orgoth created blockades both upriver and along the main roads, limiting access and trade with the region.

Caspia would persist in virtual isolation for the next several centuries, its population steadily decreasing and in some years existing in worse conditions than those of the conquered cities. Later when the seeds of rebellion were planted, Caspia became a safe haven for escaped slaves and others who fled Orgoth rule. The city benefitted from the ingenuity and courage of these rugged survivors and their descendants.

OCCUPATION

With the exception of Caspia, the Orgoth tyrants maintained their tight grip on the human kingdoms for four centuries. This is considered the darkest era in the history of western Immoren, a bleak time when the advances that had been achieved in the late Thousand Cities Era were destroyed, forgotten, or simply unavailable to the vast majority of the populace. This era set back innovation and intellectual advancement for centuries.

Due to the harsh constraints throughout the Occupation, reconstructing life under the Orgoth lash has been difficult for modern scholars. Additionally, the Orgoth destroyed most of their own records, and so understanding their goals and relationship with their own homeland is nearly impossible.

VAST ENSLAVEMENT

Many of the greatest atrocities committed by the Orgoth transpired in the early decades of the occupation, when they were engaged in conquest and establishing their domain. The appetite of the Orgoth for slaves was vast and they clearly saw no need to treat their captives with any mercy or care. Using an enslaved work force combined with servants animated from the dead, the Orgoth quickly erected tremendous fortresses and temples in black stone. They connected these fortresses with a network of paved roads. While the blood of many innocents would be shed in this work, these trade ways would eventually benefit the region's inheritors, one of the few positive aspects of Orgoth rule.

The vast slave camps required by the Orgoth were squalid and inhumane, and the loss of life in these places was beyond modern reckoning. Clear cases of Orgoth necromancy in harvesting both the souls and bodies of the dead lend an aspect of unnatural horror to these arrangements. This has left a strong legacy of loathing for the practice of slavery that would persist long after the Orgoth were gone. A vast number of slaves were shipped across the Meredius to whatever homeland spawned the Orgoth. It is unknown what became of these people.

As a sign of how horrible these times were, the people took comfort in unlikely places. The most famous folk hero to arise in the early occupation era was a man named Aidan. A thief and grave-robber, Aiden became renowned for evading the Orgoth authorities at every turn. Twice he was captured and escaped his chains. He evaded the Orgoth for years, inspiring countless tales of his exploits. His death through betrayal resulted in Aidan's dark ascension in 344 BR, joining Thamar in the ultimate escape from earthly bondage. Though few had success in following is example, his cult would experience a resurgence during the rebellion in later centuries.

For all this oppression, once the Orgoth pacified the region they conducted themselves in ways that seem almost indulgent. They required absolute subservience from the conquered people, but were not in the habits of closely managing the daily lives of the conquered. For much of this era the Orgoth kept apart from the Immorese. There may have been a strong taboo among the Orgoth related to intermingling with those they had subjugated, as the mixing of Immorese and Orgoth bloodlines was very rare.

For most of the Occupation the Immorese were allowed to continue to practice their faiths and to maintain other tightly held traditions. While many churches and temples had been destroyed during the invasion, the Orgoth allowed them to be rebuilt and for services to be attended. The invaders did not seek to spread their own faith, which they kept to themselves.

The subjugation period was particularly detrimental to the Temple of Menoth. Any claims about the authority of the priest caste became empty in the face of the tyrants who ruled and who clearly lacked the favor of the Creator. By contrast, the Morrowan message continued to spread, and its humbler churches and priests were seen as a comfort to the oppressed. In the later years the message of Thamar would help kindle a strong spirit of indignation and rebellion, turning sentiments once directed at the Menite priesthood toward the Orgoth. This period would see the Morrowans quietly become the majority, while the Menite faith waned, particularly in the south.

With the Orgoth disdain for governance, life in the region resumed with the surface veneer of normality, with new cities built and commerce and trade resumed between them. Transportation was an area the Orgoth closely controlled, with most of the steam ships dismantled and destroyed, a technology the Orgoth did not wish to adopt or understand. The same was true for rail travel, with only a few tracks utilized by mining carts being preserved. The Orgoth scrutinized those who went from one region to another, requiring sealed papers authorizing trade. Corvis is an example of a major city built at the outset of this era, situated such that the local Orgoth governor could regulate and control all river traffic passing through this vital trade route. One lasting legacy of the Orgoth administration and bureaucracy would be the division of western Immoren into quarters. This shaped the subsequent emergence of the Iron Kingdoms, as these regions would eventually identify themselves.

Many local regions were governed by collaborators appointed by the Orgoth. Particularly in the first two centuries of the Occupation, the privileged upper class, those who lived the most comfortable lives, were those who cooperated willingly with the tyrants despite the enmity of those they ruled. The woman who would become Ascendant Rowan was born into one such family, living a life of privilege until she realized the suffering inflicted on the ordinary people they mastered. Rowan renounced all wealth and gave her life to aiding the suffering and making life more comfortable for the masses. By her efforts, which included passionate pleas by which other collaborator families were shamed into surrendering their comforts, the lives of thousands of poor and enslaved Immorese were eased, and she ascended in 289 BR, having achieved enlightenment through her sacrifice. Rowan became by far the most popular ascendant during the occupation era, her example leading to the conversion of many Menites.

Examining surviving logs of collaborator administrators tabulating the distribution of slaves suggests the Orgoth governors may have begun to have less regular contact with their homeland after 190 BR. Slaves and materials shipped west across the Meredius dropped off substantially, as did new arrivals from the west to reinforce those on Immoren. This may have represented a period when the local Orgoth governors were acting independently of their home empire. A shift to viewing the conquered territory as a permanent and lasting domain may have been what led to eventual measures taken by the Orgoth to crack down on the Immorese religions, where resistance to their rule persisted most strongly. Near the end of the Occupation era the Orgoth suddenly began repressive measures. In occult circles, it is thought that divine presentiment of imminent religious persecution may have led to the Gift, one of the most important and yet poorly understood events of this era.

THE GIFT OF MAGIC

Before the Orgoth, the humans of western Immoren had limited exposure to the arcane, primarily through the prayers and rites of priests and shamans. The application of magic as a science divorced from divinity was unthinkable. The Orgoth and the lords of Morrdh were the only groups witnessed manifesting such mystical powers. The only other historical figures to have studied these matters were Thamar and her scions, each vilified for dabbling in forbidden lore.

It is no wonder that the sudden emergence of magic among the Immorese was met with fear. Yet without magic, the Immorese may never have had a chance to overcome their oppressors. The sudden emergence of arcane power is known as the Gift, often referred to as the Gift of Magic, the Gift of Sorcery, or the Gift of Thamar, as the emergence of the arcane is tied to Morrow's twin.

The theological ramifications of the Gift have been the subject of heated debate in the halls of temples, churches, and universities. Menites consider the Gift to be an act of betrayal against the Creator and hold both of the Twins accountable for this violation of Morrow's guardianship over humanity.

Whatever the source of this power, in 137 BR the first known sorcerer was born, a young girl named Madruva Dagra, who manifested the ability to throw fire from her hands when angered. Defending her sisters from Orgoth soldiers, she

might pass that ability to their children. The emergence of this potential proved to be highly unpredictable, which meant it was impossible for the Orgoth to stamp it out.

Not long thereafter arose a number of brave and brilliant scholars who began to make a systematic study of arcane matters. The most notable and successful was a genius named Sebastien Kerwin. He was the first to postulate the methodologies that would give rise to subsequent arcanists theorizing that magic was a type of supernatural energy that was responsive to intelligent will. In 96 BR he published his *Dissertations on Thaumaturgical Formula* which was a study of how magic could be controlled by the use of formula comprised of special runes.

Kerwin would write a number of other seminal works that laid the foundation for this new arcane science, including *The Essence of Divine Magic* in 90 BR, *Principia Arcana Magus* in 73 BR, and most importantly *Synthesis* in 64 BR. Modern arcanists consider *Synthesis* to be perhaps the most important text ever written, as within its pages Kerwin theorized the mechanisms by which alchemy captured and stored arcane energy. By bringing methodical systems employed for arcane study to alchemy, this book revolutionized what was possible in that field, which had until this time been a haphazard practice of trial and error. More significantly, this work would lay the foundation for mechanika, a related field by which alchemy, the arcane, and engineering could be combined. Many of the possibilities suggested by his work would not come to fruition until the centuries after Kerwin's death.

THE CIRCLE OF THE OATH

The Orgoth never bothered to repress alchemy, seeing it as largely inconsequential. Kerwin and his devotees realized their work might reverse this and arouse the suspicion of the tyrants. They implemented a number of secretive efforts by which they could communicate and share information. These became the first arcane societies, such as the Arcanist's Academe founded in 81 BR. The first occult secret society of this age was the Circle of the Oath, which may have existed as early as 150 BR as a small sept of Thamarites given early portents of the Gift and preparing by gathering occult lore. Kerwin and his group formally joined this confederation in 67 BR and shifted its focus to the systematic exploration of the arcane.

This followed on the heels of several acts of defiance against the Orgoth, including a raid in 69 BR by Dominic Cavanaugh, a disciple of Kerwin, to rescue over three hundred Thurian slaves. The Orgoth tracked down those responsible and killed them. The Orgoth believed the Church of Morrow responsible for this uprising and committed one of the most brutal

managed to slay three of them before fleeing into the woods of the Olgunholt. In retaliation, the Orgoth slaughtered her entire bloodline, but this did not prevent more sorcerers from appearing across western Immoren in subsequent years. Wherever they surfaced the Orgoth responded in a similar fashion, culling the bloodline and putting homes to the torch. This reaction was so swift and brutal it seemed fearful and suggests a familiarity with arcane awakening.

It is now understood that sorcerers were just a symptom of a sweeping change across the Immorese—the unlocking of arcane potential in all humans. While most would live ordinary lives, this power laying dormant in them, some exceptional few had such a strong connection with this font of power that they manifested sorcery spontaneously. Others were born with the potential to work magic but required training and effort to master the Gift. Even those who could not wield the arcane

COSMOLOGICAL IMPLICATIONS OF THE GIFT

Given how little is known of the thoughts and plans of the gods, the mechanism behind the Gift is unknowable. Occult scholars unearthing records from this period and studying the writings of Thamar and her scions believe the Gift may have required an arrangement between the goddess and infernal powers. The infernals are mysterious but vastly powerful entities that dwell beyond Caen and Urcaen, perhaps in some other realm. They are intent on acquiring mortal souls, which they use for inscrutable purposes. Infernals are allegedly prodigiously skilled in the arcane, and some believe the "dark gods" of the Orgoth were themselves higher order infernals.

Thamarite lore contains an apocryphal story to explain the Gift. In this tale, Morrow as the Prophet is shown occupied peering into the future where he sees the ultimate extinction of his faith at the hands of the Orgoth. While Morrow fretted over these portents, Thamar took action. She determined that empowering humanity would allow them to stand against their oppressors, and informed her brother that she had arrived at a solution. Morrow chose not to gaze too closely upon Thamar's course of action, only to discern its inevitable conclusion. Looking ahead to the future, down the single strand made possible by his sister, he saw the light of hope. So it was he consented to her plan while avoiding knowledge of its exact nature.

Even in this fable, the actual cost of the Gift is not described, although it is suggested elsewhere that the Immorese will pay some great accounting nine centuries hence. This prophecy of a vague doom connected to a lingering debt remains a popular subject of folklore and superstition.

---

reprisals of this period: the Vicarate Slaughter. The leading priests of Fharin were murdered and violence spread to outlying townships. By the end of the year over five hundred Morrowan priests were executed.

These reprisals had the opposite of the intended effect on Kerwin and his followers. The Circle of the Oath became as devoted to working against the Orgoth as refining arcane principles. Unfortunately the desire to disseminate arcane knowledge made it easier for Orgoth spies to discover this cabal in the Thurian city of Ceryl. The Orgoth launched an attack in 63 BR which culminated in a pitched battle where Kerwin was killed, although not before he annihilated hundreds of Orgoth in the most destructive display of formulaic magic up until that time. Kerwin's body was never recovered.

In an effort to ensure that the knowledge gained by the order was not lost, Agathius Nerrek, Kerwin's most powerful disciple, took control of the order and in subsequent years established safe houses in cities across Thuria, Tordor, the Midlunds, and Rynyr. The Orgoth commenced the so-called Wizard Hunts in 54 BR and killed hundreds of aspiring arcanists, ultimately shattering the Circle of the Oath. However, the order's efforts succeeded in spreading Kerwin's teachings. The Order of the Golden Crucible was founded in 25 BR by survivors who sought to obscure their purposes under the cover of simple alchemy. When the spirit of true rebellion began to kindle and spread, the Order of the Golden Crucible contributed and ultimately played a key role arming those courageous enough to defy their oppressors.

REBELLION AGAINST THE ORGOTH

With the seeds of unrest planted, the subjugated population began to stir. The hunts organized to stamp out bloodlines of sorcerers and wizards did not arouse much general sympathy due to the suspicion with which most people viewed workers of magic. More than anything else, it was Orgoth interference in organized religion that created an atmosphere ripe for rebellion. The Vicarate Slaughter became the example of what continued life under the Orgoth yoke would bring.

The final spark came at the end of 1 BR when the Orgoth governor stationed at the fortress in Fharin declared that the city must send a tithe of eight thousand slaves across the ocean. These would be chosen by lots, and as the lottery was implemented it became obvious that the Menite and Morrowan priesthoods were targeted, as every priest of both faiths in the city was chosen. In response, Fharin's citizenry rose up in a spontaneous and unorganized rebellion, seizing pitchforks, spades, clubs, and anything else that resembled a weapon. Members of the city's Order of the Golden Crucible distributed alchemical explosives to the uprising. Orgoth troops and warwitches were overwhelmed and killed, the fortress gates blasted open, and the Orgoth governor's head stuck on a pike and paraded through the streets.

Word of the uprising spread across the central region and soon became an organized rebellion. This was called the Iron Fellowship, and it stated its declaration of war against the Orgoth in 1 AR, drawing a vast following from across what had once been Thuria, the Midlunds, and Caspia. Despite early successes, the Iron Fellowship survived for only six years and was quashed by the Orgoth in 7 AR, its leadership scattered, and these territories taken back. Despite brutal reprisals, the rebellion had begun and would not be stopped. The rebels might have balked had they known it would require two hundred years of bloody battles to regain their freedom.

Modern historians are convinced that the rebellion was an inevitability, but that its success was not. The spirit of the people was willing, but the weapons to overcome the Orgoth had yet to be developed, and would ultimately require tools and talents relying on the Gift of Magic. An unsung hero of this era was an occult scholar named Nivara, an uncompromising but brilliant arcanist whom Thamarites deem the rightful successor to Kerwin. Nivara innovated many of the fundamental principles in the utilization of arcane energy as a weapon of war. She trained dozens of arcanists in these techniques and many of her disciples became the rebellion's most notable battle-wizards, presaging the warcasters of future eras. Nivara was also known for her ingenious clockwork puzzles she used to train students in mastering arcane formulae. These dangerous and mentally taxing devices were loathed by those students, but would play a key role in a subsequent inventions that were key to toppling the Orgoth. Nivara ascended in 25 AR as a scion of Thamar, an event that cast a shadow over her legacy and prompted many former students to disavow her.

THE INVENTION OF THE FIREARM AND THE ARMY OF THUNDER

In 28 AR Aurumn Alchemist Oliver Gulvont invented the first firearm, a weapon that utilized alchemical blasting powder to propel shot. The need for such a weapon was soon proven in one of the great early battles of the rebellion, when in 32 AR a large region of Tordor became a bloody battlefield of smoke and fire. This would later be called the Battle of the Hundred Wizards, the first great unveiling of Immorese battle-wizards fighting alongside conventional forces.

Supported by local nobles, these formidable students of Kerwin and Nivara together with many sorcerers saved from Orgoth extermination managed to repel the Orgoth entirely from the old Tordoran borders. Wielding elemental powers of fire, lightning, earth and frost, and in overwhelming numbers the sorcerers and arcanists bested the arrogant warwitches of the Orgoth. This battle so was so decisive that it would require eight years for the tyrants to retake the region. The Orgoth recaptured Tordor in 40 AR and executed hundreds of suspected arcanists. The people of Tordor continued to resist by whatever means they could.

Working primarily out of the city of Leryn, the Order of the Golden Crucible improved firearm design by 80 AR and set to work in hidden laboratories manufacturing them as quickly as its voluntary laborers could manage. The legendary Army of Thunder rose up to liberate Rynyr in 84 AR wielding these new weapons to deadly effect. The riflemen of this army left the smoky streets and fields of Leryn and Merywyn slick with Orgoth blood.

As with previous rebellion efforts, the Orgoth proved they would not be easily cowed, and quickly counterattacked to drive the Army of Thunder back to the towering walls of Leryn. At the Battle of the Thunderhead in 86 AR, Leryn held strong and repelled an army of over ten thousand Orgoth with an arsenal of battle magic, alchemical grenades, and row upon row of riflemen firing deadly volleys. While the rest of Rynyr was reoccupied, this city held firm and became a bastion of hope— the first city since Caspia to hold against the enemy.

THE RIP LUNG PLAGUE

A terrible plague known as rip lung hit the region from 83 to 93 AR. It is uncertain whether this deadly disease took a greater toll on the Immorese or the Orgoth, but both were affected and

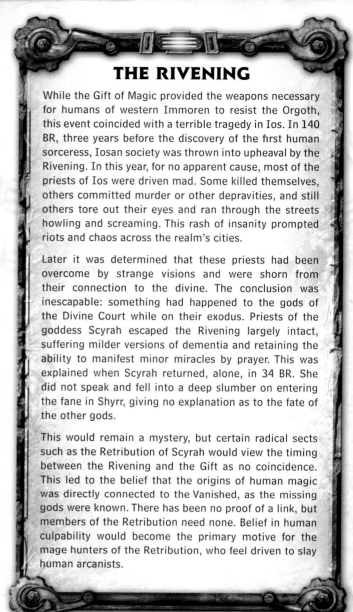

THE RIVENING

While the Gift of Magic provided the weapons necessary for humans of western Immoren to resist the Orgoth, this event coincided with a terrible tragedy in Ios. In 140 BR, three years before the discovery of the first human sorceress, Iosan society was thrown into upheaval by the Rivening. In this year, for no apparent cause, most of the priests of Ios were driven mad. Some killed themselves, others committed murder or other depravities, and still others tore out their eyes and ran through the streets howling and screaming. This rash of insanity prompted riots and chaos across the realm's cities.

Later it was determined that these priests had been overcome by strange visions and were shorn from their connection to the divine. The conclusion was inescapable: something had happened to the gods of the Divine Court while on their exodus. Priests of the goddess Scyrah escaped the Rivening largely intact, suffering milder versions of dementia and retaining the ability to manifest minor miracles by prayer. This was explained when Scyrah returned, alone, in 34 BR. She did not speak and fell into a deep slumber on entering the fane in Shyrr, giving no explanation as to the fate of the other gods.

This would remain a mystery, but certain radical sects such as the Retribution of Scyrah would view the timing between the Rivening and the Gift as no coincidence. This led to the belief that the origins of human magic was directly connected to the Vanished, as the missing gods were known. There has been no proof of a link, but members of the Retribution need none. Belief in human culpability would become the primary motive for the mage hunters of the Retribution, who feel driven to slay human arcanists.

it certainly slowed the rebellion. Rip lung scythed through the streets of urban centers leaving thousands of bodies in its wake. The Orgoth put entire sections of cities to the torch rather than bury the massive volume of the dead. This act in itself did much to arouse the ire of the people, for it had long been taboo to burn the dead without the proper oversight of priests, as this act endangered the passage of souls to Urcaen.

Eventually an arcanist and alchemist of tremendous skill named Corben was able to derive a cure for the disease. Even more impressively, he was able to implement a system whereby the treatment could be produced quickly and efficiently by other alchemists. Corben's efforts saved hundreds of thousands of lives, and perhaps also salvaged the spirit of rebellion. By 93 AR the epidemic had been halted among the Immorese, although it continued to trouble the Orgoth who lacked similar alchemical solutions. Corben's ascension nine years later was a miracle that invigorated the Morrowan rebels. In the long term, this ascension legitimized the efforts of arcanists and alchemists in the eyes of the Church of Morrow and its adherents, and Morrowan churches began to offer sanctuary to rebellion arcanists.

THE MECHANIKAL REVOLUTION

Firearms had done their part to free Leryn and had been formidable weapons in the hands of rebellion soldiers. However, this technology was stolen by the Orgoth, who responded by manufacturing their own crude firearms called blackdrakes. The true potential of the Gift to aid the Immorese would come to pass in the form of mechanika. This would be the science that would blend engineering with the power of magic and bring inventions that would bring the downfall of the Orgoth.

While the Order of the Golden Crucible continued to work from Leryn, efforts were underway in old Thuria to restore Kerwin's work. In the occupied city of Ceryl a group of dedicated arcanists came together to recover lost lore of the Circle of the Oath. Their fellowship resulted in the founding of the Fraternal Order of Wizardry in 111 AR, which would become a bastion of pure arcane theory and push the boundaries of the new art of mechanika. The wizards of the day had a better understanding of arcane energies than in Kerwin's times, and the potentials suggested in *Synthesis* became a reality. One of the first developments was the runeplate, whereby arcane formulae could be permanently inscribed on metal and invested with arcane power.

Much of this work was only made possible by the protection provided these wizards by the Church of Morrow in Ceryl. Underground routes between houses of worship allowed for much to transpire in the city without the governor's awareness. Courageous couriers risked their lives to carry papers describing ongoing work between the Fraternal Order and Order of the Golden Crucible arcanists, and together these two groups achieved substantial advancements. After the rebellion, these orders would become jealous rivals and prone to hoarding knowledge and secrets, but at this time they were united by hatred of a shared enemy.

A great step forward occurred when Aurum Magnus Phineas Bainbridge of the Order of the Golden Crucible succeeded in creating a stable arcanodynamic accumulator, a keg-sized device that could store arcane energy for an extended time. It was deemed too large but was a proof of concept and the Crucible alchemists soon found ways to make this device smaller, lighter, and considerably more powerful. Engineers and arcanists began to work on schematics and diagrams for weaponry that might exploit the potential of improved accumulators.

Several other developments in this era seemed tangential but would have major repercussions. A number of Immorese engineers had been working to bring back the steam engine, so pervasive before the Orgoth. This led to the crucial work of Maximillian Nivin, an alchemist and one of the first arcane mechaniks who was fascinated with clockwork. He had been trying to create small steam-powered automatons, primarily for the technological challenge. He had difficulty finding a means by which it could control its motions rather than being simply a sophisticated puppet. On the advice of colleagues,

Nivin made contact with the Fraternal Order and was soon invited to join their number.

Nivin soon learned of an area of abstract study that had reached an impasse and which might have bearing on his project. A number of the order's magi had been seeking to create a self-sustaining circuit of arcane formulae that could emulate the thinking processes of a living mind. Their work was based on runic puzzles left behind by Scion Nivara and preserved by the order. Excited at the possibilities, Nivin devoted himself to this study, submitted himself to Nivara's puzzles, and quickly thereafter succeeded in creating the first cerebral matrix, which could mimic some of the reasoning capacity of a living mind. Together with his apprentice Elias Decklan, Nivin created the first man-sized automaton in 158 AR. Decklan continued to innovate the design after Nivin's death, and to work on refinements which would ultimately prove crucial to the rebellion.

Opposition to the Orgoth rule continued in the form of small uprisings across western Immoren. While each was quashed in turn, these succeeded in diverting resources and made it difficult for the Orgoth to retaliate. Up until 147 AR the scope of the rebellion had been limited to the Midlunds, Thuria, and Tordor. But in this year descendants of the proud Umbrean horselords gathered and led an army of nomads to liberate Korsk and Rorschik from the tyrants. In 149 AR the Orgoth laid siege to the Khards and their Umbrean allies at the gates of Korsk, but were repelled by unyielding northmen. Cracks had begun to develop in the Orgoth domination.

Adopting a name chosen in homage to the original Iron Fellowship, the free cities of western Immoren became the Iron Alliance. Comprised of armies from Korsk, Rorschik, Leryn, and Caspia, they came together under the leadership of the newly formed Council of Ten in 164 AR. While primarily a human alliance, the ten leading generals included Grindar of Tolok Kriel who represented the Thornwood trollkin who had suffered at the hands of the Orgoth. All of the Dhunian races living outside of Rhul and Cryx had endured hardship during the Occupation as the Orgoth viewed them as animals, driving their tribes deeper into the wilderness. Of these races, only the trollkin joined in the Council of Ten and contributed major forces to the Rebellion.

THE COLOSSALS

The work of arcanists in Ceryl was known to the Council of Ten, who urged these great thinkers to relocate to Caspia for their protection. Among those smuggled to Caspia was Elias Decklan, whose exposure to the great foundries of this free city changed his thinking on the scope of automatons. The first cerebral matrix had been simple and crude, but he had theorized a much larger device, one sufficient to emulate more complex thought.

When Decklan presented this idea to other peers, its potential use as a towering weapon of war became clear to all. Decklan soon drafted schematics for a steam and magic driven behemoth which could assail even the greatest of Orgoth fortresses. The Council of Ten was persuaded that here at last was a unique weapon the Orgoth could not counter. For the next decade the greatest minds in western Immoren drafted,

debated, and planned the most significant engineering feat ever attempted by humanity. Not only would these colossals require coordination to construct, but a huge volume of raw materials, including iron-rich ore and rare metals and minerals needed for the cerebral matrix.

The plan had obstacles, including the necessity to conduct work in secrecy. When it originated in Caspia, few outside the city knew of the undertaking. But soon others in the Rebellion learned of the project, prompting an uproar among the Khards which reignited long-buried rivalries between north and south. As Korsk was also a free city and every bit as prepared to forge great weapons as Caspia, the northerners began constructing their own colossal foundries in turn, going so far as to steal design schematics from their allies when these were not voluntarily handed over.

A solution for raw materials came from an unexpected source. Since early in the rebellion, various groups had sent emissaries to Rhul asking for intervention. All of these had been turned down, but the political atmosphere in the Moot of the Hundred Houses had begun to shift. Repeated pleas for help and the increasing successes of rebellion forces finally persuaded the Stone Lords. Rhul had begun to pay greater attention to affairs beyond their borders and had gathered sufficient awareness to recognize the Orgoth as poor neighbors compared to the native Immorese.

The tipping point came when emissaries of the Council of Ten revealed the plan to construct the colossals, a calculated risk at that time. The Rhulfolk became fascinated by the possibilities of such technology, having been unaware of the advances made by human arcanists and engineers. An agreement was made whereby in exchange for knowledge of the alchemy behind firearms, the secret of the cerebral matrix, and schematics for colossals, Rhul would give its support. It would not directly intervene in the fighting, but agreed to ship vast quantities of materials—not only ore but Rhul-smelted metals and alloys, as well as completed parts created in the forges of Ghord. These contributions and later shipments of coal proved vital in the years ahead.

In 188 AR, the Orgoth discovered the Khardic facilities and assailed the free city of Korsk. The Khards were overwhelmed, their foundries were destroyed, and captured alchemists and wizards suffered indescribable torments at the hands of the Orgoth. The Khards immediately suspected betrayal, believing Rhul had entered into their arrangement with the Council of Ten only after making secret arrangements with Caspia that the colossals would stay out of the hands of the northmen. Either the Rhulfolk or the Caspians are said to have betrayed the Council by informing the Orgoth about the Korsk facilities. In doing so not only would the northerners be deprived of colossals but the battles in the north would occupy the Orgoth, letting the northmen take the brunt of the Orgoth's wrath. The truth of this conspiracy is unknown, but belief in this betrayal among the Khards intensified animosity between north and south.

Following the assault on Korsk, the Iron Alliance tripled its efforts in Caspia and the first colossal strode from that city's gates in 191 AR. With five more completed in rapid succession, the Iron Alliance was ready. Controlled by battle wizards of the Fraternal Order, these colossals and the armies marching with them destroyed the Orgoth fortress near Fharin, along with a major garrison. So began a decade long struggle as rebellion armies took back lands that had been under Orgoth rule for centuries. The colossals crushed all opposition.

While the Orgoth were driven quickly from the southeastern provinces, the rebel armies were hindered by supply lines and had difficulty pushing deep into enemy territory in the early years. The colossals consumed a prodigious volume of coal and water and required constant supervision and regular repairs. The enemy adapted, finding it easier to destroy the wizards controlling the machines than the colossals themselves. Deprived of controllers, colossals were diverted away, isolated, and destroyed.

Rebel armies had to change their tactics. Small armies followed each colossal, using it as their vanguard while safeguarding those with the arcane skills to control these great machines. This arrangement and the example of the rebellion battle wizards are seen as the precursor to modern warcasters and their battlegroups.

As the Orgoth were steadily pushed back to the sea they initiated the Scourge. The fleeing Orgoth did their best to destroy every record they had written and every structure they had once held. Their great black keeps were demolished rather than allowing them to fall to the enemy. The Scourge reduced dozens of cities and towns to waste. The Orgoth salted fields, poisoned wells, scorched the earth, and slew untold multitudes of slaves as they fled to their blackships and sailed west. The Scourge was so thorough that not one map of the Orgoth homeland has been unearthed in the centuries since. Very few writings in the Orgoth tongue survived, leaving their culture and beliefs an enigma. Yet in 201 AR, the Orgoth were driven from the continent and never returned.

THE IRON KINGDOMS ERA

While the beginning of a new epoch was marked by the stirring of the Rebellion in western Immoren, it had been a long and terrible struggle. It was not until 202 AR that the new era was born with the Corvis Treaties. This was a gathering of the Council of Ten, necessitated by some of the difficulties of the immediate aftermath of the Orgoth, where each region was wrestling with establishing order and organizing to provide relief to thousands who were suffering.

THE CORVIS TREATIES

The Council of Ten met in the city of Corvis and discussed the borders of the newly independent kingdoms. The Orgoth had left horrible scars upon the region, not only from their long occupation but the destruction left by the Scourge and the battles of the Rebellion. The new nations established by this treaty would come to be known as the Iron Kingdoms.

While there was some discussion of restoring the old kingdoms that had predated the Orgoth, this was rejected. The people had come to identify with the larger regions set down by the Orgoth governors. This gave rise to four kingdoms:

- Cygnar in the south, encompassing the Thornwood, the Midlunds, Caspia, and a significant portion of Thuria.

- Khador in the northwest, including the old Khardic lands, Kos, Skirov, and western Umbrey.

- Llael in the northeast including what had been Rynyr and the eastern lands of old Umbrey.

- Ord in the west, unifying northern Thuria and Tordor.

Certain groups had already seized authority among the Council of Ten. Caspian noble bloodlines laid claim to governing Cygnar, and none could refute the role of the City of Walls and its industry in the Rebellion. The old Khardic nobility was well positioned to claim governance over Khador and the Tordorans rose to rule Ord. The once proud eastern Umbreans did not contest the Ryn for rulership of Llael; Umbrey had suffered particularly heavily under the Orgoth, with many of its eastern noble bloodlines extinguished. The Ryn had the resources to rebuild the shattered region and so cemented the loyalty of the surviving eastern Umbreans of this area.

Not all were in agreement over these borders and the debates were heated. The Khadorans left dissatisfied, for they had pressed to restore lands once claimed by the Khardic Empire, which included a substantial portion of what would be ceded to Ord, Llael, and the northern Thornwood. But in the wake of the Rebellion, their bluster had no bite. The destruction of their colossal factories combined with the ravages of war left the Khards in a weak position. No one but the Khards wanted to see the Khardic Empire restored.

RECONSTRUCTION AND THE NEW ARCANE ORDERS

The early decades after the Rebellion were dominated by tremendous efforts of reconstruction across the new kingdoms. Technological gains provided many benefits, particularly in the swift reemergence of steam-powered machinery. In 211 AR, the newly established Steam and Iron Workers Union consolidated the labors of hundreds working to meet the demand of engineered production and repair work. Within twenty years steam-powered boats were again traveling the waterways.

The minds of arcanists and mechaniks soon turned to finding other uses for technologies. The arcanists of the Fraternal Order of Wizardry were involved in expanding arcane lore. Experiencing unprecedented freedom, many of the order's cabals followed once forbidden lines of research. Others expanded their influence, establishing major branches in most significant cities, particularly in Cygnar, Ord and Llael. Establishing new chapter houses and acquiring lucrative contracts for mechanikal fabrication work or arcane consulting necessitated paying bribes and doing favors for nobles and government officials, often of dubious legality.

This led to a major scandal in 232 AR when a pious magus named Copernicum revealed that the Fraternal Order was riddled with corruption. Copernicum and a number of his followers left the order after accusing many of its highest officers of black magic and other illegal activities. The Order would weather this scandal, although its reputation was besmirched and a number of mages were tried and executed after being convicted of practicing necromancy and infernalism.

Copernicum went on to establish the Morrowan Order of Illumination. The Order became a significant agency of the Church, specialized in matters of the arcane. While the order included pious mages seeking to follow in the footsteps of Asc. Corben, it became most notable for its role as the church's dedicated witch hunters. The Order of Illumination vowed to stand vigilant against black magic in all forms, rooting out infernalism, necromancy, mesmerism, and Thamarite cultists responsible for spreading these nefarious arts.

Fraternal Order arcanists continued their innovative works. Among their accomplishments was the refinement of the cerebral matrix. Reducing its size and experimenting with more complex arcane relays resulted in the invention of the first cortex, a tremendous improvement which allowed for smaller and more practical automatons. The first steamjack was built in 241 AR by the Fraternal Order Magus Bastion Rathleagh, working with the aid of the Steam and Iron Workers Union. Designed to be machines for labor instead of war, more followed, made in a variety of sizes and configurations. Improved cortexes allowed steamjacks to follow complex orders and their smaller size required considerably less fuel and water. The demand for steamjacks created an entire industry, while also bringing a tide of wealth into the Fraternal Order of Wizardry.

Khador meanwhile continued to seethe over her lost territories and the need to rely on a private agencies like the Fraternal Order for its cortexes and the Order of the Golden Crucible for blasting powder. Having restored much of its industry and expanding both its mining and manufacturing capabilities, this northern nation had begun to restore its armed might. The Khadoran sovereign, King Lavesh Tzepesci, was aware that his nation stood in peril and could never properly defend itself so long as colossals remained solely in the hands of the Cygnarans. Secretly he ordered new foundries built in Korsk. Lavesh's spymaster contacted arcanists of Khadoran blood who had gone abroad to learn the secrets of various arcane orders.

A conspiracy began amongst the northern arcanists, including several that had gained the trust and confidences of higher officers in the Fraternal Order's Stronghold in Ceryl as well as the Thunderhead Fortress of the Golden Crucible in Leryn. In 243 AR these conspirators stole hundreds of irreplaceable tomes

of arcane lore, alchemical formulae, and cortex fabrication schematics. On their return, these patriotic arcanists were rewarded by Lavesh, many with titles, and they formed the Greylords Covenant, an exclusively Khadoran order that quickly became an extension of the Khadoran military and connected to that nation's spy network. Khador could now manufacture her own cortexes and as much blasting powder as access to raw materials allowed.

THE TROLLKIN AND COLOSSAL WARS

Cygnar did not immediately respond to Khador's rearmament, being caught up in massive trollkin uprisings which swept the Gnarls and the Thornwood starting in 242 AR. While the trollkin kriels of these regions had been given allowances in the Corvis Treaties, the kriels had found their lands violated by humans seeking resources to fuel reconstruction efforts. Combined with human efforts to exploit every waterway for shipment of goods and materials, the kriels saw themselves being overrun and pushed out of several regions in disregard for old agreements. Unrest escalated into a full war which swept northern Cygnar and southern Ord.

Eventually Cygnar committed its colossals to battle against the trollkin, and where these giant machines strode, the trollkin fell in droves. In 247 AR after suffering several brutal setbacks, the trollkin surrendered and this ended the First Trollkin War. By this time Cygnaran spies had learned of great foundries working on war materials in Korsk. Accordingly, the Cygnaran colossals remained in this region rather than returning to Caspia. These colossals and warcasters became the Colossal Guard, headquartered out of Deepwood Tower in the Thornwood, where they could watch the border shared with Khador.

Just three years later King Lavesh committed to massive attacks against both western Llael and northern Ord, striking to seize lands that had once been part of the old Khardic Empire. The ensuing war engulfed all the nations of the Iron Kingdoms as Llael, Cygnar and Ord fought together against the Khadorans. For the first time colossals clashed face to face as those built by Khadoran hands contested with those from Cygnar.

Older Cygnaran colossals did not fare well in early battles, suffering against more recently designed and heavily armored Khadoran machines. Cygnaran foundries blazed day and night to produce newer and better colossals. The Colossal War was a seven-year conflict that saw the old peace of the Corvis Treaties permanently shattered. Massive iron giants tore each other apart amidst fields of rifle fire, bloodied pikes, and explosive displays of arcane magic.

Ultimately Khador's war industry proved incapable of sustaining the pace of production. Not only were Khador's attacks repulsed, but the allied armies of the three southern nations made advances onto Khadoran soil. Khador finally surrendered in 257 AR after losing decisively at Volningrad. The Khadorans suffered the indignity of agreeing to dismantle their remaining colossals as well as the foundries where they had been built. Cygnar ceded back lands seized from Khador in the conflict, having had no expectation of permanently occupying them.

While Khador was pacified, the trollkin kriels of the region had regained their strength and had grown more militant, organized, and indignant about the human armies marching through their lands. Trollkin incursions into Ordic and Cygnaran territory escalated into the Second Trollkin War by 262 AR. The trollkin had learned from previous battles and conducted their strikes strategically, taking advantage of the terrain to cover retreats and make it difficult for the Colossal Guard to retaliate. The gigantic machines had begun to show their limits, having been designed for attacking fixed positions, other colossals, and masses of enemy forces. They had difficulty negotiating the dense forest while fighting enemies using skirmish tactics. Several times trollkin and the full-blood trolls fighting alongside them managed to incapacitate colossals using primitive means, which shamed Cygnaran military leaders.

In response, Cygnar's King Woldred ordered his generals to innovate new weapons. Arcane mechaniks along with consultants from the Fraternal Order of Wizardry presented the concept of warjacks, making use of smaller but still formidable chassis employed for labor steamjacks, but modifying them for war. The first warjacks served in the final years of the Second Trollkin War, proving their effectiveness as the trollkin were driven back. King Woldred personally attended peace talks with representatives of the kriels to end hostilities at Hadriel Fields in 267 AR. The Cygnaran crown deemed the trollkin had legitimate grievances and granted the kriels expanded lands and paid sums for the restoration of destroyed villages in addition to granting the trollkin regular fees for the use of certain waterways. The trollkin were to be subject to Cygnaran law except within the narrow confines of their kriel lands where they could govern themselves.

Military strategists and the younger generation of warcasters were quick to see the advantages of the new warjacks. These constructs had been built with the latest and more sophisticated cortexes, had much greater range of motion and could be fielded more easily alongside infantry. A combination of advances to cortexes along with their ability to independently negotiate terrain meant a warcaster could more easily control multiple warjacks. In 286 AR King Woldred decommissioned the colossals and had his engineers convert those great foundries to warjack production. Production of similar machines was embraced in the other nations as well.

While war fabrication proceeded apace, the peace was strengthened by a changing of royal dynasties in Khador. The long and dark reign of Lavesh Tzepesci the Tormentor ended with his death to old age in 272 AR. King Dmitry Dopatevik ousted the warlike Tzepesci line and proved to be a more peaceful and diplomatic sovereign, willing to engage in negotiations with foreign ambassadors. Indeed, an amicable relationship was established between Kings Woldred and Dmitry as the two shared similar ruling philosophies.

THE GRIM YEARS OF KING MALAGANT

The political situation in Cygnar changed after King Woldred drafted his Accord-By-Hand Covenant in 286 AR. Woldred's Accord allowed the Cygnaran king to choose his own successor, even outside his bloodline, so long as that successor was of sufficiently noble blood. To satisfy probity, Woldred required the terms of succession be witnessed and implemented by the Menite priesthood who had long overseen royal succession as keepers of the True Law. While the Menite religion had waned to minority status in Cygnar, they retained significant sway with the nobles and retained authority as an ancient right.

While this accord would prove its merits stabilizing the Cygnaran succession in subsequent centuries, Woldred was unable to benefit. He died suddenly in 289 AR and his own terms disappeared. The Menite priesthood came forward to act on his wishes but faced a sudden coup by Woldred's nephew Malagant, who led a small army to claim the crown. Called the Grim King, Malagant proved to be a bloodthirsty tyrant who consolidated his power by executing rivals and gaining a stranglehold on the Royal Assembly. After an outbreak of public outcry, Malagant entered into an alliance with the Church of Morrow, which had been seeking to establish its supremacy as the kingdom's majority religion.

The Church of Morrow's endorsement of Malagant's right to the throne served to pacify many of the kingdom's pious citizens and nobles. But when the Caspian Temple of Menoth refused to do the same, Malagant accused its priests of treason and had them arrested, tried, and executed. By the end of 290 AR, over 200 Menite priests and officials had been sent to the gallows. This provoked years of religious unrest that created a lasting rift between these religions in Cygnar. Two separate assassination attempts on King Malagant gave the king the justification he required to make the royal decree in 293 AR that the Church of Morrow was now the state religion of Cygnar. The ancient rights once granted the Menite priests were revoked.

In a dark time for Menites in Caspia; many old temples in the western city were desecrated and several were set ablaze. Acting allegedly to protect ordinary Menites, Malagant ordered hundreds of families forcibly relocated to eastern Caspia, and many of their assets were seized. A large portion of the city east of the Black River became home to the city's large Menite minority. While this reduced the violence, it cemented the division between Caspia's faiths.

THE BORDER WARS

King Dmitry of Khador was assassinated in 286 AR and the throne was claimed by his wife, Cherize. She proved to be a bloody minded monarch who quickly set about preparing for war. Queen Cherize hoped to take advantage of the Cygnaran succession problems by seizing the northern Thornwood. She hoped to gain access to the Black River, which would enable Khador to disrupt trade along that vital waterway.

Cherize entered into an unusual arrangement with the savage Tharn tribes of the Thornwood—some of the last descendants of the Molgur—encouraging them to attack Cygnar while Khador's armies made their advance. The Tharn proved to be formidable adversaries in this familiar terrain. Cygnarans put aside their

DISCOVERY OF CYRISS, THE CLOCKWORK GODDESS

In 283 AR, an astronomer of the Fraternal Order of Wizardry named Aldophous Aghamore discovered a celestial body, a "Dark Wanderer," by use of powerful new telescopes. Soon thereafter, Aghamore was beset by strange dreams which he claimed were visionary. Through these he learned the name of this planet, Cyriss, and became convinced he was in communion with a divine being. Aghamore wrote of the planet as the body of the "clockwork goddess" or "maiden of gears." Aghamore was discredited by his peers until other reputable astronomers began to have similar dreams and started to correspond and then meet in person. This gave rise to the Cult of Cyriss, western Immoren's newest religion.

Cyriss' place in the cosmology is not well understood by theologians. Her worshipers believe Cyriss to be a hidden primal goddess—not a "new" deity, only newly discovered. She embodies fundamental natural principles, in particular those that govern the movement of celestial bodies and the means by which the world can be understood through mathematics. Her domain is astronomy, mathematics, and engineering, and her adherents claim she was awaiting discovery by those intelligent enough to unravel her location and to decipher clues revealing deeper mysteries. Enigmas and puzzles are central to this cult's relationship with the goddess, as they believe she provides portents through hidden codes and solutions buried in obscure mathematical formulas. Rumors about "clockwork priests" that have surrendered their bodies to gain immortality as machines seem perilously close to necromancy by Morrowan standards, but these rumors have not been confirmed.

religious differences in light of this new threat, and the crown mustered its own armies while also hiring large mercenary forces to bolster its numbers. This was the start of an extended conflict that would eventually be called the Border Wars.

The early years of this conflict have assumed legendary proportions. Cherize has been described as a sorcerer-queen of Khador, vilified in the southern kingdoms as a Thamarite. Khadorans have refuted this, but Cherize was certainly feared by her own people and was suspected of having killed her husband. The involvement of the Tharn tainted these battles as these savages conducted barbarous rites including feasting on the flesh of the fallen. While King Malagant was a tyrant, the barbarity of his enemies combined with the support of the Church of Morrow brought many Morrowan knights and priests into the conflict on his side. The war in the Thornwood was proclaimed a struggle between light and darkness, a claim supported by Tharn manifesting fell blood-sorcery while Morrowan battle-chaplains evoked miracles through fervent prayers.

Adding to the mystery surrounding this war were the peculiar ends of both sovereigns. Cherize vanished in 295 AR and her body was never found. King Malagant suffered a number of personal tragedies in the course of the war, including the betrayal of one of his most trusted champions leading to the death of his beloved queen. Two months after Cherize disappeared, he died of a wasting disease. The fighting in the Thornwood proved inconclusive, and the Border Wars would outlast both Cherize and Malagant.

The Cygnaran succession had been cast into turmoil by the rise of Malagant and the dismissal of the Menite priests, leaving the kingdom for twelve years without a king. During this time the Royal Assembly and various military leaders attempted to govern the nation, but with limited success. Khador proved quick to take advantage of the situation. Their own succession placed a child queen on the throne, but she was supported by the ambitious Lord Regent Velibor who ruled in her stead. Seeing the weakness of the Cygnaran position, Velibor launched the First Expansion War, the most successful years of the Border Wars for Khador.

Rather than confronting Cygnar, Velibor urged his armies to strike against northern Ord. While some of the initial assaults were repulsed by the stalwart Ordic defenders, the Khadoran Army gained momentum and began to make solid gains. The Ordic crown appealed to Cygnar for aid, but were only given token military support as the Cygnarans were torn by political division. Velibor expanded his operations and sent a smaller army against eastern Llael.

The war ground on over several years as both Llaelese and Ordic armies failed to halt the Khadoran advance. The Ordic King Alvor Cathor I was killed in the Battle of the Broken Sword in 301 AR, heroically leading a charge against the enemy. His broken weapon was recovered and became an important Ordic symbol representing defiance. The Khadorans pressed on and in the next year gained the greatest victory with the seizure of the northern port city of Radahvo.

THE SIEGE OF MIDFAST

One of Velibor's shrewdest maneuvers amid this extended conflict was finding a way to turn an internal conflict to his benefit. Even as the trollkin inside Cygnar undermined Woldred's peace, Khador struggled with its tribal peoples, remnants of a forgotten age. A large number of barbarian tribes persisted in the frozen northern mountains and forests. The last great alliance of these tribes assembled late in 304 AR, intent on pillaging the fertile farmlands of the interior which had been left undefended. Velibor met with tribal leaders and convinced their horde to strike at the south, where the gains and glory would be greater.

The barbarians turned their numbers against Ord, laying siege to the heavily fortified city of Midfast. Velibor intended to use them as shock fodder to presage his invasion deeper into Ord. The Ordic defenders had been pushed back to a long line of rugged hills stretching west and east from Midfast, which had

proven difficult to assault. Seeing Midfast as the lynchpin of Ordic defenses, Velibor hoped to crush the city beneath the horde and sweep on to the capital.

Midfast held for weeks against the horde while its defenders dwindled. The Siege of Midfast would become one of the most famous battles in the history of western Immoren, remembered for the heroism of Captain Markus Graza, an Ordic officer and devout Morrowan who led the defenders after the deaths of his superior officers. Even before his legendary last stand, Markus proved his skill and dedication, holding against vastly superior numbers. Despite his efforts, an expected reinforcement army from the capital did not arrive, bogged down amid muddy roads.

As Midfast's ammunition stores dwindled and its wounded defenders faced exhaustion, Markus went alone from the city under a banner of truce. Drawing on his knowledge of the beliefs of the northern tribes, Markus offered a ritual challenge to the chiefs of the horde. By their terms Markus was required to fight all fourteen chiefs, each in turn, a seemingly impossible task. As the gathered barbarians and the defenders on the wall watched, the siege was put on hold for a week as Markus faced two duels a day with the mightiest barbarian chiefs. Amid this crucible, Markus won victory after victory, suffering grave injuries on the fifth and sixth days. His resolve daunted the remaining chiefs. By the final day even the barbarians of the horde cheered for Markus above their own. In the last battle Markus found the inner reserves to endure, calling on his faith. Ascendant Katrena manifested in the sky above as Markus defeated the last chief and collapsed.

The light of Markus' ascension to join Katrena awed all gathered even as the reinforcing Ordic army finally arrived to advance on the horde. Thousands of barbarians were so stunned that they surrendered at once, casting weapons aside. Those that fought were swept from the field and ridden down. The Khadoran Army had been camped to the north of the barbarians and witnessed the miracle of ascension—seeing Morrow stood against them, their ranking kommandant ordered them to quit the field. Against all odds, Ord stood victorious. The northern barbarian tribes never regained their strength, while Markus became a revered figure among Morrowan soldiers.

Despite this defeat, the Khadoran Army persisted in the months ahead and the Border Wars continued for eight long and bloody years. The Siege of Midfast is seen as a major turning point, as Khador had no significant gains after this and Velibor became increasingly hated and despised. Juliana the Maiden Queen took the Cygnaran throne in 308 AR and sent armies in support of both Ord and Llael. Cygnar soon entered into a formal alliance with Llael, and Cygnaran soldiers and warjacks became a common sight in the last battles of this period.

Queen Ayn Vanar V assumed her majority in 307 AR but it was not until 313 AR that she realized Velibor and his military advisors had bankrupted the kingdom treasury. Ousting the former lord regent and his cronies, she put an end to the war and negotiated peace. Laedry was ceded back to Llael but the Khadorans retained Radahvo, which they named Vladovar.

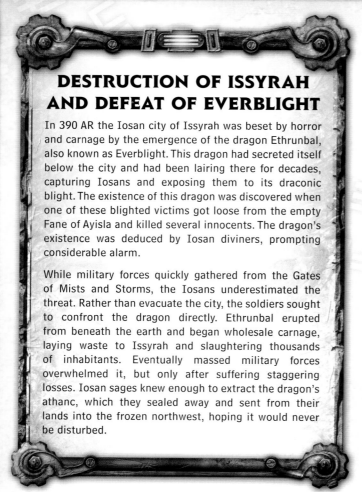

DESTRUCTION OF ISSYRAH AND DEFEAT OF EVERBLIGHT

In 390 AR the Iosan city of Issyrah was beset by horror and carnage by the emergence of the dragon Ethrunbal, also known as Everblight. This dragon had secreted itself below the city and had been lairing there for decades, capturing Iosans and exposing them to its draconic blight. The existence of this dragon was discovered when one of these blighted victims got loose from the empty Fane of Ayisla and killed several innocents. The dragon's existence was deduced by Iosan diviners, prompting considerable alarm.

While military forces quickly gathered from the Gates of Mists and Storms, the Iosans underestimated the threat. Rather than evacuate the city, the soldiers sought to confront the dragon directly. Ethrunbal erupted from beneath the earth and began wholesale carnage, laying waste to Issyrah and slaughtering thousands of inhabitants. Eventually massed military forces overwhelmed it, but only after suffering staggering losses. Iosan sages knew enough to extract the dragon's athanc, which they sealed away and sent from their lands into the frozen northwest, hoping it would never be disturbed.

Velibor was exiled and lived the rest of his days as a pariah, remembered for having wasted a generation of Khadorans in his wars. While the cost was deemed too high, Velibor succeeded in expanding the borders of the Motherland and would be remembered less harshly by later generations.

THE QUIET CENTURY

The time known as the Quiet Century was an era closer to a hundred and fifty years where the kingdoms thrived and prospered without being marred by open war. This would be a time of tremendous invention and growth, and also saw the start of the rising middle class across several of the kingdoms as the gains from industrialization began to manifest.

Though conflict was inescapable, the character of warfare in this period shifted from open declarations of hostilities between the Iron Kingdoms to smaller scale sporadic battles as the kingdoms tested borders and added new innovations to their armed forces. Espionage and sabotage became the more common expression of hostility in this period. The Quiet Century saw a resurgence of the mercenary tradition that had thrived in the Thousand Cities era. With kingdom armies reluctant to engage but governments still competing, it became common for mercenary companies to be hired to conduct proxy wars, earning considerable coin for their paymasters.

This century saw the founding of several significant universities and military academies, while systematic efforts were put forth to expand scholastic pursuits, mastery of mechanika, and the training of military officers equipped for the changing face of warfare. A number of mechanikal wonders were created in this gap between major wars and conflicts. In 343 AR, Magus Julian Montfort created the first prototype for warcaster armor. The founding of the Khadoran Mechaniks Assembly in 393 AR did much to promote and encourage engineering in that nation. This would eventually lead to military advances such as Man-O-War armor and the implementation of the first major railroads. While costly to build and slow to develop, rail lines began to be implemented in numerous regions, first to expedite mining but later employed for a wide variety of shipping. In 436 AR Cygnaran Magus Ashlan Halstead invented the arcantrik relay, precursor to the modern arc node, a mechanism that greatly enhanced the tactical options for warcasters on the battlefield.

Religious scholarship achieved advances as Sancteum theologians sought to reconcile the beliefs of major faiths, leading to a cohesive cosmology. Several tomes of scholarly study were printed describing the memories of those who had died briefly but then been returned to life by miraculous intervention. This led to the publishing of *Accounts of Urcaen* by Exarch Rudyin Goresecha in 320 AR, an account of the geography of the afterlife that proved to be extremely popular. The Caspian Temple of Menoth responded fifteen years later with *City of Souls*, a vivid depiction of the City of Man, Menoth's domain, with exhortations for humanity to heed the words of the Lawgiver.

As a reminder of Thamar's pervasive influence on Immoren, the city of Mercir was nearly burned to the ground in 415 AR by Stacia Versh, who had been branded a witch by the demand of the city's Order of Fraternal Wizardry. Evading capture she subsequently declared war upon the city's arcane society and nearly consumed the city in a conflagration before her dark ascension. Stacia's struggle emboldened a number of independent arcanists who struck out at the Order believing it was unfairly hording arcane lore. Caspian spies took advantage of this by paying bribes to encourage thefts of specific materials and thereby acquired schematics for their own use. The Cygnaran Armory subsequently began to construct its own advanced military grade cortexes.

SECOND EXPANSION WAR

Canon fire off the coast of Ord sounded the end of the Quiet Century when Khadoran and Ordic navies clashed in 464 AR. What began as a dispute over privacy soon erupted into the Second Expansion War, as King Mikhail Vanar ordered the invasion of Ord. The naval battles of this war were among the largest and most impressive ever conducted in western Immoren, involving hundreds of warships in massed battles. Turning to her naval power, Khador bypassed Midfast with its great army, landing forces to storm Corbhen instead.

While Cygnar was not allied to Ord, King Hector Sunbright II foresaw future peril if this neighbor was compromised. He sent his northern fleet from Ceryl to harass the Khadoran ships while his land forces secured the Rohannor River, preventing Khador from taking Berck, creating a stalemate by winter. This worked against the Khadorans, as they were overextended and their supply lines from Corbhen remained vulnerable. After two years of bitter fighting, the mixed Cygnaran and Ordic soldiers pushed the northmen back. A large number of mercenary companies from as far away as Llael and Caspia joined in the conflict.

When the Khadorans were pushed back to Corbhen in late 467 AR, Cygnar withdrew. The Ordic treasury was sorely pressed by the hungry mercenaries and could no longer pay their wages. The loss of the Cygnarans and mercenaries extended the war another year before the beleaguered Ordic Army liberated Corbhen and a truce was declared in 468 AR. The Khadorans lost their taste for battle as King Mikhail fell into illness and died just weeks before the end of the war.

CYGNARAN CIVIL WAR

While internal strife had been overlooked amid other conflicts, Cygnar simmered with a rising tide of religious animosity between Menites and Morrowans. This had occasionally erupted into isolated incidents of bloodshed, but previous clashes were nothing compared to the rift that would tear Caspia in half starting in 482 AR.

Among the Menites of the eastern city arose a charismatic and vocal ranking priest named Sulon. He put forth a summons calling on all Cygnaran Menites to come to Caspia and attend his words. This summons spread quickly and tens of thousands of Menites gathered from all corners of the kingdom. Before these masses, Sulon proclaimed himself hierarch, a special title associated with the absolute power of the priest-kings of old. He simultaneously seized control of Caspia east of the river, driving out any not of the faith. Thinking a riot was at hand but

THE COIN WAR

A minor but notable conflict broke out during this time in Llael. Seeing Cygnar's swept up in civil war, Khador invested in mercenaries to assault this smaller nation. Llael hired its own mercenaries to defend its territories. The Coin War was an escalating series of battles conducted almost entirely by proxy. This was an extremely lucrative time for mercenary companies in the region as they entered into bidding wars with both sides. This war ended inconclusively, but with both the Llaelese and Khadoran treasuries diminished. This had the result of forcing Llael to reduce its standing army, and after the end of the Civil War, Cygnar felt obliged to send additional troops into the region to protect its ally. This period marks the start of Llael's growing dependence on Cygnaran military support.

unaware of the nature of the Menite throngs, the Caspian city watch tried to disperse the crowds. This prompted a frenzied revolt as thousands of pilgrims rose up and slew over three hundred watchmen.

This incident ignited the Cygnaran Civil War, which raged from 482–484 AR. Zealous Menites nearly razed the river districts on the west bank of the city in the fighting that followed. The fate of Cygnar's capital seemed to hang in the balance until Sulon fell in battle. His death dealt a great blow to the morale of the Menites and opened the door for peace. High Prelate Shevann, head of the Morrowan Church's treasury and a woman of spotless reputation, stepped forward. Serving as spokeswoman for Cygnar's King Bolton Grey V, she entreated Sulon's successor, Visgoth Ozeall, for an end to violence. After protracted discussions with concessions on both sides, the Protectorate of Menoth was created to end the religious strife.

For a time this succeeded. The Menites were ceded an expanse of land east of the Black River and the entirety of eastern Caspia, which they renamed Sul in honor of Hierarch Sulon. The Protectorate had leave to govern their people as they saw fit without interference by the Cygnaran throne. It was understood that the Protectorate would remain part of Cygnar and subject to disarmament and taxation. Shevann ascended to join Morrow in 500 AR and is prayed to by any negotiating for peace or signing contracts made in good faith. The peace she achieved would not last indefinitely, but Shevann's name is still invoked by those trying to soothe religious disputes.

EXPANSION OF THE PROTECTORATE

The Sul-Menites quickly expanded into the harsh territories east of the Black River. These largely barren lands were seen as a challenge from Menoth and their subjugation a divine mandate. The Protectorate would over time convert most of the Idrian tribes. A great earthquake in 504 AR amid one of the largest of these conflicts devastated the Idrians and left the Sul-Menite soldiers intact. This was seen as a sign of divine intervention and prompted the conversion of tens of thousands of Idrians to the Menite faith, bringing with them the large settlement of Imer. This city would become increasingly important as it was built up through great construction efforts before being transformed into the capital of the Protectorate.

The Sul-Menites soon discovered a number of previously unknown resources. This included abundant diamonds that could be bartered with foreign powers and massive underground deposits of a flammable oil which was processed into Menoth's Fury, a powerful incendiary liquid. Additionally, the hills east of Imer proved to be rich in iron and other minerals, and in time the Sul-Menites discovered long-abandoned quarries allowing the construction of great temples and towering buildings in Imer. One of the greatest finds of the era was the rediscovery of Ancient Icthier and what remained of the walls bearing the original True Law. Through these and other signs, the Sul-Menites grew resolved in the notion that their settling this region was preordained and would facilitate restoring Menoth's faith across western Immoren.

FIRST THORNWOOD WAR

Crowned in 489 AR, five years after the end of the civil war, Cygnar's King Grigor Malfast led his nation into an era of growth not seen since the days of Woldred the Diligent. Steamjacks became prevalent, and the once-depleted Cygnaran coffers filled with coin. Instrumental in this was Malfast's trusted vassal, Archduke Vinter Raelthorne II. The archduke would play a major role in the conflicts of the region.

The Khadoran King Ruslan Vygor was a man of dark tempers and simmering rage. While no one dared speak it openly, Khadoran nobles deemed their king mad—Vygor saw himself as Khardovic reborn. While fired with Menite zeal, his mental instability made him a difficult man for the Khadoran Menite priests to embrace. Vygor nursed a hatred of Cygnar and its prosperity and accordingly he initiated a wild plan of conquest.

Despite his dubious sanity, King Vygor implemented numerous lasting reforms to Khador's military. At Vygor's request the nation invested in more warjacks than had ever been produced, and he also increased the scope of martial organizations like the Iron Fangs, trained to fight enemy warjacks. After working to create the greatest army seen in the modern age, in late 510 AR, Vygor sent a portion of this force, including the bulk of the renowned Khadoran cavalry, to harass the border defenders of Llael, knowing this would force King Malfast to respond. As predicted, Cygnar's king sent its main army led by Vinter Raelthorne north to beat back the impending invasion. At the same time Vygor personally led an even larger force of warjacks and the full might of Khador's heavy infantry straight into the Thornwood hoping to drive south and take key Cygnaran territories unopposed. No one suspected Vygor's ruse.

The Khadorans chopped straight through the Thornwood, razing a path two hundred miles long that later came to be called the "Warjack Road." If not for the work of scouts from Fellig who discovered this column, Cygnar may have felt the full brunt of an unexpected Khadoran army deep behind its borders.

Soldiers hastily drawn from the nearest towns and cities met the Khadorans at the Dragon's Tongue even as the main army rushing to defend Llael was recalled in a desperate attempt to intercept the Khadoran advance. The Battle of the Tongue in early 511 AR remains one of the bloodiest clashes in the history of the region, seeing a loss of more warjacks in a single battle than ever before. The war ended with Vygor's demise on the blade of Vinter Raelthorne II. This short but costly war left an imprint on both kingdoms, deepening old hatreds and seeing improvements to their respective militaries.

THE MODERN ERA
THE MODERN DYNASTIES OF THE IRON KINGDOMS

The decades after the Thornwood War saw many changes across the Iron Kingdoms as each of these nations entered modernity. Industrialization began to be embraced in full, with factories built and railroad lines beginning to cross the region. Each of the kingdoms was ruled by a dynasty that would shape their emergence into the modern era.

THE VANARS OF KHADOR

Khador's crown returned to the Vanar dynasty after the death of Vygor, much to the relief of that kingdom's people. In the decades ahead Khador began to experience true change as a rising merchant class called the kayazy became influential as they amassed great fortunes and put this wealth to bettering the nation's infrastructure and industry. The abolishment of the serfdom in 549 AR brought many eager workers to freshly built factories.

The beloved Vanar dynasty that controlled the throne in these years brought innovation and modernization to Khador while retaining the kingdom's national spirit. King Ivad Vanar maintained the throne for an unprecedented 38 years, bringing tremendous prosperity. The crown passed to his granddaughter, who was just born when Ivad died. Throughout her minority the great industrialist and statesman Simonyev Blaustavya ruled as regent. He accepted not only the responsibility of commanding the nation, but also raising Queen Ayn Vanar XI, whom he loved like his own daughter. Ivad Vanar and Blaustavya had dreams of restoring Khador to an empire, and these dreams passed to Ayn, who would see them fulfilled.

THE CATHORS OF ORD

Ord's transition into the modern era would come at the direction of the Cathor dynasty which had established the longest rule in that nation, only occasionally interrupted by their hated rivals, the Mateus. While generally admired, the Cathors have been an unpredictable bloodline. King Stagier Cathor II might have helped bring a swift end to the Thornwood War but was too paranoid to trust his advisors and insisted his armies remain neutral. This steadfast policy of neutrality marked the Cathors in the modern era. Ord learned its survival required looking after its own interests first.

Stagier's successor King Merin IV had an uneventful reign before being assassinated. His brother Fardini attempted to make the Menite faith the state religion though Ord was strongly Morrowan, but his reign was brought to a quick end with his execution when evidence came to light proving his involvement in his brother's murder. He was succeeded by the popular King Alvor IV, a shrewd politician who saw to the needs of his castellans but neglected the masses. His elder sons would prove to be unlucky, as Alvor the Fifth was killed in a fluke storm at sea after just 3 months of rule, while Brogan sat on the throne two months before collapsed stonework ended his life.

This brought the Ordic crown to a man who had never hoped or dreamed of being king: Baird II. A notorious gambler and wastrel who kept to bad company, many thought Baird would bring ruin to his nation. Yet King Baird II proved as shrewd and wise a king as ever sat the Ordic throne, establishing an extensive spy network and taking measures to bring fair taxation to the masses, shifting this burden onto the wealthier castellans instead. Beloved of the people, if hated by some of his embittered nobles, Baird enjoyed allowing others to underestimate him while proving adept at the games of politics. Like his predecessors, Baird maintained the neutrality of Ord even amid terrible wars—he only occasionally committed his nation's navy against Cryxian interlopers while keeping his army in reserve to defend his cities and borders. Baird has begun modernizing Ord, but this has been limited by the nation's paucity of resources.

THE MARTYNS OF LLAEL

Llael was less fortunate in its sovereigns, with a line of weak and ineffectual kings contributing to an internecine court focused on petty intrigues. The Martyn family which held the throne of Llael from 396 AR produced no great leaders. Artys di la Martyn V who ruled during the Thornwood War was purely a puppet of the Council of Nobles. Artys VI attempted to exert his power but only succeeded in enraging one of his archdukes into strangling him at court. While Artys VII was a scholar and an intellectual who proved to be more focused on writing than ruling his nation.

The last king of Llael was Rynnard the Fruitful, who would rule for over thirty years and proved to be quite popular and charismatic, although he brought no significant reforms. Famous mostly for his virility after siring sixteen known offspring with various wives, this did not preserve his dynasty after his death from old age. The Llaelese nobles fell into a scheming feud and a series of assassinations managed to result in all of Rynnard's known heirs being slain. The Archduke of Southryne, Prime Minister Deyar Glabryn, seized control amid this chaos and became ruler of his kingdom in the absence of any legitimate royal. While shrewd and ruthless, Glabryn is thought to have played a key role in the imminent downfall of his nation.

HIERARCHS OF THE PROTECTORATE OF MENOTH

While the Protectorate has no dynasties in the proper sense, it entered into the modern era under the firm direction of several visionary hierarchs, each of whom moved this nation toward a greater role in the affairs of the region. After the Protectorate recovered Icthier during the reign of Hierarch Turgis and its borders had been greatly expanded, his successors began to secretly arm the theocracy despite prohibitions against such measures imposed by Cygnar. Hierarch Kilgor Ravonal preached a doctrine of emancipation and worked to expand the Knights Exemplar and Temple Flameguard, shaping them into elements of a modern army.

This work was accelerated by Hierarch Garrick Voyle, who expanded warjack production and implemented the Vassals of Menoth as a means for the Protectorate to craft its own cortexes, beginning by kidnapping knowledgeable arcanists from other kingdoms. Voyle vowed to see the Protectorate as an independent kingdom, and would have his chance to put his armies to the test with the launching of the Great Crusade. These battles led eventually to his own death in the streets of Caspia and the rise of his successor, Hierarch Severius, who continued the crusades.

THE RAELTHORNES OF CYGNAR

In Cygnar, just a few short years after the Thornwood War, King Malfast fell ill and on his deathbed by way of Woldred's Covenant, he handed his crown to Vinter Raelthorne II. In 515 AR, Vinter II ushered in the Raelthorne dynasty which still rules Cygnar today. Vinter ruled with the same prudent approach he had adopted managing Malfast's kingdom, priding the utilitarian over the frivolous. In 539 AR the crown passed to his son, Vinter Raelthorne III, who filled the kingdom's coffers through burdensome taxes to bolster the navy and secure the western sea-lanes from pirates. While unpopular, Vinter III ruled Cygnar with a firm hand and strengthened the kingdom.

Vinter III had two sons: his heir, also named Vinter, and Leto. When Vinter III died with suspicious suddenness in 576 AR, the kingdom fell to his eldest son Vinter IV. Vinter IV proved to be paranoid and tyrannical. Some of the darker inclinations of his line took firmer root in him, and he bore a hatred of the Church of Morrow that defied all reason. Perceived dissidents were silenced or forced into obedience. His paranoia gave rise to the Cygnaran Inquisition, when he transformed his father's network of spies into a merciless system of judges and executioners. With their assistance Vinter ruled by terror and murder. The targets of the Inquisition were alleged witches, but more often those targeted and convicted were innocent of any crime.

THE RETURN OF VINTER

While Vinter IV was thought to have perished in his journey into the Stormlands, rumors of his death proved premature when he returned at the head of a strange army in 603 AR. Crossing the Bloodstone Marches alongside a race called the skorne, a brutal and cruel people. Vinter proved his ambition to seize back his throne when he attacked the city of Corvis. His invasion failed. The exact circumstances of Corvis' liberation are still poorly understood but seem to have involved an old Morrowan prophecy related to an entombed legion of mercenaries from the time of King Malagant. Vinter IV survived and fled back to the east with the remnants of his inhuman army. The skorne have more recently reemerged from the desert and begun to build fortifications in the Bloodstone Marches.

The middle years of Vinter's reign were marked by a rise of Cryxian activity as Cygnar was battered by coastal assaults known as the Scharde Invasions. From 584–588 AR, blackships emerged from the mists to send rapacious raiders into unsuspecting villages and towns, bent on slaughter, arson, and pillage. Graves were despoiled and slain soldiers were dragged away to feed the industries of the Nightmare Empire. Counterstrikes against the Scharde Islands resulted in the loss of a great number of ships and their crews, but both King Vinter IV and Prince Leto led armies in this war, proving their commitment to the defense of the nation. Eventually the Cryxians were driven from Cygnaran shores.

While such heroics made that kingdom's people more accepting of King Vinter IV's extreme measures, years of brutal treatment reminded them he was a tyrant. As rumors of torture at the hands of the Inquisition persisted, many began to doubt their king's sanity. Prince Leto felt driven to act and with the aid of the Morrowan Church he overthrew his brother during the Lion's Coup of 594 AR. Before King Leto could submit his brother to a trial, the Elder escaped, using Leto's queen as hostage to seize an experimental airship at the top of the palace. He rose out of reach of his pursuers but fell mercy to the whims of the wind and drifted east over the arid Bloodstone Marches.

The Royal Assembly conducted a trial for Vinter IV in absentia whereby they stripped him of all powers for his proven crimes and dark alliances. He was convicted of high treason, and his life was declared forfeit. Leto Raelthorne proved true to his word in the years after the coup by abolishing the Inquisition and restoring the nation. The next decade under Leto's rule was seen by many as a golden era of unprecedented growth, mechanikal inventions and advancements, flourishing trade, and the harmony and efficiency that is the hallmark of a fair and just government. But he was not the only sovereign working to strengthen his nation, and the schemes and ambitions of other rival powers would soon see this nation beset on multiple sides.

THE LLAELESE WAR

With little warning, Khador massed their full might and launched an invasion against Llael in the last month of 604 AR. This attack was carefully planned and executed by Kommandant Gurvaldt Irusk, the Motherland's foremost military genius with extensive knowledge of Llael's defenses. Irusk had determined the key to victory would be seizing an overwhelming advantage before Cygnar could march its armies to reinforce its longtime ally. The assault in the winter was planned knowing Khadoran soldiers were better prepared and equipped to fight in this season than its enemies. Llael's prime minister collaborated in betraying his nation in the months leading up to invasion, undermining the Llaelese Army and delivering key information to the Khadorans. The western border was penetrated in days and the Khadoran Army marched on the interior.

Cygnar rushed to its ally's defense and was caught up in a series of increasingly desperate battles across the Llaelese countryside. A brutal series of battles took place at the northern city of Riversmet, which boasted key bridges over the Black River. Ultimately Khador proved victorious and made a demonstration of this city to break the will of Llaelese still resisting in the eastern regions. Riversmet was razed to the ground and bloodthirsty doom reavers unleashed on its surviving population. This demoralized the Order of the Golden Crucible army holding the fortified city of Leryn, whose leaders subsequently opened its gates and surrendered.

The last and most intense battles of the war took place in defense of the Llaelese capital, Merywyn, which endured a long and difficult siege. On hearing of Khadoran forces moving on the Thornwood, Cygnar withdrew its armies to defend its border, and soon thereafter the capital fell. The war lasted less than six months before Llael's nobles surrendered. Khador entered a new phase of the conflict, this time battling on Cygnar's soil.

Meanwhile, a burgeoning Llaelese Resistance was born in the captive cities and the one free city of Rhydden, but would face many difficulties trying to organize against Llael's conquerors. Many of Llael's assets were seized by Khador and its industrial cities were quickly turned to supporting the Khadoran war effort. With the lands of Llael in her grasp, Ayn Vanar declared herself empress and announced the dawn of the Khadoran Empire.

THE CASPIA-SUL WAR
AND THE GREAT CRUSADES

The timing of the Llaelese War was difficult for Cygnar. Relations with the Protectorate of Menoth had worsened considerably in the preceding years and it had become clear that the Sul-Menites were in violation of its disarmament agreements. King Leto had been debating measures to enforce compliance when war in the north erupted. Hierarch Garrick Voyle capitalized on the distraction provided by the war to call a crusade against the enemies of the faith. This coincided with the arrival of a Harbinger of Menoth to the Protectorate capital of Imer, a holy messenger who spoke Menoth's will. Not only did this woman and her miracles revitalize the Menite faith, but word of her arrival resulted in thousands of Menites from other kingdoms giving up their old allegiances to join the Protectorate.

War quickly erupted between Caspia and Sul, with attacks also taking place inside Cygnar's interior as Menite forces snuck past the border patrols to conduct acts of sabotage. Cygnar was forced to divide its military forces between defending its capital and the war in the north, while also preserving garrisons along its western seaboard against the threat of Cryx. Indeed, it soon became apparent that Cryx had infiltrated the mainland in greater strength than had ever been suspected. Cygnar's spymaster eventually concluded that the Scharde Invasions had been used as a complex diversion to land forces unseen.

With turmoil in the south steadily worsening, King Leto consented to isolate Cygnaran citizens of the Menite faith in this region lest they commit treachery. At the same time, in response to the Protectorate's failed siege on Caspia, the Cygnaran Army launched an invasion of Sul. Sul's previously impenetrable walls were breached and Cygnaran forces swept into the city. Religious fervor gave the Sulese defenders desperate fortitude and led to an exhausting year of street-to-street fighting. With Cygnar's army unable to seize a quick victory, the Menites regrouped and eventually drove the Cygnarans back. Led by Hierarch Voyle, Caspia was in turn invaded by the Sul-Menites. King Leto joined the defense personally but was nearly slain in battle with Hierarch Voyle. It was not until the Menites were at the gates of Castle Raelthorne that the tide turned at last. Like Sulon in the Civil War, Hierarch Voyle was struck down. This victory arrived only after Voyle had carved a tremendous path of destruction through the ancient capital.

While fighting was taking place in the streets of Caspia and Sul, other forces of the Protectorate were on the march. Grand Scrutator Severius had led the Northern Crusade deep into the Thornwood. Armed for war, the Harbinger of Menoth joined him, hoping to eventually deliver Menoth's message to the Menites of Khador. In a bold campaign this crusade destroyed the Cygnaran city of Fisherbrook, obliterated an important Morrowan monastery outside Fellig, and helped thwart the Cryxian Lich Lord Asphyxious who had seized control of an old buried Orgoth temple in the Thornwood. Not resting on these accomplishments, Severius led the Northern Crusade into Occupied Llael and soon used holy manifestations to seize the city of Leryn as a northern stronghold for the Sul-Menites. After Voyle's death, Severius was chosen as the new hierarch to lead his nation in the Great Crusade.

FALL OF NORTHGUARD, INVASION OF THE THORNWOOD

While Cygnar would ultimately hold its capital and arrive at a fragile cease-fire with Sul, she faired worse in the north where a rag tag network of trenches around the fortress of Northguard forestalled the Khadoran advance. For months Cygnar and Khador fought a grueling war of attrition across a blasted no man's land of craters and barbed wire. Attempting to end the stalemate, Khador twice attempted to overrun the Cygnaran defenders. While the first full assault on Northguard in late 606 AR was a costly failure, with Cygnar holding out against a numerically superior foe, Khador proved swifter at recouping its losses. While Cygnar struggled to reinforce Northguard, a second massive attack was launched in 607 AR and this time

succeeded in toppling this fortress. Cygnar's northern army endured a fighting retreat through a Cryx-filled forest to regroup along the Dragon's Tongue River. Khador seized the Thornwood for itself, but has discovered it to be swarming with many Cryxian undead, making for supply line difficulties.

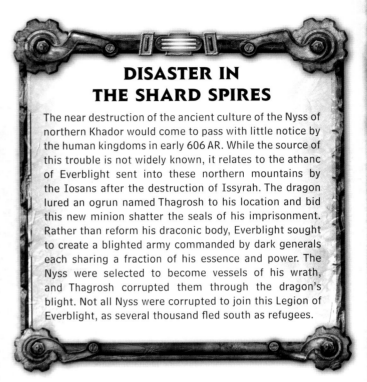

DISASTER IN THE SHARD SPIRES

The near destruction of the ancient culture of the Nyss of northern Khador would come to pass with little notice by the human kingdoms in early 606 AR. While the source of this trouble is not widely known, it relates to the athanc of Everblight sent into these northern mountains by the Iosans after the destruction of Issyrah. The dragon lured an ogrun named Thagrosh to his location and bid this new minion shatter the seals of his imprisonment. Rather than reform his draconic body, Everblight sought to create a blighted army commanded by dark generals each sharing a fraction of his essence and power. The Nyss were selected to become vessels of his wrath, and Thagrosh corrupted them through the dragon's blight. Not all Nyss were corrupted to join this Legion of Everblight, as several thousand fled south as refugees.

While Khador was victorious in war, she has endured threats from other quarters. Earlier in 606 AR an inexplicable Cryxian fleet sailed north past Ordic waters to assail the Khadoran Navy stationed at Port Vladovar, dealing a crippling blow to Khador's naval strength and inflicting severe damage on this port city. Additionally, the catastrophe in the northern Shard Spires which destroyed the Nyss people has had unexpected fallout which has affected Khador more than other nations. There are rumors of bloodthirsty dragonspawn together with blighted Nyss that have terrorized a number of outlying communities among the northern mountains. Nyss refugees have fled the north to seek refuge anywhere they can find it, particularly in the Khadoran capital of Korsk.

This is the state of affairs in western Immoren at the present, in the year 608 AR. Fighting between Khador and Cygnar has stalled, albeit each side is arming along the Dragon's Tongue River. Battles between Cygnar and the Protectorate have entered a clandestine stage. Yet while there is a lull in the conflicts, it is tense. Each side continues to mass its soldiers and stand at war readiness. Additionally, the trollkin kriels of both Khador and Cygnar are stirred up and ready for battle after intrusions on their lands. That fighting will resume is certain, with the rising menace of Cryx along the coasts as well as within the Thornwood. It is a troubling time for all the nations of the Iron Kingdoms.

Life in the Iron Kingdoms is full of contrasts. Laborers and merchants engage in their generations-old trades, but they do so in the midst of an industrial revolution. They pray to the same gods their families have worshipped for centuries, but their traditions are challenged by a rapidly changing world. The wonders of mechanika—the merging of technology and magic—are increasingly commonplace in some cities, but populations far from the walls of civilization still fear the beasts and savages of the wild. In the year 608 AR, the Iron Kingdoms are nations on the edge, with the wonders made possible by an age of reason on one side and the abyss of total war on the other.

THE IRON KINGDOMS

The nations of the Iron Kingdoms comprise the human powers in western Immoren. These are the diverse kingdoms whose borders were initially defined in the Corvis Treaties signed in the aftermath of the Rebellion against the Orgoth. Those borders have changed considerably over the centuries, and many of the current wars are extensions of ongoing territorial disputes. In 608 AR the Iron Kingdoms are in a momentary lull in an era of tremendous strife when nations have toppled nations and others have been pushed to the brink.

In these uncertain times the people of western Immoren continue on as best they can, laboring in factories and on farms and hoping the winds of war do not sweep up their homes and livelihoods. There is great opportunity for those willing to take up the sword in defense of their nation or their principles or simply in the pursuit of coin and adventure.

CYGNAR

One of the great powers in the Iron Kingdoms, the southern nation of Cygnar is beset by enemies within and without. She is ruled by a king most consider just and is the most rapidly modernizing state in western Immoren. Her people are proud of the freedom and opportunities available to them, counting among their numbers some of the most brilliant minds on Caen. They are aware they enjoy higher quality of life than many others in the region, who understandably envy their prosperity. Even the lower classes in Cygnar live better lives than those elsewhere, due to advances in mechanika and laws implemented under the current sovereign reforming labor practices.

Cygnar has become a center of industry and trade known throughout the Iron Kingdoms. Blessed with abundant resources, a long coastline, a diverse geography and citizenry, and many other assets, the nation is sometimes referred to by her people as the "Jewel of the Iron Kingdoms." Her blue and gold banner features the heraldic symbol of Cygnar,

the unmistakable Cygnus. The Cygnus dates back to the unification of Cygnar at the end of the Rebellion, formalized during the Corvis Treaties, and was chosen as a symbol of the solidarity of the southern peoples. It also represents the bright future of this new nation, whose people relied on their combined faith and courage to battle the Orgoth and forge the weapons that would ultimately defeat those tyrants.

Traditionally, Cygnar has been the nation most accommodating to outsiders and other races—in addition to humans of all ethnic groups, gobbers, trollkin, dwarves, and ogrun are welcomed for the most part. Her lands are split between many feudal duchies and provinces, but Cygnar's cities are her greatest strength. The nation's bustling capital, Caspia, is called the City of Walls after the towering fortifications surrounding it and running throughout its varied districts. The walls of Caspia are so massive and ancient that entire neighborhoods and thoroughfares exist within them. More than a million citizens live and work within the maze of these walls.

A hub for commerce by ship, road, and rail, Caspia is also one of the oldest cities in western Immoren. It is home to both the throne of Cygnar and the Sancteum, a sovereign city within the city that is the seat of the Morrowan faith. Cygnar was initially founded by Menites, and Caspia still retains many impressive temples to the Creator. The civil war that divided the capital into the twin cities of Caspia and Sul resulted in most southern Menites relocating to the Protectorate of Menoth, with the result that today Cygnar is predominantly Morrowan. Although the nation feels the strain of the Protectorate's crusades, the Crown nonetheless still advocates religious tolerance, and its small Menite minority have a proud legacy going back to Priest-Kings Golivant and Cinot.

Cygnar's cities are among the most modern in western Immoren, her people among the best educated. Most Cygnaran cities feature solid infrastructures with reliable plumbing, well-maintained roads, and measures to combat corruption and foster vital industry and public health. Only the poorest quarters of cities are squalid, and even there, representatives of the Church of Morrow make efforts to help the truly destitute. Cygnar boasts a large middle class of successful craftsmen, merchants, mechanikal innovators, and scholars, and the gap between the poor and those of means is less pronounced than in other nations.

Ceryl, to the northwest, is the nation's second-largest city, once the heart of the ancient kingdom of Thuria. Now it is a shipping center that is home to the northern fleet and is famed for the skill and lore of its arcanists. In the northeast, Corvis sits at the confluence of two major rivers, where a steady flow of riverboats passes through the bustling docks amid multiple-storied buildings that are slowly sinking into the muddy ground. Far to the south is Mercir, a city only easily reached by boat. In this relative isolation, Mercir has developed its own distinct culture, including a larger than normal population of trollkin, who are sometimes exploited as cheap labor. Highgate, in the west, is seen as a guardian of the Broken Coast. From its perch among the Wyrmwall Mountains, its massive steam-powered cranes hoist ships from the waters to safeguard them from Cryxian pirates. These cities and the other major Cygnaran towns are all vibrant urban centers conducting vital manufacturing work amid complex local politics. Many boast pioneers in industry and scientific advancement as well as a number of prestigious universities. Yet with prosperity comes other dangers, and each city and major township is preyed upon by criminal communities seeking to exploit any opportunity.

The civilized Cygnaran countryside with its lush farmlands is divided by several untamed regions, including the extensive Wyrmwall Mountains, the Gnarls, and the Fenn Swamp. Though the nation maintains several highways and rail lines, these wild areas remain inhospitable and are populated by savage humans, wild trollkin kriels, and all manner of predatory beasts. Travel between major cities can be risky, with occasional military patrols and overworked road wardens able to protect only the main roads and railways.

In the past few years Cygnarans have seen the fall of their allies in Llael, the loss of the northern Thornwood Forest to the encroaching Khadoran Empire, and years of turmoil in their capital and neighboring Sul due to open warfare with the Protectorate. Cygnar remains on friendly terms with the nation of Ord but that kingdom's sovereign has proven reluctant to enter into a formal alliance and has shrewdly negotiated for considerable concessions in return for even the most grudging and minimal military assistance.

Cygnar's King Leto Raelthorne has a reputation as a just and resourceful monarch who has ruled with intelligence in an extremely difficult time. A far cry from his hated brother, Vinter Raelthorne, Leto took the crown and freed Cygnar from tyranny. Despite holding strong against multiple enemies, though, King Leto has seen his support eroded by years of strife and several significant—if arguably unavoidable—defeats. While many military experts insist no monarch or general could have done better in the same circumstances, the loss of Llael and the Thornwood combined with considerable trollkin-related unrest have given considerable fuel to Leto's detractors, particularly in the north of Cygnar. He retains many staunch supporters, but increasingly strident voices claim he has been too indecisive amid the nation's wars.

The recent clashes between Caspia and Sul are a testament to Cygnar's precarious position. Hostility began during the Llaelese War while Cygnar's troops abroad were engaged against Khador, with Protectorate forces laying siege to Caspia's eastern gates. This was unsuccessful but demanded retaliation, and the Cygnaran Army eventually breached the walls of Sul. Their invasion into this city proved to be costly and extended, consuming the lives of thousands on both sides. Eventually the Protectorate reclaimed Sul and conducted a counter attack on the streets of Caspia, one which seemed near to swallowing the entire city in conflict and threatening the palace. Disaster was only narrowly averted after a prolonged battle in which the king himself took up his blade. In the end, the battle ended when the Protectorate's hierarch was struck down by one of Cygnar's commanding warcasters. Their morale broken, the Sul-Menites withdrew, and there has been a tense cessation in hostilities between the two cities. Massive garrisons in both cities stand ready to continue the conflict at the slightest provocation.

Despite these threats, Cygnar is well defended. Many say Cygnar's greatest asset is her advanced mechanika; indeed, the nation is unequalled in the synthesis of magic and science. Her advanced technology is no more evident then in her specialized military forces such as the fabled Stormblades and gun mages. But even frontline infantry field high-quality rifles and other ordnance and fight alongside some of the most sophisticated warjacks ever designed. Cygnar's ability to manage the division of military resources between its armies has been key to its endurance. Each operates independently to confront various threats, one in the north, one in the east, and one in the southwest, all supported by the reserves of the smaller Fourth Army. Similarly, the Royal Navy has divided its fleets between theaters of operation. Cygnar's navy is peerless in its technological might and has become pivotal in preventing incursions from the sea.

It would seem war is changing the pace of Cygnar's technology as swiftly as it is changing the pace of her people. Her foundries produce more weapons, warjacks, alchemical components, and material to support the war effort, and goods and rare materials throughout the kingdom are now rationed for the military. In truth, the Cygnaran spirit preserved in the hearts of her soldiers is the nation's true strength. The people of Cygnar are bloodied but unbowed. Every Cygnaran knows at least one friend or family member who has died as a consequence of war, but even after massive losses over recent years, many citizens are still eager to take up arms in the defense of their crown and country. They are more than willing and ready to defend themselves and their beloved kingdom from those who would crush the principles of freedom and all for which Cygnar stands.

THE KHADORAN EMPIRE

Khador is a land of sweeping expanses, fertile plains, imposing mountains, and dense forests. Her people are the stalwart inheritors of an ancient civilization that once dominated the north. This history is ever present in the minds of the Khadoran people, as every generation repeats the tales of the legendary horselords. These fierce warlords banded together, conquered the weaker tribes, and fashioned the proud Khardic Empire. Some say the empire never truly fell but simply endured a dark age until it could emerge and evolve into the modern nation of Khador. In 606 AR, bolstered by sweeping military conquest, Khador's sovereign declared herself Empress Ayn Vanar, and the kingdom of Khador became the Khadoran Empire, a continuation of this ancient legacy.

Since the dawn of the Iron Kingdoms, the Motherland has looked on her neighbors with contempt; the Khadorans never felt compensated for their suffering at the hands of the Orgoth.

At the Corvis Treaties, Cygnar, Ord, and Llael all claimed lands that had once belonged to the Khardic Empire, a bitter pill to swallow combined with the suffering of the Khardic people in the centuries of the Occupation. It was not long before the proud Khadorans sought to readdress these borders. Over the centuries Khador has made numerous attempts to expand her holdings. Time and again Khador's monarchs have felt the call to reestablish the empire of old, blurring boundaries with the blood of border wars.

The Khadoran people see their empress, Ayn Vanar XI, as the personification of their nation and call her the Pervichyi Rodinovna, the "Prime Daughter" of the Motherland. The conquest of Llael fulfilled the ambitions of generations, and this success has only emboldened the empress. More than imperialism, more than nation-building, for this ruler the ongoing war is the expression of a manifest destiny. The Khardic people by right should rule the Iron Kingdoms, and she is willing to expand Khador's dominion by any means necessary. Her armies have marched south and struck down the great Cygnaran fortress of Northguard and with it claimed the entirety of the Thornwood Forest. Having redrawn Khador's southern border at the northern bank of the Black River, the High Kommand and its legions pause to regroup before their next campaign begins.

To match her rivals, over the past centuries the Motherland has taken great strides toward reinventing herself as a major industrial power. As a result of unchecked mechanized growth, most Khadoran cities lie shadowed under a constant canopy of smoke and soot. Khador's industrial revolution has wracked her citizens with growing pains, but the kayazy merchant princes and other royal supporters have no intention of backing from their goal of total superiority. While some noble families may wonder if the cost to ancient tradition is worth the rewards of the modern age, the grip of industrialization now spans the empire.

Khadorans are assiduous laborers who fervently devote their sweat and blood to their way of life. Patriotism is in their nature, and service is a badge of honor. Khador comes first, with religion and ethnicity following. Though the citizens are narrowly split between the Morrowan and Menite faiths, ancient religious feuds have been set aside for the call of the Motherland. Members of Khador's Menite Old Faith practice their religion much the same as the ancient horselords did, and many of the aristocratic families are devout followers. Even so, the recent emergence of the Harbinger in the Protectorate threatened that solidarity as tens of thousands of citizens chose to heed her call to join the Protectorate's crusades, and more may follow.

Khador's steamjacks are built in accordance with the Motherland's emphasis on endurance and raw strength, and her railway is a source of much pride. A nation once comprising pockets of ethnic societies, isolated in their remote forests and mountains, has transformed into an empire rising on a tide of nationalism. Her capital of Korsk is every bit as impressive as any southern city with its great factories, schools of higher learning, and glorious cathedrals.

The people of Khador have not enjoyed the fruits of the modern era as thoroughly as their southern neighbors, a fact that fuels their dreams of empire. Most Khadorans still work as unskilled laborers, although every year more of them join the ranks of craftsmen and the great cities of the north house branches of the Khadoran Mechaniks Assembly as professional and innovative as any of their Cygnaran counterparts.

Military service is required of every adult male in Khador, and women are equally accepted, though not compelled. More citizens pursue military careers than in other nations, and combat skill is well respected in all arenas of life. Even the politically powerful have served their time, creating lasting bonds that transcend class barriers. Only a small number of Khadorans seek to evade military service, generally those found among the criminal fraternities of Korsk and other major cities.

DIVIDED LLAEL

A fallen and fragmented nation, Llael's demise began in the winter of 604 AR when, in a lightning attack, Khador invaded and caught its people and their Cygnaran allies completely off guard. Seven months later, the Llaelese War ended with the surrender of Merywyn, the former capital. This has entirely changed the face of the nation, entering Llael into four long years of turmoil and constant adaptation to the changing face of their nation as it has been occupied, conquered, and repeatedly battled over by foreign powers. Most of the people had no desire to host the largest conflicts by the battle-ready armies of the Iron Kingdoms and desperately desire some return to normality, even if that means accepting foreign flags and masters. A minority of patriotic, stubborn, or embittered and enraged individuals refuse to give up the dream of Llael and fight on, forming the core of a Llaelese Resistance whose struggles become more desperate with each passing week. At present, what was once western Llael is increasingly accepting its lot and has begun rebuilding. A sizable number of citizens of Umbrean descent look on the new era with some optimism, as their once-divided people have been reunited with bloodlines from the west. Eastern Llael contains several Resistance havens but is increasingly dominated by the Northern Crusade of the Protectorate of Menoth and their religious zealotry.

In truth, Llael was a failed state well before the Khadorans marched on their shared border. The last strong Llaelese king died of old age almost ten years before the onset of this war, and his death plunged Llael's nobles into a frenzy of self-consuming plots and politics. This included the assassination of all the former king's heirs as well as a number of duels and assassinations further thinning the ranks of the nobility. Prime Minister Deyar Glabryn took power and proved to be a corrupt and self-interested leader more intent on lining his pockets than governing his nation. The small and poorly funded Llaelese Army was further reduced in favor of mercenary contracts and an overreliance on Cygnaran aid. The Cygnaran Army spent considerable lives seeking to slow the inexorable Khadoran advance but was ultimately forced to withdraw to defend Cygnar's own borders. It is widely believed Glabryn collaborated with the Khadorans by weakening the nation.

Prior to the invasion, Llael had a centuries-old reputation as a haven of court intrigue and shrewd financiers. Llael maintained sovereignty through intense political brokering. Its income came from the collection of tariffs made possible by its central location between several of the major powers of western Immoren. The region, in the midst of the trade route between Cygnar and Rhul, is of considerable strategic importance. This has been a blessing and a curse, filling Llaelese pockets in times of peace but constantly drawing the covetous eyes of Khador since the signing of the Corvis Treaties.

Despite the recent turmoil, most of its surviving citizens simply try to carve out lives for themselves as best they can and see to the needs of their families. After almost four years under Khadoran rule, most have come to terms with being part of the Khadoran Empire. Their lives, similar to those in Cygnar and Ord before, have in some respects improved under the efficient management of the Khadorans.

Many opportunities have come into this region as a result of Khadoran investment, including work extending rail lines as well as considerable military industry, particularly in the capital of Merywyn and the large western city of Laedry. There is no doubt the Khadorans have improved the nation's infrastructure. Despite these factors, resentment toward the Khadorans lingers, particularly in parts of Llael that saw the worst of the war. The tally of deaths from the invasion remains unknown. Tales of the burning of Riversmet and other wartime horrors reverberate throughout the kingdoms. It will take more than a few years for these incidents to be forgotten.

In both Merywyn and Laedry there has been something of a reversal of fortunes between the Ryn and the Umbrean people. While many Llaelese Umbreans were proud of their nation, they were also marginalized, with military service their only hope for advancement. Many of the most fervid were killed in the invasion, fighting to save their homes. Those who remain remember the lack of respect they suffered from the Ryn. A renewal of Umbrean spirit has swept the region, and increasingly Umbreans are gaining positions of authority and influence, while Ryn scramble to curry favor. For the Umbreans in particular, life has improved under the new government, even if the region remains in turmoil.

Llael also possesses natural resources that for centuries enabled it to stay competitive with its larger neighbors, notably a high content of coal and, in the northern mountains and particularly around Rynyr, great quantities of the minerals required for making blasting powder. With nobility owning the lands, Llael's upper classes increased their wealth from coal and powder profits while the nation's poor did all the work. Indeed, the disparity between the classes appeared more clearly in Llael than anywhere else in the kingdoms, yet thousands of workers from all over western Immoren arrived daily to work the mines.

THE LLAELESE RESISTANCE

Life among the Resistance is hard; food is scarce, and one must remain constantly on the move. Any Llaelese found to be supporting the Resistance in any capacity, even by unknowingly providing food or shelter, face execution at the hands of the Khadorans. Rhydden is the last city in the hands of the Resistance and has transformed from a tranquil city of wine into a heavily fortified encampment. Elsewhere operatives must make do with the dubious security of safe houses and underground dens in Merywyn and Laedry.

The Llaelese Resistance is in a state of transition but remains fiercely dedicated to its cause, perhaps all the more so as the dream of restoring Llael becomes even more unlikely. In Rhydden their emphasis is on the immediate needs of the citizens collected there, ensuring their preservation amid desperate circumstances. The objective of the Resistance outside Rhydden has become the disruption of Khadoran bureaucracy and harassment of the military however possible rather than the pursuit of conventional military gains. The surviving Resistance leaders have years of experience fighting difficult battles while outnumbered and outgunned; some of them are former members of the Llaelese Army or held prominent positions in esteemed groups like the Order of the Amethyst Rose, gun mages who have long dedicated themselves to the kings of Llael. These veteran commanders are training the next generation of warriors for a different sort of war, one fought in alleyways and by small groups seeking to evade detection as they strike at their enemies and exact a cost in Khadoran blood for the occupation.

Funding for the Resistance has also changed. Much of its financial support has come from a group identifying themselves as the Highborn Covenant, former nobles of Llael who feel betrayed by the former prime minister. Many of these nobles, now living in exile in Cygnar or Ord, are still willing to support those fighting at home, but as their own situations have changed, the funds they supply have dwindled. Increasingly the Resistance relies on alternative sources of support, including selling their services as mercenaries and raising sympathy for their cause among displaced Llaelese. Fundraising for the Resistance has taken place wherever former Llaelese have settled, most particularly near Corvis in Cygnar and in certain Ordic cities like Five Fingers, Berck, and Tarna. Both fulfilling mercenary contracts and the need to raise funds, sometimes by questionably legal means, often requires Resistance agents to go abroad on a variety of dangerous missions.

Little has changed except that now Khadoran laborers work alongside former Llaelese citizens and the fruits of their toil puts food on the tables of the kayazy industrialists rather than the Rynnish aristocracy.

Though battles between the Llaelese Resistance and the Khadoran occupiers still flare, the central conflict in this nation changed with the arrival of the Sul-Menite Northern Crusade. Technically allied to the Resistance, the Northern Crusade has seized vast swaths of Llaelese land for the Protectorate of Menoth. New battle lines have been drawn between the Khadorans who have conquered the region and the Sul-Menites, with the Black River as the main divider.

Eastern Llael past the Black River remains in greater chaos, with the southern portion still held by the most dedicated leaders of the Llaelese Resistance and the northern city of Leryn and its environs in the grip of the Northern Crusade. The relationship between these allies of convenience became strained after the Protectorate moved into Leryn and it became clear the Menites were more interested in gaining a foothold and converting the Llaelese citizenry than in driving out the Khadorans. Many here who are not of the Menite faith have begun to wonder if their lives might have been better under Khadoran rule. For others, the difficulties of the last several years have provoked renewed piety, and they pray for salvation, miracles, divine intervention, or mercy. The faith of both Morrowans and Menites in the region is stronger, and some Llaelese see the Northern Crusade not as invaders or occupiers but as deliverers.

Another significant power in the region is the looming presence of Rhul to the north. Even the Khadoran Empire respects Rhul's military might and are aware of its interests here due to ongoing vital trade through the region. Many southern Rhulfolk disapprove of the Khadoran Empire and its conquests—a number of Rhulic citizens who lived and worked in Llaelese cities were casualties of the war—but ultimately the preservation of trade is their priority. Rhul trades with the Khadoran Empire as much as with other nations so has been unwilling to take sides.

Despite Khadoran control of the Black River through Llael, Rhulic shipments have found ways to reach Cygnar and Ord. Some degree of Khadoran complicity seems likely, even if only in the form of bribes. In truth, the costs to Rhulic interests are not substantially greater than they were before the war; the coin once paid to Llaelese nobles and merchants as exorbitant tariffs is simply now spent on bribes and smugglers.

The simmering strife makes the region a considerably less desirable place to live, but it also provides opportunities for the courageous and ambitious. This is particularly true for mercenaries, as there is no end to clients looking for armed and skilled individuals. Whether motivated by greed or by sympathy for the locals, warriors-for-hire have flocked to the region, and a variety of commerce and services have sprung up to accommodate them. Locals may disdain such trade as war-profiteering, but they also may find themselves needing to rely on the sell-swords for protection.

ORD

The kingdom of Ord is a land of fog-shrouded moors, rolling highlands, and rocky coasts. Bordered by the hungry Khadoran Empire to the north and east and the powerful Cygnarans to the south, Ord has maintained its sovereignty through skillful diplomacy backed by stalwart soldiers and a navy capable of holding its own against any fleet on Meredius.

The Ordic people are descended from two mighty kingdoms, Thuria and Tordor, and its people are proud of that ancestry. For some the tales of ancient glories help distract from their difficult lives, as this nation has widespread poverty and a sharp divide between the wealthy and the poor. The Tordorans dominate the upper classes and are particularly populous in the north, where they own and control the most fertile and prosperous lands. Many of the wealthier Tordorans have made their fortunes in livestock; the region is famed for its cattle, goats, sheep, and horses. The Thurians, more numerous in the south, are far scarcer in the halls of power; even those families that have risen to power are generally subordinate to their Tordoran counterparts. Those Thurians who have attained any success have had to do so with wits and hard work.

The nation's ports are home to the finest sailors and dock men in western Immoren. Ordic fishermen and sailors exert a great deal of control over seaborne trade routes all across the western seaboard. True, some Ordic ports are pirate havens and thieves' dens, but the goods their merchantmen procure from all over the Iron Kingdoms can make even the most disreputable cities worth the trip. Ord's largest city and most thriving trade center is Berck, where the leaders of merchant houses dominate city politics. While it is a city with a dark criminal underbelly, it is considered the fair face of Ord and is home to the famed Ordic Navy.

Equally important and of far darker reputation is Five Fingers, also known as the "Port of Deceit," a city sprawling across numerous islands at the mouth of the Dragon's Tongue River. Five Fingers is a city that has made an industry of vice, including smuggling, gambling, and extortion. The seemingly lawless environment here, combined with Ord's neutrality in the wars abroad, makes Five Fingers appealing to mercenary companies, and it has garnered a reputation as a place where deals can be struck for anything under the sun. As dangerous as it is, for many the unique opportunities offered in Five Fingers outweigh the risks.

Ord is the poorest kingdom in western Immoren. Aside from peat harvested from hundreds of bogs, Ord has little natural resources, with livestock the only other significant export. The coal deposits in the riverbanks near Merin are considered abundant but are only sufficient for the needs of the capital and the northern city of Midfast. Inland residents tend toward farming, raising livestock, or trade in peat or wool.

Like the craggy hills and boggy moors, the people of Ord are rugged, weathered, and difficult to tame. They are mostly a common people who enjoy a wide variety of sport and gambling diversions from their everyday lives of dock work, shipbuilding, or tilling fields. Those born to wealth live on large estates high above the lowlands. Both classes can fall prey to the numerous brigands that plague the nation despite the efforts of its kings to eradicate them.

While more famed for its navy, Ord has an army that has earned respect in countless border wars. The Ordic Army has managed to repel numerous Khadoran invasions throughout history despite its chronically dated arms and relatively small size. Its soldiers are traditionally well trained and brave, but the nation lacks the economic might to outfit them with the advanced mechanika now common in the other armies of the Iron Kingdoms. Much of Ord's security has been derived from the rugged border between Khador and the Ordic interior, jagged hills fortified with dozens of holds and fastnesses. The recent seizure of the Thornwood by Khador has imperiled that, prompting the Ordic Army to increase recruitment and commit to a frenzy of construction along their eastern border.

Ord's King Baird Cathor II, known as "the Baird" among his people but sometimes called "the Bandit King" behind his back, relies on shrewd political maneuvering to ensure his kingdom's survival. Some say he earned his less flattering moniker as much from his shady associates as from the curses of castellans complaining of his high taxes. While he presents himself as a simple pleasure seeker, he has proven to be one of the shrewdest and best-informed monarchs in the kingdoms and possesses an expansive network of spies. Since the outbreak of war, he has carefully maintained his country's neutrality even as he attempts to play other nations off one another. While Ord has suffered repeated attacks from Khador over the centuries and Baird's sympathies rest with Cygnar, he is too pragmatic not to exploit opportunities to enrich his struggling kingdom.

Such opportunities lately have bestowed the nation with the chance to become a more significant power. As the only kingdom not yet actively engaged in war, Ord is in an advantageous position. After the fall of Llael many refugees, some possessing valuable skills, sought refuge in Midfast and Merin. This led to the Free Order of the Golden Crucible establishing its new headquarters in Midfast, bringing with them a wealth of alchemical expertise as well as considerable income from their far-flung membership. Cygnar seeks to solidify an alliance with the kingdom now that Llael has fallen, and the Ordic throne

recognizes its increased value to Cygnar. This has resulted in some exchanges of services and mechanika between the Cygnaran Armory and the Ordic Navy, spearheaded by King Baird's second son, a distinguished naval officer who has taken up the cause of modernizing the kingdom's military assets.

The annexation of the Thornwood by Khador resulted in an unexpected development when the Cygnaran city of Fellig was cut off from the rest of its nation after the fall of Northguard. Mercenaries working together with the Ordic Army were able to provide the city relief from a Khadoran siege, and now Fellig has become an Ordic possession, creating a stalwart northeastern bastion for the Ordic Army. Cygnar's King Leto has seen fit to allow this situation to persist, at least until his nation can recapture the Thornwood. For now, it is better that Fellig be in Ordic rather than Khadoran hands. The city's citizens find themselves in a peculiar position, as it is populated by proud Morridanes who remain fiercely patriotic to Cygnar; most residents are grateful to Ord but become prickly at any talk of the city being anything but Cygnaran. Nevertheless, the

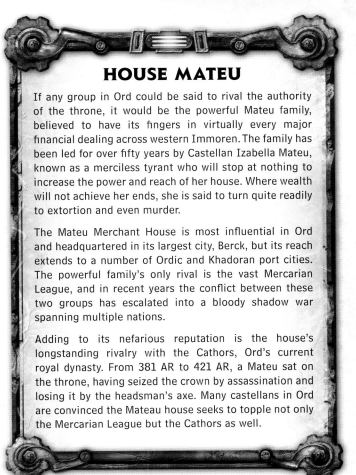

HOUSE MATEU

If any group in Ord could be said to rival the authority of the throne, it would be the powerful Mateu family, believed to have its fingers in virtually every major financial dealing across western Immoren. The family has been led for over fifty years by Castellan Izabella Mateu, known as a merciless tyrant who will stop at nothing to increase the power and reach of her house. Where wealth will not achieve her ends, she is said to turn quite readily to extortion and even murder.

The Mateu Merchant House is most influential in Ord and headquartered in its largest city, Berck, but its reach extends to a number of Ordic and Khadoran port cities. The powerful family's only rival is the vast Mercarian League, and in recent years the conflict between these two groups has escalated into a bloody shadow war spanning multiple nations.

Adding to its nefarious reputation is the house's longstanding rivalry with the Cathors, Ord's current royal dynasty. From 381 AR to 421 AR, a Mateu sat on the throne, having seized the crown by assassination and losing it by the headsman's axe. Many castellans in Ord are convinced the Mateau house seeks to topple not only the Mercarian League but the Cathors as well.

influx of Ordfolk including fresh soldiers has been a boon, and the city is in the midst of finding its new identity.

Thus far Khador has proven reluctant to test Ordic borders. As Khador's only source of outside commerce, Ord is a market the kayazy wish to preserve. Like the tides from which the kingdom derives much of its livelihood, Ord's outlook seems to ebb and flow from day to day, and her leaders and king cast their nets into the choppy seas of politics and intrigue to see what bounties they might draw forth from the deep.

PROTECTORATE OF MENOTH

The newest of the nations recognized as the Iron Kingdoms was not forged in the fires of the Rebellion and defined at the Corvis Treaties but was born from civil war and religious strife. It is unique in many respects, most notably for being a strict theocracy, ruled by the iron hand and watchful eye of the Temple of Menoth. Religion and government go hand-in-hand in the Protectorate of Menoth; religious faith and the worship of the Creator is an aspect of daily life for even its most ignorant laborers. While not every citizen of the Protectorate is equally pious or zealous, there is no escaping the omnipresent influence of the

Menite priests, who control the nation's government, police, judges, and executioners. Ardent believers view themselves as the last bastion of the true religion of mankind and see around them endless examples of heresy and blasphemy. Their nation and faith are inseparable, and now they are part of a key moment in history when a great crusade has been called to bring the wayward back into the fold.

The Protectorate began as a compromise during the peace talks at the end of the Cygnaran Civil War in 484 AR, and for most of its history it was beholden to Cygnaran authority. Even in the earliest years the Cygnaran Crown preferred to leave the Sul-Menites to govern themselves. The only stipulations imposed on the people of the Protectorate were that they continue to pay taxes to the throne and that they not create a standing army. Even these mild limits would eventually fall by the wayside, and for the last several decades the Protectorate has acted as an increasingly sovereign state. The situation reached a head during the Llaelese War when the Protectorate launched attacks against Cygnar and the two severed all lingering ties.

Over the last century, the Protectorate developed a unique culture centered on a strict caste-based theocracy. While the Menite priests like to think of their role as an extension of ancient beliefs, their theocracy is a uniquely modern invention and includes many reinterpretations of sacred text. The leaders of this nation are both more fanatical than Menites of the recent past and pragmatic when it comes to making use of developments such as mechanika. The Protectorate is noted for extremely strict laws controlling virtually every aspect of its citizens' lives. Within the walled cities and fortress temples of the Protectorate, Menoth's will is the Law meant to govern all mankind, honored above all else and followed without question or hesitation.

In past decades the Protectorate was heavily taxed by Cygnar, which stoked the fires of enmity. In retaliation, the theocracy prohibited the use of Cygnaran coinage within their borders. Visiting merchants and travelers had to change their coins at exorbitant rates for Protectorate currency or risk engaging in illegal transactions. When making arrangements with those who would not accept their currency, the theocracy has paid in uncut diamonds harvested from its mines—to the surprise of the Cygnarans who had ceded the land believing it barren and devoid of resources.

Despite the accord in 484 AR that ended the Cygnaran Civil War, Sul-Menites view the Cygnaran Crown and adherents of the Morrowan faith as Menoth's enemies. The Sul-Menites believe the Morrowan faith usurped the rightful place of the Creator to gain influence over most of western Immoren. With such deep and fundamental disagreements with the Morrowan way of life, a renewal of this conflict was perhaps inevitable. This sentiment has become increasingly entrenched among the Sul-Menites since the rule of Hierarch Ravonel, who had overseen the initial development of the Protectorate's nascent standing army. Ravonel's work was carried forward by his successor, Hierarch Voyle, who continued to expand the Menite war machine and went so far as to state that the

Civil War had never ended but that there had simply been a prolonged ceasefire.

By the terms of the treaties allowing its relative independence, the Protectorate was prohibited to establish an army, a law that proved futile. Publicly the visgoths agreed to Cygnar's conditions for peace, but they continued to train soldiers in secret and hide stockpiles of arms. When Cygnaran dignitaries raised the question about the increasingly obvious militarization of the Protectorate, the standing forces were justified under the pretext of protecting holy sites from "the savage natives."

The Sul-Menites had indeed become involved in armed conflict with local Idrian tribes dwelling east of the Black River. In one of the first and most spectacular miracles manifested by Menoth in the modern era, a massive earthquake struck the largest Idrian city even as they waged battle with the Menite crusades in 504 AR. The Sul-Menite forces were untouched, while thousands of resisting Idrians were swallowed by the earth and their homes demolished. This demonstration of Menoth's power ultimately saved many more lives than it took, as the majority of the local Idrians immediately surrendered and converted to the worship of Menoth, joining the new nation and eventually becoming a significant portion of its population. The blend of converted Idrians and Sulese (once Caspians) would give rise to the rich culture of the Protectorate, which over time would adopt a number of Idrian customs. The event did not end Idrian resistance to the spread of the Protectorate, however, and more far-flung tribes continued to refuse to give up their beliefs and fought and died by the thousands in the following decades. Despite this contentious past, Idrians have become a vital part of the theocracy, particularly valued among the Temple's martial orders for their loyalty, discipline, and fighting prowess.

Geographically, while the Protectorate lacks fertile farmland as well as forests to harvest wood, it has other resources in great abundance. Modern mining techniques have unearthed rich iron veins in the hills east of Imer. Several high-grade quarries have been excavated in this region, fueling the expansion of the capital, Imer as well as other great structures like Tower Judgment in the north. The harsh wilderness of the Protectorate is blessed with rich diamond veins, and the lands have proven rich in the crude oil that can be refined into Menoth's Fury, a highly flammable substance that has become vital in the defense of the nation. The greatest blessing has undoubtedly been the Idrians themselves, a people who have bolstered the numbers of the Sul-Menites and brought with them skills at warfare, numbers useful for labor, and a fierce dedication to their adopted faith.

For decades, the Protectorate quietly stockpiled weapons, bribed inspectors, and gathered its strength. This included the production and refinement of steamjacks, purportedly for labor but in fact as weapons of war. The adoption of warjacks was one of the first pragmatic concessions made by the Synod of Visgoths in the early days of the Protectorate. The religious tenets of the Menite faith have long disapproved of any magic that was not invoked through the prayers of Menite priests, including inventions made possible through mechanika. The Cygnaran

Civil War amply proved the worth of these machines in battles waged in Caspia's streets, and the Synod decreed these and other weapons might be used by the faithful if cleansed through prayer and other rites. Each warjack built by the Protectorate was therefore purified and blessed as it was assembled and made ready for battle, a practice that continues today.

Other related doctrinal concessions have been made in more recent decades. While Protectorate foundries were capable of creating the basic chassis and weaponry for warjacks, they were initially unable to produce the cortex, a highly technical and advanced piece of mechanika. Early on, its artificers had to rely on foreign-built cortexes salvaged from fallen machines or smuggled into the nation, such as from Menite sympathizers in Khador. This ended when Khador launched the Llaelese War and declared all cortexes too valuable to be sent abroad, even to a power hostile to its enemy. Those involved in the smuggling trade were declared traitors, and the Protectorate was left to find other means of acquiring cortexes. This gave rise to the founding of the Vassals of Menoth, an extreme measure that began with the capture and enslavement of foreign arcanists capable of cortex construction. Several highly skilled arcane mechaniks from Ord and Cygnar were forced to create new cortexes and train others to do so. As with the purification of warjacks, the Protectorate believes this work is dangerous and involves unholy energies but that the proper measures can reduce this taint and allow for cleansed weapons to be built in order to bolster the Great Crusade. Today, mechanika has become an accepted part of life in the Protectorate, even if the arcane is still treated with suspicion.

Well before Hierarch Voyle's declaration of the Great Crusade, relations between Cygnar and the Protectorate had been on a steady decline. While the Sul-Menites had taken measures to hide the full extent to which they were preparing an army, it was quite obvious they were not in compliance with the treaties that had ended the Civil War. Just as his predecessor had, Cygnar's King Leto Raelthorne chose not to enforce these treaties, knowing armed conflict would be the result. Furthermore, Hierarch Voyle intentionally forestalled the conflict for which he was preparing by periodically sending emissaries to discuss grievances between the two powers, leaving the impression a diplomatic solution might be possible.

Several key factors inevitably converged to whip the Protectorate into the frenzy required to launch its crusades. The first and most important of these was the rise of the Harbinger of Menoth in the northern Protectorate. A young girl emerged from a small village, one who had clearly been chosen by Menoth to serve as the Creator's prophet on Caen. Floating in the air by dint of holy power and capable of channeling the raw might of the Lawgiver, the Harbinger was also gifted with visions wherein the will of Menoth was revealed to her, and through her, to the Synod and the hierarch. For centuries Menoth had been a remote presence, occupied by higher matters in Urcaen and rarely deigning to pay heed to Caen. The arrival of the Harbinger sent shockwaves through the religious communities of western Immoren as a tangible sign not only that Menoth was willing to intervene in the world but also that he clearly supported the Sul-Menite cause. Together the Harbinger and the hierarch decided the time for crusade was upon them, particularly with Cygnar distracted in the north with the onset of the Llaelese War. Knowing Caspia might be left vulnerable, hostilities erupted in full.

A mighty armed expedition marched north from the Protectorate, led by Grand Scrutator Severius and accompanied by the Harbinger. This would become known as the Northern Crusade, and it would battle heathens in Cygnar and the Thornwood and eventually seize gains in eastern Llael. Meanwhile, southern forces laid siege to Caspia in the opening salvo of what would become the Caspia-Sul War, a fierce and extensive clash between the two adjoining cities that has only recently ended. This war was costly on both sides and included a full invasion into Sul followed by nearly a year of turmoil in its streets, and then a counter-invasion into Caspia after regaining Sul. Neither city escaped these conflicts unscathed, and the inhabitants of both remain at high alert. The conflict came to an end with the death of Hierarch Garrick Voyle and the retreat of the crusading armies. The leadership of the nation passed to Hierarch Severius. Sul has since entered a period of rebuilding, and a tense cease-fire has been established between the garrisons on either side of the Black River, although smaller intermittent conflicts between these armed powers still erupt elsewhere along the border.

While the battles between Caspia and Sul resulted in each side retaining their respective cities, the Protectorate has made great gains in recent conflicts. The Northern Crusade seized the Llaelese city of Leryn, an extremely defensible mountain fastness that has become the home of the crusade and the center of ongoing operations in that region. Imer remains the capital, but Hierarch Severius has made Leryn his temporary seat and from there supervises the Northern Crusade, which boasts a sizable portion of the Protectorate's military might. The Synod continues to govern the Protectorate's heartlands in the south, their actions continually scrutinized by junior scrutators loyal to the hierarch. In addition to furthering the plans of the Great Crusade in the north, the seizure of additional lands has brought additional converts and resources to the Protectorate. The Llaelese region is far more fertile than the barren soil in the southeast, and such gains may well be a boon to the Sul-Menites in the long term.

Such gains take time to trickle down, particularly in a time of war, and the citizens of the Protectorate live in austere conditions, even compared to the smaller towns of the Khadoran north. All citizens are expected to contribute to the temple, in terms of both goods produced and strength of arms when needed. In theory the citizens require little more than their faith, but not everyone is equally devout. The scrutators maintain a watchful presence, as do Menite monks dressed as ordinary citizens who watch for any who would speak out or act against the theocracy. Such blasphemers can be incarcerated and subject to punishment at any time and requiring no evidence beyond the suspicion of temple authorities. While most Sul-Menites are pious and love their Creator, there is no question that worship services are zealously attended by all as much from fear of the scrutators as out of pure religious sentiment.

LIFE BEYOND THE IRON KINGDOMS

The nations of the Iron Kingdoms are not alone in western Immoren. Other civilizations and empires have existed for millennia beyond their borders, separated from the kingdoms of men by mountains, seas, and secrets. In the wilderness great forces are stirring to heed ancient calls, and from the east comes an army of cruel invaders.

CRYX

Just across the waters west of Cygnar lie the Scharde Islands, home to Cryx. Lord Toruk, the Dragonfather, is the unquestioned ruler of this empire, though he rarely condescends to the vulgarities of governance, leaving such trivialities to his council of twelve lich lords. Ancient chronicles place the dragon's arrival at the Broken Coast around 1,000 BR, but even older evidence indicates he has plagued western Immoren for more than four millennia. Toruk may be the oldest known entity on Caen, which makes his self-proclaimed status as a god extremely convincing.

In the western seas, sheltered by rings of razor-sharp reefs, a long and foreboding coast of jagged peaks juts from dark waters like the fangs of a monstrous creature hungry for the flesh of the sky above. On the main island in the shadow of its jungles and mountains, terrible creatures inhabit putrid cities and villages of collapsed and crumbled architecture, communing and festering like ticks on a mangy wolf. Though Cryx is the host to Lord Toruk's undying legions, its black cities house desperate, disposed mortals attempting to eke out their lives within the borders of the Nightmare Empire. In these wretched places, the weak survive at the mercy of the strong, and the strong know no mercy.

Toruk rules from his capital of Skell, where the blight emanates from him like a sickening fog. The major island and several nearby are awash in this blight, darkening all aspects of life. The living cannot abide proximity to Toruk, and Skell is populated only by the dead and those few priests of the Dragonfather in the final stages of their deathless transformation. All things on the main island are corrupted. Nothing is untouched, and very few outsiders who journey to Cryx, however briefly, can say they left unchanged. Even the familiar races are often blighted and twisted into forms alien to their mainlander kin. In addition to the many necromantic monstrosities haunting the islands, Cryx is home to Satyxis, trollkin, ogrun, and gobbers, all of whom have a stake in—and are subject to the predations of—the Nightmare Empire. Although humans account for the majority of the population, Toruk's kingdom is clearly not a place ruled by living men.

The wilds of the Scharde Islands are home to terrible beasts of fiendish cunning. They are driven by more than instinctual hunger, for the beasts of this land are capable of malice and

THE DEATH BELOW

The people of the Iron Kingdoms have never comprehended the machinations of Lord Toruk and his lich lords. For centuries, Cryxian raiders struck the coasts of Cygnar, Ord, and Khador seemingly at random, slaughtering entire villages without warning. Occasionally, Cryxian raiders struck further inland, but their purposes were obscure. Only a few decades ago, in what came to be known as the Scharde Invasions, Cryx carried out a series of brutal raids along the Cygnaran coast. The Cygnaran Armory's close examination of the events resulted in the Hurstwallen Report, which drew the disturbing conclusion that the seemingly random raids and attacks contained a sinister purpose: to draw attention away from Cryx's drive into the mainland interior.

Such action have borne a dark fruit in several hidden locales, including the Wyrmwall and beneath the Thornwood Forest. The Cryxians possess a tremendous network of tunnels there, within them a factory complex to rival any in the Scharde Islands. The twisted passages were inherited from a race called the cephalyx who were eager to join with the undead minions of Toruk for purposes known only to them. With this alliance in place, the dominion of the lich lords has begun to spread across the Thornwood and beyond. Necrotechs labor endlessly to create a legion of helljacks and bonejacks to exceed any Cryxian army in history, and the thralls at the disposal of the lich lords now number in the tens of thousands.

The Cryxian armies have begun to stir, preparing to carry out the next stage of Lord Toruk's plans. The Iron Kingdoms know Cryxian activity has increased in the mainland, but they do not suspect the extent of the death that lurks beneath their feet. Nevertheless, no one travels alone through the Thornwood, where even armed patrols have begun to disappear, and those who live on the edges of the great forest whisper of sinister shapes moving in the night.

cruelty, a subtler effect of Toruk's pervasive blight corrupting even farther than is visible to the eye.

Toruk's legions have spread plague, death, and famine across western Immoren for ages. Before the Scharde Invasions, the Dragonfather and his servants were a mysterious and formless threat preying on the outskirts of civilization. But in recent decades they have begun to make their presence known across the mainland. The days when Cryx was known by little more than legend and the sporadic predations of its blackships are no more.

It is no great secret Toruk has designs on western Immoren, though not for the frivolous motivations of mortal conquerors. The Dragonfather is consumed with an ancient war and longs for the day his legions will raze the lands of men and drive his progeny from their hiding places where they will be consumed by his deathless rage.

IOS

The forested interior and mountainous borders of Ios have never welcomed visitors. It is a nation of dreadful secrets and enduring tragedy. Few visitors have ever been invited in, and any who have attempted uninvited entry have vanished. Scholars and historians know little of the history of the Iosan people—only that they are the diminished remnants of the great Empire of Lyoss that endured for millennia before annihilating themselves in a moment of great hubris. Academics who have studied and spoken with the few Iosans that venture into the Iron Kingdoms believe the barren, wasted Stormlands beyond the Bloodstone Desert may have been generated by whatever force smote the Empire of Lyoss.

Since settling in western Immoren, the Iosans have maintained only limited contact with their neighbors, an isolationism that has become almost total in the past three decades. This isolation comes from a deep source of misery. Ios is ill. Its people struggle with a terrible cancer, for the nation is slowly dying from the inside. This sickness has led them to mistrust anything unfamiliar, and it grows ever worse. Before 581 AR, Ios sometimes sent emissaries and diplomats beyond their borders. Though always aloof and reluctant to part with their secrets, these ambassadors made an effort to negotiate commerce and maintain some relations with the other kingdoms. Today the Iosans no longer entreat the other kingdoms whatsoever.

The reclusive nature of this nation is facilitated by a number of geographical barriers, including looming mountains to the north and south and a vast and maze-like western forest. Beyond the forests and mountains, monolithic cities of stone and glass are filled with wonders beyond the comprehension of men, but there are also wide tracts of land that much of the time are cloaked in a drifting brume of pale gray that obscures sight and distorts sound. It is said this mist is sentient, that it has a life of its own and whispers in ill-defined voices. Some Iosans say it is the mist that takes the souls of those born soulless and that the whispers are the anguished spirits of those souls casting vengeful aspersions at the living. Amid the natural beauty of the wilderness abandoned cities lay in ruin, as do forgotten temples to dead gods. Many of these sites are inhabited by dangerous and horrific spirits, and worse. The Iosans themselves tread as carefully as any outsider in some portions of their lands for fear of awakening things ancient, terrible, and vengeful.

Travelers who stray too near the region invariably discover fortresses called aeryths manned by merciless riflemen, archers, and swordsmen. These warriors line their ramparts and patrol their borders in search of any who venture too deep into their sacred domain, for the footsteps of outsiders despoil the earth and weaken their lost gods with every stride.

Iosans possess a deep and unique understanding of the arcane and have mastered principles radically different from the traditions of human arcanists. They use tremendous stones shaped and laid with expert precision to create their imposing structures, many of which are pyramidal, made of massive terraced stone blocks. Portions of the stonework are covered with ancient engravings and reliefs. Incredible engineering has gone into these fantastic structures; some feature giant doors made from a single slab of stone hundreds of tons in weight yet balanced so perfectly that a child can push it open. The architecture seems to defy physics, and it is a mystery whether this is an illusion or actual magic at work.

At the center of Iosan society, hundreds of noble houses called *hallytyr*, or "high house," oversee the various aspects of culture. Representatives of the fifteen most powerful hallytyr constitute the Consulate Court, which has ruled Ios for many centuries.

The sickness that plagues Ios is due to the departure of their deities, known as the Divine Court or simply the Vanished. Of the eight gods that once lived among them, only two are known to still exist, and both are uncommunicative with their faithful. Most Iosans worship Scyrah, the goddess of spring, who appears to move closer to death each day. For centuries her priests had no answers to what ails their goddess or how they should proceed, but in recent years things have changed rapidly. In the aftermath of a violent civil war, the marginalized group known as the Retribution of Scyrah has risen to sudden prominence in Iosan politics. This has been accelerated by the recent discovery that another of the elven gods has survived—Nyssor, the god of winter. Proclaiming that the answer to the sickness of their gods lies in the death of all human arcanists, the Retribution is increasingly urging the nation to prepare for war.

The threat of annihilation weighs heavily on the people of Ios, but they have begun to see the Retribution's argument that there is a chance, as desperate as it is, for salvation. Others still believe the Vanished may yet be found, and a small group called the Seekers is dedicated to investigating any leads about the missing gods. This group has not succeeded in convincing the majority of their beliefs, and recently even they have become more sympathetic to the Retribution's goals.

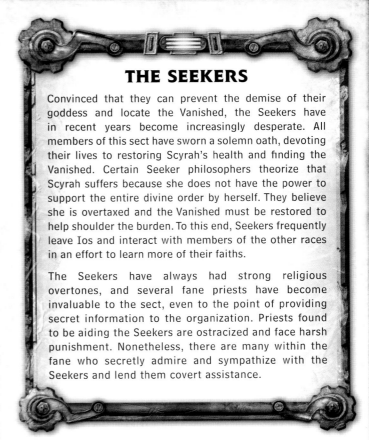

RHUL

Rhul is a great expanse of soaring peaks, rugged mountains, sheltered valleys, and deep gorges. The landscape is both beautiful and terrifying, for the Borokuhn Mountains, Silvertip Peaks, and Glass Peaks boast some of the tallest mountains in western Immoren. Crossing the outer mountains from the south or west requires knowledge of the dangerous icy roads and trails created by the dwarves over the centuries. Some lead into chokepoints, run under massive fortifications, or twist back on themselves as they climb the mountains, allowing watchers to observe those venturing inward. The outer clans that man the major fortresses like Horgenhold and Hammerfall take their duties seriously, and only those travelers who ask permission and pay the proper tolls are given easy passage. Nestled safely within these barriers, the great lake Armsdeep stabilizes the harsh northern weather and provides life and livelihood for over a million dwarves and a hundred thousand ogrun.

The greatest cities of Rhul rest on the shores of this lake. The timeless capital of Ghord and its sister city Ulgar are sprawling complexes of intricate stonework that have taken dozens of lifetimes to complete. The Rhulic gift for crafting metal and stone is second to none in the kingdoms. Even minor landmarks, roads, and towers rival Caspia's Sancteum in grandeur and perfection. The mountains of Rhul contain vast quantities of ores and minerals, including rich deposits of otherwise rare minerals difficult to find elsewhere.

Some of these minerals are required for advanced metallurgy, and Rhulic genius at this craft has placed the dwarves and their ogrun clanmates at the pinnacle of smithcraft. Some clan lords, for instance, wear armor that seems truly impenetrable. A portion of the peerless goods produced by these craftsmen find their way down the Black River from Armsdeep, one of the primary trade routes to the southern lands.

The dwarves of Rhul claim to have the oldest and most stable civilization in western Immoren, with records dating back over eight millennia. They have always lived in the great northern mountains and seem to have no thirst for conquest. They once enjoyed friendly trade arrangements with Ios but now find those borders sealed to them as well as humans.

Rhul keeps a close eye on the politics of the Iron Kingdoms. Though it has maintained neutrality in the affairs of humans for thousands of years, it started to change this policy during the Rebellion against the Orgoth. For the first time raw materials and Rhulic industry were loaned to humans to aid in the construction of the Colossals. The Rhulfolk have since taken an interest in the south, impressed by the innovations of humanity and see great opportunities. Many dwarves are pragmatic by nature, and those involved in affairs abroad prefer not to let opportunities for profit or industrial advancement pass them by; others watch humanity knowing foreign politics could threaten their own security. Having enjoyed trade relations with Cygnar and Khador as well as Llael, the merchants of Rhul suffered in the recent wars when they lost direct routes to the south through Llael. They have since found solutions to some of these issues, but it seems they must increase their dealings with the growing Khadoran Empire.

Life in Rhul has always centered on the clan, a tightly knit extended family of shared bloodlines and marriages. Clans vary considerably in size, with the most important encompassing thousands of members. New clans are periodically formed by youths seeking to branch out from their family and start a fresh tradition or industry. In marriage the wife usually adopts the clan of her husband, but the reverse may also occur. Clan lord is the most fundamental rank in Rhul; these leaders are the patriarchs or matriarchs of their extended families. Clan lords are given respect and deference proportionate with the size, prosperity, and honor of their clan. The thirteen most powerful clan lords are known as the "Stone Lords of Rhul," the ultimate authority in the nation. They are responsible for the defense and prosperity of the dwarven people and handle all interactions with foreign ambassadors and sovereigns. Not all stone lords are equally talented, intelligent, or suited to their position, yet each is descended directly from one of the Great Fathers and is thus deemed worthy of respect and obedience.

The internal politics of Rhul revolve around complex tallies of clan influence, honor, and industry. Disputes among individuals within a clan are resolved by their clan lord, but those between members of competing clans can be settled by lawful duels. Larger disputes between entire clans can also be resolved by legally sanctioned feuds which can extend across decades or even centuries. While violent, these martial clashes are governed by strict laws and rules and bear no resemblance

THE OGRUN OF RHUL

Millennia ago, the dwarven clans provided shelter and food for neighboring ogrun tribes during a famine. The ogrun placed the same great value on duty and honor as their dwarven saviors, and in only a few generations the ogrun had become citizens of Rhul. Over time they have grown much more civilized than their forebears, but they retain a unique, if complementary, culture within Rhulic society.

Ogrun culture is strongly feudal in nature, with young warriors seeking to improve their martial prowess and provide good service to a strong lord. This allowed them to adjust easily to dwarven society with its clan lords, and in some cases entire families of ogrun look to a specific clan and its lord to lead them. To the ogrun this ties into a vital concept called *korune*, a highly personal relationship. In traditional ogrun culture, there could be several layers of korune, whereby a young warrior serves his korune, and that senior ogrun is himself sworn to an even more influential korune. The oath-sworn bond of korune is very strong, broken only in death. Those in service to a korune are willing to offer their lives to protect their lord.

Ogrun may spend years or even decades seeking a korune, during which they are termed *bokur*, which means "unsworn." Bokur are in a continuous state of seeking a worthy master to whom they can dedicate themselves, all the while honing their own battle prowess so as to impress their future lord and be worthy of service. Bokurs will often lend themselves temporarily to a cause or a specific individual in order to get to know his merits and determine whether a more permanent oath should be sworn. It was once unseemly for a bokur to extend this status too long, but this is no longer the case. Rhul and its martial clans increasingly offer their services as mercenaries and have encouraged the ogrun to join them. Experienced bokurs are highly valued for their loyalty and fearsome skill. They might spend their professional careers as bokur and wait to swear this ultimate oath of fealty to their clan lord when ready to retire. Such aged but highly experienced ogrun make for excellent bodyguards and advisors to the Rhulic clan lord and are almost always welcomed.

Even when they have not yet declared their korune, most Rhulic ogrun are full members of dwarven clans and are thus subordinate to its clan lord, whom they obey and treat with great respect. Such fealty is still binding but less personal than the oath-bond for a korune. In purely ogrun communities korune will speak for their vassals, and there may be a single great korune who leads the entire community through a chain of vassalage.

to the chaotic brawls of other races. Indeed, duels and feuds are often fought as a matter of spirited competition between clans seeking to secure the rights to certain building projects or contracts for major work. As in most extended families, the clans typically set aside their conflicts whenever they are threatened by outside forces.

The solidarity of Rhulfolk versus outsiders is legendary in western Immoren, and it is well known that any dwarf will put aside other concerns should the homeland be threatened. Indeed, Rhul has no "standing army" in a conventional sense, yet it boasts perhaps the largest and best-armed fighting force in western Immoren, as so many of its citizens stand ready to rally for national defense. Each clan has its own host of disciplined warriors, who work together in border regions to garrison major fortresses and could be gathered under the stone lords against outside aggressors were it necessary. Any of the stone lords could quickly muster as large of a Rhulic force as would be needed for any conflict, though this has rarely been necessary.

Law is a sacred principle among the dwarves, inextricable from religious belief. The legal system in Rhul is governed by the Codex, a living record of all judicial decisions made in Rhul since its founding that contains at its core the Edicts of the Great Fathers, the central principles set down by the progenitors and gods of the Rhulic people. Its interpretation and the enforcement of its rules are supervised by grim judges of the Moot of the Hundred Houses, Rhul's major legislative and governing body. The priests of the Great Fathers are respected as arbiters of dwarven honor and jurisprudence. The members of the Tribune, the highest-ranking priests, are frequently consulted in matters of state.

The authority of clan lords over their families is absolute, but even these lords must obey the laws of the Codex and heed the commands of the Moot and the stone lords, who alone have the right to declare feuds with rival clans. Clan lords are advised by master builders, martial champions, and priests. These roles are of equal import to the Rhulfolk who approach battle, construction, and religion as three expressions of the divine laws they obey.

Throughout Rhulic history, strong clan lords have banded together in councils to oversee the counties, towns, and cities, with the most important body being the Moot itself. The Moot is Rhul's central legislative and judicial body and meets frequently to discuss the concerns of the nation. Only the hundred most powerful clans can send speakers to attend. Membership changes periodically as clan fortunes rise or fall, but most of the top clans have held their status for centuries. Moot judges are special experts appointed by the stone lords. These are well-educated arcanists, priests, or scholars who spend their lives studying the Codex. Moot Judges have jurisdiction over entire clans and can pass judgment on clan lords. While this system has worked well to maintain stability, the Moot is often criticized for being slow to make decisions.

Several dwarven enclaves have been established abroad in the human kingdoms, with the largest in Khador and Cygnar. These communities usually work closely with neighboring humans and have been a great asset to those nations' labor and industry. They were created after the Corvis Treaties as a way of recognizing the Rhulfolk for helping construct the colossals by which the Orgoth were defeated. These communities are considered Rhulic soil and are governed by Rhulic law, although citizens are expected to be respectful of the ordinances of the host nation. When these communities were established, they attracted many ambitious and younger clans who felt they had little hope for advancement in Rhul. Working in one for a time remains a tradition among young dwarves seeking their own fortunes before deciding where they will settle permanently. The same is also true for many of the ogrun who belong to dwarven clans.

THE PEOPLE OF WESTERN IMMOREN

HUMANITY

Mankind holds sway from the far north of Khador all the way to Bloodshore Island in the south. There is great diversity among humanity. A traveler across western Immoren can expect to encounter numerous ethnic and regional groups, most of which identify themselves based on the most prominent old kingdoms from the Thousand Cities era before the arrival of the Orgoth. Those cultural identities are deeply rooted despite the rise of the modern kingdoms defined after the Corvis Treaties. Cultures and appearance can vary dramatically among these groups, as most of these identifications were regional rather than based on bloodlines.

CASPIANS AND SULESE

The most numerous people of western Immoren are the Caspians and Sulese, native to the southern region that has been home to their ancestors since the founding of ancient Calacia. The distinction between the two is very recent but very important to both. Those descended of the ancient Caspians and living west of the Black River in Cygnar refer to themselves by the old name of "Caspians." People of the same ancestry east of the Black River in the Protectorate of Menoth refer to themselves as Sulese to honor Hierarch Sulon, who initiated the Cygnaran Civil War and who is the namesake of the city of Sul, which was once eastern Caspia. While this may seem a matter of semantics, in can be argued that in the century since that war the Sulese have established a distinct culture, largely due to their intense religious beliefs.

Even the appearance of the two peoples differ, as the less comfortable living conditions experienced by the Sulese in the Protectorate of Menoth often weathers their features. Both groups share common traits, although the populations that melded into this region were diverse enough that there is a tremendous variance. Many Caspians tend to have cream-colored complexions and lighter hair, while others are darker hued and have black hair. Intermarriage between Sulese and Idrians is relatively common, contributing to further subtle changes over the last several generations.

IDRIANS

The Idrians of today were once made up of a number of diverse tribes native to the eastern region known as the Bloodstone Marches. These formerly nomadic tribesmen have largely taken up the worship of Menoth, although some tribes have remained outside the Protectorate and retain some of their older traditions. While the Idrians were labeled as worshipers of the Wurm before their conversion, their spiritual beliefs were more varied. Some were indeed followers of the Wurm, while others practiced a variant of ancestor worship. Both were deemed intolerable to the Menites of the Protectorate, and crusades were conducted to bring these people back to the faith of the Creator. Idrians typically have olive skin, dark brown or black hair, and almond eyes.

KHARDS

North of Ord, the Khadoran Empire is dominated by the second-largest culture in western Immoren, that of the Khardic people, descendants of the empire that ruled the north before the coming of the Orgoth. Over a thousand years ago, the Khardic Empire and its western horselords conquered many small nations, city-states, and tribes, and the Khards of the present day descend from the strongest bloodlines of those times. Like the other peoples of the north, they tend to be tall and physically robust on average, generally larger than their southern counterparts, mostly with pale skin. At its height the Khardic Empire stretched across a sizable portion of western Immoren and included many different peoples.

KOSSITES

In the far northwest the once-wild Kossites have preserved much of their culture. They are a tall and lanky people, descendants of the forested tribes of Kos. The Kossite people are notoriously hostile to outsiders and retain certain tribal customs, even within larger towns and the great city of Ohk. Kossites have a reputation for wood lore and survivability in impossibly harsh conditions, deserved after centuries negotiating the frozen Scarsfell Forest. They are frequently sought after as scouts and trackers, and many serve the Khadoran Army in this capacity.

MIDLUNDERS

The populous Midlunders of northern Cygnar dominate that nation's northern heartland. They are a rugged and practical people who have embraced an attitude outsiders sometimes mistake for stubbornness. During the Thousand Cities Era the Midlunds was a vast region with numerous farmlands and townships, and it was arguably the unification of the pragmatic Midlunders with the urbane Caspians after the Corvis Treaties that has given Cygnar its cultural identity. Many of the career soldiers of Cygnar's armed forces are Midlunders, particularly along the northern and eastern borders. Even from ancient times this was a region that saw the blending of dozens of different cultures, and so there is no particular look that defines them, although more are dark-haired and ruddy-skinned than fair.

MORRIDANES

Hailing from the bogs and forests of the Thornwood, the Morridanes are the descendants of the lost kingdom of Morrdh, territories that fall largely within the borders of modern Cygnar. Outsiders sometimes hold them in poor regard for their rustic ways and taciturn demeanors, but beneath that exterior the Morridanes are shrewd, stalwart, and loyal individuals. Physically, they are noted as being shorter of stature and slighter of build than their southern countrymen.

RYN

The eastern nation of Llael was dominated by the fair-skinned Ryn, a people of slight build and short stature who made up the majority of that nation's populace. Much of the Llaelese nobility were of Rynnish blood. Ryn were particularly dominant in the Llaelese capital and eastern farmlands. They consider themselves the inheritors of a long and esteemed history and are proud of their language and culture but now face the fact that their nation lies divided, most of it conquered by Khador, while the east has fallen to the Protectorate's Northern Crusade. The Ryn take credit for inventing the firearm and refining the arts of pistol dueling in particular but were a shrewd and well-spoken people with a fondness for negotiation, the fine arts, and alchemy as well as a taste for ornate architecture. Thousands of Ryn fled during the Llaelese War and scattered abroad, swelling the nearest cities in both Ord and Cygnar, while some even sought sanctuary in Rhul.

SCHARDE

Over time, as civilizations rose and fell, some of their people fled west to the Scharde Islands. The people here are thought to be primarily a blend of those who were once Morrdh, Molgur, Tordorans, and Thurians. Before the coming of Toruk the forbidding archipelago was fertile enough to support a thriving population, and it became a haven for pirates and raiders that preyed on the mainland while erecting fortified fiefdoms. When the Dragonfather arrived he seized control here, transforming the pirate lords into undead and immortal lich lords who would oversee the squalid lives of the petty mortals that were beneath his notice. Over time his powerful blight has seeped into everything here, transforming the people and the land. The generations spawned by the survivors of Toruk's arrival and the rise of Cryx have been irrevocably tainted by the presence of the Dragonfather. These people, now called Scharde, are easily recognizable by their ritual scarification, tattooing, and bone body piercings. Some, however, bear the taint of draconic blight more obviously. Solid black eyes, razor-sharp teeth, scaled skin, and other deformations are common. Even those less blatantly corrupt have been influenced by the dragon's proximity, and the Scharde are largely a cruel and violent people.

SKIROV

The other once-wild people of the north that were tamed by the Khards were the Skirov, the people of Khador's northern mountains. These thick-bodied and imposing people are among the most stoic and fearsome of Khadorans, noted for their strong passions and intense piety. The people of this region have long been deeply religious—in ancient days they were zealous worshipers of the Wurm, but most took to Menite conversion after the crusades of priest-kings emulating Khardovic. Many mountain communities are counted among the most stalwart supporters of the Old Faith, while others converted to the faith of Morrow and embraced its principles with a similar intensity. Great temples and churches dominate these rustic mountain towns, and the people of this region are among the most superstitious and distrustful of those suspected of witchcraft. Skirov are fairer of skin and generally have lighter hair than most other Khadorans.

THURIANS

Thurians are one of two major cultures that dominated the western seaboard in ancient days. The Thurians of today are descendants of a kingdom now divided between northwestern Cygnar and southern Ord. Thurians have long prized sharp wits and the accumulation of secrets and lore; sorcery is unusually common among them, and this region has seen more than its fair share of prestigious arcanists. Organized human magic has its roots in this region, and the Stronghold of the Fraternal Order of Wizardry is based in Ceryl, the heart of what was once Thuria. Like Caspia and the Midlunds, Thuria was a welcoming kingdom that brought many diverse peoples into its community, and thus the physical features of Thurians vary considerably, though a slightly higher than average number have red hair and green eyes. Many Sinari, discussed below, settled in Thuria early in the kingdom's history and left a legacy of dark-skinned, black-haired individuals. Both proudly call themselves Thurians and can trace lineages back before the Orgoth.

TORDORANS

The other great western culture was the Tordorans, who are rightfully proud of their ancient traditions, particularly related to mastery of the sea. Ord's northern regions and particularly its aristocracy are dominated by the descendants of Tordor, a nation that conquered Thuria before the arrival of the Orgoth. Tordorans rarely marry outside their own ethnicity and so have a more distinct and identifiable appearance than many of the region's dominant cultures, with black hair and olive skin. The ruling castellans are known as High Tordorans, but even lowborn Tordorans pride themselves on their blood and ancestry.

UMBREANS

Several other distinct cultures have survived in Khador amid the trackless wastes and vast wildernesses that naturally divide the nation. In southeastern Khador and western Llael are another once-divided people, only recently unified under Khadoran rule after the Llaelese War. Heirs to the ancient eastern horselords of old, the Umbreans once contested with the Khards for domination of this region, and distrust and animosity persists between them. Tales of the ancient battles fought between Khards and Umbreans are still told in this region, particularly near the grim battlefields where generations of blood have been spilled. Umbreans have intermingled with many other groups but retain a strong sense of cultural identity, and many harbor dreams of a nation of their own. Their size and build are similar to that of the Khards, but they usually have slightly darker skin and black hair.

OTHER HUMAN ETHNICITIES

There are several other smaller ethnicities in the Iron Kingdoms. The dark-skinned Radiz and Sinari are nomadic peoples found across the southern Kingdoms, some living in caravans moving across western and Central Cygnar. Both of these groups have dwindled over the centuries as families have abandoned the old ways and integrated with other cultures, bringing greater diversity to the Thurians, Midlunders, and Caspians in particular. Pocket ethnic groups in Cygnar include the Gnasir and the Arjun, both of which shun contact with outsiders and speak their own somewhat incomprehensible dialects. In northern Khador a number of isolated groups persist that once contended with the Skirov and Kossites for resources, including the Vindol, the Ruscar, the Bolotov, and the Yhari-Umbreans. Some of these people live in tribes little changed since the days of the Molgur and still proudly display totemic emblems of the wolf, the bear, and the raven.

NONHUMAN RACES

Although humanity accounts for the greatest part of the populations of the nations of the Iron Kingdoms, many other races are also present, particularly in Cygnar. Gobbers are a common sight in most major Cygnaran and Ordic cities, having adapted well to urban life. They are encountered less often in Khador and Llael. Khadorans tend to be more insular and distrustful of other races, who may not share their bold nationalistic feelings, but gobbers can still be found in major industrial centers like Korsk and Khardov.

Though the Iron Kingdoms themselves can rightly be thought of as human nations, all are also inhabited by a variety of races who possess varying degrees of loyalty and recognized citizenship. Other races are most common in the major cities, where they are drawn to seek employment. By and large, members of the other races are treated with tolerance by urban dwellers where they lead similar lives to humans, although sometimes they are pressured to settle in ghettos or communities of their own. They are less welcome among rural communities, where prejudices are stronger, particularly in areas that sometimes endure raids from nearby wilderness tribes or kriels. Where larger groups of certain races have settled in a city, they may retain some of their tribal organization within their district or quarter, and often their leaders become influential outside of the community as well. It is not uncommon for places with large communities of trollkin to find that the kriel's elders wield significant clout in city affairs; the threat of strike is a potent weapon in modern labor disputes.

GOBBERS (GOBLINS)

There are two distinct species of goblins found in western Immoren, and attitudes toward each are markedly different. Gobbers are the most numerous of the two species and have had great success in integrating into the communities of other races, including human cities. Their small stature—most of them are around three feet tall—makes them appear non-threatening, and they have undeniable aptitude for mechanikal devices and alchemy. Next to humanity, gobbers are the race that has most successfully adapted to urban life. Inquisitive, cunning, and entrepreneurial, some gobbers have earned their place in society as owners of small businesses, often running salvage, scrap, and repair services. Less civilized tribes of gobbers with shamans and tribal chieftains still exist in the wilds, but by and large, the race has moved into the cities.

BOGRIN (GOBLINS)

By contrast, bogrin are a largely reviled species of goblin usually only encountered in the wilds, with only a few established communities existing in human cities, such as Five Fingers. Bogrin are larger than gobbers, are recognizable by the distinct ridge on the top of their heads, and are likely to display body piercings and tattoos. They are generally considered more violent and aggressive than gobbers, and repeated conflicts have pushed them away from most townships and cities. Accordingly they encounter considerably more prejudice than their cousin race, even in cases where an individual has demonstrated a willingness to coexist in society. They are most numerous among the Scharde Islands.

TROLLKIN

Trollkin largely live in the traditional communities of kriels centered on villages far from human civilization. Until recently, the trollkin were a scattered people, living in much the same way as they have for centuries, but recent warfare and displacement have shattered their lives. Some leaders among them have begun to foment radical ideas, and previously peaceful trollkin communities are uniting in war against all those who would oppress them.

Trollkin are also commonly found throughout the cities of the Iron Kingdoms and are particularly valued in industries that depend on freight or heavy labor, although their size and strength can also be intimidating. In most cases, they work for lower wages than human workers and may face other difficulties as they are often treated as lower-class citizens. Some kriels have transplanted in entirety and live as communities among the populations of major cities. These urban kriels face trouble adjusting from their traditional lifestyle, and many of their youth have begun to give up the old ways in favor of human culture.

RHULFOLK (DWARVES)

With records dating back over six millennia, the dwarves of Rhul have the oldest and most stable continuous civilization in western Immoren. Though they have officially maintained neutrality in the affairs of humans for thousands of years, Rhulfolk keep a close eye on the outside world and periodically do involve themselves in outside affairs. Rhulfolk have become a common sight among humanity, both on and off the battlefield. Although Rhul itself seems to have no interest in conquest, its leading clans do seek profit and happily adopt mankind's technological developments. In some parts of eastern Khador and the Upper Wyrmwall Mountains mixed communities of humans and Rhulfolk have been established, though recent tensions between Khador and Cygnar sometimes threaten their safety.

OGRUN

The ogrun of Rhul are fully integrated members of Rhulic society despite constituting a minority of the population. Ogrun are also found among some human communities, especially those that are home to mercenary companies. The raw strength of the ogrun also makes them highly valued laborers, particularly in regions that see heavy shipping traffic, and the sense of honor treasured by most ogrun makes them prized as bodyguards. It is worth noting that many of the ogrun of Rhul refer to themselves as "Rhulic" although the term "Rhulfolk" is usually reserved for dwarves. There are also a number of ogrun tribes living outside Rhul, most numerously among the northern mountains of Khador and also among the tainted people of Cryx.

IOSANS (ELVES)

Though the nation of Ios closed its borders years ago, a few of its people can still be found among the Iron Kingdoms. Notoriously tight-lipped regarding their home, Iosans are poorly understood, and most people react to them with unease. Some few of them are found roaming far and wide, consulting ancient libraries and scholars on historical minutiae. A very small number make a life as mercenaries, plying a bloody trade for a coin in which they seem barely interested.

NYSS (ELVES)

The Iosans can seem almost loquacious in comparison to their cousins, the Nyss. They are a highly insular people who until recently were rarely seen outside of the farthest reaches of the north. In the past few years refugees have begun to make their way to the cities of Ios, Khador, and Ord, fleeing some great disaster about which they are reticent to speak. Skilled hunters and trackers, the Nyss are a proud and self-reliant people; that their tribes have been scattered implies a tragedy of profound consequence.

OTHER RACES

There are other races across the expanse of western Immoren, but they have little truck with the civilized nations of the Iron Kingdoms and their neighbors in Rhul and Ios. Scholars have grudgingly admitted that certain species such as gatormen, farrow, bog trogs, and croaks are technically intelligent, although they are usually seen as a menace and often labeled as monsters. The same is true for groups like the Tharn and the Satyxis, both of whom may once have been human but who have transformed into distinct—and hostile—species. Additionally, there are some possibly intelligent but ferocious creatures that occupy an uncomfortable middle ground between beast and people, such as ravenous trolls, satyrs, and the eastern cyclopes.

Only a few years ago the vanguard of a great army of invaders arrived on the western edges of the Bloodstone Marches. The skorne are a truly vicious race that honors its warriors above all others. Few citizens of the Iron Kingdoms have met a skorne outside of a battlefield, and little is known of their culture. Since they seem bent on the complete subjugation of western Immoren, they are likely to remain an enigma. Very little contact has been made with other possibly intelligent species from eastern Immoren, such as the efaarit, which may be a race of gobber, or the primitive lethians. Somewhere in remote eastern Immoren there are rumored to be highly intelligent giants, but such reports are often looked upon as fanciful legends.

LANGUAGES OF THE IRON KINGDOMS

Languages in western Immoren have been evolving since before recorded history. In certain eras there has been a proliferation of tongues even more bewildering than the war-torn political landscape of the so-called Thousand Cities. Language has followed in the wake of culture, and warfare between tribes has resulted in the dominance and subjugation of tongues, while dialects have sprouted and evolved in isolated communities. Each of these tongues has a complex and varied history and many regional variances, and dozens of lesser languages linger on the fringes. It is quite common for inhabitants of western Immoren to speak multiple languages with various degrees of fluency. Being able to communicate effectively in two or three different tongues is common, as is exposure to multiple dialects of each. Written fluency is another matter and varies from kingdom to kingdom. For many there is a wide gulf between spoken comprehension and written fluency.

Languages are grouped based on their origins. Among human languages, there are four main language families, each named after their respective major languages: Caspian, Khurzic, Molgur, and Morridane. Of these, only Molgur is still spoken; the rest are known only to those interested in ancient documents.

CASPIAN LANGUAGES

While Caspian itself is no longer a living language, it is the largest language family and therefore of great interest to scholars and theologians. It spread with both the Menite and Morrowan faiths before it changed and fragmented into distinct regional languages with some commonalities, such as the alphabet they use. Several languages descended from Caspian are still in common use; the most significant are described here. Additionally, there have been a number of intermediary Caspian languages; most are of interest only to linguists, but some are still spoken in certain regions, although rarely as a primary tongue.

CASPIAN (EXTINCT)

Caspian is a descendant of several ancient languages of the first major Menite communities in western Immoren, including that used in Ancient Icthier. The first written documents, such as text of the True Law, were in a tongue that predates Calacian, which was the immediate precursor of Caspian. The Caspian language reached its height during the Thousand Cities Era and became the language of educated discourse. Most ancient Morrowan and Menite texts in the south were written in Caspian, with the most modern and internally consistent version being set down by Ascendant Angellia when she presented the definitive translation of the Enkheiridion.

CYGNARAN (AND SULESE)

The language most directly derived from Caspian, Cygnaran is the dominant language of the southern Iron Kingdoms, having been widely adopted by the people of the Midlunds and Caspia itself. It is used throughout the region as a trade language and is the national language of Cygnar and the Protectorate of Menoth, although the latter refers to the language as Sulese. It is a rich language that includes a number of words borrowed from the Orgoth tongue that came into use during the Occupation as well as many commonly used trade terms for alchemy, engineering and the arcane.

Given its broad geographical region, Cygnaran has numerous dialects. Sulese is easily understood by any Cygnaran speaker but has adopted a number of Idrian terms and phrases and includes distinct religious terms. The riverfolk and swamp denizens of the northern stretches of the Black River are infamous for their "Swampie" language, a dialect that includes many terms from Morridane and is thus difficult to understand by the uninitiated. The Arjun employ a similarly dense dialect that mixes old Thurian with Cygnaran.

LLAELESE

Llaelese is a direct evolution of the Ryn language of Rynyr and has changed very little since before the Orgoth Occupation. The people of this region have always been proud of their language

as an essential element of their culture, although most Llaelese also speak Cygnaran. Since the nation's occupation by the Khadoran Empire, inhabitants have begun to learn to speak Khadoran, but the Llaelese still use their traditional language among families and friends.

ORDIC

The modern descendant of Tordoran, Ordic is the most widely spoken language of the Ordic people, who are very often multilingual. The vocabulary includes many words from Thurian as well as a number of Orgoth terms. Other words have been borrowed from a variety of languages, likely as a result of Ord's status as a seafaring melting pot. Ordic is notable for having established many widely accepted nautical terms, which are familiar to sailors of all nations.

SCHARDE

There has been some debate as to whether Scharde, spoken throughout the Broken Coast and among the denizens of Cryx, can be considered its own language or should be classified as a dialect of Cygnaran. As the Nightmare Empire of Cryx has absorbed denizens of every mainland kingdom, its language includes words from Molgur, Morridane, Ordic, Llaelese, and Khadoran. Many traders and sailors of the Broken Coast become passably familiar with the Scharde Tongue.

KHURZIC LANGUAGES

Most Khurzic languages have begun to fall by the wayside in favor of modern Khadoran, which is spoken pervasively across the Khadoran Empire.

KHURZIC (EXTINCT)

The roots of the Khurzic languages are difficult to trace, stretching back to prehistory in the north. It is believed several of these tongues came with pilgrims from the southern Exodus who spread Menite teachings into the northlands. Their disciples sought to translate the True Law into local tongues and preserve these scriptures in writing. Khurzic uses a distinct alphabet, although it was likely derived from the pre-Caspian alphabet used in Icthier. Like Caspian, Khurzic is no longer spoken but is studied by scholars of ancient history. Most other Khurzic languages have begun to fall by the wayside in favor of modern Khadoran, which is spoken pervasively across the Khadoran Empire.

KHADORAN

The language of the Khadoran Empire is the enduring language of the north and has been learned by many in the regions bordering its expanding territories. Over the generations Khadoran has steadily swallowed up rival languages in the north, incorporating a variety of words and phrases from the other Khurzic tongues. Khadoran includes a number of Orgoth-derived terms as well as some taken from Molgur. Most Khadoran speakers can communicate easily with one another despite regional accents and colloquialisms, although fewer Khadorans in the rural regions can read and write compared to those in other kingdoms.

KOSSITE

Kossite is now a little-used tongue, perhaps due to its scarcity of written literature. The Kossite people were largely illiterate for most of their history, even after many tribes converted to Menoth. In some remote forest communities and among certain families the language is preserved, but Khadoran has nearly swept it aside.

UMBREAN

Umbrean is a distinct language, although it bears strong similarities to Khadoran; they share a structure as well as an alphabet and contain many similar words. Umbrean has been preserved by the people of eastern Khador and those of what was once western Llael and is still spoken both in homes and among other Umbreans. There are distinct Umbrean translations of the True Law, which differ in small but noteworthy ways from their Khadoran counterparts. This language has persisted despite the prevalence of Khadoran, although most Umbreans speak both, and many also speak Llaelese, Ordic, or Cygnaran.

MOLGUR LANGUAGES

Although Molgur has given rise to a number of distinct languages, they share many roots and elements; with a bit of exposure and familiarity, speakers can often make themselves understood to one another, although conveying complex ideas can be difficult. One of the most distinct dialects of Molgur is that used by the Tharn, who have their own words and phrases but whose language is otherwise quite similar to ancient Molgur.

MOLGUR

The most ancient living tongue, Molgur originally spread across western Immoren with the dominance of that tribal people before the Warlord Era. It was once pervasive among Devourer-worshipers, but its use is now confined to fringe settlements and dialects adopted by Dhunian races. Due to its association with the Wurm, it is sometimes referred to as the "Berserker's Tongue."

GOBBERISH

While some linguists disdain to consider this a distinct language, it is arguably as divergent from the original Molgur as Molgur-Trul and is difficult for outsiders to comprehend. Gobberish is less cohesive and consistent than the other Molgur tongues, frequently becoming an amalgam including local human tongues of the region. The most broadly spoken dialect includes many Cygnaran terms. Since most southern gobbers can also speak Cygnaran, they sometimes seem to employ Gobberish just to confuse humans that annoy them. They also use it to speak privately to one another, often speaking particularly quickly to further confound outsiders.

MOLGUR-OG

Molgur-Og is common to the ogrun, who have added their own words and particularly expanded the language's range of curses and swearing. There is no written form of Molgur-Og. Those ogrun who make their homes in Rhul write in Rhulic, and even in speech this language has become increasingly prevalent. Molgur-Og is on the decline among Rhulic ogrun, who retain its use primarily for Dhunian services and family matters.

MOLGUR-TRUL

Molgur-Trul is the most widely used Molgur tongue and is used by trollkin throughout western Immoren. It has diverged more dramatically from its linguistic roots than other Molgur languages to become the most versatile in that family. The trollkin possess a rich tradition of runic carving, and their written language is as versatile and expressive as their speech. Use of this language spread to other troll species, including full-blood trolls, pygmy trolls, and dire trolls, although their vocabularies and sentence construction are much more limited.

MORRIDANE LANGUAGES

The most obscure and least widespread of the human language families, the Morridane languages are in serious decline. While Morridane has a distinct ancient alphabet, the two living tongues in this family abandoned it long ago.

MORRIDANE (EXTINCT)

The language of the people of Morrdh, Morridane is one of the more difficult ancient tongues, subject to far less scholarly study than Caspian. Morridane and Caspian are distantly related, having diverged from one of the tongues of Icthier after the Exodus prompted by the Time of the Burning Sky. The ancient writings of Morrdh are highly prized by occultists. Morridane's original alphabet shares only a few symbols with the Caspian one.

IDRIAN

Idrian is on the decline but is still spoken among the remaining tribal nomads on the fringes of the Protectorate of Menoth and elsewhere in the Bloodstone Marches. The majority of Menite Idrians switched to Sulese after converting a century ago. Idrian is classified as a Morridane language even though it was heavily influenced by other tongues used in this eastern region. In ancient times a number of Idrian tribes were conquered by Morrdh, which had a tremendous impact on their language. Idrian also incorporates many Molgur terms. Although written Idrian once had its own alphabet, it has been largely forgotten. Most who speak this tongue cannot read or write its original alphabet. Idrians converted to Menite worship who still speak Idrian use the Caspian alphabet for writing it. Other tribes have taken up the Molgur alphabet instead.

THURIAN

The most widely spoken of the Morridane languages, Thurian has persisted in Ord and northwestern Cygnar, as the descendants of Thuria are proud of their ancient roots. Thurians do not consider themselves descendants of Morrdh, but their kingdom had regular contact and periodic wars with the dark kingdom and eventually adopted a variant of Morridane mixed with tongues local to the coasts and bogs of the Thurian region. Thurian has evolved considerably away from its Morridane roots into one of the most distinct of western Immoren's living tongues, making it difficult to learn by outsiders, although most Ordsmen know some Thurian as a matter of course. It is considered a "low" language in Ord compared to Ordic or Tordoran, a matter of dispute between these two peoples. Thurian literature is quite popular among the nobles of northwestern Cygnar, where the tongue has a more romantic connotation. Modern Thurian is written with the Caspian alphabet.

The so-called "Five Cant" is an artificial dialect of Thurian blending old Tordoran, Cygnaran, and Caspian. It is a very fast-spoken and intentionally confusing dialect used extensively in the town of Five Fingers that originally arose among the port's criminals and has spread to the criminal circles of other cities.

RHULIC

All dwarves and most northern ogrun speak Rhulic, and this language is not generally well known outside of Rhul. Although some human scholars have undertaken its study, particularly in communities with dwarven enclaves, dwarves trading with humans prefer to speak in Cygnaran or Khadoran. Written Rhulic is complex, consisting of numerous runic combinations of geometric shapes. The alphabet also has a distinct variant used for written correspondence that differs from the angular variant used for inscribing text in stone or metal. Most ogrun of Rhul can speak Rhulic with fluency and some can even read and write it as a second language, which is useful when aiding the Rhulic mercenary companies with their copious records. The language contains a variety of minor dialects, with the most distinct used among clans who associate least with outsiders. The miners of Ulgar have a distinct dialect, for example, as do the dwarves of remote eastern Farhallow.

SHYR

The Iosans speak a language called Shyr, a name shared with their capital in Ios. This is an ancient and extremely complex language, with rigid rules of syntax and grammar entirely dissimilar from human and dwarven tongues. Written Shyr is not phonetic and uses thousands of intricate glyphs. Shyr is almost never heard outside of Ios, and as the Iosans guard their language as tightly as all their secrets, only a handful of scholars outside Ios are familiar with its written form. There are distinct dialect differences between the language used in Shyrr, Iryss, and Lynshynal as well as among those used in some of the outlying fortifications. Additionally, the numerous houses have developed terms specific to their use, although these do not generally represent a barrier to communication. Members of the Retribution of Scyrah have created an extensive system of gestures to be used in place of spoken language for certain tasks.

AERIC

Aeric, the language of the Nyss, is related to Shyr but diverged considerably after the Nyss left Ios and settled in northern Khador. The written form bears no similarities to Shyr's.

Written Aeric is closely connected with Nyss religion and learned almost exclusively by priests and sorcerers.

OBSCURE LANGUAGES

There are many other languages in western Immoren, including dozens of tongues among isolated areas on the fringes of Khador or other nations. Some are obscure like Satyx, the language of the Satyxis, and the nearly incomprehensible Thrallspeak utilized by the more advanced undead. Some are guarded, blasphemous tongues such as the words of infernal entities or the occult runes of the Telgesh script studied by Thamarites. The Thousand Cities era saw the development of dozens of tongues now of use only to scholars attempting to piece together the distant past.

STEEL, SMOKE, AND CITIES

THE CHANGING FACE OF THE IRON KINGDOMS

The rise of industry has defined the lives of the people of the Iron Kingdoms more profoundly than any war, plague, or treaty. In the modern era innovation and technology build upon one another at a feverish pace, transforming the landscape itself in ways undreamed of by previous generations. Smokestacks rise to the sky in every major city, belching smoke that creates a perpetual haze above the streets. Steam-powered ships ply the rivers and oceans, braving currents that could not be overcome by sail alone and opening trade between distant ports. The blast engines of great factories burn day and night, producing mighty machines of war that have revolutionized battle.

As more and more people have become employed as factory hands, textile laborers, or ironworkers, society has changed radically. No longer does the average person expect a life spent toiling at his family's farmstead. Instead, he looks to the cities, where he can earn a fair coin for his labor and enjoy some of the benefits of the modern era. The rulers of nations see opportunity for immense wealth and innovation in warfare, and the many soldiers carry weaponry of startling sophistication. None of these marvels would have been possible were it not for the invention of the steam engine and the subsequent fusion of magic and technology known as mechanika.

Magic is still a fearful mystery to most, but its application is increasingly common. The roots of industrial thaumaturgy lie in alchemy, a skill known to humanity long before the Gift of Magic. By the careful preparation and mixture of sometimes rare but mundane ingredients, alchemists can create solutions with arcane properties. While wizardry and sorcery remain exotic and uncommon, their practitioners are increasingly accepted as valued members of society, particularly in the cities. The arcane mechanik is a figure respected by even the common man, as his most wondrous creations—steamjacks—are among the most iconic symbols of the modern age.

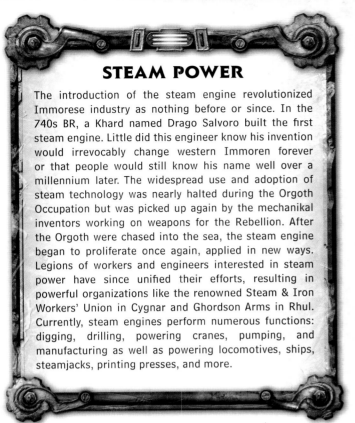

STEAM POWER

The introduction of the steam engine revolutionized Immorese industry as nothing before or since. In the 740s BR, a Khard named Drago Salvoro built the first steam engine. Little did this engineer know his invention would irrevocably change western Immoren forever or that people would still know his name well over a millennium later. The widespread use and adoption of steam technology was nearly halted during the Orgoth Occupation but was picked up again by the mechanikal inventors working on weapons for the Rebellion. After the Orgoth were chased into the sea, the steam engine began to proliferate once again, applied in new ways. Legions of workers and engineers interested in steam power have since unified their efforts, resulting in powerful organizations like the renowned Steam & Iron Workers' Union in Cygnar and Ghordson Arms in Rhul. Currently, steam engines perform numerous functions: digging, drilling, powering cranes, pumping, and manufacturing as well as powering locomotives, ships, steamjacks, printing presses, and more.

Even divided by national borders, imposing wildernesses, and language, the people of the Iron Kingdoms share many experiences in their daily lives. The common people of every nation are ruled by powerful aristocrats, priests, or industrialists, and sometimes by all three. The elite choose how to rule, how much they tax their subjects, and how to govern. Having known no other form of governance, few people question such feudal monarchies.

Serfdom has been largely abolished; most people rent their homes and the lands they work and keep any profit in their own pockets. In some cases the poorest may be so indebted to land owners that their freedom is arguably illusory, but for most of the common people this has brought a greater degree of liberty and increased opportunity to earn a comfortable living. Every year more people give up farming and toil in the country in favor of city life, while others continue to live as their families have for generations.

Most city dwellers find work in labor or manufacturing, typically related to the dominant industries of the cities in which they live. Coastal cities like Highgate employ numerous stevedores and shipwrights as well as crews for the numerous steam-powered cranes, but a laborer in Ironhead Station would be more likely to find employment in a steel mill or hauling mineral ores. Some institutions, such as textile mills or freight transport interests, are common to almost every city and employ huge numbers of individuals across the Iron Kingdoms.

Employment in the cities does not necessarily equate to a better standard of living. There are far more people seeking work than there are available positions, even with industry booming in the midst of ongoing wars, and the positions that are available are usually for the most onerous and unpleasant work. This demand means industrialists can choose to pay poor wages or demand tremendous working hours from their employees. Not every factory boss is greedy or unreasonable, but enough are that labor has begun to organize in resistance. The Steam & Iron Workers Union, or the "Union Steamos," as they are more commonly known, provide a powerful organization to demand fair pay and vocational training to its members in return for reasonable yearly dues.

THE RAVAGES OF INDUSTRY

The industrialization and mechanization of the modern era is wreaking havoc on the land, air, and water. Countless acres of forests are destroyed to carve out regions for farming and grazing livestock and to satisfy the great demand for timber. Often, conflict arises in areas claimed by groups and races that do not recognize the authority of those conducting these harvests. Loggers commonly report run-ins with hostile trollkin kriels, bogrin, or blackclads, sometimes leading to bloodshed.

The burning of coal, especially during the winter months, commonly creates a smoke hazard in the more populated areas of Immoren. Cities in cooler climes, such as Korsk and Khardov, with their burgeoning industries and dense populations, live almost constantly blanketed in soot and fog, as do many of the cities of Cygnar. Both Corvis and Fharin are renowned for smoky fogs and for the foul-smelling coal fumes known as "stinking fogs." Some cities have made proclamations limiting the amount of coal that can be burned, but such regulations rarely succeed in spite of the threat of fines and more drastic deterrents. Industry is too important to the Iron Kingdoms to be slowed.

The tanning and slaughtering industries have added greatly to the diminishment of the rivers with the dumping of chemicals and other byproducts of industry. Areas with thriving alchemy production add even more exotic and often lethal waste products. Municipal statutes attempt to regulate such matters, just as they do the leaving or throwing of garbage, but in most cities all of this—loss of forests, unbreathable air, poisoned water, and litter—is an ever-growing concern.

TRANSPORT BY LAND AND SEA

The staggering demand for resources has spurred rapid growth of transportation on both land and sea. While small components and trade goods are often still moved by caravan, material resources like lumber, ore, and harvested grains are now required in quantities for which roads are insufficient. The resulting rail boom of the past century has entirely changed how people judge distance and travel time across western Immoren.

RAIL TRAVEL

The first true rail line was a Khadoran innovation. Completed in 487 AR after twenty-seven years of construction, it connected the cities of Korsk and Skirov. A crowd of hundreds gathered in Korsk to witness the launch of the *Korska*, the first steam-powered locomotive. This engine could pull thirty tons with a

INDUSTRY AND AGRICULTURE

Farming and ranching are essential functions, and a significant portion of the population in each kingdom are employed working the land. Thriving cities and marching armies need food. Many people would starve if not for markets filled with fresh produce and meats. Those working and living on the fringes of rural regions are more vulnerable to dangers from the wilderness, however. Nobles who own these lands are expected to defend lease-holders, but these efforts are often retaliatory, too late for victims of trolls, Tharn, undead, or other horrors.

Most of the wealth from food production remains in the hands of nobles. The wealthiest are those whose lands encompass the most fertile and varied farmland and pastures. Controlling the food supply for the capitals and major centers of industry gives such nobles political clout beyond their rank and station. That said, a number of private interests have made inroads into industries such as the shipment and distribution of essential goods, using trains and wagon caravans to bring produce and livestock to market. Wealthy merchants of the middle class have begun to compete with nobles for control over the farmlands and herds, sometimes buying lands and even noble titles to legitimize their family lines. Established families treat these new nobility with disdain.

The old professions of farming and herding cattle have changed significantly as a result of modernization and industry. Larger consortiums and progressive nobles have access to steamjacks that can be used to plow difficult land, remove rocks and other debris, and so on. Other advances include steam-powered pumps that extend natural irrigation and the breeding of weather-resistant strains of grain. These developments allow larger tracts of land to be worked by fewer hands as well as opening up regions for farming once deemed useless.

maximum speed of sixteen miles an hour and could make the 218-mile journey in roughly fifteen hours. Though primitive by modern standards, the Korsk-Skirov line was a tremendous achievement noted by every power in the Iron Kingdoms.

In just a few decades the Cygnaran military and the Steam & Iron Workers Union had collaborated to lay tracks connecting Caspia and Steelwater Flats and then, through a miracle of engineering, dug sixty miles of tunnel through the Upper Wyrmwall Mountains connecting the line to Ironhead Station. In 577 AR the Cygnaran engine *Caspian* ran the line bearing a load of forty tons in just under four hours. The rail boom in western Immoren had truly begun.

Rail lines now interconnect the major cities of Khador and Cygnar, and steam locomotives have captured the imagination of people across the continent. Though trains were first built in Khador, the refined look and function of the Cygnaran steam locomotive have become the standard by which all trains in the Iron Kingdoms are judged. The engine car that hauls the train is dominated by a massive steam engine at its fore. Atop this, smokestacks vent huge streams of coal smoke, making the train visible for miles. Within the car the engineer uses the engine's instruments to slow and accelerate the train and to monitor boiler pressure, while his assistants fuel the great boiler system. A huge firebox at the front of the engineer's cabin converts stored water into the steam that drives the locomotive forward. The engine hauls a set of cars mostly devoted to freight and, increasingly, military troops on their way to the front lines. Many trains also include armed cars or even carry guardian warjacks when traveling near battlefields or across dangerous tracts of wilderness.

Life as an engineer is rarely dull; in times of strife, trains are often military targets, and it is not uncommon for them to encounter savage war parties far from civilization. As these engines are considered vital to national interests, most kingdom militaries have taken efforts to bolster their security. Cygnaran soldiers and Khadoran Rail Korps are frequently stationed aboard their nation's trains to protect them. Khador has gone so far as to equip many of its trains with gun turrets and other armament. Train crews also tend to travel well armed, and only the best-prepared or most foolhardy bandits will attempt to rob a train.

The use of passenger cars is increasing, especially in Cygnar, but they are still something of a novelty. For now, most individuals seeking passage take whatever space is available among the freight in exchange for their coin. While expensive, rail travel offers one of the fastest ways to cross long distances, greatly accelerating the spread of news.

STEAMSHIPS AND STEAMBOATS

The application of the steam engine has revolutionized travel on water as well as land. With steam power the ships of the Iron Kingdoms are no longer at the mercy of the waves, winds, and tides, and the combination of engine and paddlewheel has greatly expanded the industry of trade-by-water. A steam-powered, flat-bottomed paddlewheel craft can travel farther upstream than most sailing ships through its ability to fight currents and to keep moving without rowers when the wind is not favorable.

Towns like Riversmet and Cherov-on-Dron sprang up almost overnight, and the size of others such as Khardov, Merywyn, and Corvis easily doubled or even tripled thanks to increased river trade. Once steam was profitably applied to the rivers and seas, the popularity of ships relying solely on wind power began to decline. The paddlewheel and the ship's engine were indeed pricey and difficult to maintain, but travel stability, especially upstream, more than made up for the cost. Steamships have the added advantage of being able to outrun many pursuers when voyaging in remote stretches, although their paddlewheels are easily damaged by the larger aquatic predators found in some regions.

In due course, steamships became the craft of choice for the more progressive and prosperous river traders, and even on the seas the retrofitted steamship has become an increasingly common sight. Today, sailing ships remain widespread in the deep waters, but even these are mostly hybrids that utilize auxiliary steam engines and paddlewheels to give them reliable motive power regardless of the winds. Without a doubt, shallow-keeled, steam-spewing, coal-powered vessels have overtaken the rivers and streams.

Like all travel across western Immoren, river trade is not without its perils. River pirates and vicious primitive tribes of bog trogs and gatormen sometimes attack merchant ships. Cygnaran and Khadoran authorities conduct patrols, but most merchants who wish protection either contract mercenary vessels to accompany their fleets or hire sell-swords to travel alongside their crews.

Increasingly common sights aboard the steamers, especially below decks, are the pint-sized, grease-smeared gobbers. The reasoning here is simple: they are small and just as proficient at technical matters as any human. Gobbers keep steam engines running and squirm into places many humans cannot in order to make fast repairs. Cognizant of nearly every detail, they make excellent quartermasters, and just as on dry land, many water-faring gobbers are able cannoneers. In a human, these traits make for a good sailor; in a gobber who takes up less than half as much space as a human, this package of traits can be indispensable to many a captain. Gobbers also use up half the resources and are rarely known to be lazy. They are often the equals of their human counterparts even aside from their brute strength, and not many humans can match a gobber's zeal in tackling a troublesome repair.

THE RISE OF THE CITY

Western Immoren's growing cities represent the true face of the Iron Kingdoms. These bustling centers of industry offer incredible opportunities, but no opportunity is without risk, and urban life brings with it unique challenges.

Each of the cities of the Iron Kingdoms is a reflection of its history, its rulers, and the aspirations of its citizens. The ancient walls of Caspia enclose a teeming populace and the heart of both the Cygnaran crown and the Morrowan Church, the Sancteum. Just across the Black River, Caspia's sister city,

BLAUSTAVYA SHIPPING & RAIL

Founded in 551 AR by Kayaz Simonyev Blaustavya, a man who rose to become lord regent in 572 AR and great vizier in 606 AR, Blaustavya Shipping & Rail is the foremost mercantile power in the Motherland. It moves goods, food, and coal across the entire breadth of Khador. BS&R also has a substantial interest in commercial fishing and merchant security out of Ohk, dealings with heavy industry in Korsk, and a massive distribution center based out of Khardov. Most other merchant companies and guilds live in the shadow of "Big Iron."

With rail stations in Ohk, Khardov, Korsk, and Skirov, BS&R moves goods rapidly, effectively, and inexpensively. It is the largest commercial user of steam engines and steamjacks in all of western Immoren and has acquired several companies that produce the parts to maintain its equipment. Big Iron steamjacks, trade trains, and other vessels all carry the image of "the stack;" a stylized smoke stack billowing plumes of smoke. The icon is stamped on the sides of their armored trains, displayed on placards on their warehouse walls, and emblazoned on the sails or smoke stacks of their ships. Since the creation of the first rail line in Khador, Blaustavya has become a household name in the nation's metropolitan centers. BS&R is the largest private employer in Khador and offers better working conditions and pay than any of its competitors. Laborers, alchemists, technicians, and arcane mechaniks alike make their livings at Big Iron.

Sul, is not only an industrious modern city but a site of Menite pilgrimage. At prayer time the bustle of commerce in Caspia is matched in Sul by crushing silence. Far to the north lie the urban centers of the fallen state of Llael. The tread of occupying forces gives rhythm to the alchemists and industries of Laedry and Merywyn, whose populations are already beginning to resign themselves to Khadoran rule. Farther north and west is Khador's capitol, Korsk, a massive city thrumming with the power of conquest as its people endure hard labor to support the efforts of their empress. Still, they endure less hardship than their comrades in the city of Khardov, where the wheels of industry grind day and night, turning their sky to ash in order to advance Khador's engines of war.

Technology, alchemy, and mechanika have all undergone incredible revolutions over the past decades, and whole industries have arisen. For centuries, most of the inhabitants of the Iron Kingdoms made their livings as craftsmen, soldiers, or field workers, but in the modern cities people have a greater choice of professions. However, most individuals seeking work are untrained and lack the education and capital to found merchant ventures of their own. Thankfully, the demands of progress have created countless jobs for the common citizen, driving many to seek opportunities in the cities and transforming small trading hubs into smokestack-littered centers of industry.

THE RULE OF LAW

Each kingdom has its own laws and those tasked to enforce them, and there is considerable regional variance. Most ordinary people live their lives without much concern for law, mindful that wrong-doers will be punished and that this protection keeps them safe. Nonetheless some areas are more unregulated and lawless than others and some regions house particularly biased judges and enforcers. Citizens may need to learn to cope as a matter of survival, such as by paying bribes or for protection. If such measures are a minor burden and are enforced predictably, they might not unduly affect daily life.

The law is often more consistently applied in major cities. City watchmen or their equivalents, such as Winter Guard garrisons, are charged with keeping the peace, and experienced veterans among their number are tasked with investigating noteworthy crimes. Certain capital offenses receive considerable attention and funding to track down the guilty, particularly if pressure is applied by ranking nobles or clergy. But for petty street crime, those responsible are only arrested when caught red-handed. In cases where the local watch seems disinterested, crime victims might seek freelance help instead by hiring their own investigators, placing a bounty on the heads of those who wronged them, or offering a reward for the return of stolen goods. Bounties are a common incentive for hunting down the guilty for both lesser and greater offenses, and it is not uncommon for nobles or others in the government to offer hefty bounties for wanted criminals. Freelancers with the proper skills are often better equipped and experienced at tracking down such wrongdoers than the local watch and can make a good living as bounty hunters.

It is also common for major organizations to enforce internal rules and laws on members, carrying out certain punishments without involving the authorities. Traditional apprenticeships give considerable leeway for a mentor to discipline his apprentice, for example. Other groups are also allowed some legal control over their sworn members, including major religious institutions such as the Church of Morrow or Menite temples as well as mercenary companies, arcane orders, and several major craft and trade guilds. Usually these groups have limited jurisdiction and will have to turn members over to the authorities if requested. In much of western Immoren, the Church of Morrow has specific rights to investigate and persecute cases of occult maleficia. For other unusual crimes, properly qualified specialists might be empowered to assist local law.

In most areas, the accused is considered guilty until proven innocent and his case heard by a judge or tribunal, depending on the city and country. Policies for the enforcement of law and execution of punishments against violators varies considerably from nation to nation, as does the degree of justice across class lines. While nations like Cygnar and Ord have implemented measures to promote fair treatment of commoners, in practice those lacking in wealth or influence may be powerless and could even face summary judgments. In the Protectorate of Menoth, for example, every priest has tremendous authority and can legally dispense justice without trial. That said, Sul-Menite priests are themselves watched by the scrutator caste, and internal corruption is not tolerated. In Occupied Llael, suspected troublemakers may be immediately flogged by Winter Guard without proof of wrongdoing, something that would never happen to a Khadoran citizen.

Citizens in Khador, Ord, and Cygnar can generally expect a trial and to face their accusers, although specific judges may have their own biases that will affect the outcome. The word of the privileged—whether noble, priest, or head of a major merchant house—is always trusted above that of a common laborer or freelance sell-sword. Where guilt can be clearly established, however, even those in the highest positions can fall before the weight of public outrage or by being dishonored before their peers. Every nation also has its own penalties for various offenses and may prioritize crimes differently. Some crimes are universally dealt with severely, most particularly murder, treason, and piracy. In some corrupt cities a highly skilled arbiter or a properly greased palm can transform murder into justifiable homicide, treason into a simple lapse of judgment, and piracy into authorized privateering. But if these attempts prove unsuccessful, those facing capital crimes can expect execution, sometimes by gruesome means.

Standard methods of execution include hanging and beheading, but in some regions it is common to be burned alive or to suffer torture before execution, and gibbeting is a typical penalty for piracy in particular. The Protectorate of Menoth has the harshest penalties of the Iron Kingdoms, with the scrutators being specialized in extracting confessions and dispensing painful justice. Other severe offenses deemed not worthy of execution warrant branding or maiming, although this is less commonly done in the modern era. Imprisonment combined with forced labor is an option favored in Khador and the Protectorate. Cygnar has set aside Bloodshore Island as a prison for those deemed dangerous but for whom execution is undesirable— generally politically connected prisoners or those who may have information making them too important to be eliminated. For minor crimes, flogging and public shaming is the most usual punishment, although perpetrators can sometimes evade this by paying fines. Others who cannot pay may be imprisoned for at least a short duration.

Many laws simply do not apply to nobles, and they may legitimately be able to act with greater liberty than their lessers. It has long been the practice that landed nobles are not to be prosecuted on petty offenses such as drunkenness, improper speech, small acts of theft, burglary, or in some cases, even extortion and assault. Bringing serious charges against any

THE MERCARIAN LEAGUE

Founded in the Cygnaran city of Mercir as a confederation of traders and noble interests, the Mercarian League has become arguably the most powerful mercantile interest across western Immoren. The league wields vast power over the financial markets of the kingdoms. While most prevalent in Cygnar, it has significant holdings in Ord and even influence in Khador through shadow ownerships or secret partnerships. Most of the league's wealth is related to shipping, and in the centuries since it was founded it has accumulated a formidable and well-armed navy to protect its merchant vessels.

The league maintains a network of influential contacts within many major cities and has established a virtual monopoly over several of Cygnar's major ocean-based trade routes. It has also taken part in trading in shares to acquire investment capital for extended voyages and is one of the few groups in western Immoren that has been willing to invest in exploration beyond the immediate shores. The intelligence-gathering arm of the league is known as the Eye of Mercir, and while primarily involved in commercial espionage, the league has no fear of dabbling in politics.

One of the greatest recent gains of the Mercarian League happened in 593 AR when it won a power struggle over the control of an Ordic company called the Berck Imports House. Once owned by the Mateu Merchant House, this company was the pioneer that established successful trade with the southern continent of Zu, bringing back a wealth of exotic imports, including spices, fabrics, ivory, and other luxury goods. The struggles around control of this trade route have resulted in allegations of kidnappings, murders, and worse. The two mercantile groups remain bitter and dangerous rivals, each going to almost any lengths to sabotage the efforts of the other. Meanwhile, the Mercarian League continues to invest in additional expeditions abroad, having been chartered by the Cygnaran crown to find other untapped resources and potential trade routes. The first Immorese settlements on Zu have sprang up the last few years, drawing a number of adventurous individuals to risk their lives traveling abroad to start a new life.

control staggering wealth. In times when borders are hostile, the lucrative trade of black-market goods is tempting for those willing to risk life and limb. Extortion, theft, and smuggling are the crimes of choice for these groups, with banditry and piracy outside the cities.

EDUCATION

Though the state of general education varies from nation to nation and city to city, the Iron Kingdoms are home to a number of prestigious establishments of higher learning. Institutions like the centuries-old Corvis University and Khadoran Institute of Engineering are bastions of intellectual respectability. The best universities are typically recognized by royal charter and offer prestige and a moderate amount of wealth to the highly qualified professors that comprise their staffs. The support and maintenance of such institutions is invariably a matter of national pride, as they exist for the betterment of society, and they produce some of the finest minds in the Iron Kingdoms.

Graduates of academic institutions may find employment as professors themselves, but many set out to explore more practical applications of their studies or conduct research in the field. Those whose expertise lends itself to mechanikal, alchemical, or physical engineering may well establish independent workshops outside the university, presenting papers on their inventions and discoveries out of a sense of duty in advancing the state of knowledge or the mere vanity of recognition by their peers. If their experiments might be useful in warfare, they may find themselves courted by the military academies of their nations. Scholars who specialize in the natural sciences or historical pursuits may spend significant time in the field.

Field expeditions may include several professors of disparate studies who band together to make the most effective use of their grant funds. Traveling far afield in the pursuit of knowledge, they might seek out an ancient ruin where one of their number can study inscriptions in the language of Morrdh while a colleague researches the habits of the razor bats that now live in those ancient tunnels. Such expeditions are often fraught with peril and invariably budget for mercenary protection. The scholars themselves typically possess a certain aptitude in self-defense—as well as surprisingly lethal artifacts of their former expeditions.

Any citizen may attend university lectures, but only registered students have access to many university facilities, such as housing, libraries, workshops, and laboratories. Most universities charge tuition on an annual basis, although this rarely covers more than a portion of operating expenses. While these fees are not onerous for the wealthy, they are too much for the poor to endure easily. Particularly promising young minds may be forced to find patrons among the clergy or the nobility, often with strings attached. Tuition fees must be paid before a prospective graduate can stand before a panel of professors to be tested for expertise in his chosen field. These opportunities arise once a year; those who fail must either enroll for another year or abandon their aspirations. If this final assessment is passed, the aspiring scholar receives a sealed and signed certificate attesting to their qualifications. Proof of graduation

landed noble or government officer is a difficult and risky proposition; the evidence must be overwhelming, and the accusation can prompt reprisals. This extra burden of proof for the nobility is found in every kingdom with a noble class and was particularly exploited in Llael prior to the Khadoran occupation. Khadoran great princes and their heirs, Cygnaran dukes, and Ordic lord castellans are more or less above the law barring intervention by agents of the Crown with charges of treason. While the Protectorate does not have nobles, the priest caste is treated similarly. There is comparatively little corruption there thanks to the watchful eye of the scrutators— but with the latitude given priests, the standard for abuse of authority is far different than in other nations.

The threat of punishment seems to do little to deter many lawbreakers, and most cities are home to countless criminals, professional or otherwise. Many people who have moved from the countryside in search of jobs that were unavailable turn to lives of crime. Some criminals are quite sophisticated, or at least well connected. The Iron Kingdoms are rife with criminal organizations like the notorious gangs of Five Fingers and the vicious *bratyas* of the Korsk underworld. Some of these criminal fraternities wield significant political power and

is valued by those interested in becoming professors or making a name in research or academia.

The great military academies of the Iron Kingdoms are another bastion of learning. By and large, these state-supported academies are devoted to the grooming of military officers. In Cygnar, the Strategic Academy educates all commissioned officers, while the Trident naval academy trains Ord's most promising students in the arts of war. The Druzhina is Khador's elite officer training school. It is in these places that those who command men in battle learn their trade at the hands of instructors who almost invariably graduated from the same institutions in decades past. Most of these academies spend at least one year instructing pupils on practical combat tactics, warjack deployment, logistics, military history, theories of command, and the application of drills.

Warcasters usually begin their formal training at these academies. Their instruction includes the mundane studies of their peers but is supplemented by intense arcane training under the tutelage of senior warcasters. Warcasters are numbered among the most valuable assets of their nations' militaries, and their training is exhaustive and lengthy. They are instructed in both the direct application of their arcane abilities and the control of warjacks. This academic training typically lasts for over a year before the warcaster begins field training as a journeyman.

Military academies are also home to more esoteric schools. In Cygnar the Strategic Academy controls several specialized branches, including the Militant Order of the Arcane Tempest, devoted to the training of Cygnaran gun mages. In Khador, the Druzhina likewise provides academic and occult training for newly inducted arcanists of the Greylords Covenant.

COMMERCE AND TRAVEL

Cities have been the birthplace of new institutions, spurred by increasing trade and travel between regions. The rise of banks and other financial institutions could not have occurred without the safety and security provided by city walls and stable governance. Merchants and travelers alike have found it necessary to keep large sums of coin on hand to handle business transactions. Given the sometimes unfavorable exchange rates, it is also advantageous to have a source of local currency.

International travel is supervised. To allow for trade, every government has a trade board that regulates travel and dispenses licenses, or "Letters of Request," notarized by public officials. To gain these papers, a traveler typically goes through an interview process and pays a nominal fee set by the local trade board of the target destination along with any taxes or duties. Indeed, often travelers journey with trade or diplomatic caravans to avoid interrogation at borders, toll houses, city gates, and harbor docks. Though it has become easier, travel has by no means become safer; carrying large sums through the wilderness can be extremely risky, as bandits and brigands plague the major travel arteries.

Due to the strained relations between nations, the roads of the Iron Kingdoms are more dangerous to traverse these days than they have been in some time. Foreign trade is especially challenging but also much more profitable. The necessity of safeguarding roads, rivers, and trade has led to the advent of the professional road warden. In Cygnar, these individuals are paid by the state to travel the nation's highways to keep them clear of brigands and threatening beasts. Most road wardens

COINS OF THE KINGDOMS

Each kingdom mints its own coinage as a right of sovereignty. Standard weights for coins of each major precious metal were established during the Corvis Treaties, so Khadoran and Ordic coins generally have similar weight (though not always size, shape, or purity) as Cygnaran ones. Most coins have different images stamped on each side, with one bearing the face of the monarch reigning when the coin was minted. All coins include decorative features intended to discourage counterfeiting, but some currency is more trusted than others.

Gold, silver, and copper have been favored for currency, with copper falling out of use for commerce but still widespread among the lower classes. Many reputable establishments refuse to trade in anything less than silver. With the exception of Cygnaran gold crowns and silver shields, which are widely accepted across western Immoren, most establishments refuse payment in foreign coin or will require a substantially higher rate. Dedicated money changers operate in most sizable towns, usually taking a percentage service fee.

Of other currencies, Rhul's coin is trusted due to the dwarves' exacting standards for weight and metal purity, but as its traders use Cygnaran coin abroad, Rhul's currency is rarely seen outside its borders. Khadoran and Ordic coins are accepted inside their nations of origin but are devalued elsewhere. Coins produced by the now-defunct state of Llael are essentially without value beyond their basic worth as precious metal, and much of this coin has been melted down and re-minted as Khadoran currency. Inhabitants of the Scharde Islands do not mint their own coin but will usually possess an assortment of currencies.

The Protectorate of Menoth was originally forbidden from minting coins. Shortly after the Protectorate's founding, the scrutators created a special currency to prevent citizens from amassing wealth or seeking to trade outside Protectorate borders. This coinage, made from fired clay, is worthless in other nations. For trade abroad, the Protectorate uses gemstones and raw materials.

NATIONAL COINAGE	COIN NAME	METAL	VALUE
Common Cygnaran Coinage:	crown	gold	trade standard
	shield	silver	10 shields = 1 crown
	farthing	copper	10 farthings = 1 shield
Uncommon Cygnaran Coinage:	swan	gold	2 crowns
	half-crown	gold	5 shields
	half-shield	silver	5 farthings
Khadoran Coinage:	koltina	gold	eq. crown
	denescka	silver	eq. shield
	kuppek	copper	eq. farthing
Llaelese Coinage: (no longer minted and rapidly depreciating)	goldbust	gold	eq. crown
	keep	silver	eq. shield
	kettle	copper	eq. farthing
Ordic Coinage:	royal	gold	eq. crown
	silverweight	silver	eq. 2 shields
	galleon	silver	eq. shield
	half-galleon	silver	eq. 5 farthing
	blackpenny	copper	eq. farthing
Protectorate of Menoth Coinage:	decastave	clay	eq. 10 crowns
	stave	clay	eq. crown
	mark	clay	eq. shield
	trace	clay	eq. farthing

operate in small groups, sometimes accompanying caravans. When they anticipate threats beyond their own abilities they may hire mercenaries to aid them at the kingdom's expense. In more remote areas, wardens are almost unheard of, and travelers must rely on their own wits and resources against attacks. The Khadoran government sometimes similarly employs wardens but generally prefers to use Winter Guard to patrol.

Roadhouses along the highways provide periodic stopping points between cities and towns, some just outside them and others far from any settlement. Some are little more than supply shops with outlying areas for camping in relative safety, while others serve as some mix of inns, taverns, or brothels. Others are posts for road wardens that may double as royal messenger

relay stations, and remote roadhouses are often fortified for defense. When visiting a privately owned roadhouse, travelers are well advised to remember that the proprietor's word is law.

Every kingdom has soldiers patrolling its borders, though Cygnar's are far the most plentiful. Alert for enemy troop movements and unlawful smuggling operations, these patrols regularly stop and search both land and river traffic and question travelers. Generally made up of four to twenty soldiers, patrols are very suspicious of heavily armed groups, particularly those including improvised warjacks or strange beasts.

MILITARY SERVICE

Every kingdom maintains its own standing army, and military service is a common element of many people's lives. The military forces of most nations offer a modest wage, regular food and board, and some possibility of advancement, although it is rare for enlisted men to rise to the rank of a commissioned officer. Still, advancement by merit is possible and more likely in times of war. Those born into nobility or wealth typically enter service at military academies as cadets and on graduation become officers by purchasing their commissions. Today most armed forces make some attempt to promote the most competent and skilled officers rather than indulging the privileged, but an officer from a good family can still expect to rise more quickly in the ranks.

Modern warfare emphasizes combined arms. Every soldier has a role and is expected to heed orders while fighting alongside more specialized and elite forces as well as the steam-powered warjacks that are often essential to victory.

The citizens of almost every nation, especially those near threatened borders, can readily see that their ways of life are endangered. Among the people of Cygnar the loss of the Thornwood, the fall of Llael, and the invasion of their capital has caused a surge of patriotism. Many are doing whatever they can to support the war effort. Khadoran citizens have less choice, as military duty is mandatory for all male citizens over the age of seventeen and open to females of the same age range, but most Khadorans are proud to serve their nation when called. While only four years of service is required, many Khadorans voluntarily serve longer. The life of a Khadoran soldier is hard but brings considerable honor and respect.

Citizens of the Protectorate of Menoth can be called upon for military service at any time, no matter their age. In rare emergencies militias are formed from whole villages, arming anyone capable of holding a spear. Professional soldiery is an honored profession among the Sul-Menites. The ranks of the Temple Flameguard are full of citizen-soldiers eager to do their part to protect their faith.

Military service is on the rise even in the neutral nation of Ord, which has bolstered its border defenses and increased patrols hoping to prevent a similar fate as Llael. Serving in the Ordic Army does not carry the same peril as for those nations at war but is still hazardous. The borderlands frequently become battlefields, and the presence of Khadoran soldiers marching through the Thornwood has created a new region of vulnerability for Ord along its eastern border. Khadorans have long made a habit of launching small incursions across Ord's borders to test defenses and to season their elite branches with combat experience. King Baird II has been keen to improve and modernize his armed forces, aware of the looming threats to his kingdom.

MERCENARIES

The long history of bloody conflict in the Iron Kingdoms has created endless opportunity for those willing to do violence for pay. War is so ubiquitous in the Iron Kingdoms it is only natural that a certain breed approach it like any other trade. These are the mercenaries, soldiers of fortune generally loyal only to the paymaster currently filling their pockets. Where war thrives, mercenaries inevitably follow.

A longstanding code of conduct called simply "the Charter" defines the rules and strictures under which mercenaries operate. The foundation of these codes arose from extensive mercenary activity during the Thousand Cities Era, but the Charter was formalized and widely adopted in its modern form after the Corvis Treaties. The Charter clarifies how mercenaries are expected to treat employers, civilians, opposing and allied militaries, prisoners, and other mercenary companies. It offers rules for claiming territory, dividing loot, and ransoming prisoners. It also lays out what constitutes armed rebellion and what orders a company-for-hire can lawfully disobey, such as the slaughtering of civilians.

Every mercenary company is obliged to operate under the terms of the Charter. The Charter is supplemented by the specific codes and oaths sworn by individual mercenaries and companies. These lesser charters define the kinds of contracts

COMPANY CHARTERS

A mercenary company is incorporated by a charter, which is a contract between a consenting government and the mercenary commander. Possession of this contract represents ownership of the company and can be passed down to successors. When the contract is burned or otherwise destroyed, the company is disbanded.

Company charters often detail day-to-day operations, including pay shares, ranks, recruitment (which is usually, but not always, voluntary), and length of service. All mercenaries employed by a company must observe its chain of command. Violation of this tenet can result in arrest, disciplinary action, or even execution in the case of severe insubordination or desertion. Company officers are responsible for the behavior of their men. Mercenaries are expected to behave with honor. Looting, torture, and the execution of prisoners is prohibited.

Once contracted, a mercenary company must fulfill its obligations to the letter of the contract. Breaking a contract to switch sides in the midst of battle for reason—such as on offer of better pay—is unlawful and dishonorable. Once a company has fulfilled its contract, it is free to depart or negotiate new terms of service. If a contract stipulates a cooling-off period, the hired company cannot accept contracts against its previous employer for a specified period. Furthermore, a company can never take action against the authority that approved their founding charter. It is for this reason many mercenary companies prefer to incorporate their companies in Ord, a historically neutral nation.

Less legitimate outfits tend to have vague, incomplete, or contradictory charters, or simply take the expedient of operating with no charter at all. Despite the sanctions, there are always renegade mercenary companies who refuse to follow the old codes, along with private interests willing to hire them.

Most mercenary companies are relatively small, usually led by a seasoned military commander with some years of service with a national army or a charismatic negotiator capable of securing new work. The majority of these outfits comprise fewer than thirty members bound under the company's charter, although the more successful can deploy hundreds of soldiers at a time. Quality of life in the smaller mercenary companies varies considerably, depending on that group's leadership, skill, reputation, and clientele as well as the stability of the Iron Kingdoms at any given time.

Many small companies are simply a collection of individuals willing to fight together for coin. Companies with strong reputations can be picky and will turn away thugs, but almost any company is eager to snatch up those with arcane or mechanikal talents. Since many companies spend protracted time in the field (and are expected to provide for themselves while doing so), they are often on the lookout for cooks and people with wilderness survival skills. The more respectable companies tend to be highly professional and specialize in certain combat roles. These groups are often in high demand, especially during the traditional campaign season starting in the early spring.

a company will accept and the types of combat they engage in. Companies or individuals deemed in breach of these rules can suffer legal and even military retaliation—what was once a proud mercenary company can become a band of brigands or outlaws. Bounties offered for these criminals can serve as an incentive for other, once-competing companies to hunt them. Even if an outlawed company keeps a low profile and avoids destruction by force of arms, they might face the most ignominious of fates: death by unemployment. Most nations consider it a matter of policy never to employ those who violate the Charter, although times of extended war bring inevitable corruption and can prompt individual paymasters to be less particular in their hiring policies.

Most successful mercenary companies have become adept at interpreting the letter of their charters to suit their needs. Additionally, any mercenary worth his salt must learn contract negotiation and trade laws as a side vocation.

The best-equipped companies bring with them one or more warjacks and armed laborjacks. The presence of a 'jack or two on the battlefield can be a powerful force multiplier, and those mercenaries who can afford to purchase and maintain these expensive machines are always in demand. While warcasters remain rare among mercenary bands, 'jack marshals are not uncommon. Mercenaries who spend more than a few years in this line of work are invariably exposed to warjacks, and many take the trouble to learn the basics of commanding them in combat.

Not all mercenaries join companies. Many begin their careers as lone swords or guns-for-hire. Some individuals bring such highly valued skill sets to the battlefield they can pick and choose whom they work with. Warcasters, alchemists, arcane mechaniks, and combat arcanists of all stripes possess abilities that are always in demand. It takes skill to remain independent, and those without the chops are either left littering the battlefield or recruited into a larger outfit. In general, the life of a solo mercenary is short and dangerous.

Not every mercenary works for national interests; there is no shortage of wealthy private individuals or organizations with a need for hired soldiers. In practice, anyone with deep enough coffers and a large enough grudge can hire a small army. Private armies make local governments uneasy unless they are undertaking duties that presents at least the façade of legitimate work, such as assisting in maintaining public order. Large private armies are rare, but can provide the muscle to afford their considerable political liberties. Several of the most powerful nobles and merchant princes in Cygnar, Khador, and Ord have access to such forces and deploy them to serve their private agendas.

MAGIC

Magic is an undeniable force in the lives of the people of the Iron Kingdoms. Priests invoke blessings and perform small miracles as proof of the power of the divine. Sorcerers intuitively brandish raw elemental energies, while arcanists learn to use powers capable of defying the ordinary laws of nature by way of formulae. Rightly shunned by society and working from the shadows, necromancers and infernalists make truck with dark and corruptive forces. The mysteries of the occult are still held in awe by the common people even as the work of arcanists shapes industry and occasionally spills over to affect daily life.

There are myriad methods by which magic is invoked. The practice of controlling that power is not fully understood, however, even by those who spend their lives in its study. Every race and culture has its own relationship with the arcane and shuns some aspects while incorporating others into religion, warfare, and industry. A number of races, such as the Nyss, Iosans, Rhulfolk, and trollkin, are perfectly comfortable with their people practicing magic in both its divine and arcane forms. These cultures believe that priests and arcanists alike are practicing gifts passed down by the gods but approaching that power by different means. This perspective is quite distinct from that of the humans, whose relationship with magic has remained complicated over time.

While there are many shades of complexity to human attitudes toward magic and the countless individual disciplines by which its power can be harnessed, most can be distilled to two fundamental distinctions. First is the differentiation between divine and arcane magic. Second, controlled and "legitimate" magic is set apart from that which is unrestrained and unregulated.

For most of recorded history, humanity openly acknowledged only divine magic and had little exposure to systematic studies of the arcane. Only priests who communed with the gods and spent time in prayer were known to wield magic, which was deemed divine intervention. These powers might be malevolent

RUNES OF MAGIC AND TELGESH GLYPHS

The first sorcerers gained glimpses of glowing runes of power as they began to manifest their powers, and soon learned these arcane glyphs played a role in shaping reality. As the barely controlled arcane energies poured through them, they manifested ephemeral circles of runes in the air about their hands and bodies.

Over the centuries arcanists have taken a more systematic and scientific approach to the study of runes and formulae. Initially arcanists accepted these glyphs as fundamental to magic but knew little of their origins nor how to innovate new combinations, relying only on the genius of early arcane innovators like Sebastien Kerwin recorded in early tomes. In time occult scholars began to scrutinize those old documents and other, once spurned, occult texts. They began to confront the unsettling but unmistakable fact that the arcane runes they wield bear some relationship with Telgesh, the ancient occult glyphs first penned by Thamar in the years just before her ascension. Whatever their origins, by studying these runes, properly gifted individuals learn to master the arcane arts, able to craft complex formulae which have in turn revealed new runic combinations, some of tremendous power.

and fearsome curses or beneficial and protective blessings, but in all cases, magic was thought to originate from the gods and require their chosen vessels as intermediaries.

Only a few instances of arcane magic can be found before the arrival of the Orgoth, limited primarily to the dark rites and necromancy of Morrdh and several isolated cases of self-empowered occultists. In life, Thamar was counted one of these, and some believe her dogged pursuit of these secrets was the key to her ascension. All the ancient tales of pre-Gift magic include elements of necromancy and infernalism, dark practices drawing on the energies of death and compacts with sinister intelligences from some realm beyond Urcaen.

This legacy of the tainted nature of magic was reinforced by the arrival of the Orgoth, who demonstrated such destructive and corruptive power. The invaders were horrifically profligate in human sacrifices and gathering the souls of the slain to fuel their dark rites and erected black temples to accumulate and store tormented spirits. In the era when the Orgoth dominated, priestly magic from both the Twins and Menoth did little to help the inhabitants of western Immoren resist their oppressors.

It was at this time of despair that the Immorese were given a seed of hope. The so-called Gift of Magic is an event more legendary than factual. But it is widely believed, particularly by occult practitioners, that this "Gift" was made possible by

MAGIC AMONG THE OTHER RACES

The elves of Ios mastered unthinkable arcane energies at a time when mankind still lived in primitive tribes, barely able to build shelters to protect them from the elements. Some of the Iosans' secrets were lost in the aftermath of the collapse of the Bridge of Worlds, but the descendants of Lyoss remain potent masters of the arcane. Iosans do not utilize mechanika but rather their own arcane fabrications called arcanika. These items serve a similar function but operate from very different principles. Iosan sorcerers are more likely to manifest power over fire than cold.

The Nyss evolved their own culture, in which sorcery became a valued and vital aspect of religion. Sorcerers and priests were the only Nyss who learned the written form of Aeric, their language, and this fascination with the written word aided in their mastery of the arcane. Nyss sorcerers are predisposed to ice magic, perhaps as a link to their frozen god.

In Rhul, the gift of the arcane is a rare talent, firmly controlled by the Brand of Odom, a reclusive cabal, well respected by the nation's ruling bodies despite its secretive nature. They closely guard the mysteries of Great Father Odom and take a conservative approach to the use of the arcane, governed by the laws set forth in the Codex. It is the Brand of Odom that controls and oversees the production of Rhulic steamjack cortexes. Among their sorcerers, fire, earth and cold are all relatively common.

The trollkin are unusual among Dhunian species to have a strong affinity for the arcane; sorcerers are born with some frequency among them and are capable of gaining high status in their kriels. Many trollkin sorcerers are born as albinos, their pale skin tone a sign that potent forces await their command. The trollkin have several sorcerous traditions, the most pervasive and organized being among those with the power to shape stone.

Ogrun and gobbers have no affinity for arcane magic and no history of sorcery. The closest they come to working magic is the intuitive grasp on alchemy possessed by many gobbers. Alchemy is an art that allows magic to be released indirectly, by combining substances that have inherent power or that release power in certain mixtures and combinations.

Thamar, Morrow's dark twin, who found a way to grant to humanity powers never bestowed to them by Menoth. Thamar found a way to break this sanction and deliver unto the humans of western Immoren arcane potential.

From this point forward, human sorcerers began to be born with regularity in western Immoren. These intuitive spellcasters wield primal elemental magic and sometimes have difficulty controlling their power. Their emergence was later seen as just a symptom or side-effect of a deeper change that had happened across western Immoren, where now many others were born with the talent to unlock their inner potential to wield magic. Growing groups of arcanists began to study and develop the principles that would become the fundamentals of all modern arcane theory.

Even so, the people of western Immoren retain a conflicted and suspicious attitude toward magic and those who wield it. Through the association with Thamar, human magic unquestionably suffers a dubious reputation, a fact that has occupied many priests, particularly of the Menite faith. And yet without magic, it is likely the current nations and their prosperity would not exist, and that the very religions that view magic with skepticism would have been extinguished amid a continent of slaves.

Most people of the Iron Kingdoms have gradually become more accepting of magic that does not have a divine origin, but it has not been a smooth or steady process. In many remote and rural communities, suspicion of arcanists remains rampant and there is still the widely held belief that all of this power is tainted and turns to evil. In urban centers attitudes are considerably more accepting, given the benefits of mechanika in particular are evident in all walks of life. In these areas, there is more of a distinction between regulated and accepted magic contrasted with those who are seen as dangerous and unprincipled wielders of this power. A number of prominent arcane orders have reputations for being solid and upstanding contributors to their communities, offering their services and wares as would any other crafts guild. Among Morrowans, the practice of magic became more widely accepted after the ascension of Corben. His example is seen as proof that whatever the dark origins of magic, it is a tool that can be put to good use or ill.

Nonetheless, not all magic is accepted, and sorcery in particular has retained a darker reputation due to its spontaneous and often uncontrolled nature. Sorcerers have occasionally been responsible for dramatic accidents in the course of mastering their unpredictable powers. Similarly, it is known that some arcanists turn to the black arts of necromancy and infernalism in their pursuit of unearthly knowledge. All of these groups have endured various degrees of persecution, and ensure that magic is still seen as a potentially insidious practice by the pious.

SORCERERS

Sorcerers are the most intuitive of spellcasters; they are individuals who are born to the arcane without prompting or tutelage. Unfortunately, many are consumed by their own powers before they gain the sophistication to control their deadly gift. Sorcerers are predisposed to the control of one of the elements. Many only manifest their sorcerous powers in the face of extreme danger or stress, or in response to some crisis. A person's first encounter with his own abilities is usually as frightening to him as it is to those who witness it. There are tales of sorcerers consumed within the conflagration of their first poorly channeled spell, destroyed along with whatever enemy had caused them to manifest their lethal powers.

Though the Gift is known to appear spontaneously, it is particularly strong in some hereditary lines. The spark is unpredictable, however, and can die with passing generations just as it can flare to life in new bloodlines. In certain times and places in the past, the persecution of sorcerers was common. Angry mobs have burned more than a few sorcerers at the stake, and despots have given sanction for them to be hunted like dangerous beasts. In the modern era, society has become more accepting, but it is still not unknown to find an accused sorcerer or witch swinging from a tree on the outskirts of some remote village, accused of acts of black magic. Some sorcerers look for acceptance through military service or make use of their talents as adventurers or outlaws.

ARCANISTS

Arcanists are the learned practitioners of the magical arts. Harnessing magic as an arcanist requires a steady hand and a clear and confident mind. Unlike sorcerers, arcanists are drawn to study arcane formulae, which unlocks in them the buried capacity to work magic. That said, some sorcerers eventually feel compelled to adopt a more systematic approach to their magic through training and disciplined study. Arcanists view untrained sorcerers as undisciplined, ignorant, and sloppy

Traditionally trained arcanists begin their study under a mentor, although some brave few have undertaken self-directed studies. Apprenticeship traditions vary widely across western Immoren but usually require thankless years of grueling study, menial labor to instill discipline, and long preparation while learning the fundamentals of magical theory. If an apprentice proves dependable and skilled, he might eventually be inducted into the order of his master. Opting to join a different order is usually perceived as a serious insult and can have serious ramifications. Some orders, like the Greylords Covenant in Khador or the Protectorate's Vassals of Menoth, require membership by practicing arcanists as a matter of law.

The arcane orders of the Iron Kingdoms have attempted to maintain a tight grip on magical knowledge in order to further their own interests. This has resulted in insular habits that promote neither ingenuity nor invention. Although arcanists are considered the foremost experts on abstract magic and its deeper principles, their usefulness in society is sometimes debated. Particularly in the modern era, arcane mechaniks are

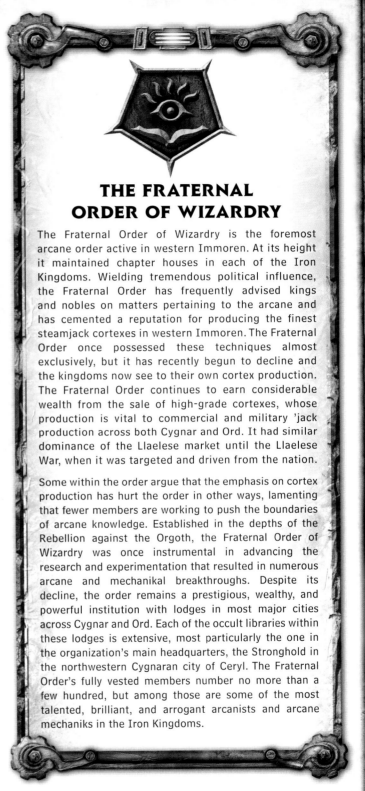

THE FRATERNAL ORDER OF WIZARDRY

The Fraternal Order of Wizardry is the foremost arcane order active in western Immoren. At its height it maintained chapter houses in each of the Iron Kingdoms. Wielding tremendous political influence, the Fraternal Order has frequently advised kings and nobles on matters pertaining to the arcane and has cemented a reputation for producing the finest steamjack cortexes in western Immoren. The Fraternal Order once possessed these techniques almost exclusively, but it has recently begun to decline and the kingdoms now see to their own cortex production. The Fraternal Order continues to earn considerable wealth from the sale of high-grade cortexes, whose production is vital to commercial and military 'jack production across both Cygnar and Ord. It had similar dominance of the Llaelese market until the Llaelese War, when it was targeted and driven from the nation.

Some within the order argue that the emphasis on cortex production has hurt the order in other ways, lamenting that fewer members are working to push the boundaries of arcane knowledge. Established in the depths of the Rebellion against the Orgoth, the Fraternal Order of Wizardry was once instrumental in advancing the research and experimentation that resulted in numerous arcane and mechanikal breakthroughs. Despite its decline, the order remains a prestigious, wealthy, and powerful institution with lodges in most major cities across Cygnar and Ord. Each of the occult libraries within these lodges is extensive, most particularly the one in the organization's main headquarters, the Stronghold in the northwestern Cygnaran city of Ceryl. The Fraternal Order's fully vested members number no more than a few hundred, but among those are some of the most talented, brilliant, and arrogant arcanists and arcane mechaniks in the Iron Kingdoms.

at the forefront of practical innovation, leaving traditionalists behind. Nonetheless, major groups such as the Fraternal Order of Wizardry and the Greylords Covenant possess a wealth of arcane lore and are political and social forces as much as affiliations of like-minded arcanists.

GUN MAGES

In recent centuries a number of arcane specialties have developed to meet the needs of society and the military. One of the most notable is that of the gun mages, arcanists who combine firearm skill with the ability to channel magic through rune-inscribed bullets. Gun mages carry a particular mystique in the minds of the people. To the average citizen, they are seen as romantic figures: dashing officers and arcanists as skilled with their weapons as with magic. In truth, these arcanists practice their magic as a dedicated martial discipline. Two notable orders have arisen to master and pass down their techniques: the Militant Order of the Arcane Tempest in Cygnar, which has been a recognized branch of the Cygnaran Army for several decades; and the Order of the Amethyst Rose, whose remaining members can be found either assisting the Llaelese Resistance or selling their skills for hire.

To fully harness their abilities gun mages make use of special firearms called magelocks, made of an expensive heat-resistant and magically responsive steel alloy. Some might consider a gun mage's reliance on firearms and ammunition to be limiting compared to other arcanists, but the deadly effectiveness of a practiced gun mage in battle is indisputable. Firearms are potent weapons in their own right, but augmented by a gun mage, a magelock pistol becomes an incredibly versatile weapon.

NECROMANCY

Perhaps the oldest of human arcane arts, necromancy is almost universally reviled. Though the actual rituals and practices of these dark arts are veiled in superstition, the horrific reality is known all too well by the people of western Immoren. The Iron Kingdoms are plagued with undead, including restless, vengeful spirits, as well as the shambling creations of necromancers.

There is power to be had if one is willing to delve into the forbidden lore of necromancy, and the kingdoms bear witness to the foul creations and experiments of dark mages. More sinister yet are the organized groups that have made a dedicated study of furthering these dark arts: Thamarite necromancers of the Shroud as well as the necromantic generals of Cryx. These two groups are the foremost experts in this horrid field and are both feared for their knowledge and power.

The necromancers of Cryx, slaved to the twelve lich lords that govern the Nightmare Empire, are each a fulcrum of necromantic power and research. Cryxian necromancers arguably boast a more pervasive and advanced mastery of the necromantic arts than any others, a result of Cryx being one of the few places on Caen where this magic is openly practiced. Cryxian necromancers want for nothing—corpses, living victims, terrible ichors, forbidden tomes, and even the blood and knowledge of Toruk himself are all within their grasp.

Though Cryx casts a long shadow over Immoren, there are subtler threats originating within the Iron Kingdoms themselves. Even independent practitioners of the necromantic arts may possess formidable power. The Thamarite Shroud sept in particular has a wealth of necromantic lore drawn from centuries of occult

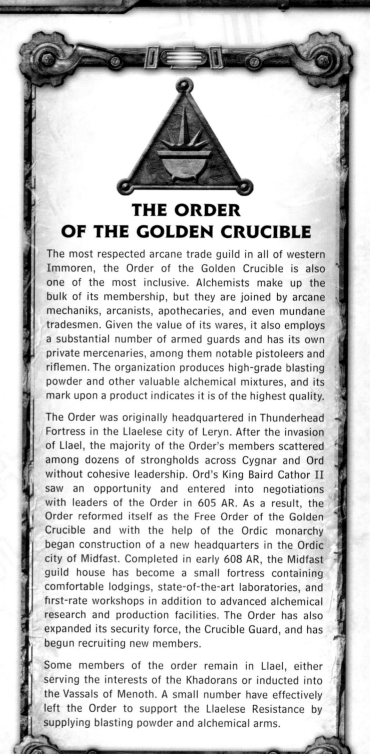

THE ORDER OF THE GOLDEN CRUCIBLE

The most respected arcane trade guild in all of western Immoren, the Order of the Golden Crucible is also one of the most inclusive. Alchemists make up the bulk of its membership, but they are joined by arcane mechaniks, arcanists, apothecaries, and even mundane tradesmen. Given the value of its wares, it also employs a substantial number of armed guards and has its own private mercenaries, among them notable pistoleers and riflemen. The organization produces high-grade blasting powder and other valuable alchemical mixtures, and its mark upon a product indicates it is of the highest quality.

The Order was originally headquartered in Thunderhead Fortress in the Llaelese city of Leryn. After the invasion of Llael, the majority of the Order's members scattered among dozens of strongholds across Cygnar and Ord without cohesive leadership. Ord's King Baird Cathor II saw an opportunity and entered into negotiations with leaders of the Order in 605 AR. As a result, the Order reformed itself as the Free Order of the Golden Crucible and with the help of the Ordic monarchy began construction of a new headquarters in the Ordic city of Midfast. Completed in early 608 AR, the Midfast guild house has become a small fortress containing comfortable lodgings, state-of-the-art laboratories, and first-rate workshops in addition to advanced alchemical research and production facilities. The Order has also expanded its security force, the Crucible Guard, and has begun recruiting new members.

Some members of the order remain in Llael, either serving the interests of the Khadorans or inducted into the Vassals of Menoth. A small number have effectively left the Order to support the Llaelese Resistance by supplying blasting powder and alchemical arms.

study dating back not only to Thamar herself but also Scion Delesle, who was the terror of the Menite priesthood. Those who practice these forbidden arts are in a constant state of war with those who would stop them, such as the Morrowan Order of Illumination, and these battles sometimes spill over onto innocent victims amid the dark alleyways of major cities.

INFERNALISM

The study and invocation of infernal entities is a discipline more blasphemous and feared than necromancy. Few are mad or desperate enough to truck with these creatures from realms beyond Caen and Urcaen. Contacting the infernals is perilous, and those who possess the knowledge guard it jealously. Despite having learned how to summon infernal creatures, bind them into service, and make terrible bargains with them, infernalists often know little about the creatures themselves or what deeper desires they may foster beyond a hunger for the souls of the living. Most infernalists are arcanists who have opened a font of power that grants them frightening and terrible gifts. The price is invariably paid in souls, and infernalists often barter pieces of their own essence as well as selling souls stolen from others The dreadful actions of infernalists have magnified the suspicion and distrust heaped on all who practice magic, making them as hated by other magic practitioners as by the pious.

ALCHEMY & APOTHECARIES

Alchemy, the synthesis of arcane formulae with the systematic study of naturally occurring elements, chemicals, and substances, is one of the most diverse and respected arts in all the Iron Kingdoms. Alchemical salves, unguents, and potions are used to address all manner of needs. A learned student of alchemy can produce solutions to quicken the healing of dire wounds, produce useful acids and distillations, or subtly poison even the most vigilant of victims. Alchemy is a vital component of modern industry, as many technological, metallurgical, and mechanikal marvels of the modern day require the use of alchemical processes.

The study of alchemy began millennia ago in arts practiced by tribal shamans seeking primitive medicines from naturally occurring plants and animal parts. As they experimented with substances available from nature many tribes accumulated a thorough knowledge of the world around them. Eventually this study became formalized by apothecaries, naturalists, and poisoners. This field was already thriving in the Thousand Cities Era but truly came into its own during the decades before and after the Rebellion, playing a key role in the development of mechanika and assisting in countless industrial tasks.

Scholarly practitioners experiment with naturally occurring substances and produce many of the mundane reagents needed in the manufacture of more advanced alchemical substances. For the most part, apothecaries deal in the creation and extraction of naturally occurring acids, antitoxins, purgatives, and other medicinal aids and poisons. The study of poison is essential to understanding medicine, although the occurrence of opportunists specializing in this field in order to supply would-be assassins has given some apothecaries a dubious reputation.

Today's alchemists are professionals and innovators whose services are in high demand. The best among them may join powerful trade guilds or serve their kingdom's war industry. Many aid in the fabrication of mechanikal accumulators and other essential components. The creation of blasting powder and other explosives for munitions has become highly valued in both commercial and military markets. Other alchemists prefer to make their livings as private dealers of medicinal alchemical substances. Some open permanent shops, while those with less coin (or shadier reputations) travel from town to town by wagon to hock their wares.

MECHANIKA

Of all the benefits of magic that have come to western Immoren, it is mechanika, the synthesis of the arcane and the mechanical, that has had the most profound impact. Mechanika has revolutionized industry and warfare in every way imaginable, and its innovators continue to create new marvels. Utilizing magic to overcome engineering obstacles, mechanika allows for the reliable production of tools and weapons that harness arcane energies and apply them in useful ways. Many gifted individuals make their livings as arcane mechaniks, practicing industrial thaumaturgy to craft potent devices.

The merging of magic and technology began in the midst of the Orgoth Occupation, in the work of arcanists and alchemists seeking weapons by which to defeat their oppressors. The first applications of the arcane to mundane mechanical items arose from Sebastien Kerwin's early theories and research into the formalization of arcane formulae. Kerwin had proposed that arcane energies could be harnessed through the application of such runic formulae to specially crafted components made from rare and precious metals. Eventually these efforts led to the first functioning mechanika devices. Crude by modern standards, these items nonetheless contained the most fundamental component of all mechanikal devices: the accumulator.

The first accumulators, massive and bulky, were anything but portable, housed in immense, porcelain-lined vats. The result of hundreds of years of scientific progress and experimentation, modern accumulators are much more efficient, capable of storing vast amounts of arcane energy. A small accumulator easily fits in the palm of a hand and holds enough energy to power mechanikal weapons or armor.

Alchemy also delivered the next mechanikal innovation. Sebastien Kerwin's notes described attempts to transcribe mystical runes used to control magic, in which he quickly discovered that parchment burst into flame if such written runes were empowered. Seeking a more durable solution, he hypothesized it should be possible to inscribe arcane formulae into specially treated steel and then empower the runes by channeling accumulator charges through the plate. While it would not be confirmed until generations after his death, this hypothesis proved to be true, resulting in the development of runeplates. As Kerwin theorized, a mechanika user can trigger the plate's captive arcane force by channeling energy through the plate using an accumulator. Inscribing runes on moving parts with interlocking gears and coils has led to even more sophisticated inventions, such as the arcane turbines used in warcaster armor.

All this development has given birth to new disciplines. Any good mechanik can assemble and maintain a piece of mechanika, but, arcane mechaniks—the leaders in this rapidly growing field—focus on creative and innovative utilizations of runeplates and more specialized components.

STEAMJACKS

To most citizens, steamjacks are but one of the greatest modern mechanikal wonders, but their impact is far-reaching, as their use has revolutionized warfare, industry, and agriculture. Laborjacks work in logging camps, freight yards, docks, and construction sites throughout western Immoren, and every citizen of the Iron Kingdoms is familiar with the fearsome warjacks—steamjacks armed with dedicated military weaponry and possessing the highest grades of cortexes. Wherever they are found, steamjacks embody progress in the modern age.

NECROTECH

The necromancers of the Cryxian Empire acquired the secrets of mechanika from the mainland. After stealing the corpses of arcane mechaniks and arcanists, they were able to compel the dead to share their secrets. In just a few decades the servants of Cryx had not only learned the fundamentals of fabricating mechanika but also managed to modify and improve these processes to suit their own methods. By using necromantic shortcuts, they were able to craft their devices more quickly, giving birth to a hideous fusion of mechanika and the magic of death, an arcane science known as necrotech. The existence of this dark science is abhorrent in the eyes of the mainland kingdoms, and the use of such technologies there is punishable by death.

Necrotechs also benefit from access to sources of fuel and energy too grotesque for others to consider. The foul mineral called necrotite, found in grounds thick with carnage and resonating with atrocity, is one example. Extremely concentrated, it functions similarly to coal but is able to burn far longer. Necrotite is as toxic as it is efficient, however, and both the smoke and the residue produced from burning it is harmful to the living.

Necrotechs have also toyed with older, darker power sources, including those adapted from the Orgoth. One of these inherited pieces of nefarious technology is the soul cage, a device that captures and imprisons souls freed from the body during death and trapping them indefinitely until they can be tormented and drained to fuel other necromantic devices.

These constructs combine all the principals of mechanika. The melding of magic and industry in their manufacture shows how well the two disciplines can together create something truly amazing. Steam-driven engines power metal chassis driven by a cortex, the steamjack's mechanikal brain. Though not as smart or adaptable as people, steamjacks do possess a native intelligence and the ability to solve specific sorts of problems, which makes them incredibly valuable as heavy laborers. 'Jacks that see prolonged use typically develop quirks and even distinct personalities that may reflect the proclivities of their operators.

While these iron giants are expensive to manufacture, their industrial applications are so varied that all the nations of western Immoren consider them indispensable for a wide range of tasks. Laborjacks are the backbone of Cygnar's and Ord's transportation and mercantile efforts, making it possible to move goods in massive crates and handling containers, increasing commercial efficiency. In Khador, the tireless creations work in massive forges pounding metal plates and other parts for locomotives, steamjack manufacture, and other heavy industry. While the Protectorate has prioritized producing warjacks over laborjacks, the latter can still be found assisting in construction efforts and other heavy tasks, and such machines can quickly be armed if the need arises. Khador and Cygnar are the two largest producers of commercial and military steamjacks, although both Ord and the Protectorate have dedicated 'jack foundries as well. Llael was the smallest producer of 'jacks before it was invaded, but its foundries are now under the control of its occupiers.

WARCASTERS

Few in number, warcasters are powerful arcanists born with the innate ability to mentally contact and control the cortexes within steamjacks. Their intuitive connection to the arcane also enables them to bond with other mechanikal devices, providing vessels for their channeled power. Warcasters are much sought after by the militaries of the Iron Kingdoms for their martial and magical prowess.

Most warcasters begin experiencing extraordinary perception of the world before they realize the nature of their gift. Their senses begin to awaken to the flows of mystical energy around them, and some may start to feel a strange sensation near advanced mechanika as their minds detect the energy moving through conduits and runic formulae. Such power can lie dormant for a lifetime; only through rigorous training and mentoring can a warcaster's potential be fully unlocked. Developing these skills requires tutelage that is nearly impossible to find outside of a kingdom's military or one of the major mercenary companies where a fledgling warcaster can find a mentor capable of instructing him in the finer points of controlling his power.

While not all who have this ability are eager to join the military, warcasters enjoy a revered station in any army. The militaries of the Iron Kingdoms expend considerable resources to equip their warcasters with steam-powered and mechanically augmented armor, which affords them far better protection than most soldiers of similar rank. Warcaster armor

THE CORTEX

One of the greatest early mechanikal inventions was the cerebral matrix, which was subsequently refined into the cortex. This artificial mind can give life to a steam-powered automaton and allow it to respond to commands. As it accumulates experiences a cortex is capable of slowly learning over time, although this can lead to unexpected quirks as well as improved performance.

The cortex serves as the intermediary between a steamjack's chassis and the sensory apparatus by which it perceives its environment. 'Jacks rely on vision and sound to react to the world and are usually designed to operate within a specific environment, such as a factory, a dockyard, or the battlefield. Although they may seem quite clever when focused on a familiar task, cortexes of the simplest grades do not adapt well to unfamiliar environments and require supervision when operating out of their element.

A laborjack might adroitly handle even fragile crates and perceive when a damaged one requires attention from its handler. All 'jacks can discern the identities of their handlers by appearance and voice and are generally capable of reacting to unexpected threats. Steamjacks with higher-grade cortexes can handle a wider variety of environments and are better at acting with limited instructions, although they still have limits. A warjack is extremely skilled at recognizing friend from foe on the battlefield and negotiating obstacles to seek its targets but is more likely to require supervision on a bustling city street where danger is not always easily apparent.

utilizes an arcane turbine to provide a constant flow of energy used to reduce the perceived weight of the armor and generate a protective power field.

The presence of a single warcaster can turn the tide of a battle. Even the most powerful and sophisticated warjack can perform only a limited number of combat functions under the guidance of a 'jack marshal, but a warcaster can command warjacks like finely tuned instruments of war, often controlling many of the devastating machines at one time.

Due to the tremendous powers they harness and the importance of their role, each nation's warcasters seem larger than life to its citizens who most often do not understand the difficulty of their jobs and the stresses under which they operate. The more famous warcasters, known by name across their kingdoms, are treated as heroes.

RELIGION

While the modern era has brought many changes from the spread of industrialization, urbanization, and greater education, the importance of religion in peoples' lives is undiminished. Religious institutions form a bedrock of stability for the cultures of western Immoren and help define the deeper beliefs of their inhabitants, shaping views on morality, spirituality, and the hopes and fears regarding the afterlife. The most successful religions of western Immoren have adapted over the centuries to accommodate evolving societies, and every era has experienced the rise of new faiths and cults that threaten established beliefs.

While most people outside the clergy do not spend much of their daily lives in religious contemplation, the faith of a person's upbringing has a major impact on attitudes toward neighbors and outsiders. Levels of piety vary widely, from near indifference to absolute devotion, but even less pious citizens may turn to spiritual leaders during life transitions, like weddings and funerals. Major churches and temples exercise considerable social and political influence, while subversive cults work to advance secret agendas while hiding from those who would hunt them. Unsettling supernatural events plague western Immoren, including the insidious plots of otherworldly infernals, necromantic horrors rising from despoiled graveyards at the behest of necromancers, and attacks by monstrous creatures lurking beyond the city walls. These dangers lend gravity to the admonitions the clergy deliver during religious services.

No one doubts the existence of the gods or their influence on the world, even the obstinately impious. Priests can invoke power through ritual, and their prayers have tangible and irrefutable impact, whether through withering curses, blessings during battle, or small miracles that reduce the suffering of the diseased or infirmed. Witnessed acts of divine intervention, while rare, have been recorded often enough over the centuries to become accepted as fact. Superstition is widespread, particularly among the less educated and in the rural quarters. In many areas, belief and superstition mingle to create customs that bear little resemblance to sanctioned religious practices yet have no less importance to those practicing them.

The tremendous diversity of religious sects and practices across western Immoren can lead to dangerous misunderstandings. Religion can be a comfort against a hostile world but can also prompt violence and bloodshed between faiths. Local laws and social pressures reduce such incidents, but they still occasionally erupt. Those of like beliefs tend to congregate and avoid those whose faith offends them, although in the larger cities it is common for citizens of different faiths to coexist in close proximity. Sometimes an otherwise peaceful town is thrown into religious uproar over unexpected events at home or abroad. In even the most civilized kingdoms, persecution of sorcerers and overly zealous witch-hunting is remembered, and not everyone believes such extreme measures are unwarranted.

On the other hand, churches and temples serve as vital gathering places where citizens of different classes can discuss the issues of the day as well as conduct important rites of passage. Often the climate of a given community can be gauged by what transpires at houses of worship. During times of war, families gather to honor the fallen dead, complain about the choices of nobles and kings, and point fingers of blame at shared enemies and clamor for action. The priests who lead congregations wield considerable power to either reassure the faithful or fan the flames of zealotry.

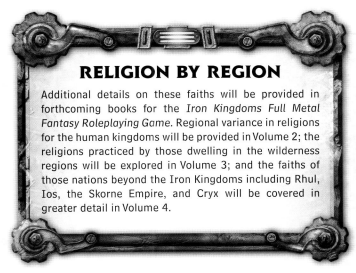

RELIGION BY REGION

Additional details on these faiths will be provided in forthcoming books for the *Iron Kingdoms Full Metal Fantasy Roleplaying Game*. Regional variance in religions for the human kingdoms will be provided in Volume 2; the religions practiced by those dwelling in the wilderness regions will be explored in Volume 3; and the faiths of those nations beyond the Iron Kingdoms including Rhul, Ios, the Skorne Empire, and Cryx will be covered in greater detail in Volume 4.

DOMINANT FAITHS OF THE IRON KINGDOMS

There are two broadly accepted religions among the nations of mankind, represented by the Church of Morrow and the Temple of Menoth. The relationship between these religions is complex and has changed over the centuries, alternating between periods of relatively stable peace and ones of strife and violence. Usually the tensions between these religions are more subtle. In most large communities, members of these faiths have learned to coexist.

Exclusive communities exist, particularly in the Protectorate of Menoth, a nation arising from a religious schism in Cygnar and one that is nearly exclusively Menite. Even in communities such as these there can be differences in beliefs and the possibility of multiple sects. People attending a specific church or temple share similar beliefs, but those beliefs may be starkly different from the ones held by people attending church in another quarter of the same town. Any sizable town or city will have dozens of smaller churches and temples and usually a larger cathedral, central temple, or abbey that is overseen by the highest-ranking priest of the community's majority faith. In cities with multiple sects, this hierarchy is less clear, and some priests may act independently.

The worship of Menoth is particularly ancient, as this god is the Creator of Man. In many regions, however, this faith began to diminish as it was replaced by the rapid spread of the Morrowan faith after the ascension of the Twins. The Menite religion entered a drastic decline during the Orgoth Occupation, when the oppressed population increasingly turned to the comforting teachings of Morrow.

Morrowans do not consider themselves opposed to Menoth, whom they acknowledge as humanity's Creator, but they have chosen to entrust their spiritual wellbeing to Morrow and his priests. The Morrowan belief in free will and personal accountability combined with the sympathetic examples of the various ascendants prompted the rapid spread of this faith across western Immoren. The Morrowan faith is presently the majority religion in Cygnar, Ord, Occupied Llael, and Khador.

Many historians believe the advances in engineering and mechanika that define the modern age were made possible only after the teachings of the Twins, which promoted critical thinking and challenged old beliefs. Menite theologians argue instead that these faiths gave rise to widespread corruption and exposed mankind to insidious and unholy influences. There may be truth in both perspectives. Morrow's dark twin, Thamar, is a pervasive shadow in every Morrowan community, with her worshipers and teachings existing in those places Morrow's light cannot reach. The Twins remain philosophically connected, and it is impossible to examine the faith of one without the other.

THE CHURCH OF MORROW

Across western Immoren, the Church of Morrow is indisputably the dominant faith, with a sizable majority in every human kingdom except the Protectorate of Menoth. Khador is the only kingdom with a substantial minority of Menites, but even there Empress Vanar is a recognized Morrowan and the church has tremendous reach and influence. Ord and Cygnar both recognize the Church of Morrow as their state religions, as did Llael when it was independent. The Morrowan faith emphasizes the individual as a potential agency of good and stresses how each person can contribute to society. Its beliefs resonate with people in many walks of life and social strata, advocating improvement through self-reflection, good works, honorable conduct, and self-sacrifice.

Core to the Morrowan faith is the idea of Volition—that every person in life makes choices that determine whether they will be a force for positive empowerment or for selfish gain. By association, pious Morrowans are seen as good and reliable citizens while those who succumb to the "dark path" of Thamar are seen as evil, self-serving, and destructive. This is a simplistic reduction of the subtleties of Morrow's and Thamar's respective philosophies, but clear distinctions appeal to the masses. The more nuanced aspects of the Twins are left to theologians and scholars. Before his ascension, Morrow was both a philosopher and a soldier, a thinker who endorsed the virtues of peace but who allowed that armed conflict was sometimes necessary. The Morrowan faith teaches that honor can be maintained amid violent strife if applied judiciously, such as to defend the

network of contacts and spies to keep its leaders well informed of matters abroad. The heart of the Church of Morrow, the Sancteum, is a sovereign nation with its own armory, soldiers, and warjacks dedicated to protecting the faith, its clergy, and its holy sites. Lower-ranking priests are spiritual bastions for local congregations, while the highest-ranking ones stand as trusted advisors to nobles and sovereigns.

CHURCH HIERARCHY

One of the great strengths of the Church of Morrow is its extremely cohesive and inclusive hierarchy, allowing it to function as a single body despite being spread across multiple nations and being arguably the most pervasive human organization in western Immoren. While there are many individual interpretations of Morrow's message nearly all are welcomed into the larger hierarchy. Only a few unusually radical reinterpretations of the message of the Twins have been excluded from being recognized as official arms of the Church. Individual priests within the hierarchy are given considerable leeway in following their own paths to enlightenment and finding a personal connection to Morrow and his ascendants.

Individual churches are similarly given considerable autonomy but are supported by the larger hierarchy. Such a large organization requires a sizable bureaucracy, handled by priests with an aptitude for administration as well as pious laypersons chosen for the task. There is regular correspondence between church leaders and their superiors. In the aggregate these reports provide the Church's hierarchy with a high degree of awareness of events occurring across the Iron Kingdoms. Kingdoms. Ranking church officers and their clerks make decisions based on incoming reports as well as personal inspections and determine when additional support or shifts in personnel might be required. For example, a local priest who suspects a cult of Thamarites in his community would send an urgent plea to his superiors for assistance, who might in turn hand the matter over to the dedicated witch hunters of the Order of Illumination, who would then dispatch an armed investigative force.

As the center of this faith, the Sancteum in Caspia is afforded sovereign status as a state in its own right, a courtesy afforded to church grounds across the Iron Kingdoms. Although it prefers to remain neutral in ongoing wars, the Church has considerable military might and can field small armies fully equipped with modern mechanika and warjacks if need be. Most of this armed might is housed in the Sancteum, but elements of its arsenal may be sent abroad to protect cathedrals or commit to battles

helpless. Morrow insisted the better side of man's nature could rise to the fore even amid the bloodiest of conflicts. This allows his message to have impact in times of both peace and war and to appeal to soldiers as well as those they protect.

The preeminent status of the Church of Morrow is a relatively recent phenomenon; before the arrival of the Orgoth this faith existed with the reluctant sufferance of, and occasional bloody clashes with, members of the Menite temples. Morrowans look back on that time as a period of religious oppression, when they were forced to pay burdensome tithes and attend Menite temples despite their true beliefs. They were quick to reverse this situation after the Orgoth were driven from Immoren. Since the Corvis Treaties were signed, the Church of Morrow has worked to unravel the hold the Menite clergy maintained over the ruling castes of the various kingdoms.

These efforts have largely succeeded, with the Morrowan church now holding primacy of religion outside the Protectorate and having tremendous sway over all walks of life, from commoner to noble and among laborer and scholar alike. The church has a hand in kingdom politics and cultivates its own formidable deemed vital to the Church's interests. The Church's size and scope make it difficult for the organization to act quickly or decisively to intervene in foreign matters, as any action it can take is likely to be opposed by some branch of its membership.

The current leader of the Church of Morrow is Primarch Arius, who rarely leaves the Sancteum—or even the Archcourt Cathedral, which is his ecclesiastical seat. Primarch is a lifelong position, and new primarchs are elevated only after the death of their predecessors. They are selected through a display of divine approval that includes a manifestation of archons representing the Host of Morrow. This gives the primarch a degree of authority rarely found in other faiths, but each is nonetheless a mortal who serves as best he can, making the crucial decisions for this far-flung faith. Primarch Arius has close ties to the Cygnaran government, being a mentor and personal advisor to King Leto Raelthorne. Because of this, some foreigners consider him too careful of Cygnaran interests and biased against Morrowans of other nations, especially Khador. His detractors are vocal but have been largely ineffective in changing the situation. For the moment the Church of Morrow seems strongly invested in the security and safety of Cygnar. Arius is an aged priest, and eventually mortality will claim him, necessitating another to take his place.

The primarch is aided in governing the church by the Exordeum, a governing body of thirty-six leading priests with the lifelong rank of Exarch who manage the majority of day-to-day matters. While they also convene and dwell within the Sancteum, the exarchs are drawn from across the Iron Kingdoms and include prominent members from Khador, Ord, and the Llaelese region. Exarchs are appointed by the primarch to replace those who die—or, rarely, those who withdraw from the post. The dictates and decrees of the Exordeum are passed to vicars who are the seniormost priests dwelling outside the Sancteum and who oversee sizable regions called vicarates. Most vicars are organized into Vicarate Councils, each composed of seven vicars, which are present in many major cities, including: Caspia, Ceryl, Fharin, and Mercir in Cygnar; Merywyn in Llael; Merin in Ord; and Khardov, Korsk, Ohk, and Skirov in Khador. Answering to these councils are the prelates and high prelates who oversee Church business in individual cities and towns, taking care to ensure myriad smaller churches are adequately staffed and tending to the faithful. The church also counts among its membership hundreds of battle-chaplains, members of the military in multiple nations who serve as soldiers while performing church services, tending to the injured, and providing last rites.

THE ENKHEIRIDION AND ITS MYSTERIES

The Enkheiridion is a complex and difficult sacred text that contains the writings of both Morrow and Thamar accumulated before their respective ascensions. These ancient books include many deliberately cryptic passages. The original Enkheiridion was written in Old Caspian and is kept in the Archcourt Cathedral of the Sancteum. Immediately after their ascensions, Thamar's and Morrow's writings were lost. It was several centuries before they were restored by the woman who would become Ascendant Angellia, who compiled them in their present form. Asc. Angellia was also the first to copy and translate the texts into formal Caspian, which at the time was the language preferred by the educated. Modern copies of the Enkheiridion are copied by hand from Angellia's text—itself a sacred relic—to preserve its complex inscriptions, notations, illuminated pages, and intricate symbols. In Khador a similarly precious translation of the original book exists in Khurzic, translated by Khardic Angellian monks.

Due to the cost to produce these tomes as well as the nature of the ancient languages, the Enkheiridion is not accessible to the common layperson. The text is studied by clergy or university educated scholars. Morrowan priests have long warned against allowing untrained laity from reading Thamar's portion of the Enkheiridion in particular, as Thamar's teachings are considered highly subversive and dangerous to unprepared minds.

The religious text commonly used by the vast majority of the faithful is a heavily abridged and translated catechism. Varying slightly by region, catechisms are written in the common vernacular tongues, such as Cygnaran, Ordic, Llaelese, or Khadoran, and are produced by church printing presses. The most widely available catechisms focus almost exclusively on Morrow's teachings and include only a select few passages from Thamar to highlight the Volition. They also include tracts written by later ascendants, particularly Asc. Angellia and Asc. Rowan. Some catechisms include explanatory notations by revered theologians.

Different Morrowan sects emphasize different passages of this holy text or focus on a specific ascendant as a lens for understanding Morrow's philosophies. The most widely read collection of Morrowan doctrine is the *Prayers for Battle*, a tome focusing on Morrow's life as a soldier as well as lore about the Martial Trinity of Ascendants: Asc. Katrena, Asc. Solovin, and Asc. Markus. *Prayers for Battle* describes honorable conduct in warfare and the last rites for those who die by violence. This book is favored by pious Morrowan soldiers and is fundamental to martial orders allied to the Church of Morrow. A less widely distributed collection called *The Flickering Flame* is required reading by agents of the Order of Illumination and includes passages by Asc. Corben and Asc. Solovin but also a large number of Thamarite references, including tracts by Scion Ekris, Sc. Delesle, and Sc. Nivara in addition to Thamar herself. This collection is deemed vital to witch-hunters but is kept within the order lest its contents encourage the profane cults the order battles.

A number of specialized groups and orders serve the Church. Dozens of regional martial orders exist to protect holy grounds and cathedrals, one of the most prominent being the Precursor Knights of Cygnar, members of which sometimes march to war alongside the Cygnaran Army. The Order of Keeping is a monastic and reclusive branch interested in the preservation and protection of the Church's greatest relics and secrets, and its well-armed and armored knights sometimes serve as bodyguards for high-ranking priests. The Church has sanction to root out organized Thamarite sects as well as those practicing the dark arts of necromancy and infernalism and is aided in this capacity by the Order of Illumination, a powerful and militant group of witch-hunters and pious arcanists. The Exordeum and the primarch are extremely well informed about current events abroad by their vast network of contacts and informants, including those stationed in high office. Intelligence gathering is overseen by the Llaelese Exarch Dargule, one of Primarch Arius' most trusted confidants.

THE CHURCH WITHIN THE COMMUNITY

In most of western Immoren, when a person speaks of going to church or attending to prayers, it is presumed they are speaking of Morrowan services. Small churches of Morrow are numerous in most cities, excepting those few townships that are exclusively Menite. Generally there is a church or sheltered shrine for every few hundred Morrowans. In some cases the faithful may be tended by a pious lay preacher rather than a consecrated member of the clergy with formal religious training.

Larger and more established churches become centers of their communities and are among the most impressive and well-built structures in their townships. These are usually assigned at least one ordained priest, along with supporting novices and pious volunteers who attend to the grounds, cooking, and other needs. Ordained priests vary widely in temperament and intelligence, depending on their natural gifts. By and large priests are literate and well educated, being versed in Morrowan philosophy, history, law, and extensive study of the Enkheiridion, the sacred text of the faith.

Priests are expected to make themselves available to their congregation to advise them on matters of spirituality and morality in addition to conducting regular services and performing significant ceremonies. Funeral rites are deemed one of the most important and essential of Morrowan services, particularly in recent years, as the evidence of the misuse of corpses through necromancy has been on the rise.

Through training and faith, priests can pray to manifest small miracles, acts of sacred magic that can be a boon to their community. This includes attending to the injured and diseased. These efforts are limited; despite the expectations of the suffering, priests cannot erase all illness or affliction with the wave of a hand. Morrowan priests following the example of Asc. Solovin are well versed in the mundane aspects of caring for the wounded, such as splinting broken bones, binding cuts, and applying alchemical salves to cleanse wounds and prevent infection. Such priests can lend their prayers to quicken the healing process, but primarily for superficial injuries. In most cases a body must heal naturally, and particularly grievous wounds require extended bed rest even when closely attended by the most capable of Morrowan healers. Truly miraculous healing requires the direct intervention of the divine, which rarely happens and can only be invoked by the most spiritually potent priests when the need is tantamount for the common good. Such great miracles usually come with unpredictable repercussions, as the raw energy of the divine does not easily manifest on Caen.

A priest does not have the time or ability to attend to every injury or complaint among his congregation and must manage expectations. In large cities major churches are inundated by those seeking assistance, requiring strict policies to maintain public order while providing charitable aid. These policies vary from church to church and priest to priest, with those emulating Asc. Rowan being the most accommodating to the masses. Overworked priests may refer petitioners to neighboring churches or recommend nearby apothecaries or physicians.

Each community is expected to donate time and funds toward the upkeep of local churches, although the clergy prefers voluntary donations and does not impose strict tithes—a point of differentiation with Menite temples. Major construction projects or commissions for significant works of sacred art, stained glass, or sculpture are supported by funds drawn from the Sancteum treasury, often augmented by sizable donations from sponsoring local nobles. Supporting the church is expected of landed nobles, who gain good will among the common people and preferential treatment for burial rites and entombment. In regions where Church leaders are actively involved in politics, having the sympathy of the clergy can be of pragmatic value.

Among the greatest works of architecture in the modern age are the massive cathedrals of the Church of Morrow, found in many major cities, with notable examples in the capitals of Cygnar, Khador, Ord, and Llael. These vary considerably in style and ornamentation, drawing on the regional cultures where they stand, but most are intricately ornamented and set with gargoyles and other statuary depicting legends from the long history of the faith. The Archcourt Cathedral in the Sancteum—which houses the primarch and the Exordeum— was built just before the arrival of the Orgoth and is counted a wonder of western Immoren. The construction of cathedrals and major abbeys are tremendous works, requiring decades of labor by hundreds of craftsmen and thousands of laborers.

These structures are major attractions for their cities, drawing an influx of pious pilgrims and other visitors, thus supporting commerce in the city. Many of these cathedrals preserve relics of the faith, items of great historical and spiritual significance, often associated with specific ascendants or notable holy priests. Only a handful of relics of Morrow himself exist, and these are preserved either in the Sancteum or in the hidden Divinium, the old seat of the Morrowan Church. The wonders of the Sancteum bring hundreds of thousands of pilgrims to Caspia every year, along with donations and vows of support. Major holidays like the Ascension Feast draw additional worshipers, pilgrims, and funds.

Smaller churches in remote areas may be more modest, but the Church of Morrow as a whole is an extremely wealthy

WITCHCRAFT AND BLACK MAGIC

Witchcraft and black magic are legal terms in the Iron Kingdoms that can be acted upon by the authorities, particularly the Order of Illumination, which has a mandate given by the Morrowan Church to investigate and persecute offenders. A witch is defined as an individual who is practicing black magic, a charge that can carry severe penalties, including execution.

Within the Morrowan Church, black magic and witchcraft have traditionally been defined by the primarch and Exordeum. The current standard is any magic used for the following:

1) Infernalism—the practice of communicating with and negotiating with infernal entities.

2) Necromancy—the practice of animating the dead, interfering with the immortal soul, or using magic that draws in whole or in part on the energies released by death or suffering.

3) Mesmerism—any magic that interferes with free will by forcing a person to make decisions or actions not their own.

The third category is the most difficult to prove or disprove and is consequently the most rarely utilized in accusations. This definition has sometimes been deemed inadequate by specific sovereigns or other authorities, who have implemented broader stipulations. For example, during the reign of Vinter Raelthorne IV, the Inquisition in Cygnar created an extremely broad standard for witchcraft that included anyone born a sorcerer, though there was special dispensation given to those employed by the Cygnaran military. The Inquisition did not leave these matters to the Church but conducted its own investigations and was notorious for its excesses, as virtually anyone could be accused of and executed for witchcraft, even those incapable of magic.

organization. Ranking priests allocate this wealth to broadening the reach of the faith through the construction of new temples, shrines, and cathedrals as well as printing and distributing religious texts and fostering charitable works. Considerable funds are also spent on special branches of the church responsible for its protection, including its own well-armed soldiers and groups like the Order of Order of Illumination. In addition to remaining ever vigilant for signs of infernalism, the Illuminated Order is also a prime reason the Church has remained free of widespread corruption despite its wealth, for it sees that senior Church officers are subjected to scrutiny and regular tests of piety. These efforts have largely eliminated self-serving pretenders, so while it is possible for priests to be lured down the wrong path of the Volition, compromised individuals rarely reach the upper ranks. Scandals over local priests corrupting Morrowan philosophies are dealt with swiftly by Illuminated agents while rumors are quashed by the church hierarchy, often with the help of pious nobles.

Most people view the Church of Morrow as a positive, benevolent organization. The criticisms it does receive are most often for simply not doing enough. There are many who clamor for the Church to exercise its power to intervene in specific kingdoms. The Church has a history of neutrality in times of war, rarely participating in the conflicts except to defend its holy sites. Regional biases are nevertheless inevitable, which has sometimes threatened the cohesiveness of the church leadership. Ranking members of the clergy are eager to avoid a schism, but the divide between the northern and southern church is expanding.

While unified by a single hierarchy, the Morrowan faith is far from homogenous, differing considerably by region and particularly by nation. These distinctions can be seen at every level, from church architecture to worship rites and holy days. Such differences can cause friction between the faithful of different sects, but they illustrate an essential part of the Morrowan philosophy.

ASCENDANTS AND ARCHONS OF MORROW

Caught up in the trials and tribulations of ordinary life, most who follow the faiths of Morrow and Thamar—even exceptionally pious priests who give their lives to worship—have no expectation of ascending themselves. In the centuries that followed the Twins' lives, however, some exceptional few rose to prominence and paved their own paths to ascension. Those associated with Morrow are known as ascendants and are revered as saint-like paragons; those linked to Thamar are called scions, seen by outsiders as unholy beings that spread corruption to mortal minds, yet to Thamarites honored as singularly holy and proof of the myriad routes to enlightenment. These beings are not treated as gods by either faith, being subordinate to Morrow or Thamar, but are vital intermediaries with the divine.

After ascension, each individual became part of the religious canon, held as examples to demonstrate the vastly different ways in which both Morrow's and Thamar's teachings could be interpreted. The rise of a new ascendant or scion is a major and exceptionally rare historical and theological event. Each of the spectacular miracles by which the ascendants have transformed into divinity has demonstrated the proof of Morrow's teachings and provided an ideal toward which the pious strive. Scions are seen by Morrowans as proof that the dark twin continues to exert her own insidious influence on the world.

The ascendants play a vital role in Morrowan worship, and many individual churches and cathedrals are dedicated to one or more of them. Most Morrowans see them as approachable and comprehensible examples of their faith. The ascendants are thought to hear prayers closely tied to their spheres of influence and on extremely rare occasions have even

SYMBOLS AND PATRONAGES OF THE ASCENDANTS OF MORROW

In addition to their use as ascendant talismans, the symbols of the ascendants are sometimes imprinted, embossed, or engraved on items associated with their areas of patronage. Religious books bear on their spines the symbol of Asc. Angellia. Asc. Corben's symbol can be found on alchemical formulae. Battlefield hospital tents or rooms set aside to attend the sick or dying bear Asc. Solovin's mark. Asc. Markus' symbol is found on keystones of city arches and gates, Asc. Doleth's symbol is branded into the prows of ships, and Asc. Gordenn's symbol is affixed to the hafts of farming implements. Asc. Katrena's symbol is engraved on the arms or inside the armor of nobility and protectors of the church. Bank documents and other contractual papers often include the symbol of Asc. Shevann.

Asc. Angellia (f) ascended 1027 BR
Patron of history, lore, and the written word

Prodigious Rynnish scholar, historian, and linguist. Wrote the definitive history of western Immoren up to her time. Recovered the lost Enkheiridion and wrote its definitive notated translation.

Asc. Corben (m) ascended 102 AR
Patron of alchemy, astronomy, and the arcane

Notable arcanist who advanced astronomy, mechanika, and alchemy. Cured Rip Lung plague. Ascension seen as sign of Morrow's endorsement of arcanists who apply their powers to good works.

Asc. Doleth (m) ascended 1411 BR
Patron of sailors, boatmen, and fishermen

Fisherman on the western coast. Followed quiet, solitary path toward enlightenment. Meditated on Morrow's teachings while at sea. Selflessly rescued victims of shipwrecks amid storms of the Meredius.

Asc. Ellena (f) ascended 1590 BR
Patron of pilgrims, proselytizers, travelers, and messengers

Conducted pilgrimages in a particularly dangerous era. Spread teachings of Morrow to farthest corners of continent. Proselytizing ensured rapid spread of the faith. Performed charitable works where Menite temples had turned a blind eye to suffering.

Asc. Gordenn (m) ascended 812 BR
Patron of farmers and family

Monk and farmer devoted to alleviating suffering during Time of the Long Sun, a horrible drought. Credited with countless miracles, such as turning barren farmlands fertile and calling down rainfalls. Saved thousands from starvation.

Asc. Katrena (f) ascended 1810 BR
Patron of valor, knighthood, and nobility

First Ascendant, born in frozen north, ascended after protecting Morrowan priests and thinkers from the Menite Purging. One of the first and greatest defenders of Morrowan faith. Died from wounds suffered in battle with Menites defending one of the first primarchs.

Asc. Markus (m) ascended 305 AR
Patron of soldiers and city watchmen

Ordic soldier who single-handedly stalled an invading barbarian horde at the Siege of Midfast by challenging its fourteen chiefs to a series of duels. Died and ascended as the siege was lifted.

Asc. Rowan (f) ascended 289 BR
Patron of the poor and downtrodden

Lived during height of the Occupation. Renounced all material wealth and spent her life alleviating the suffering of the enslaved Immorese. Achieved enlightenment through self-sacrifice.

Asc. Shevann (f) ascended 500 AR
Patron of merchants, oratory, and conciliation

Most recent ascendant. Negotiated peace with the Sul-Menites after the Cygnaran Civil War. Considered patron ascendant of Caspia.

Asc. Sambert (m) ascended 605 BR
Patron of craftsmen, artists, and builders

Masterful sculptor, architect, painter, mason, and engineer with skill to manifest the divine on Caen through craft. Revolutionized sacred architecture with Archcourt Cathedral and other buildings in the Sancteum.

Asc. Solovin (m) ascended 1253 BR
Patron of healers, battle-chaplains, and midwives

Soldier and priest from Thuria who visited countless battlefields to treat wounded regardless of their affiliations. Sacrificed himself to destroy Scion Remel.

manifested on Caen to lend their aid through visions or more overt displays of holy power.

Each ascendant has a history, a distinct philosophy, and associated rites and prayers. The remains and possessions of each ascendant are holy relics that are preserved and displayed at various major cathedrals and monasteries. Most of these are reputed to possess miraculous properties and serve as conduits for the divine. Occasionally a revered priest will receive similar treatment after death. Each of primarchs join Morrow after death, transfigured into special messengers called archons. Their remains are preserved in the catacombs below the Archcourt Cathedral, contributing to the holiness of this most sacred ground.

Ascendants and archons are reputed to sometimes manifest before chosen faithful to deliver signs and portents from Morrow, the Prophet. These manifestations are sometimes translated into cryptic prophecies, the meaning of which is studied and interpreted by theologians. All witnessed manifestations of ascendants and archons are preserved and recorded in church records and are frequently the subject of religious art and sculpture.

The faithful sometimes feel a closer relationship with their patron ascendant or ascendants than with Morrow himself and spend much of their time in prayer addressing this patron. It is common for Morrowans to keep spiritual tokens on their person, most commonly a necklace bearing the Radiance of Morrow together with coin-like talismans representing ascendants. These vary in detail and quality. The finest of these talismans are minted in the Sanceum and sold to pilgrims who visit the holy city. Even the less pious will often superstitiously pray to or name an ascendant when engaged in a difficult task related to their areas of patronage. A physician cleansing a difficult wound might mutter a prayer to Asc. Solovin, for example.

THAMARITE CULTS

While Morrow has become the most prominent deity of the Iron Kingdoms, the cults devoted to his twin sister Thamar exist in relative obscurity, a fact her adherents prefer. Despite this, the teachings of Thamar have had tremendous impact on the Morrowan faith, forming a conceptual counterpoint by which their beliefs and morality are defined. To adhere to Morrow's path one must reject Thamar's, and vice versa. Thamar has had just as profound an impact on the thinking and philosophies of mankind as her brother, but her legacy is cast in shadow since Thamar's faith is inherently subversive and is associated with the darker aspects of human nature.

The concept of transgression as a gateway to enlightenment is fundamental to Thamarite belief. For this and other reasons, this faith has always been relegated to cult status, and its adherents are both feared and loathed by the dominant religions. Those who truly understand Thamarite philosophy know there are many roads to unlocking one's own inner potential, some subtler

than others. Thamar is seen by her faithful as the goddess of knowledge in all forms. She is a champion of the downtrodden, the outcast, the vengeful, and the iconoclastic. She is a goddess of freedom, self-expression, and perseverance. Those drawn to her darker aspects for their own sake or who use their faith as an excuse to justify atrocious deeds are blind to her true path. Besides the nefarious villains among her faithful there have also been heroes advocating the liberation and freedom of the spirit. When it has suited their ends, Thamarites have even shown a willingness to come to the defense of pious Morrowans.

The relationship between Morrow and Thamar and their respective paths is complicated and difficult to quantify even for theologians. On one hand, Morrowan doctrine suggests it is natural and inevitable that some people will choose the "dark path of Thamar" when confronted with the Volition. Church doctrine suggests these people are to be pitied and treated humanely, advising that those who have taken this turn might be set back on the path of light. The Church of Morrow makes a significant distinction between those who have unknowingly fallen under Thamar's sway and those who outright worship the goddess, forsaking all other faiths. Those who act from selfish or misguided desires but who have not actually devoted themselves to the Dark Twin can be redeemed, while those who have sworn allegiance to Thamar are enemies of the faith.

There is a broad spectrum of people labeled Thamarites, among them many who do not actively worship the goddess or her scions. The Church of Morrow has sometimes placed emphasis on "unknowing worship" as a proof of Thamar's corruptive influence seeping into a community and to frighten the wayward back to lives of rectitude. Anyone prone to pursuing vices can be subject to this scrutiny, and this has led to persecution by groups like the Order of Illumination, which is charged with rooting out Thamarite cults.

Even as Morrow and his ascendants look after those who are kind and generous, Thamar is thought to watch over and lend aid to the wicked. Those raised in Morrowan communities who turn to lives of crime may seek Thamar's benevolence, knowing Morrow would not accept them. This is particularly true for those contemplating imminent death and an uncertain afterlife. Thamar's followers encourage this, supporting the notion that Morrow's faith is judgmental while Thamar is welcoming. Her worship finds the warmest welcome in underworld and criminal circles, where her teachings most easily take root.

Nearly all acts of transgression, crime, and pathos are seen as the purview of Thamar. For Thamarites morality itself is an enslavement of the spirit. Acts of crime and rebellion for their own sake are hollow in the goddess' eyes, however. Thamar and her followers find enlightenment only in unshackled spirit and the triumph of the individual over the many. She is the patron not of selfishness but of self-accomplishment.

While the broad persecution of Thamarites may seem unjust at times, the septs of Thamar do include many genuinely dangerous and insidious individuals. To those who follow the dark goddess, nothing is forbidden.

THE MANY PATHS

In life Thamar had a strong fascination for the occult and ardently pursued arcane lore at a time when such powers were almost unknown. Delving into these matters was key to her ascension. She pieced together an occult alphabet called Telgesh that is related to the arcane alphabets used by all arcanists in western Immoren who shape reality by force of will and that is believed to be fundamental to necromancy. She also obscured knowledge of her own path by placing enigmas and riddles in her writings, intending her followers actively pursue enlightenment their own way. Indeed, this need to work through the tortuous philosophical conundrums to understand the secrets of reality is a central tenet of Thamarite faith.

According to Thamar's words, every path to ascension is different and every worshiper must find his own interpretation of her teachings. Some beliefs and aspects of her faith have been codified over time, however, and like-minded worshipers drawn to a particular aspect of the goddess may form septs. Most often a sept is a small group, but the most prominent septs contain hundreds or even thousands of worshipers scattered across western Immoren. Some argue that banding together in this way is inherently antithetical to Thamar's teachings, but the scions who have ascended prove that some paths are more viable than others. Septs are a means for Thamarites to work together toward common ends and to share insights, lore, and rituals. Several of the largest septs are dedicated to specific areas of forbidden knowledge, such as necromancy or infernalism.

Thamarites reject the term "priest" for those who study the goddess, preferring to call themselves advocates. At the heart of the most lasting septs are advocates of an intellectual inclination who seek to better themselves by understanding Thamar's philosophies and acting upon the goddess' words and the examples of her scions. There is no single organization that unites all the divergent Thamarite advocates, although some of the larger septs have established hierarchies and rules. Thamar's symbol, called the Ternion Brand, is adopted by dedicated followers as a sign of their commitment. It is sometimes displayed openly in defiance of authorities but more often is kept hidden.

Thamarite advocates do not usually channel her power through prayer like priests of other faiths; while dark miracles have been known to manifest when her name or those of the scions are invoked, this is exceedingly rare. Most believe the best way to gain power over reality is to master the arcane arts. Thamar is the goddess of magic as well as knowledge, as it was she who bestowed the Gift on humanity. Arcane practitioners are thought to carry forward the mystical work Thamar began before her ascension. No arcane path is forbidden to Thamarite worshipers, at least in theory. Necromancy in particular has been embraced as one of the oldest and most primal of arcane arts, inextricably linked to life, death, and the power of the immortal soul.

The Church of Morrow brands all Thamarites malefactors, a term conveying the belief they are irredeemably profane. Thamarites are viewed as a major threat, an enemy of civilization itself. They are actively persecuted by both Menites and Morrowans. The Church of Morrow's belief in the Volition

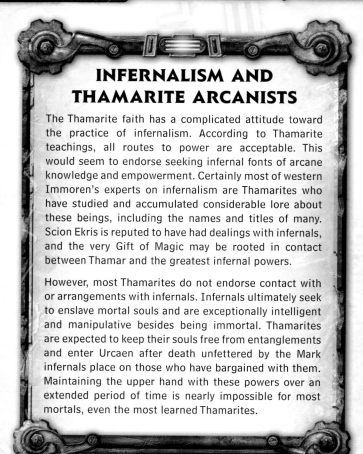

INFERNALISM AND THAMARITE ARCANISTS

The Thamarite faith has a complicated attitude toward the practice of infernalism. According to Thamarite teachings, all routes to power are acceptable. This would seem to endorse seeking infernal fonts of arcane knowledge and empowerment. Certainly most of western Immoren's experts on infernalism are Thamarites who have studied and accumulated considerable lore about these beings, including the names and titles of many. Scion Ekris is reputed to have had dealings with infernals, and the very Gift of Magic may be rooted in contact between Thamar and the greatest infernal powers.

However, most Thamarites do not endorse contact with or arrangements with infernals. Infernals ultimately seek to enslave mortal souls and are exceptionally intelligent and manipulative besides being immortal. Thamarites are expected to keep their souls free from entanglements and enter Urcaen after death unfettered by the Mark infernals place on those who have bargained with them. Maintaining the upper hand with these powers over an extended period of time is nearly impossible for most mortals, even the most learned Thamarites.

extends mercy only to those who unknowingly walk the dark path and can be brought back to the light; those who consciously choose to explore Thamar's teachings are deemed worse than damned. In most nations the Church of Morrow is lawfully empowered to capture, interrogate, and sit in judgment over Thamarite malefactors. For these reasons most Thamarites seek to hide their religious beliefs, particularly in regions where the Church of Morrow is prominent. Thamarites with position in society pretend to be Morrowans, at least to a minimal degree, attending church services and keeping Morrowan iconography prominently on their persons.

The most pious followers of Thamar keep a small, secret shrine for worship. This usually includes a small metal or clay statue of Thamar and possibly a second smaller statue representing one or more of the scions. Due the secrecy of Thamarite worship, open funeral services are rare. More often, Thamarites are buried in Morrowan ceremonies.

SCIONS OF THAMAR

Even as Morrow has saint-like ascendants, there have been a number of individuals who have ascended to a higher state of being at the moment of death by heeding Thamar's teachings and seeking their own distinct paths. In keeping with the iconoclasm endorsed by this faith, these individuals have often been branded by history as notorious criminals and madmen, as infamous as Morrow's ascendants are revered. To the Morrowan majority the list of scions is a roster of villainy, while to Thamarites it represents the infinite ways in which an

SYMBOLS AND PATRONAGES OF THE SCIONS OF THAMAR

It is quite rare to find the symbols of the Thamarite scions on anything other than a small coin-like talisman a worshiper may carry for luck or to use in prayer. These symbols are sometimes used in underworld circles as markings to designate access to areas utilized as safe houses or meeting places, such as hidden shrines.

Sc. Aidan (m) ascended 344 BR
Patron of thieves, relic seekers, and the hunted

Outlaw and grave robber who undermined Orgoth rule defying their laws and evading those hunting him. Desecrated Morrdhic, Rhulic, and Orgoth tombs to acquire occult lore.

Sc. Bolis (m) ascended 271 AR
Patron of gamblers, smugglers, and fences

Criminal mastermind and entrepreneur. Popularized gambling as a gateway to deeper vice and laid foundation for Five Fingers to become a free haven of crime, manipulating Ord and Cygnar to do so.

Sc. Delesle (f) ascended 1610 BR
Patron of necromancy, rebellion, and self-determination

Conducted campaign of terror against Menite temples and priesthood in the early Thousand Cities Era. Desecrated burial grounds and animated the dead to make war on Menites. Shielded Morrowan communities from scrutators during the Menite Purging.

Sc. Drayce (m) ascended 1400 BR
Patron of liars, politicians, and pleasure seekers

Most charismatic and subtle of Thamar's scions. Influential leader, master of human weakness, singularly ruthless and manipulative politician, and notorious hedonist. The full scope of his influence was not realized until long after his ascension.

Sc. Ekris (m) ascended 1780 BR
Patron of secrets, diviners, and forbidden lore

First Scion, alleged disciple and lover of Thamar before her ascension. Peerless occultist who determined Telgesh glyphs derived from Morrdh. Expanded early mystical writings of Thamar. Made pacts with infernals to extend his life and complete enlightenment.

Sc. Khorva (f) ascended 1250 BR
Patron of duelists, assassins, and criminal enforcers

Peerless assassin and killer. Assassinated Primarch Lorichias in the Divinium. Her actions and ascension were witnessed by a Menite delegation. This eventually ended the Menite Purging, allowing Morrowans and Menites to coexist.

Sc. Lukas (m) ascended 995 BR
Patron of the depraved, the mad, and the visionary

Sadistic hunter and killer, least understood of the scions. Sought immortality through a legacy of horror by murdering and torturing hundreds, including Morrowan priests. Chose victims based on prophetic visions and dreams. Feared even by Thamarites.

Sc. Nivara (f) ascended 25 AR
Patron of arcanists, artificers, and teachers

Most influential arcanist of the early Rebellion. Kerwin's true successor, who innovated use of arcane power in war. Her rune-inscribed puzzles laid the foundation for the cerebral matrix.

Sc. Remel (m)
Pscended 1700 BR, destroyed 1253 BR
no current patronages

Ancient scion noted in Morrowan records as destroyed during the ascension of Solovin. Most modern Thamarites disavow his existence.

Sc. Roth (m) ascended 687 BR
Patron of bandits, mercenaries, and outcast soldiers

Bandit lord who carved out a fiefdom along the Dragon's Tongue River leading an army of cutthroats. Displayed brilliant tactics when he was almost victorious against three vastly superior armies in the Battle of Roth's Stand.

Sc. Stacia (f) ascended 421 AR
Patron of arsonists, revenge, and the persecuted

Sorceress of tremendous power branded a witch and sentenced to death. Defied authorities in Mercir, where she obliterated every arcanist in the area and consumed three-quarters of the city in an inferno.

individual soul can cast aside its limits to transcend mortality. These ascensions have been infrequent but spectacular events.

The scions are thought to hear prayers closely tied to their spheres of influence, and records of the Church of Morrow relate incidents where scions have worked through mortal intermediaries by bestowing visions or outright possessing them and manifesting remarkable powers. On extremely rare occasions they have manifested on Caen for direct intervention. Each scion is associated with a unique path to ascension, a distinct philosophy, and associated prayers. The remains and possessions of each scion are relics that are preserved in secret places by the most powerful of Thamar's septs. They are reputed to possess miraculous properties and serve as conduits for the divine.

THE MENITE TEMPLE

While the Menite religion played a central role in the rise of human civilization, this ancient faith has been on the decline for centuries. Only in the Protectorate of Menoth are Menites the overwhelming majority, as that strict theocracy was established specifically to restore the faith to prominence. In the Protectorate life is quite different than anywhere else in the Iron Kingdoms, as religion is an inextricable part of life. The Sul-Menites of the Protectorate claim to have restored the old traditions of their faith, but in many respects their society is unique and does not resemble that of ancient times. The priest caste is in absolute control of the government, with the temple's hierarchy filling the positions held by the nobility in other kingdoms. The leader of the temple is also the head of state, a position presently occupied by Hierarch Severius, a formidable scrutator who leads armies of the faithful to war. The Protectorate's army is simply an extension of the temple, and its clergy also enforce the law.

Sacred rites and rituals pervade all aspects of life, and these, too, require the guiding hand of priests. Though not all people who live in the Protectorate are equally pious, all are affected by religion daily in countless ways. The hardship of working the barren lands east of the Black River only amplifies the prayers of the faithful who look to Menoth to improve their lives and shelter them in the afterlife. For the poor, the promise of Urcaen has more appeal than daily existence, which lends greater fervor to prayer. The best chance many have to improve their standing is to serve the temple more actively and directly, such as by joining the Temple Flameguard that serves as the Protectorate's citizen militia or by aspiring to other temple positions.

As a matter of course every Menite in the Protectorate is aware they may have to take up arms to defend the faith. They each know to whom they must report should the call to arms be given, and there are weapons stashes in most communities for this eventuality. The prospect of war and crusade is a real fact to every Menite in this nation, since they believe themselves to be the last bastions of their faith, a religion that has been under constant attack by the godless for centuries. This attitude stands in contrast with that of Menites in other kingdoms, who have had to learn to live alongside their countrymen of other faiths.

Unlike the Church of Morrow, the "Temple of Menoth" is not a single organization, but many. The Sul-Menite temple is distinct from the Old Faith of Khador, and independent temples exist in both Ord and Cygnar with no connection to these groups. While this may change in the course of the Sul-Menite crusades, at present the Menites do not share a hierarchy.

This has become a topic of heated debate after one of the most momentous spiritual events in the last decade—the appearance of the Harbinger of Menoth in 603 AR. This young woman is a conduit for the divine and can speak with the words of Menoth himself as she channels miracles on Caen. Her arrival first served to spark a call Menites from all over western Immoren to the Protectorate then to ignite the Great Crusade, reinforcing the Sul-Menite claim to being the true successors of Menoth's chosen people on Caen. Word of the Harbinger's existence sent shockwaves through Menite communities in other kingdoms. In addition to an initial rush of converts who left their communities to join the Protectorate, the Harbinger has been the cause of ongoing dissent within Menite communities as spiritual leaders try to reconcile their beliefs with this clear sign of divine favor.

MENITES LIVING AS A MINORITY FAITH

Menites are a significant minority across the Iron Kingdoms, where they conduct their lives much the same way as their neighbors except on days of worship, when they attend their temples. Most Menites carry a small Menofix, a symbol representing their god as well as the creation of humanity. Menites are generally hard workers, as their faith emphasizes diligence; the most pious among them eschew sloth and self-indulgence. They are not often found in taverns, gambling halls, or other common places of entertainment. Because of this, they may be viewed as insular, humorless, and disapproving by Morrowan neighbors, who will admit they are also serious and productive in their chosen trades. Menites in turn disapprove of the indolent lifestyles they believe to be rife among Morrowans. Small daily friction sometimes masks religious tensions lying below the surface, and relations between these faiths have become increasingly strained. In large communities, incidents of religion-inspired violence are not uncommon.

Of the kingdoms, Cygnar has the smallest proportion of Menites compared to the rest of its population. The end of the Cygnaran Civil War saw the majority of Menite families emigrate to the newly created Protectorate of Menoth, and only small Menite communities persist in Cygnar. The Protectorate's crusades have greatly escalated tensions between Morrowans and Menites in this kingdom, particularly in the east. This situation has not been helped by Protectorate missionaries and agents looking to infiltrate Menite communities to convert those citizens to their cause. Many remaining Menites choose to worship in secret, although there are no laws forbidding their beliefs and old Menite temples and shrines stand in most cities and towns. Such secrecy is particularly widespread among Menites enlisted in the Cygnaran Army. Anti-Menite sentiment is not endorsed by the Cygnaran government or ranking military officers, but as a matter of widespread and pervasive antipathy it is difficult to address.

In Ord, Llael, and Khador there are sizable and respected Menite communities with deep roots. Yet even here the spread of the Protectorate's crusades has had an impact. In war-torn regions, the loyalties of such communities may be called into question, particularly since the appearance of the Harbinger. Away from the front lines, Menites live in relative peace and cooperation with the Morrowan majority. Khador is notable for having a particularly large Menite population, most belonging to a sect called the Old Faith, which did not suffer as great of a decline as other Menite sects during the Orgoth Occupation. There are many exclusively Menite communities in Khador as well as cities where they represent a substantial segment of the population. The Old Faith has the largest organized hierarchy of any Menite sect in western Immoren outside the Protectorate of Menoth but lacks centralized leadership. Its ranking visgoths are scattered and focused on attending to the temples in their respective regions. Below the visgoths are influential priests called sovereigns who oversee individual temples.

Menite communities usually demonstrate higher levels of general piety than Morrowan ones, perhaps due to strict upbringing and more consistent traditions of teaching religious doctrine to the young. Even the less pious prefer lives of discipline and adherence to the rule of law. Many Menites adapt readily to military service and acquit themselves admirably, with career soldiering being a respected profession. Menite communities prefer to self-govern where possible, adhering to the dictates of the Canon of the True Law, their core religious doctrine. Originally inscribed on the stones of Ancient Icthier, this ancient text has been translated and interpreted numerous times. The most widely used Old Faith transcription of the Canon differs from the one used by Sul-Menites in important respects, particularly in its explanation of the authority of the priesthood.

MENITE PRIESTS AND SCRUTATORS

Throughout Menite communities, the masked priests of the Lawgiver are viewed as legal authorities, although those outside the Protectorate must obey the laws of the kingdoms where they reside. In communities in which Menites have the right to self-rule, there are two castes of clergy: priests, who preach, teach doctrine, and lead religious services; and scrutators, who serve as judges and executioners among their people. In areas where the Menite faith is particularly strong, the authority of the scrutators over Menite citizens is all but absolute and rarely challenged. Only in the Protectorate of Menoth, where Menites are the overwhelming majority, however, does a true theocracy exist.

All Menites attend temple on days of worship, with exceptions made only for those who are severely ill, attending to other temple business, or otherwise legitimately unavailable. According to ancient law, Menites are also required to donate one-tenth of their yearly earnings to the temple. Failures to attend religious services or pay tithes are crimes and subject to punishments commensurate with the severity of the infraction. The ability of the temple to enforce this varies considerably, but the scrutators and the Knights Exemplar who serve them often take an active role in enforcing temple law, even if such measures are not supported by secular law. In most cases government officials are reluctant to interfere in the internal affairs of these communities.

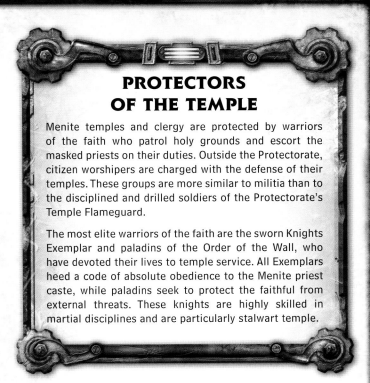

PROTECTORS OF THE TEMPLE

Menite temples and clergy are protected by warriors of the faith who patrol holy grounds and escort the masked priests on their duties. Outside the Protectorate, citizen worshipers are charged with the defense of their temples. These groups are more similar to militia than to the disciplined and drilled soldiers of the Protectorate's Temple Flameguard.

The most elite warriors of the faith are the sworn Knights Exemplar and paladins of the Order of the Wall, who have devoted their lives to temple service. All Exemplars heed a code of absolute obedience to the Menite priest caste, while paladins seek to protect the faithful from external threats. These knights are highly skilled in martial disciplines and are particularly stalwart temple.

MENITE ATTITUDES TOWARD OUTSIDERS

Regardless of their specific sect, most Menites do not understand how those of other faiths can easily separate spiritual matters from daily life. Menites often find it unconscionable that so many people have foresworn their Creator to bow to another god. To a Menite the gifts that humanity possesses derive from Menoth alone and should not be squandered. In the centuries before the Orgoth, when the Menites were the majority, Morrowans were forced to heed the True Law, including paying tithes and attending temple, and traditionalists among the Menites yearn for their temple to return to such prominence.

Menite communities outside the Protectorate must grudgingly accept Morrowans but are not tolerant of other faiths. Menites see the Devourer Wurm as the ancient foe of their god and its cultists as deserving of violent extermination. This is one area where Morrowans and Menites fundamentally agree. Historically, Menite confusion about the distinction between Dhunia and the Devourer Wurm has prompted violence against trollkin, ogrun, and gobber tribes as well.

Similarly, most Menites are uncomfortable with the arcane. Menites see the spread of the Gift as an affront to the Creator by Morrow and Thamar. As a consequence, those born with strong arcane abilities within Menite communities have difficulty coming to grips with their powers, sometimes denying them outright. Others feel compelled to purify themselves through ritual and prayer. In remote Menite communities, local priests have been known to put to death young children manifesting sorcery. In the Protectorate of Menoth, the only sanctioned arcane practitioners are those belonging to the Vassals of Menoth. This group performs works vital to the Sul-Menite war effort, but its arcanists are kept under constant supervision and are treated akin to indentured servants of the state, enjoying only limited freedom.

OTHER FAITHS

While Morrow and Menoth are the most pervasive religions in the Iron Kingdoms, a number of other faiths exist, especially among the other races that call western Immoren home. The degree of awareness that humans have of other religions varies but is usually limited. Most people in western Immoren are aware that Iosans, Nyss, Rhulfolk, trollkin, ogrun, and gobbers have their own faiths but are rarely interested in the particulars.

The primary exceptions to general acceptance of other faiths are the cults of the Devourer Wurm that have long been seen as an enemies of civilization.

CULT OF CYRISS

Despite the relatively recent discovery of the goddess Cyriss, her following has spread rapidly among the members of specialized technical fields, including astronomy, mathematics, engineering, and mechanika. Her faith has adherents at most major universities, observatories, and machine shops.

The worshipers of the Clockwork Goddess have yet to experience much persecution. They are fortunate to have risen to prominence in an age when the more tolerant Morrowan faith holds the majority. Furthermore, its adherents have no longstanding animosities and few religious rivals. Unlike Thamarite and Devourer cults, they are not associated with black magic or unwholesome rites. In certain areas of Cygnar the worship of Cyriss has even gained nominal acceptance, and the Crown has sanctioned the construction of a large temple to Cyriss in Caspia.

Most followers of the Maiden of Gears worship discreetly, reluctant to identify themselves as believers to outsiders. They quietly practice their faith by engaging in scientific pursuits, working on mathematical theory, crafting intricate pieces of machinery or mechanika, studying astronomy, or deciphering codes and enigmas. Members may carry a small token of their belief to identify themselves to one another, such as a pendant inscribed with her symbol amid interlocking gears. While this faith is not actively persecuted, many Menites and Morrowans view its members with suspicion. Rumors among them suggest inner cabals that practice peculiar rites related to the celestial cycles. These cults are said to have built sizable hidden temples across western Immoren, each filled with a dizzying array of wondrous machinery and protected by automated guardians. Some even whisper that high-ranking priests of Cyriss can transfer their souls into machine bodies to attain immortality.

That the cult possesses different layers of membership is true. Those who prove their loyalty and impress ranking priests with their intelligence and skill may eventually earn access to the cult's inner workings. With its own distinct beliefs, goals, and purposes, this group is almost a different faith, its members separate from the worshipers who simply revere Cyriss as a patron.

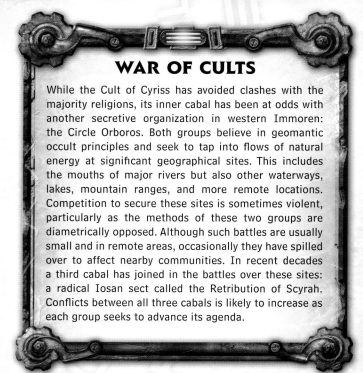

WAR OF CULTS

While the Cult of Cyriss has avoided clashes with the majority religions, its inner cabal has been at odds with another secretive organization in western Immoren: the Circle Orboros. Both groups believe in geomantic occult principles and seek to tap into flows of natural energy at significant geographical sites. This includes the mouths of major rivers but also other waterways, lakes, mountain ranges, and more remote locations. Competition to secure these sites is sometimes violent, particularly as the methods of these two groups are diametrically opposed. Although such battles are usually small and in remote areas, occasionally they have spilled over to affect nearby communities. In recent decades a third cabal has joined in the battles over these sites: a radical Iosan sect called the Retribution of Scyrah. Conflicts between all three cabals is likely to increase as each group seeks to advance its agenda.

CULTS OF THE DEVOURER WURM

Cults of the Devourer Wurm are considered dangerous and worthy of expunction by both Menites and pious Morrowans. Adherents of the Beast of All Shapes can be found among barbaric humans, bogrin, trollkin, and several other wild races, although they are fewer in number in the modern era. The Devourer-worshiping Molgur, which included many of these races, left a legacy of fear that lingers still.

With the memory of Devourer-worshiping barbarians engendering such strong antipathy, it is no coincidence that most Devourer cults exist on the fringes of civilization or deep within the untamed wilderness. With few exceptions, these cults are isolated, have no shared religious accord, and demonstrate a wide variety of rites and rituals. Each Devourer cult has its own customs, adornments, and depictions of its multifaceted god. The so-called Beast of All Shapes has been portrayed countless ways, most often as a predatory totemic animal such as a wolf, serpent, bear, eagle, or shark. There are also groups that worship the Wurm under another name. Many gatorman tribes worship an entity called Kossk, described as a primal alligator or gatorman with a voracious appetite, for instance; blackclads of the Circle Orboros consider this another aspect of the Wurm rather than a distinct entity.

Human worship of the Wurm was still practiced by large numbers as recently as 305 AR, which marked the last great gathering of uncivilized human tribes from northern Khador. These tribes endured massive casualties and conversions during and after the Siege of Midfast and never recovered their numbers. Remnants of these people and similar tribes persist in the more remote wilderness regions, particularly in the northern mountains and forests of Khador, on several of the outer Scharde Islands, deep in Cygnar's Wyrmwall Mountains, and in the Bloodstone Marches.

Most Devourer cults revere the moons, particularly Calder, which they associate with the Wurm, and feast rites are conducted both when Calder is new and when it is full. Bloodletting rites are common, with human sacrifice and cannibalism also practiced, although cannibalism has never been as widespread as attributed by Menite and Morrowan clergy. The most feared of cultists are the Tharn, attributed with supernatural transformative abilities as a birthright of their long association with the Wurm. The Tharn were thought on the verge of extinction but have had a recent resurgence as a result of an alliance with the blackclads who inhabit the wilderness.

DHUNIAN FAITHS

While in ancient days the worship of the Wurm was widespread, the fall of the Molgur led to the adoption of Dhunian practices by surviving trollkin, ogrun, and goblin tribes. The worship of Dhunia is accepted in the human kingdoms, though many view it as primitive. This religion was ignored by human theologians until recently, and most humans still know little about it. The rare shrines to Dhunia found in human towns and cities are generally located in districts with sizable resident populations of trollkin, gobbers, or ogrun. These are usually outdoor monuments in stone with rune-carved columns but may include a large central abstract depiction of the pregnant goddess. Much larger and more impressive Dhunian holy sites exist in dedicated communities of these races.

For most Dhunians, worship is a private affair; they rarely congregate except at seasonal rituals. Dhunians pray to the goddess in times of travail and seek her blessings for childbirth or conception, as fertility is one of her main concerns. Her connection to the passing seasons leads her worshipers to make offerings and conduct celebratory feasts during the equinoxes.

Dhunian communities often support at least one, and often several, shamans, who have studied the ways of the goddess and instruct others in spiritual beliefs. A shaman's role is similar to that of a priest, but he may also serve as a chief or an advisor to a chief. Dhunia favors those who are stalwart in the defense of their families, and although she is not depicted as aggressive, some of her shamans are accomplished warriors and invoke her name when entering battle. While most shamans are rooted to a specific community, some prefer a nomadic existence and travel from village to village, offering spiritual council and sharing news. Among the trollkin, Dhunian shamans are often looked to for lore concerning the full-blood trolls that coexist with wilderness kriels and serve as beasts of labor and war.

Each Dhunian race has different ways of revering the goddess, but it is common for pious believers to keep runic necklaces or adornments on their person or weapons. These are often small pieces of stone or metal inscribed with simple runes believed to bring good fortune and protection. Some of these are ancient and carry considerable symbolic importance. The runes do not

BLACKCLADS OF THE CIRCLE ORBOROS

The most organized and widespread organization associated with the Devourer Wurm is the Circle Orboros, known by most as the "blackclads." These druids wield tremendous power to control the chaotic forces of nature. Contrary to rumor, the esoteric beliefs of this group do not involve worship of the Wurm, but they know a great deal about this god and its cults. Blackclads describe the Wurm as one aspect of a larger natural power called Orboros, from which their power derives. Reclusive and few in number, blackclads are shunned by civilized communities who fear their powers and consequently avoid confronting them. They are reputedly involved in unsavory activities like human sacrifice and kidnapping children, and there is some truth to both accusations.

Blackclads have extensive contact with the diverse Devourer cults scattered along the fringes of western Immoren. These communities respect and revere the blackclads as prophets of the Wurm and willingly do their bidding. Drawing from these communities, the Circle has created a martial organization to serve them called the Wolves of Orboros.

name Dhunia herself but describe desirable attributes or convey meanings of protection or prowess in battle. They are looked upon as akin to permanent prayers to Dhunia requesting her blessings for those who wear them.

The Dhunian faith has no specific holy text, with beliefs passed orally through the generations. Runic writings inscribed on columns near Dhunian settlements typically describe the deeds of notable members of the community. This is particularly common among trollkin, who prefer to immortalize the stories of their ancestors in stone. These writings may be copied onto parchment scrolls by charcoal rubbings from the original stone inscriptions, with such scrolls often carried by shamans and chroniclers who speak Dhunia's praises through the example of those she has blessed.

For the Dhunian races, there exists a primal connection between Dhunia and the Devourer Wurm; Dhunia is "the mother" and the Wurm "the father." This divine relationship is a violent one, as the Wurm represents baser instincts such as hatred, jealousy, and envy. They seek to control these dangerous impulses and find solace through Dhunia. Given the tremendous stigma associated with the Wurm in human communities, the connection between Dhunia and the Devourer is rarely broached with outsiders. Similarly, most Dhunians know better than to discuss their belief that Menoth was also born of Dhunia and the Wurm, a belief outright heretical to Menites and Morrowans alike, except perhaps to a handful extremely open-minded Sancteum theologians.

CHURCH OF THE GREAT FATHERS

The dwarves of Rhul worship the Great Fathers, thirteen progenitor gods that sired their race and established their system of laws. Each of the Great Fathers embodies a different aspect of Rhulic culture, but their clergy is devoted to them as a pantheon, offering praises to each in turn. There are rituals throughout the year devoted to specific Great Fathers, and Rhulfolk will occasionally invoke individual names when engaging in activities relevant to each one's purview.

All thirteen Great Fathers are represented by influential clans in Rhul bearing their names. Each of these clans is led by a stone lord who bears additional responsibilities as the inheritor of a divine legacy. While the nation is an oligarchy, the thirteen stone lords are empowered as heads of state and work with Rhul's governing body, the Moot of the Hundred Houses, represented by the hundred most powerful clans.

Religion and government have overlapping roles in Rhul. The central holy text of the Church of the Great Fathers is the Codex that records all of Rhul's extensive records of legal precedence. Similarly, the practice of law and jurisprudence is inextricable from religious rites among the dwarves. Despite this, Rhul is not a theocracy, and the role of the priesthood is to serve as judges and arbiters of jurisprudence. Clan lords are the ruling class of Rhul, but disputes between clans may provoke intervention by Moot judges, appointed members of the clergy recognized for expertise in Rhulic law. Arbitration takes up more of many priests' time than the study and preaching of religious doctrine. At any time when Rhulfolk cannot resolve a dispute, either party can seek a member of the clergy to witness a lawful duel or to arbitrate grievances. Their decisions carry the full weight of law and are recorded in the ever-expanding Codex.

As a legacy of the legend of the Claywives, the wives of the Great Fathers, women have traditionally dominated the Rhulic clergy, occupying many of the highest ranks, although both genders are accepted into the priesthood. The Claywives have accumulated a body of their own legends, and although the practice is frowned upon by traditionalists their names are sometimes invoked in prayer in a similar fashion as Great Fathers. The Cult of the Claywives is large and generally accepted, as all dwarves recognize the equal role of these progenitors in their existence.

Outsiders may make the mistake of thinking this religion is similar to that of the Menites. In mixed dwarven and human communities there is some natural sympathy between these faiths, as both religions emphasize hard work and adherence to lawful conduct. On closer examination, however, the doctrines of the Church of the Great Fathers bear far more similarities to those of the tolerant Church of Morrow, advocating self-improvement and intellectual challenges rather than absolute obedience. Rhulic jurisprudence encourages debate and argument, in stark contrast to Menite law. Rhulic and human secular laws also differ in many respects—the legal dueling and feuding accepted among Rhulfolk would be deemed an egregious breach of the peace in the human Iron Kingdoms.

Dwarves have generally had an easy time integrating into human cities and have never faced significant religious strife. Many of the laws of the Codex are pertinent only to Rhul and have no bearing on dwarves living among mankind. Rhulic morality is largely in line with that of the human majority religions, and this faith has never sought to proselytize.

FANE OF NYSSOR

While it has long been one of the smallest faiths of western Immoren, the Fane of Nyssor is now reduced to a fraction of its former size. This has long been the religion of the Nyss of northern Khador, whose culture and society were nearly destroyed by the rise of the Legion of Everblight. Even as Nyss culture has been torn apart, their homelands lost and abandoned, many of their people murdered or converted into blighted monstrosities, the religious practices of the Nyss have suffered as well.

The Nyss were once part of the Iosan people. In the days following the Cataclysm, the survivors of the Empire of Lyoss followed their gods in an exodus from eastern Immoren. As each god settled into a different city of Ios, those who would become the Nyss dwelled in Darsael, now a forgotten ruin. After the Divine Court left Ios in its unsuccessful quest to return to the Veld, these people abandoned Darsael and made the long trek into the northwestern mountains seeking their patron, Nyssor.

The people of Darsael had long been shunned by other Iosans, who did not value the qualities of winter, and so their departure was not mourned. It was not the scorn of their neighbors that motivated their travels, however. Rather they responded to the words of their prophet Aeric, who had received a vision calling them into the frozen mountains to await the return of their god. Over the centuries the Nyss became a distinct people turned to a life of semi-nomadic tribes, hunting from the land, living in many ways akin to the old tribes that had prowled eastern Immoren before the unification of Lyoss.

Little did the people of Ios know that Nyssor would, in fact, return to his chosen people. Suffering from some inexplicable malady, however, the god of winter was forced to encase himself in ice to slow the degradation that ailed him. In this way Nyssor became the frozen god but remained the heart of religion for the Nyss, whose priests attended him faithfully. Priests and sorcerers associated with the fane were entrusted with the secrets of written Aeric, the language of the Nyss, and with preserving the lore and prophecies of the god.

With the arrival of Thagrosh and the Legion of Everblight, the Nyss experienced something akin to a second cataclysm. More than half the Nyss were corrupted and joined the dragon's blighted horde, while many others were slain. The rest fled, taking with them the vault of their god. Become a refugee people, the Nyss travelled south, enduring much hardship. Like their Iosan cousins, the Nyss are reticent to discuss matters of spirituality with outsiders, although they are also strongly pious and conduct private prayers to the god of winter.

FANE OF SCYRAH

Among Iosans the worship of the goddess Scyrah, the goddess of spring, is all but universal. At the same time, there is no race more secretive and unforthcoming about their religion or spiritual beliefs than the elves. Even those who have been exiled and no longer dwell among other Iosans rarely speak about their faith. With the Iosans' reputation for being aloof and unapproachable, this is not particularly surprising to outsiders, but it does mean very little is known of Iosan religion. In previous centuries, before Ios sealed itself from the outside world, some minimal communication on the topic reached human theologians, but they know little more than that an elven pantheon exists. Rumors persist that the Iosan gods walk among their people, but on this topic Iosans are particularly silent.

This is a social taboo so strong it crosses all class and sect lines, for the simple reason that it is imperative outsiders do not know of the doom awaiting their race. Scyrah has long been their last savior, and upon her shoulders rests the wellbeing of an entire civilization, yet she lies in fitful slumber and is prophesied to die in less than a century. Even the recent discovery of Nyssor has not changed this, and most elves consider it too early to hope. Given their reluctance to show outward signs of their faith, some outsiders may gather the impression Iosans are a non-spiritual people, but nothing could be further from the truth. Considering that the death of Scyrah could occur within the lifetime of most Iosans, they are intensely pious, feeling a close connection to Scyrah mixed with grief, fear, and uncertainty. The prospect of death is terrifying to Iosans, as they take no comfort or assurances in their fate in the afterlife. The Veld is vacant of the gods who once defended it.

The piety most Iosans living outside of Ios feel is a deeply private affair, with spiritual rituals and prayers undertaken in isolation. Iosans still pray to the Vanished, and it is not uncommon for the pious to offer nominal praises to the other gods at certain times. In ancient days each of the Divine Court was given attention at times related to their purviews. Lacyr was at the forefront of every prayer, Ossyris prayed to at times of war or turmoil, Ayisla worshiped at the onset of nightfall, and Nyrro worshiped at daybreak. Scyrah received considerable devotion at the start of spring, Lurynsar at summer, Lyliss at autumn, and Nyssor at winter. Many of these praises still take place in private, with Scyrah now at the heart of all rituals and ceremonies, as since her solitary return to Ios she is seen as regent for Lacyr.

In Iosan religion, the fane is both a church and a physical home of a god. Once there were eight occupied fanes, one for each of the gods, but now only Lacyr's former fane in Shyrr is inhabited—and Scyrah, who rests there, is sleeping and largely insensate. The physical proximity and tangibility of the goddess nevertheless resonates with all Iosans, as the center of this church where the goddess of spring lies is literally holy ground. Most Iosans visit the fane once in their lives.

THREE SECTS OF SCYRAH

Scyrah's return and lack of communication has prompted division among those who revere her. Three distinct sects persist, both in Ios and among those citizens living abroad: the traditional and conservative Fane of Scyrah, worshiped by the majority; the Seekers, a small but dedicated group who hopes to find evidence of the Vanished elsewhere in the world; and the Retribution of Scyrah, a growing radical movement who believe human magic is responsible for the wasting of the gods.

The traditional Fane of Scyrah has been gradually losing ground as the goddess has remained silent. They are seen as protectors of Iosan spiritual traditions, and it is their role to tend to the goddess and protect her, but beyond this they are viewed as indecisive and reluctant to act. The people of Ios have looked to these priests for guidance and have not been happy with the results. Few who adhere to the traditional beliefs live outside Ios. Most exiles and travelers who leave Ios are either Seekers or affiliated with the Retribution. The distinction between these two groups is significant, but they have found common ground.

Seekers remain convinced the answers to the Vanished will require aid and communication from outside Ios. They earnestly seek out alliances and friendships as well as investigating any clues that might shed illumination on the Vanished, including delving into esoteric occult matters. Yet after decades of fruitless searching, many Seekers have growing sympathies with the Retribution, which has a more decisive and specific agenda. Seekers tend to be subtler in their interactions with other races and sometimes acquire information useful to the Retribution. These two groups have conducted a number of cautious exchanges and have occasionally worked together.

The Retribution has its own zealous priests and distinct rituals and customs that are dissimilar from those of others who worship the goddess. Their depiction of Scyrah is also different in certain ways, portraying her in a more vengeful light. Despite these doctrinal differences, the Retribution has gained tremendous support since the return of Nyssor. Thousands have joined their cause, including two of Ios' ruling hallytyr, or high houses, bringing their elite soldiers and myrmidons—the Iosan equivalent of warjacks. The gathered army in Ios is supported by many far-flung Retribution agents that have been covertly working in human lands for centuries, based in hidden safe houses scattered across the Iron Kingdoms. Many of these agents spend much of their time gathering intelligence and conducting other support activities rather than fighting directly. There are some in Ios who fear any escalation by this radical sect could bring war to their borders, but a growing number believe it is better to fight than accept extinction.

For their part, most human arcanists are ignorant of the Iosan plots against their lives. The Retribution has worked slowly and carefully in past decades, covering its tracks. Most prominent wizards, sorcerers, and other arcanists have myriad rivals or enemies and thus the occasional deaths are often ascribed to other sources. The Fraternal Order of Wizardry has become aware that a group of radical elves has targeted some of its members, but they have no idea of the scope of this group or its resources.

CHARACTERS

Your character is the persona through which you'll explore the mysteries and dangers of the Iron Kingdoms. A character's "skeleton" is made up of his archetype, race, careers, skills, abilities, and other mechanical details, but as the player, you breathe life into him by imagining his personality and roleplaying him accordingly.

As characters adventure and become more experienced they hone their abilities, refine their skills, and advance through levels that increase their potential.

All characters begin the game at Hero level.

CHARACTER STATS

What a character can do in a roleplaying game is governed by a set of statistics, or stats, that represent his attributes. Stats provide a numerical representation of a character's basic qualities and are used to determine the success or failure of a variety of die rolls while playing. The higher the number, the better the stat.

Stats are broken into two categories: primary stats and secondary stats. A character's primary stats broadly determine his fundamental strengths and weaknesses. Each primary stat is further divided into two related secondary stats.

The range of stats for most characters falls between 2 and 8. A character's race determines what his starting stats are as well as what their maximum values can be. As a character gains experience over time, the maximum allowable value of his stats increases.

PRIMARY AND SECONDARY STATS

The primary stats are Physique, Agility, and Intellect. The secondary stats are Speed, Strength, Poise, Prowess, Arcane, and Perception.

Physique (PHY): Physique is how tough, healthy, and physically durable the character is. It reflects the physical attributes of the character. This stat is used to resist poisons, illness, and physical ailments. Physique also helps determine a character's Armor (ARM), Willpower, and the number of damage circles on his life spiral.

- **Speed (SPD):** This is how fast the character moves. It determines how far a character can move during his turn and is used to calculate important derived stats like Defense (DEF) and Initiative.

- **Strength (STR):** This is a measure of the character's physical strength. Strength is used to determine how much a character can lift and is a major component of how much damage he inflicts in melee combat.

Agility (AGL): Agility is a measure of the character's reflexes and nimbleness. This stat is used when the character makes a non-combat skill roll involving coordination and reflexes. Agility helps determine a character's DEF and the number of damage circles on his life spiral.

- **Poise (POI):** Poise reflects a character's hand eye coordination and manual dexterity. It is the character's ability to focus physically. Poise helps determine a character's skill with ranged weapons.

- **Prowess (PRW):** Prowess is a measure of a character's grace, balance, and control over his body. It takes into account practice, conditioning, and training. It helps determine a character's natural talent with melee weapons and partly determines a character's Initiative.

Intellect (INT): This is a measure of the character's wits, deduction, and the speed of his thoughts. This stat is used when the character tries to figure something out or uses a skill involving knowledge or problem solving. Intellect also helps determine a character's Willpower and the number of damage circles on his life spiral.

- **Arcane (ARC):** This is a measure of the character's magical power. Arcane is also used to determine a character's skill with offensive magic. Only characters with the Gifted archetype have the Arcane stat.

- **Perception (PER):** This is a measure of how astute the character is, his attention to detail, and his awareness. It is also used in part to determine a character's Defense (DEF) and Initiative.

DERIVED STATS

Derived stats are values computed using a character's primary and secondary stats along with other factors. By combining primary and secondary stats together in various combinations, derived stats further expand the parameters of what a character can do.

Defense (DEF): This stat determines how hard it is to hit a character in combat. A character's basic Defense is the sum of his Speed, Agility, and Perception. Defense can be modified further by abilities or equipment.

Initiative: This stat is used in initiative rolls (p. 201) to determine when a character can act during combat. A character's basic Initiative is the sum of his Speed, Prowess, and Perception. Initiative can be modified further by abilities or equipment.

Armor (ARM): This is how difficult it is to cause damage to the character. A character's Armor is the sum of his Physique and the armor modifiers from the armor he wears.

Willpower (WIL): This stat determines the character's ability to resist the effects of fear and mind control magic. A character's Willpower is the sum of his Physique and Intellect.

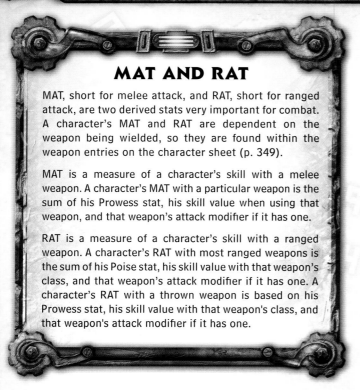

MAT AND RAT

MAT, short for melee attack, and RAT, short for ranged attack, are two derived stats very important for combat. A character's MAT and RAT are dependent on the weapon being wielded, so they are found within the weapon entries on the character sheet (p. 349).

MAT is a measure of a character's skill with a melee weapon. A character's MAT with a particular weapon is the sum of his Prowess stat, his skill value when using that weapon, and that weapon's attack modifier if it has one.

RAT is a measure of a character's skill with a ranged weapon. A character's RAT with most ranged weapons is the sum of his Poise stat, his skill value with that weapon's class, and that weapon's attack modifier if it has one. A character's RAT with a thrown weapon is based on his Prowess stat, his skill value with that weapon's class, and that weapon's attack modifier if it has one.

THE LIFE SPIRAL

Characters in the *Iron Kingdoms Full Metal Fantasy Roleplaying Game* have life spirals that determine how much damage they can suffer during play. The life spiral is split into three aspects that correspond to the character's primary stats. In other words, each aspect has a number of vitality points equal to the character's stat. The higher a character's primary stats, the more damage he can suffer during play. Each aspect splits into two branches, for a total of six branches. The numbered branches are used to determine which branch of a character's life spiral suffers damage first.

For the complete rules on how characters suffer and heal damage, see "Damage" (p. 215).

STAT MODIFIERS

There are many effects in the game that can modify stats, including spells, equipment, archetype benefits, and weapon abilities. If an effect modifies—but does not permanently change—a character's stat, the modifier applies only to that stat. It does not alter the character's derived stats or require a change to his life spiral. If one of the character's stats is permanently changed, his derived stats and life spiral must be recalculated.

ABILITIES, CONNECTIONS, AND SKILLS

While a character's stats establish his principle attributes, his abilities, skills, and connections determine his specific expertise and talents. Characters begin the game with a small selection of abilities, connections, and skills (based on their choices of starting careers), and as they grow more experienced they learn new skills and abilities and also further refine and improve the skills they already have. Abilities, connections, and skills are similar in that they influence a character's specialization, but they differ in how they function, how they are acquired, and how they advance.

Abilities represent things a character knows how to do. Abilities can be gained only once, and they do not have levels of mastery; a character either has an ability or he does not. Once a character gains an ability, he gains all the rules associated with it. The use of an ability normally does not require rolling dice to determine if it succeeds. A character must have an ability in order to attempt to use it.

Some abilities have prerequisites, usually a minimum primary stat, secondary stat, or skill level.

Connections are things like contacts the character has developed or organizations to which he belongs. A character can gain multiple connections, but each must be focused on a different network of contacts. Like abilities, connections do not have levels. Once a character gains a connection, he gains all the benefits associated with it.

Skills represent knowledge, talents, and proficiencies a character develops over time. Unlike abilities and connections, skills have levels that measure a character's mastery in that skill. Each of the character's skills has a maximum level between 1 and 4. If more than one of a character's careers includes the same skill, use the highest maximum to determine the maximum level for that skill that the character can achieve. As a character gains experience, he can increase the levels of existing skills or learn new skills available from his career choices.

COMMAND RANGE

Every character has a command range equal to his INT + Command skill in inches. A character is always in his own command range.

The use of a skill usually involves rolling dice in a skill roll to determine if the skill was successful or not. The higher the skill's level, the more likely the skill roll will succeed.

A character may be able to use a skill whether or not he has that skill on his character sheet. The difference is that a character with training in that skill is more likely to roll a successful skill roll. For more details on skill rolls, see "Skill Resolution Rolls" (p. 198).

The full list of abilities can be found on p. 156, and the full lists of skills can be found on p. 172 and p. 173. Connections are discussed on p. 168.

CREATING YOUR CHARACTER

The most important component to your roleplaying experience is the character you choose to play. The choices you make when creating your character not only determine what your character is good at, but they also influence how your character interacts with others and the world around him. The steps below for creating a character cover the basics for playing the *Iron Kingdoms Full Metal Fantasy Roleplaying Game*. For a more deeply rewarding experience, think about your character's personality, history, and motivation. Does he have a character flaw? Does he speak with an affectation? What are his biases, weaknesses, and shortcomings? Where is he from? What is he afraid of? What—and who—does he love? The more detail you put into your character, the more enjoyment you'll derive from your roleplaying experience.

Before you get started, you'll need a character sheet to record all the pertinent information about your character. You can use any system you like for tracking this information, but we have included a character sheet at the end of this book for you to photocopy and use for your characters (p. 349).

With your character sheet, you are ready to get started with character creation. In addition to the following steps, you need to name your character and think about how he knows the other characters in your adventuring group. It is also a good idea to discuss your character concept with the Game Master before you begin. Your Game Master might have a specific narrative campaign in mind that could affect the type of characters the group is playing. For instance, you might be playing a group of Nyss refugees who have escaped from the same village before it became subjugated by Everblight's legion, in which case everyone would play as a Nyss character. Or you might play as a group who met during warcaster training at a military academy, in which case each character would have Warcaster as one of his career choices.

There are five basic steps for creating a character:

1. Choose your character's race.

2. Choose your character's archetype.

3. Choose two starting careers for your character.

4. Increase your character's stats.

5. Apply the finishing touches.

STEP 1: CHOOSE YOUR CHARACTER'S RACE

You can play a human, dwarf, gobber, Iosan, Nyss, ogrun, or trollkin. Your choice of race determines the character's starting stats as well as the careers available to him. Race also affects a character's height and weight, and some races begin the game with racial benefits and abilities. The race entries list the following information:

Stat Profile: Each racial stat profile establishes the starting stats for a starting hero of each race. It also sets the upper limits for each stat at each stage of a character's experience progression. Characters begin as Heroes, so use the Hero Limit column to determine the maximum value for each of your character's stats.

Only characters with the Gifted archetype have the Arcane stat. If the character is a focuser, he starts the game with ARC 2. Will weavers start the game with ARC 3. See "Arcane Traditions" on p. 228 for details on these types of spellcasters.

Archetype: These are the archetypes available to a character of this race.

Languages: These are the languages that the character can speak and read at the start of the game. It is highly recommended that all of the characters in an adventuring party have at least one language in common.

Height and Weight: This is the range describing the average size and heft of characters for that race. These are guidelines, not hard and fast rules. You can choose to play an exceptionally tall, short, heavy, or thin member of any of the races if you desire.

Additional Characteristics: These are other bonuses or disadvantages the character begins with.

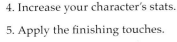

HUMAN

Humans are by far the predominant race living in the Iron Kingdoms, and perhaps across Caen itself, as they have been observed on several continents. Mankind has been prevalent in western Immoren for as long as legends have been told, with civilizations stretching back six thousand years and untold millennia before that as nomadic tribes. Humans are an adaptable and hardy race capable of a broad range of careers and thriving in every geography, from the frozen northern mountains to the arid desert wastes. Humans have been at the forefront of invention and pioneered many of the technologies that the nations of the region rely upon, including alchemy and mechanika.

The five Iron Kingdoms were the inheritors of the Thousand Cities Era, a time when countless petty fiefdoms emerged across the region. This has given rise to a proliferation of human ethnicities and cultures, each proud of its history. Many of the peoples of western Immoren have distinct physical traits and can be recognized on sight.

Humans come in a wide range of appearances, with great variance in skin pigmentation, height, hair and eye color, and body build. Most Immorese humans have pale or olive skin, but there are those who are exceptionally pale and others with very dark skin. Hair colors are usually shades of brown but include black, red, blond, and many shades between. Humans identify with one another more by shared languages and nationality than by superficial physical distinctions.

The most commonly identified ethnicities are described on p. 64, but all humans share a common stat profile.

HUMAN

	STARTING VALUE	HERO LIMIT	VET LIMIT	EPIC LIMIT
PHY	5	7	8	8
SPD	6	7	7	7
STR	4	6	7	8
AGL	3	5	6	7
PRW	4	5	6	7
POI	4	5	6	7
INT	3	5	6	7
ARC	*	4	6	8
PER	3	5	6	7

Archetypes: Gifted, Intellectual, Mighty, Skilled

Languages: A human starts the game with two languages: his native language and one other he has picked up in his travels. If a character is from Cygnar or the Protectorate, his native language is Cygnaran/Sulese (those from the Protectorate call this language Sulese, but it is largely the same as Cygnaran). If he is from Khador, his native tongue is Khadoran. If the character is from Llael, he speaks Llaelese. If he is from Ord, he speaks Ordic. A character from isolated or distinct tribes speaks the language of his people.

Height: 61–75 inches male, 55–69 inches female

Weight: 110–200 pounds male, 90–170 pounds female

Additional Characteristics:

- Exceptional Potential – Humans are extremely adaptable and talented individuals. Your character begins the game with your choice of +1 PHY, +1 AGL, or +1 INT. Add this bonus before spending Advancement Points. Note this bonus does not increase the character's racial maximum, just the starting value.

DWARF

Dwarves are the sturdy and long-lived folk who hail from the northern nation of Rhul, a sprawling mountainous civilization based around extended family clans. Rhul is the longest enduring and stable civilization in western Immoren. Rhulfolk, as dwarves are commonly known, are stalwart in body and demeanor and generally optimistic about overcoming hardships or obstacles. They readily embrace mechanika, steam power, and manufacturing. They are relatively slow innovators but have shown superlative skill in adapting and improving upon these fields. Most dwarves take considerable pride in their individual areas of expertise, whatever that may be; performing good work is a core value of their culture. This has led to Rhul's reputation for fine crafted goods as well as exceptionally disciplined and professional mercenaries and soldiers.

There is truth to the dwarven reputation as a law-abiding people. Primacy of law is vital in Rhul, where arbitration is overseen by the priests of their progenitor gods with sacred solemnity. Most dwarves do not make idle promises. This has encouraged a fondness for negotiating detailed contracts that other races may find tedious. Rhulic law includes stipulations for settling disputes by violent duels and feuds, which has led to martial traditions being enthusiastically embraced by all walks of life. Rhulfolk have been living in human cities for centuries and face no real discrimination. The solidarity of the Rhulic people is well known and well deserved, as even strangers will go to great lengths to look after one another.

Physically dwarves are shorter on average than humans, but they make up for it by being quite stout in frame. They can expect to live about half again as long as humans. Dwarves demonstrate a similar range of skin tones and hair colors as human ethnicities in the same northern regions. Most Rhulfolk have a pragmatic attitude toward clothing, armor, and weapons and prefer function over ostentation.

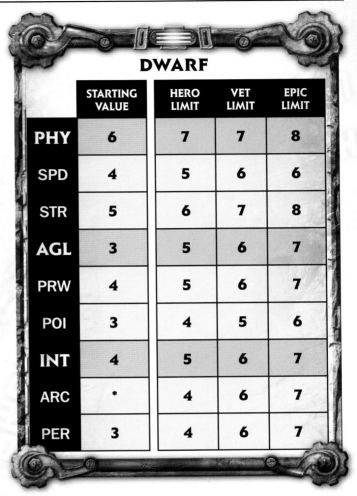

DWARF

	STARTING VALUE	HERO LIMIT	VET LIMIT	EPIC LIMIT
PHY	6	7	7	8
SPD	4	5	6	6
STR	5	6	7	8
AGL	3	5	6	7
PRW	4	5	6	7
POI	3	4	5	6
INT	4	5	6	7
ARC	*	4	6	7
PER	3	4	6	7

Archetypes: Gifted, Intellectual, Mighty, Skilled

Languages: A dwarf starts the game with two languages: Rhulic and one other he has picked up in his travels.

Height: 52–60 inches male, 47–55 inches female.

Weight: 150–190 pounds male, 105–145 pounds female.

Additional Characteristics:

- Load Bearing – Dwarf characters start the game with the Load Bearing ability (p. 164). This ability is in addition to any others the character gains from his starting career.

- Connections (clan) – Dwarf characters begin with Connection (dwarven clan) (p. 169). This is in addition to any other connections the character starts with.

GOBBER

Gobbers are an amiable and curious people inclined to violence only as a last resort, which differentiates them from their wilder cousins known as bogrin. They have had considerable success integrating into human society in both rural and urban areas. They include astute traders, skilled laborers, and innovative thinkers with a natural affinity for alchemy and engineering. Gobbers are a diminutive people, quite slender and wiry. They are hairless, and their skin is generally a mottled green-gray. This coloration can change drastically, however, often by mood, and some gobbers can control their skin coloration to a limited degree.

Gobbers are one of the three major Dhunian races that worship the mother-goddess, although religion is not a major aspect of their lives. Indeed, they seem irreverent and lacking in solemnity to some cultures, but this is merely an extension of their curiosity and general disregard for social barriers. Gobber society has little regimentation or hierarchy, with each gobber expected to speak frankly and contribute to the general well-being of his family and closest friends.

Gobbers who work and live together fall into a communal relationship where ownership of items like tools or weapons becomes meaningless, a behavior they may also exhibit with friends and colleagues of other races. Although they do not consider taking another's belongings under such circumstances theft, those living in human society understand human norms, so they cannot make excuses to evade punishments for crimes. Small in stature, extremely nimble, good climbers, and naturally skilled at evading notice, gobbers do make exceptional thieves. This has led to unfortunate stereotypes. Gobbers usually prefer to create things of lasting value by the skill of their hands and equally nimble minds than to survive by pilfering. That said, they are often exploited in low-paying jobs, so many live in poverty and sometimes turn to criminal professions as an alternative. Others live as semi-nomadic junkers, a respectable trade among gobbers, and travel from town to town salvaging broken and discarded items to repair and resell.

GOBBER

	STARTING VALUE	HERO LIMIT	VET LIMIT	EPIC LIMIT
PHY	4	6	7	7
SPD	6	7	7	7
STR	3	4	5	6
AGL	4	5	6	7
PRW	4	5	6	7
POI	3	5	6	7
INT	3	4	5	6
ARC	–	–	–	–
PER	3	4	4	5

Archetypes: Intellectual, Mighty, Skilled

Languages: A gobber starts the game with two languages: Gobberish and one other he has picked up in his travels.

Height: 34–42 inches male, 32–40 inches female.

Weight: 42–60 pounds male, 38–55 pounds female.

Additional Characteristics:

- Deft – Whether or not they have the Skilled archetype, gobber characters start the game with the Deft archetype benefit (p. 117). This benefit is in addition to any other archetype benefits the character starts with.

- Gobbers have a racial modifier of +1 DEF.

- Gobbers cannot use great weapons or rifles.

IOSAN

The learned and physically graceful people from the nation of Ios are the remnants of a once-vast empire that has long since collapsed. Though Ios has been bordered by Rhul almost as long as human civilization, these people originally came from eastern Immoren. The disaster that destroyed their old civilization led to other problems. While few outsiders know it, the race is dying; its numbers are dwindling, and the current generation faces a looming cosmological catastrophe that might occur within their lifetime. This has led to most Iosans being xenophobic and extremely secretive. Those who come to know them realize they are an intelligent and skilled people, equally well versed in combat and the arcane arts. While private about religious matters, most are deeply pious in their worship for a goddess named Scyrah.

Iosans live considerably longer than most races, which has given rise to a reputation for agelessness. Many enjoy over two centuries of life, for they are not prone to disease and rarely show the ravages of time even in their advanced years. Given the imminent doom their race faces, Iosan longevity is not seen as a great advantage. Iosans are generally pale and have a range of hair color, with some dying their hair exotic shades. Certain sects wear tattoos as a way to show solidarity, and a number have also chosen to shave their heads.

The Iosans have been reticent as long as humanity can remember, but in the last few decades their isolationism has taken an extreme turn. The nation has closed its borders and conducts little trade with outsiders. Not all Iosans have retreated to their homeland, however, and a number live among the human kingdoms. These tend to be exiles, pilgrims, or well-armed agents serving vital missions. Two Iosan religious sects have specific reasons to be abroad in human lands: the Seekers and the Retribution of Scyrah. The former tends to be friendlier than the latter.

IOSAN

	STARTING VALUE	HERO LIMIT	VET LIMIT	EPIC LIMIT
PHY	5	7	7	7
SPD	6	7	7	7
STR	4	5	6	7
AGL	3	5	6	7
PRW	4	5	6	7
POI	4	5	6	7
INT	4	6	6	7
ARC	*	4	6	8
PER	3	5	6	7

Archetypes: Gifted, Intellectual, Mighty, Skilled

Languages: An Iosan starts the game with two languages: Shyr and one other he has picked up in his travels.

Height: 65–75 inches male, 60–70 inches female.

Weight: 125–180 pounds male, 85–140 pounds female.

Additional Characteristics:

- Iosan characters begin the game with an additional ability selected from one of their careers.

NYSS

Nyss are the rugged race that once inhabited the frozen north amid the imposing peaks of the Shard Spires—a region so inhospitable even the hardy Khadorans ceded it to them. They appear markedly different from their Iosan cousins, being taller and more physically robust, with black hair and extremely pale skin. They also possess an even greater longevity than the Iosans.

The Nyss are a tribal people who live close to the land as superlative hunters, trackers, archers, and swordsmen. Also inheritors of a long and ancient line, they know the forging of superior weapons as well as the crafting of supple leather armor. Considered the chosen people of the winter god Nyssor, the Nyss have an affinity for cold. Sorcery is common among them and is seen as a blessing that allows them to manifest the powers of cold against their enemies.

At one time the Nyss were more similar to the Iosans and lived alongside them, although they were never as xenophobic or insular as their cousins. Centuries ago they undertook a spiritual exodus to the frozen wilds and adopted a new way of life. This forever changed them. Traditionally the Nyss have always been a strongly devout people who see themselves as chosen by Nyssor, but their culture was recently shattered by the arrival of the dragon Everblight, who worked through his minions to enslave most of the Nyss as part of his legion. The few who escaped the dragon's blight fled south as refugees and now eke out livings as mercenaries, hunters, or criminals. Even as they try to preserve their old ways, they know they must rely on other peoples to ensure their survival.

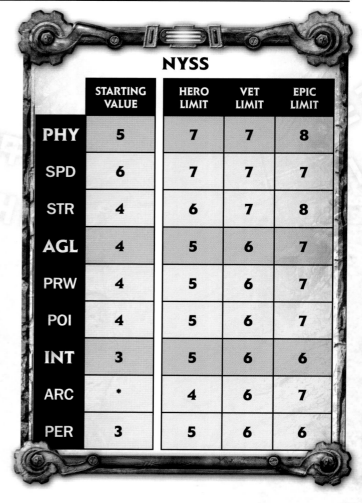

NYSS

	STARTING VALUE	HERO LIMIT	VET LIMIT	EPIC LIMIT
PHY	5	7	7	8
SPD	6	7	7	7
STR	4	6	7	8
AGL	4	5	6	7
PRW	4	5	6	7
POI	4	5	6	7
INT	3	5	6	6
ARC	*	4	6	7
PER	3	5	6	6

Archetypes: Gifted, Mighty, Skilled

Languages: A Nyss starts the game with two languages: Aeric and one other he has picked up in his travels.

Height: 67–77 inches male, 62–72 inches female.

Weight: 140–195 pounds male, 95–130 pounds female.

Additional Characteristics:

- Nyss with the Gifted archetype cannot have the Arcane Mechanik, Arcanist, Gun Mage, or Warcaster careers.

- Reduce the cost of Nyss bows (p. 262) and Nyss claymores (p. 256) by 10 gc during character creation.

- Nyss gain +1 on Initiative and PER rolls.

- Nyss gain +3 ARM against cold damage.

- Nyss suffer –3 ARM against fire damage.

OGRUN

Ogrun are fierce-looking, formidable creatures who tower over most other races and are capable of remarkable feats of strength. They are also a tremendously honorable people who have earned a place for themselves in the Iron Kingdoms, primarily as laborers and peerless warriors. While scattered tribes of ogrun still exist in isolated pockets, most have integrated into the kingdoms' cultures. The largest concentration of ogrun is found in Rhu, where they are counted as full members of the dwarven clans to whom they have sworn fealty. Ogrun loyalty is legendary, and they have a reputation for being among the most dedicated and fierce bodyguards in western Immoren. Mercenary ogrun are deemed more trustworthy and reliable than other sell-swords and can command a premium wage.

Ogrun are one of the major Dhunian races, and while their society within Rhul has changed, they remain a spiritual people. Traditional ogrun culture is rooted in a simple but effective system of feudalism whereby young warriors called bokur must eventually find worthy leaders to serve. Elder ogrun in turn hope to prove worthy enough to earn the binding oaths of young bokurs, for whom they then carry a certain responsibility. The ogrun in the leadership position is a korune—a lord—and there can be multiple layers of vassalage in an ogrun tribe, with the leader being whoever boasts the largest chain of subordinates. General obligations are secondary to personal oaths, and even Rhulic ogrun feel the urge to find a worthy korune, generally after an extended period of wandering and self-testing.

Rhulic ogrun have adopted many of the beliefs and priorities of dwarven society, including taking pride in work. While the combat arts are chosen by most, there are many accomplished ogrun smiths, masons, and mechanics who tackle these professions with the same dedication as a bokur mastering his battle-glaive.

OGRUN

	STARTING VALUE	HERO LIMIT	VET LIMIT	EPIC LIMIT
PHY	6	7	8	9
SPD	5	6	6	6
STR	6	8	9	10
AGL	3	5	5	6
PRW	4	5	6	7
POI	3	4	5	6
INT	3	5	5	6
ARC	–	–	–	–
PER	2	4	5	6

Archetypes: Mighty, Skilled

Languages: An ogrun starts the game with three languages: Molgur-Og, Rhulic, and one other he has picked up in his travels.

Height: 90–105 inches male, 82–97 inches male.

Weight: 450–500 pounds male, 330–380 pounds female.

Additional Characteristics:

- Huge Stature – An ogrun can wield a weapon in one hand that usually requires two hands to wield, but he suffers –2 on attack rolls with that weapon.

TROLLKIN

Trollkin are a strong, hardy, and tradition-minded people renowned for their tenacity and resilience. These people have been among the most successful and diverse of the races of western Immoren. Persisting outside the laws of the Iron Kingdoms, trollkin are organized into large tribal societies called kriels which are comprised of multiple families called kith. Most trollkin wear distinctive quitari patterns that denote their connection to kith and kriel. Trollkin are the most deeply religious of the Dhunian races, and their shamans are spiritual leaders as well as leaders of sizable communities.

Trollkin are large and physically imposing, with distinctive skin whose hue may range from dark blue to blue-green, though their sorcerers tend to be slighter of build with much paler skin tones. They grow colorful quills rather than hair, and the faces of the males show calcified growths that become more pronounced with age. Trollkin are blood relatives of trolls and boast similar, if reduced, resilience; a trollkin who is well fed can endure wounds that would kill a human. This vitality also leads to long lives, and they regularly live almost twice as long as humans. Some trollkin possess tremendously powerful, booming voices said to be able to crack stone and shatter eardrums.

The trollkin are divided between the wilderness kriels, who are often at odds with human civilization, and those who have integrated into the cities as citizens of the Iron Kingdoms. Few trollkin are comfortable on both sides of this divide, and most must eventually choose between them. Certain kriels have had increasingly violent clashes with human townships and armies in recent years. As a result, trollkin often face prejudice and fear in human cities, particularly in regions that have been beset by the larger, ravenous full-blood trolls. In general, trollkin are valued in cities for their seemingly inexhaustible stamina as well as their skill at a variety of crafts, particularly the art of armed conflict.

TROLLKIN

	STARTING VALUE		HERO LIMIT	VET LIMIT	EPIC LIMIT
PHY	6		8	9	10
SPD	5		6	6	6
STR	5		7	8	9
AGL	3		5	6	7
PRW	4		5	6	7
POI	2		4	5	6
INT	3		4	5	6
ARC	*		4	6	7
PER	3		4	5	6

Archetypes: Gifted, Mighty, Skilled

Languages: A trollkin starts the game with two languages: Molgur-Trul and one other he has picked up in his travels.

Height: 71–84 inches male, 63–76 inches female.

Weight: 250–330 pounds male, 150–230 pounds female.

Additional Characteristics:

- Trollkin with the Gifted archetype cannot have the Arcane Mechanik, Arcanist, or Warcaster careers.

- Tough – Whether or not they have the Mighty archetype, trollkin characters start the game with the Tough archetype benefit (p. 116). This is in addition to any other archetype benefits selected for the character.

- Feat: Revitalize – Whether or not they have the Mighty archetype, trollkin characters start the game with the Feat: Revitalize archetype benefit (p. 116). This is in addition to any other archetype benefits selected for the character.

STEP 2: CHOOSE AN ARCHETYPE

Your character's archetype largely defines his role in the game along with what career options are available to him. Each archetype has a number of archetype benefits. Your character starts with at least one of these benefits (or more, from race or other sources), and as he develops and gains experience, he can learn additional archetype benefits.

Archetypes include Gifted, Intellectual, Mighty, and Skilled.

GIFTED

Those with the Gifted archetype are born with the capacity to work magic. This potential can be latent, discovered only later in life, or it can be pronounced and defining from an early age. The Gifted archetype allows characters to take arcane careers such as Arcane Mechanik, Arcanist, Gun Mage, Priest, Sorcerer, and Warcaster.

A character with the Gifted archetype starts the game with a tradition (p. 228). This book describes two: the will weaver and the focuser. If the character begins the game with the Warcaster career, he is a focuser; otherwise, he is a will weaver.

Choosing the Gifted archetype is the only way for a character to have an ARC stat. If the character is a focuser, he starts the game with ARC 2. Will weavers start the game with ARC 3. The character can increase his ARC before the start of the game by spending Advancement Points and later by gaining Experience Points (XP).

Additionally, a Gifted character begins the game with one of the following benefits. Characters gain additional benefits as they accumulate experience points.

- Additional Study – The character delves further into the mysteries of the arcane and is rewarded with a spell from one of his career spell lists. This benefit can be taken multiple times, but a character still cannot exceed twice his INT in spells known.

- Combat Caster – When this character makes a magic attack roll, he gains an additional die. Discard the lowest die of each roll.

- Fast Caster – The character gains one extra quick action each activation that can be used only to cast a spell.

- Feat: Dominator – The character can spend 1 feat point during his turn to double his control area for one round.

- Feat: Powerful Caster – The character can spend 1 feat point when he casts a spell to increase the RNG (range) of the spell by twelve feet (2″). Spells with a range of CTRL (control area) or SP (spray attack) are not affected.

- Feat: Quick Cast – The character can spend 1 feat point to immediately cast one upkeep spell at the start of combat before the first round. When casting a spell as a result of this benefit, the character is not required to pay the COST of the spell.

- Feat: Strength of Will – After failing a fatigue roll, the character can spend 1 feat point to instead automatically succeed on the roll. This benefit can be taken only by characters with the will weaver tradition.

- Magic Sensitivity – The character can automatically sense when another character casts a spell within fifty feet for each point of his ARC stat. Such characters can tune out this detection as background noise but are aware of particularly powerful magic. Additionally, a character with the focuser tradition can sense other focusers within their detection range.

- Rune Reader – The character can identify any spell cast in his line of sight by reading the accompanying spell runes (see the "Runes and Formulae" sidebar, p. 228). He can also learn the type of magic cast (the spell list it came from) and the tradition of the character casting the spell.

- Warding Circle – The character can spend fifteen minutes to create a circle of warding runes around a small room or campsite. The names of the characters he intends to keep safe within the circle are incorporated into the runes. When any other character enters the circle, all named characters are alerted. While in the circle, non-named characters lose incorporeal, and non-named undead and infernal characters suffer –2 on attack rolls.

INTELLECTUAL

Capable of true bursts of genius, the character is exceptionally intelligent and thinks impossibly quickly and clearly. He is a mastermind capable of planning and executing the most sophisticated plots and plans. He sees all the angles and anticipates the likely course of action taken by lesser minds. Characters with the Intellectual archetype are cerebral thinkers and planners.

Intellectual characters possess a tactical genius and adaptability that gives them +1 on attack and damage rolls in combat. While in the command range of an Intellectual character, a friendly character listening to his orders also gains +1 on his attack and damage rolls. This bonus is non-cumulative, so a character can gain this bonus only from one Intellectual character at a time.

Additionally, an Intellectual character begins the game with one of the following benefits. Characters gain additional benefits as they accumulate experience points.

- Battlefield Coordination – The character is a skilled battlefield commander. He is able to coordinate the movement and attacks of friendly forces to maximum effect. While in his command range, friendly characters do not suffer the firing into melee penalty for ranged attacks and spells and do not have a chance to hit friendly characters when they miss with ranged or magic attacks while firing into melee.

- Feat: Flawless Timing – The character can spend 1 feat point to use this benefit during his turn. When he uses Flawless Timing, the character names an enemy. The next time that enemy directly hits him with an attack that encounter, the attack is instead considered to be a miss.

- Feat: Prescient – The character can spend 1 feat point to win initiative automatically and take the first turn that combat. If two or more characters use this ability, they make initiative rolls to determine which of them goes first.

- Feat: Perfect Plot – The character is a flawless planner and allows nothing to escape his attention. Assuming he is able to oversee all aspects of his plan, scout out the related sites, and do his research in great detail, he is sure to succeed. Of course this degree of planning takes time and care, but perfection is not without its cost. The character must spend 1 feat point to use this ability. A character following this character's plans gains an additional die on non-combat related rolls during the day in which the plan was enacted.

- Feat: Plan of Action – At the start of combat, the character can spend 1 feat point to use this benefit. During that combat, he and friendly characters who follow his plan gain +2 to their initiative rolls and +2 to their attack rolls during the first round of combat.

- Feat: Quick Thinking – The character's quick thinking enables him to act impossibly fast. Once per round, the character can spend 1 feat point to make one attack or quick action at the start of another character's turn.

- Feat: Unconventional Warfare – The character is quick thinking enough to assess any situation, see every potential angle and outcome, and use the environment itself as a weapon. He can use his attacks to off-balance foes and send them careening off ledges or into nearby vats of molten metal, cause them to stumble over terrain features, hit their weak spots to knock them to the ground, or otherwise maneuver them into a position of weakness and jeopardy. The character must spend 1 feat point to use this ability and explain to the Game Master how he is turning the environment against his enemy. The Game Master then determines the likely effect of the character's action or attack. Outcomes include a boosted damage roll (see p. 197), knockdown, push, slam, or a fall from a height.

- Genius – The character possesses an incredible aptitude for intellectual pursuits. The character's INT rolls are boosted.

- Hyper Perception – The character's keen senses miss few details. The character's PER rolls are boosted.

- Photographic Memory – The character has a photographic memory and can recall every event in perfect detail. During play he can call upon his memory to ask the Game Master questions pertaining to anything he has seen or experienced.

MIGHTY

The character is in peak physical condition. He is incredibly strong and inhumanly resilient. The character is capable of feats of strength that defy imagination.

Mighty characters gain an additional die on their melee damage rolls.

Additionally, a Mighty character begins the game with one of the following benefits. Characters gain additional benefits as they accumulate experience points.

- Beat Back – When this character hits a target with a melee attack, he can immediately push his target 1″ directly away. After the target is pushed, this character can advance up to 1″.

- Feat: Back Swing – Once per turn, this character can spend 1 feat point to gain one additional melee attack.

- Feat: Bounding Leap – The character is capable of preternatural feats of athleticism. Once during each of his turns in which the character does not run or charge, he can spend 1 feat point to pitch himself over the heads of his enemies into the heart of battle. When the character uses this benefit, place him anywhere within 5″ of his current location.

- Feat: Counter Charge - When an enemy advances and ends its movement within thirty-six feet (6″) of this character and in his line of sight, this character can immediately spend 1 feat point to charge the enemy. The character cannot make a counter charge while engaged.

- Feat: Invulnerable – The character can spend 1 feat point during his turn to gain +3 ARM for one round.

- Feat: Revitalize – The character can spend 1 feat point during his turn to regain a number of vitality points equal to his PHY stat immediately. If a character suffers damage during his turn, the damage must be resolved before a character can use this feat. An incapacitated character cannot use Revitalize.

- Feat: Shield Breaker – When this character hits a target that has a shield with a melee attack, the character can spend 1 feat point to use this benefit. When the character uses this benefit, after damage has been dealt the other character's shield is completely destroyed as a result of the attack.

- Feat: Vendetta – The character can spend 1 feat point during his turn to use this benefit. When this ability is used the character names one enemy. For the rest of the encounter, this character gains boosted attack rolls against that enemy. A character can use this benefit only once per encounter unless the original subject of his vendetta is destroyed, at which point the character can spend a feat point to use this benefit again.

- Righteous Anger – When one or more characters who are friendly to this character are damaged by an enemy attack while in this character's command range, this character gains +2 STR and ARM for one round.

- Tough – The character is incredibly hardy. When this character is disabled, roll a d6. On a 5 or 6, the character heals 1 vitality point, is no longer disabled, and is knocked down.

SKILLED

The character is extremely quick, nimble, and dexterous. He relies on his wits, skill, and luck in equal measure.

A Skilled character gains an additional attack during his Activation Phase if he chooses to attack that turn.

Additionally, the character begins the game with one of the following benefits. Characters gain additional benefits as they accumulate experience points.

- **Ambidextrous** – The character does not suffer the normal attack roll penalty with a second weapon while using the Two-Weapon Fighting ability.

- **Cagey** – When this character becomes knocked down, he can immediately move up to twelve feet (2″) and cannot be targeted by free strikes during this movement. This benefit has no effect while this character is mounted. While knocked down, this character is not automatically hit by melee attacks and his DEF is not reduced. The character can stand up during his turn without forfeiting his movement or action.

- **Deft** – The character has nimble fingers and steady hands. The character gains boosted AGL rolls.

- **Feat: Defensive Strike** – When an enemy advances into and ends its movement in this character's melee range, this character can spend 1 feat point to immediately make one melee attack targeting it.

- **Feat: Disarm** – After directly hitting an enemy with a non-spray, non-AOE (area of effect) ranged or melee attack, instead of making a damage roll, the character can spend 1 feat point to disarm his opponent. When this benefit is used, the enemy's weapon, or any object in his hand, flies from his grasp. He suffers no damage from the attack.

- **Feat: Swashbuckler** – Once during each of his turns, this character can spend 1 feat point to use Swashbuckler. The next time this character makes an attack with a hand weapon after using this benefit, his front arc extends to 360°, and he can make one melee attack against each enemy in his line of sight in his melee range. Regardless of the number of characters hit, Swashbuckler can trigger the Sidestep benefit only once (see below).

- **Feat: Untouchable** – The character can spend 1 feat point during his turn to gain +3 DEF for one round.

- **Preternatural Awareness** – The character's uncanny perception keeps him constantly aware of his surroundings. The character gains boosted Initiative rolls. Additionally, enemies never gain back strike bonuses against this character.

- **Sidestep** – When this character hits an enemy character with a melee weapon, he can advance up to 2″ after the attack is resolved. This character cannot be targeted by free strikes during this movement.

- **Virtuoso** – Choose a military skill. When making a non-AOE attack with a weapon that uses that skill, this character gains an additional die on his attack and damage rolls. Discard the lowest die of each roll. This benefit can be taken more than once, each time specifying a different military skill.

STEP 3: CHOOSE TWO CAREERS

After selecting your character's archetype, next choose two careers for your character. By mixing and matching different careers, you can realize a vast number of character concepts from a warcaster pirate to an aristocratic priest, as well as create a number of familiar character types found in the Iron Kingdoms.

A character's careers are more than professions; they represent his ongoing development path as well. Careers determine the character's role in society and the skills and abilities he has the opportunity to master.

When you choose your character's careers you're not necessarily determining what he does for a living, but defining the skills and abilities he's learned over the course of his life. The people of the Iron Kingdoms are a varied lot, and the heroes who become player characters are an even more diverse crowd. It is for this reason that you choose two distinct careers. You might wish to consider one career to be your character's primary occupation—the way he would describe himself. A character who is a Priest and a Rifleman most likely considers himself first and foremost a man of faith, but he's honed his skills with a repeating long rifle in response to the threats he might face at a frontier parish. On the other hand, your character's careers might represent a change in his life. Perhaps a character who began his adult life as a rifleman in the employ of the Ordic army has decided to give up the military life for the more righteous path of a clergyman, albeit a clergyman who knows the value in keeping his arms locked and loaded.

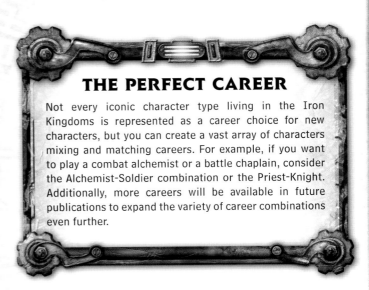

THE PERFECT CAREER

Not every iconic character type living in the Iron Kingdoms is represented as a career choice for new characters, but you can create a vast array of characters mixing and matching careers. For example, if you want to play a combat alchemist or a battle chaplain, consider the Alchemist-Soldier combination or the Priest-Knight. Additionally, more careers will be available in future publications to expand the variety of career combinations even further.

The careers you choose for your character not only determine what he knows how to do at character creation, but also what he can learn and improve over time as he gains experience. Each career description lists the benefits starting characters begin with. On your character sheet, note the skills, abilities, and connections your character gains for each career, and list the starting equipment and money. Note that many careers overlap each other in terms of their skills and abilities. If you gain the same starting skill twice, once from each starting career, your character begins the game with that skill at level 2.

CAREER	REQUIRED RACE	REQUIRED ARCHETYPE	STARTING CAREER ONLY
Alchemist	—	—	—
Arcane Mechanik	—	Gifted †	—
Arcanist	—	Gifted †	—
Aristocrat	Human	—	Yes
Bounty Hunter	—	—	—
Cutthroat	—	—	—
Duelist	—	—	—
Explorer	—	—	—
Fell Caller	Trollkin	—	—
Field Mechanik	—	—	—
Gun Mage	—	Gifted †	—
Highwayman	—	—	—
Investigator	—	—	—
Iron Fang*	Human (Khadoran)	—	Yes
Knight	Human or Iosan	—	—
Mage Hunter	Iosan	—	—
Man-at-Arms	—	—	—
Military Officer	—	—	—
Pirate	—	—	—
Priest (of Morrow or Menoth)	Human	Gifted †	—
Rifleman	—	—	—
Soldier	—	—	—
Sorcerer	—	Gifted†	Yes
Spy	—	—	—
Stormblade*	Human (Cygnaran)	—	Yes
Thief	—	—	—
Trencher*	Human, Ogrun, Trollkin (Cygnaran)	—	Yes
Warcaster	—	Gifted (Focuser)	Yes

* These careers can be paired only with specific other careers at the time of character creation.

† A character who chooses this career **and** the Warcaster career becomes a focuser instead of a will weaver.

Some careers have prerequisites that a character must meet to choose the career. A character's career choices do not change, but a character can add additional careers with experience. See "Earning Experience Points" (p. 153) and "Character Advancement" (p. 155) for details.

ANATOMY OF A CAREER

Prerequisites: Some careers have prerequisites. A character can have a career only if he also has all the prerequisites to take that career. Prerequisites usually require a specific race or archetype, but in some cases they might require the career to be chosen at character creation or for the character to have a minimum value for a stat.

Starting Abilities, Connections, and Skills: These are the abilities, connections, and skills a new character with the given career begins the game with. In addition to abilities, connections, and skills, if a career has other considerations for beginning characters (such as spells or special requirements), they are noted here as well. The full list of abilities can be found on p. 156, and the full lists of skills can be found on p. 172 and p. 173. Connections are discussed on p. 168. When a character learns a new career as a result of character advancement, he does not receive any of the starting abilities, connections, or skills associated with the new career.

Starting Assets: This is a description of any gear, equipment, or weapons a character starts with if he chooses the career at character creation. It also lists the starting funds for that character. This applies only to new characters. When a character learns a new career as a result of character advancement, he does not receive any of the starting assets.

A character keeps all the weapons, equipment, and money from both of his careers. A character who has armor listed in both his careers keeps one set of his choice.

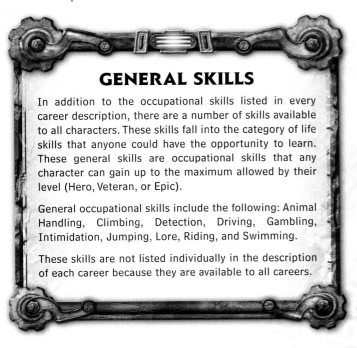

GENERAL SKILLS

In addition to the occupational skills listed in every career description, there are a number of skills available to all characters. These skills fall into the category of life skills that anyone could have the opportunity to learn. These general skills are occupational skills that any character can gain up to the maximum allowed by their level (Hero, Veteran, or Epic).

General occupational skills include the following: Animal Handling, Climbing, Detection, Driving, Gambling, Intimidation, Jumping, Lore, Riding, and Swimming.

These skills are not listed individually in the description of each career because they are available to all careers.

CAREER ABILITIES, CONNECTIONS, AND SKILLS

The following entries delineate all the abilities, connections, skills, and spells specific to each career. Characters can choose to take these options as they gain Experience Points, as noted on the Character Advancement Table (p. 154). A character who takes the career later in his advancement can choose from these options as well.

Abilities: Abilities cover a wide range of specialties a character can have. A character can choose abilities specific to his career from this listing as he gains experience. (Starting abilities are included on this list for characters who take a career later on.) Some abilities have prerequisites that must be met before they are selected, such as a certain skill rank or another ability.

Connections: Connections are things like membership in an organization and contacts with important or influential people. Like abilities, a character can acquire these later in his career.

Military Skills and Occupational Skills: Skills are aptitudes in which a character can gain greater proficiency over time and are broken into two categories: military skills and occupational skills. Military skills are focused on combat, and occupational skills focus on the non-combat related talents associated with the career. Some skills are not available to starting characters and can only be acquired later in a character's career.

CUSTOMIZATION AND OPTIONS

The careers here are intended to get players exploring the world of the Iron Kingdoms quickly. As a result they offer few choices or options for customization at the time of character creation. Some experienced players might want a greater hand in creating their characters. With the Game Master's approval, a player can:

Replace a starting ability with another ability available to that career. The character must meet the prerequisites for the new ability selected.

Replace a starting occupational skill with another occupational skill available to that career.

Replace a starting military skill with another military skill available to that career.

Replace a starting spell with another COST 1 or 2 spell from that career's spell list.

These substitutions do not have a substantial impact with regard to creating challenging encounters, but it adds some flexibility for players willing to put a bit more time into the character creation process.

A Game Master might also decide to give his players some opportunity for customization by starting their characters with a small number of experience points to add options. Starting player characters with 10 or 12 XP gives them plenty of room for customization without advancing them too far.

The list in this entry defines what skills are available to the career, as well as how accomplished the character can become in each skill. The level listed by each skill is the maximum level allowed by the career. The maximum allowable level for a skill is also dependent on the character's current experience level. **A Hero character can have skills up to level 2, a Veteran character can have skills up to level 3, and an Epic character can have skills up to level 4.** If the same skill is listed for different careers for the same character, use the higher maximum value.

Spells: This is the spell list from which a character with this career can select spells. The spell list section only appears in the entry for careers that can learn to cast spells. The maximum number of spells a character can learn is equal to twice his Intellect stat.

ALCHEMIST

PREREQUISITES: NONE

STARTING ABILITIES AND SKILLS	Abilities: Grenadier and Poison Resistance Military Skills: Hand Weapon 1 and Thrown Weapon 1 Occupational Skills: Alchemy 1 and Medicine 1
STARTING ASSETS	50 gc, alchemist's leather, gas mask, traveling alchemist's kit, any five alchemical grenades, and a grenadier's bandolier
ALCHEMIST ABILITIES	Bomber, Brew Master, Fast Cook, Field Alchemist, Fire in the Hole!, Free Style, Grenadier, Poison Resistance
ALCHEMIST CONNECTION	Connections (alchemical order)
ALCHEMIST MILITARY SKILLS	Hand Weapon 2, Thrown Weapon 4, Unarmed Combat 2
ALCHEMIST OCCUPATIONAL SKILLS	Alchemy 4, Craft 4 (any), Forgery 2, General Skills 4, Medicine 4, Negotiation 4, Research 4

The alchemist is trained in the arcane science of refining and combining rare and exotic ingredients to create alchemical items, including blasting power, healing salves, and potent alchemical grenades. He might have learned the secrets of his trade in an apprenticeship with an organization such as the Order of the Golden Crucible, or he could have received his training from one of the many freelance alchemists roaming the Iron Kingdoms.

The life of an adventuring alchemist is a dangerous one. Sometimes an alchemist has access to the resources of established organizations, but at times he might need to personally gather rare substances for use in complex alchemical creations. This often means venturing into the wilds in search of rare natural reagents—many of which are exceedingly hard to locate or must be harvested from elusive and dangerous creatures.

Playing an Alchemist: The Alchemist is the only career that can fully utilize and explore the wonders of alchemy in the Iron Kingdoms. An Alchemist character can augment his alchemical skills with the acquisition of specialist abilities like Brew Master, Fast Cook, Field Alchemist, and Free Style. A player should choose to play an Alchemist if he wishes to create alchemical items, unleash volatile alchemical compounds in battle, or utilize the field alchemy rules to mix alchemical substances on the fly. Alchemists pair well with a wide variety of careers and fill a variety of roles in a party, from the Skilled Alchemist-Thief who bombs his enemies to the Gifted Alchemist-Arcane Mechanik who supports his party with items, spells, and the Medicine skill.

Experienced alchemists gain even greater mastery of their alchemical mixology and eventually can learn the Bomber ability, granting them control over their alchemical grenades even when they miss their intended target.

ARCANE MECHANIK

STARTING ABILITIES, SKILLS, AND SPELLS	**Abilities:** Inscribe Formulae **Military Skills:** Choose either Hand Weapon 1 or Rifle 1 **Occupational Skills:** Craft (gunsmithing) 1, Craft (metalworking) 1, and Mechanikal Engineering 1 **Spells:** Arcantrik Bolt and Polarity Shield
STARTING ASSETS	50 gc and a rune etching kit. The character also begins the game with a mechanika weapon or suit of armor worth up to 750 gc, including the device's housing, power source, and rune plate.

ARCANE MECHANIK ABILITIES	'Jack Marshal, Ace Commander, Arcane Engineer, Drive: Assault, Drive: Pronto, Inscribe Formulae, Resourceful, Steamo
ARCANE MECHANIK CONNECTIONS	Connections (mechaniks organization)
ARCANE MECHANIK MILITARY SKILLS	Hand Weapon 2, Light Artillery 2, Rifle 2
ARCANE MECHANIK OCCUPATIONAL SKILLS	Command 1, Craft 4 (any specialization), Cryptography 3, General skills 4, Mechanikal Engineering 4, Negotiation 2, Research 3.
ARCANE MECHANIK SPELLS	Spells from the Arcane Mechanik spell list

Bridging the gap between machines and magic, the arcane mechanik is an arcanist with a penchant for mechanikal engineering. He is an innovative crafter of mechanika devices and has the necessary skills and knowledge to create and repair mechanika armor and weapons or the arcane systems of steamjacks. The arcane mechanik has likely spent some time as an apprentice for an established arcane mechanik or for an organization that employs them, such as the Steam and Iron Workers Union in Cygnar.

Creating mechanika is an incredibly expensive undertaking, and arcane mechaniks often turn to adventuring and mercenary work to fund their endeavors. Since their skills are in high demand, an arcane mechanik typically has little trouble finding lucrative employment. Additionally, the wild and unpredictable life of a freelance mercenary often provides the perfect testing ground for many types of mechanikal creations.

Playing an Arcane Mechanik: The Iron Kingdoms setting would not be the same without the wealth of mechanikal weapons, armor, devices, and steamjacks that shape its battles and its very way of life. No other career has the same ties to mechanikal items as the Arcane Mechanik. Arcane Mechaniks begin the game with the Inscribe Formulae ability, the key to creating the runeplates that shape the magic behind all mechanika. In addition to their mechanika crafting excellence, Arcane Mechaniks begin the game with a mechanika item and have a spell list that showcases their mechanikal affinity. Whether a mechanika-wielder, mechanika-creator, 'jack marshal, spell slinger, or all of the above, there can be no doubting an Arcane Mechanik's mechanikal mastery.

Experienced Arcane Mechaniks become even more adept at working with mechanika and with warjacks in particular. They alone gain access to the potent Resourceful ability that obsoletes the need to gain fatigue or spend focus upkeeping spells on steamjacks under their control ever again.

ARCANIST

STARTING ABILITIES, SKILLS, AND SPELLS	**Abilities:** Great Power **Occupational Skills:** Lore (Arcane) 1 and Research 1 **Spells:** Arcane Bolt, Aura of Protection, and Light in the Darkness **Special:** A character who chooses Arcanist as one of his two starting careers gains the Rune Reader Gifted archetype benefit (p. 115).
STARTING ASSETS	75 gc

ARCANIST ABILITIES	Arcane Defenses, Arcane Scholar, Great Power, University Education
ARCANIST CONNECTIONS	Connections (magical order)
ARCANIST MILITARY SKILLS	—
ARCANIST OCCUPATIONAL SKILLS	Craft 2 (any), Etiquette 2, General Skills 4, Negotiation 2, Oratory 2, Research 4
ARCANIST SPELLS	Spells from the Arcanist spell list

The arcanist is a trained arcane practitioner who manifests his magic through the precise and practiced use of arcane formulae. He might have studied under a master arcanist for years, learning complex arcane recitations, or he could have refined his innate magical abilities on his own, seeking out ancient books of arcane lore to acquire more complete control over his spells.

Arcanists often join or are recruited into established arcane organizations to gain access to tightly guarded knowledge in return for service to the order. The search for forgotten lore is a strong motivator for the arcanists of western Immoren. Many arcanists who might prefer to study in the safe confines of their residences grudgingly set out to uncover these lost or forbidden secrets. Freelance arcanists are not uncommon, and their skills provide them with no end of employment opportunities.

Playing an Arcanist: The Arcanist career is the path of a pure spellcaster with a spell list packed with spells for offense, support, control, *and* utility. Any party would be grateful to have an Arcanist along thanks to his Aura of Protection, an ARM-enhancing upkeep spell that won't even crimp his own style thanks to the Great Power ability (which allows him to upkeep a spell for free). It's important to note, however, that arcanists lack all military skills and have limited non-combat expertise outside of the arcane arts. A starting Arcanist character is defined as much by his other career as he is by the Arcanist career. Pairing Arcanist with Pistoleer, for example, creates a character who slings spells with quick

actions and fires repeating pistol shots with his attacks. Pairing Arcanist with another spellcasting career gives an even broader spell list and access to additional magic-related abilities.

Experienced Arcanists benefit greatly from additional Gifted archetype benefits and can eventually gain the Arcane Defenses ability, granting them increased protection from their enemies' spells once they've mastered their own.

ARISTOCRAT

STARTING ABILITIES, CONNECTIONS, AND SKILLS	**Abilities:** Good Breeding, Language (any), and Privilege **Connections:** Connections (nobility) **Military Skills:** Hand Weapon 1 and the choice of one other: Archery 1, Pistol 1, or Rifle 1 **Occupational Skills:** Command 1 and Etiquette 1 **Special:** A character who chooses Aristocrat as one of his two starting careers gains 50 gc each month from his family holdings.
STARTING ASSETS	**200 gc**
ARISTOCRAT ABILITIES	Advisor, Appraise, Battle Plan: Call to Action, Expert Rider, Good Breeding, Language, Natural Leader, Poison Resistance, Privilege, Rallying Cry, Swift Rider
ARISTOCRAT CONNECTIONS	Connections (any)
ARISTOCRAT MILITARY SKILLS	Archery 2, Hand Weapon 3, Lance 3, Pistol 2, Rifle 3
ARISTOCRAT OCCUPATIONAL SKILLS	Bribery 4, Command 4, Cryptography 2, Deception 4, Etiquette 4, General Skills 4, Law 4, Negotiation 4, Oratory 4, Seduction 4

The aristocrat is descended from one of the leading houses of the Iron Kingdoms. He could be a Kayazy merchant prince, a Cygnaran noble, or the heir to an Ordic castellan. It's possible that his family line stretches back to the Thousand Cities era; some noble lines are of more recent creation. Whatever the provenance of his name, station and prestige have provided the aristocrat with many advantages, including formal training in a wide variety of military and civilian skills and access to his family's wealth and estates.

The Iron Kingdoms can be a dangerous place for a nobleman. The ancient families have many enemies, and aristocrats are well trained by their houses to prepare them for the dangers of the world.

Playing an Aristocrat: The Aristocrat is a strong social career, especially in situations where the weight of his nobility can be brought to bear. The career also has access to training in a broad variety of weaponry, superior equipment thanks to his wealth, and surpassing leadership potential. An Intellectual Aristocrat is an obvious choice and pairs well with careers like Military Officer and Ranger due to their abilities that influence allies within command range. That is not the only option for a noble, however. A Mighty Aristocrat-Knight is a powerful horseman, a Skilled Aristocrat-Duelist combines sword-and-pistol combat with high society intrigue, and a Gifted Arcane Mechanik-Aristocrat can marshal steamjacks in a large area while supporting them with spells.

An experienced Aristocrat becomes an ever-greater social character but also a great leader of men. His broad access to social skills at high levels enhances the Good Breeding and Privilege abilities while his Advisor and Rallying Cry abilities are a testament to his leadership.

BOUNTY HUNTER

STARTING ABILITIES AND SKILLS	**Abilities:** Binding and Take Down **Military Skills:** Choose two of the following: Crossbow 1, Hand Weapon 1, Pistol 1, Rifle 1, or Unarmed Combat 1 **Occupational Skills:** Detection 1, Intimidation 1, Rope Use 1, and Tracking 1
STARTING ASSETS	75 gc

BOUNTY HUNTER ABILITIES	Binding, Crossbowman, Head-Butt, Language (Five Cant), Pursuit, Roll With It, Take Down, Waylay
BOUNTY HUNTER CONNECTIONS	Connections (any)
BOUNTY HUNTER MILITARY SKILLS	Crossbow 3, Hand Weapon 2, Pistol 2, Rifle 3, Unarmed Combat 4
BOUNTY HUNTER OCCUPATIONAL SKILLS	Bribery 2, Deception 2, Disguise 2, General Skills 4, Interrogation 2, Law 2, Negotiation 4, Rope Use 4, Sneak 3, Streetwise 4, Tracking 4

The bounty hunter makes his living hunting criminals, deserters, and wanted men of all stripes. He likely has a background that emphasizes tracking, military skill, or both. Since the occupation of bounty hunter often calls for capture rather than killing, he should be skilled at both armed and unarmed combat.

Bounty hunters must often take work where they can get it, and as a result range far afield and enter dangerous and even hostile territory in pursuit of their targets. Because of the danger involved in the occupation, bounty hunters might work in pairs or even teams, increasing their chances of capturing valuable targets. In fact, a number of prominent mercenary companies in the Iron Kingdoms receive a significant portion of their revenues through bounty hunting.

Playing a Bounty Hunter: Most characters in the *Iron Kingdoms Full Metal Fantasy Roleplaying Game* have a high degree of competence when it comes to killing a man. The Bounty Hunter is no different in that regard, but he's one of the few who can reliably subdue a man *without* killing him. His Binding and Take Down abilities open up whole new opportunities to an adventuring party and introduce new ways to explore social skills like Deception, Interrogation, and Negotiation. Though he does not have numerous combat-related abilities, the Bounty Hunter has plentiful military skills and can combine his talents with combat careers like Rifleman as easily as he does with more social careers like Investigator.

The experienced Bounty Hunter has plenty of room to grow in occupational skills and military skills but might rely on his other career (or careers) for many of his ability advancements. At Veteran level, the Pursuit ability becomes essential. With Pursuit, a Bounty Hunter is truly inescapable.

CUTTHROAT

STARTING ABILITIES AND SKILLS	**Abilities:** Anatomical Precision, Backstab, and Prowl **Military Skills:** Hand Weapon 1, and the choice of one other: Crossbow 1, Thrown Weapon 1, or Unarmed Combat 1 **Occupational Skills:** Intimidation 1, Sneak 1, and Streetwise 1
STARTING ASSETS	75 gc

CUTTHROAT ABILITIES	Anatomical Precision, Backstab, Blood Spiller, Camouflage, Chain Attack: Bleed Out, Fast Draw, Language (Five Cant), Prowl, Specialization (Assassin Blade), Two-Weapon Fighting, Waylay
CUTTHROAT CONNECTIONS	Connections (criminal)
CUTTHROAT MILITARY SKILLS	Crossbow 2, Hand Weapon 4, Thrown Weapon 3, Unarmed Combat 3
CUTTHROAT OCCUPATIONAL SKILLS	General skills 4, Interrogation 2, Sneak 4, Streetwise 4

The cutthroat is an unrepentant killer who makes his living by preying on those weaker than himself. He might have learned his murderous trade simply surviving in the gloom-haunted streets of Blackwater, or he could be a black-hearted assassin, slaying targets at the behest of anyone with enough coin to pay his fee. Regardless of where he learned the finer points of murder, the cutthroat is skilled at stalking his victims and then striking a fatal blow from the shadows.

Cutthroats associate with those who operate outside the law, and might band together with other nefarious rogues for a common purpose. Typically, cutthroats prefer to earn their livings by accepting payment for murder or by robbing the corpses of their victims. Some cutthroats accept employment as bodyguards or hired thugs for criminals with more wealth and power than themselves.

Playing a Cutthroat: The Cutthroat career isn't subtle in purpose: the Cutthroat is a killer. Abilities such as Anatomical Precision, Backstab, and Two-Weapon Fighting facilitate this purpose, and the Camouflage and Prowl abilities allow the Cutthroat to get in close enough for the kill. Cutthroats lend themselves to the Skilled archetype due to the additional attack and benefits like Ambidextrous, Feat: Untouchable, and Sidestep. When looking for a career to support playing a Cutthroat, Duelist, Highwayman, and Thief are all natural fits, but don't dismiss the less obvious options. The Alchemist's simple smoke is a great way to take advantage of Camouflage and Prowl, and both Alchemists and Cutthroats can start with the Thrown Weapon military skill.

As they gain experience, Cutthroats stick to their strengths. The Veteran-level abilities Blood Spiller and Chain Attack: Bleed Out are exceptional tools for a bloodthirsty character in any campaign.

DUELIST

PREREQUISITES: NONE

STARTING ABILITIES AND SKILLS	Begin with the Parry and Riposte abilities. Begin with the occupational skills Gambling 1, Intimidation 1, and Jumping 1. Begin with the military skills Hand Weapon 1 and Pistol 1
STARTING ASSETS	75 gc

DUELEST ABILITIES	Acrobatics, Fast Draw, Gunfighter, Parry, Precision Strike, Quick Work, Riposte, Roll With It, Two-Weapon Fighting.
DUELEST CONNECTIONS	—
DUELEST MILITARY SKILLS	Hand Weapon 4, Pistol 4, Thrown Weapon 3, Unarmed Combat 2
DUELEST OCCUPATIONAL SKILLS	Etiquette 2, General skills 4, Law 2, Oratory 2, Seduction 3, Streetwise 2

Possessing the requisite speed, nerve, and skill at arms, the duelist is an expert combatant. Both blade and pistol are the duelist's forte, and he must have superlative ability in one or both to defeat his opponents. The type of skill necessary to become a duelist can be acquired through innate ability and long hours of practice.

For many, the code duello is simply a way of life. Many military officers and aristocrats turn to dueling to settle their personal and public disputes. Professional Llaelese and Ordic duelists sometimes make their living by serving as stand-ins for various nobles who need to settle a score with a rival yet lack the necessary martial prowess to do so. Duelists who continue to win duels for their noble patrons can earn both fame and wealth for their endeavors. In many nations, underground fighting circuits offer the duelist a chance to ply his trade. Additionally, a duelist's skills are always in demand for those seeking capable bodyguards and mercenaries.

Playing a Duelist: Though their breadth of weapon knowledge does not quite rival that of the Soldier, Duelists hone their craft with sword and pistol into a deadly art form. From the start, the Duelist career offers a unique fighting style with the ability to weave in and out of combat thanks to Parry and to punish enemies for their failed attacks with Riposte. The Duelist career is tied more to a lightly armored, close-in fighting style than it is to a particular archetype, and Gifted, Intellectual, Mighty, or Skilled Duelists are all viable options. Though far from

an optimized social character, the Duelist also dabbles in the social skills Etiquette, Intimidation, Oratory, and Seduction, making him a good choice for combat-minded players who desire opportunities to shine in social situations.

The experienced Duelist continues to hone his deadly craft and his unique fighting style. With the addition of the Acrobatics ability, Veteran-level Duelists become truly impossible to tie down in melee combat.

EXPLORER

PREREQUISITES: NONE

STARTING ABILITIES, CONNECTIONS, AND SKILLS	**Abilities:** Big Game Hunter, Language (any), Port of Call **Connections:** Connections (patron) **Military Skills:** Choose one: Archery 1, Hand Weapon 1, Pistol 1, or Rifle 1 **Occupational Skills:** Detection 1, Medicine 1, Navigation 1, and Survival 1 **Special:** A character who chooses Explorer as one of his two starting careers gains 25 gc each month from his patron for as long as he continues to explore new regions, report back regularly, and bring his patron occasional gifts from exotic places.
STARTING ASSETS	150 gc, map case, and spyglass.

EXPLORER ABILITIES	Battle Plan: Reconnaissance, Big Game Hunter, Disease Resistance, Expert Rider, Language, Natural Leader, Poison Resistance, Port of Call, Signal Language, Swift Rider
EXPLORER CONNECTIONS	Connections (wealthy patrons), Connections (isolated tribe or people)
EXPLORER MILITARY SKILLS	Archery 2, Crossbow 2, Hand Weapon 2, Pistol 2, Rifle 3, Thrown Weapon 2, Unarmed Combat 2
EXPLORER OCCUPATIONAL SKILLS	Command 4, Craft (any) 2, Cryptography 2, Etiquette 2, General Skills 4, Medicine 2, Navigation 4, Negotiation 4, Rope Use 4, Survival 4

The explorer is an intrepid adventurer who combines academic knowledge and a wide range of practical skills with a smattering of combat expertise. He might have learned the basics of combat and scouting in a military organization, but likely has also received instruction in the natural sciences at one of the Iron Kingdom's major universities. He specializes in exploration and one or more areas of academia, but the explorer's breadth of useful skills makes him a well rounded jack-of-all-trades.

Although the nations of western Immoren boast great cities and huge swaths of settled land, there remain large tracts of unexplored wilderness between them. The explorer plies his trade here, plumbing the depths of crumbling ruins and ancient tombs for both wealth and knowledge. A number of organizations, such as the Department of Extraordinary Zoology at Corvis University, employ explorers to seek out artifacts or lore of special interest to them.

Playing an Explorer: The Explorer career is broader in scope than the dedicated Cutthroat or Rifleman. Explorers have access to a range of military skills, a diverse mix of abilities, and plentiful occupational skills. The most defining element of the Explorer is the Big Game Hunter ability. Big Game Hunter scales with the Explorer's Survival skill, so he can quickly gain exceptional accuracy against wild creatures he faces in battle. In wilderness campaigns in particular, Explorers really get a chance to shine thanks to their numerous survivalist skills and abilities along with added combat potential in the wilds. Explorers can utilize a variety of archetypes from the Intellectual

Explorer with hyper perception who never misses a detail, to the skilled Explorer with the Virtuoso archetype benefit who's a crack shot with a heavy rifle.

Experienced Explorers continue their wilderness leadership and can eventually pick up Battle Plan: Reconnaissance to complement Natural Leader and a high command range. This battle plan gives the explorer's party a real advantage in regions of difficult terrain.

FELL CALLER

STARTING ABILITIES AND SKILLS	Abilities: Fell Call: Signal Call and Fell Call: Sonic Blast Military Skills: Great Weapon 1 or Hand Weapon 1 Occupational Skills: Command 1, Fell Calling 2, Lore (Trollkin) 1, and Oratory 1
STARTING ASSETS	75 gc
FELL CALLER ABILITIES	Battle Plan: Call to Action, Fell Call: Cacophony, Fell Call: Call of Defiance, Fell Call: Ground Shaker, Fell Call: Heroic Ballad, Fell Call; Reverberation, Fell Call: Signal Call, Fell Call: Sonic Blast, Legacy of Bragg, Natural Leader
FELL CALLER CONNECTIONS	Connections (Kriel)
FELL CALLER MILITARY SKILLS	Great Weapon 3, Hand Weapon 3, Thrown Weapon 3, Unarmed Combat 3
FELL CALLER OCCUPATIONAL SKILLS	Command 4, Fell Calling 4, General Skills 4, Oratory 4, Seduction 2

Fell callers are trollkin whose lineage can be traced back to the legendary Bragg, the first of their race to harness the booming song of the fell call. The character can lift his powerful voice in song to urge his allies on to heroic efforts or simply batter his foes with focused bursts of shattering sound. Fell calling is in the character's blood, but he has probably received training from other, more experienced trollkin with the same gift.

Fell callers are respected and valued members of trollkin kriels, and they are a welcome presence among trollkin warriors. The rare fell caller that leaves his kriel to seek fame and glory in the wider world is likely to accept worthy non-trollkin as traveling companions. He doubtless expects the same level of reckless heroism from his comrades as he displays.

Playing a Fell Caller: Like the Alchemist career, a Fell Caller gains access to a whole suite of game play options unavailable to other character types. Any party that includes multiple trollkin characters would *really* benefit from a Fell Caller, but even a lone descendent of Bragg can use his voice as a powerful battlefield asset. Fell calls are a versatile tool that can bolster a Fell Caller's existing combat potential or can represent his main mode of attack. From the Mighty Fell Caller–Man-at-Arms to the Gifted Fell Caller–Sorcerer, the career offers a wealth of options. Note that unlike spells, fell call attacks

are ranged attacks, so they cannot be used in melee combat without penalties.

Experienced Fell Callers have plentiful abilities to increase their fell call options and can even gain a free fell call each turn with Legacy of Bragg. At the Veteran level, Fell Callers can learn the impressive Ground Shaker fell call that allows them to knock their enemies off their feet.

FIELD MECHANIK

STARTING ABILITIES AND SKILLS	**Abilities:** 'Jack Marshal, Bodge, and Hit the Deck! **Military Skills:** Hand Weapon 1 or Pistol 1 **Occupational Skills:** Command 1, Craft (metalworking) 1, and Mechanikal Engineering 1
STARTING ASSETS	25 gc, mechanik's tool kit, and a light laborjack with up to 200gc of weapons

FIELD MECHANIK ABILITIES	'Jack Marshal, Ace Commander, Bodge, Dodger, Drive: Ancillary Attack, Drive: Assault, Drive: Off Road, Drive: Pronto, Hit the Deck!, Iron Sentinel, Scrounge, Steamo, Tune Up
FIELD MECHANIK CONNECTIONS	Connections (mechaniks organization)
FIELD MECHANIK MILITARY SKILLS	Hand Weapon 2, Pistol 2
FIELD MECHANIK OCCUPATIONAL SKILLS	Command 3, Craft 4 (any), General Skills 4, Mechanikal Engineering 4, Negotiation 3

The field mechanik is a skilled engineer or a talented bodger who, much the way a combat medic patches up wounded soldiers to keep them fighting, can apply a quick fix to damaged steamjacks. He might have learned his trade in the military mechanik corps of a professional army or in a mercenary tinkerer's workshop. Although he has basic combat training, the field mechanik likely has experience commanding warjacks in battle, and when given the opportunity can draw upon the destructive abilities of these mighty machines.

There isn't a nation in western Immoren that doesn't have great need for the talents of field mechaniks. Those unwilling or unable to find employment in the military are always welcome in the many mercenary companies who employ aging warjacks in constant need of vital maintenance.

Playing a Field Mechanik: One of the strongest reasons a player might choose Field Mechanik as a starting career is found in his starting assets: Field Mechaniks start the game with a light laborjack! While the 'Jack Marshal ability is available to a few different careers, no one else starts with a steamjack or has the opportunity to learn as many Drive abilities as the Field Mechanik. Abilities like Bodge, Scrounge, and Steamo make it easier for a Field Mechanik to keep his steamjack in fighting condition, while Dodger and Hit the Deck! allow him to avoid personal injury. A Field Mechanik's choice of archetype and other career can lead to entirely divergent play styles. A Mighty Field Mechanik-Knight can join his steamjack on the front lines, but an Intellectual Field Mechanik-Military Officer rarely needs to get his hands dirty, instead enhancing others with Battle Plans and Drives.

As he gains experience, a Field Mechanik grows rapidly in his ability to support and repair steamjacks. Once he's achieved Veteran status, a Field Mechanik can learn Iron Sentinel to further enhance his personal survival skills and Tune Up, a quick action that allows him to coax peak performance from a steamjack.

GUN MAGE

PREREQUISITES: GIFTED

STARTING ABILITIES, SKILLS, AND SPELLS	**Abilities:** Craft Rune Shot and Fast Reload **Military Skills:** Pistol 1 or Rifle 1 **Occupational Skills:** Detection 1 and Intimidation 1 **Spells:** Rune Shot: Accuracy, Rune Shot: Brutal, and Rune Shot: Thunderbolt
STARTING ASSETS	25 gc, ammo bandolier, magelock pistol or rifle (with powder and ten rounds of ammunition), and a rune shot casting kit

GUN MAGE ABILITIES	Arcane Precision, Craft Rune Shot, Fast Draw, Fast Reload, Gunfighter, Keen Eyed
GUN MAGE CONNECTIONS	Connections (gun mage order)
GUN MAGE MILITARY SKILLS	Pistol 4, Rifle 4
GUN MAGE OCCUPATIONAL SKILLS	General Skills 4, Seduction 2
GUN MAGE SPELLS	Spells from the Gun Mage spell list

An arcanist with a penchant for gunfighting, the gun mage strikes down his enemies with rune-scribed bullets. Although the gun mage has intrinsic sorcerous abilities, his skills require very specific training. For this reason, the gun mage probably spent at least some time as a member of an established militant arcane order. There, he learned how to harness his power through the barrel of a magelock pistol (most commonly) or rifle (more rarely), unleashing spells in a hail of lead.

Deadly and skilled, a freelance gun mage is a valuable commodity who can earn substantial coin as a gun for hire, a bodyguard, and even as an assassin. Gun mages who served with an arcane order typically have experience leading men into combat and are often recruited to serve the same role in prominent mercenary companies.

Playing a Gun Mage: Although Gun Mages can be focusers or will weavers, they have an arcane style all their own. In addition to a handful of normal spells like Return Fire and Snipe, Gun Mages have a spell list packed with the iconic rune shot spells. As the rune shot rules (p. 230) explain, these spells do not require quick actions to cast, and multiple spells can affect the same shot. This effectively turns each round fired from a magelock pistol or rifle into a custom-built offensive spell with effects that vary from increased damage to continuous effects to AOEs. The Gun Mage career can pair with other arcane careers for increased spellcasting options, but many Gun Mages instead choose Duelist, Pistoleer, or Rifleman to augment their gunplay.

Experienced Gun Mages gain a great deal of flexibility as they pick up additional rune shot abilities, broadening the customization potential of each shot they take. Eventually learning the Arcane Precision ability or True Sight spell also gives the Gun Mage a way to deal with stealthy enemies that are the bane of other gunslingers.

HIGHWAYMAN

PREREQUISITES: NONE

STARTING ABILITIES AND SKILLS	**Abilities:** Ambush and Saddle Shot **Military Skills:** Hand Weapon 1 and choose one: Archery 1, Crossbow 1, or Pistol 1 **Occupational Skills:** Animal Handling 1, Detection 1, Intimidation 1, and Riding 1
STARTING ASSETS	75 gc, mask, riding horse, and tack

HIGHWAYMAN ABILITIES	Ambush, Appraise, Binding, Expert Rider, Fast Draw, Fast Reload, Light Cavalry, Prowl, Ride-By Attack, Saddle Shot, Swift Hunter, Swift Rider, Traceless Path, Two-Weapon Fighting, Waylay
HIGHWAYMAN CONNECTIONS	Connections (criminal)
HIGHWAYMAN MILITARY SKILLS	Archery 3, Crossbow 3, Hand Weapon 3, Pistol 3, Unarmed Combat 3
HIGHWAYMAN OCCUPATIONAL SKILLS	Bribery 2, Deception 3, Disguise 2, General Skills 4, Interrogation 2, Negotiation 4, Rope Use 4, Seduction 4, Sneak 4, Survival 2

The highwayman makes his living robbing those traveling western Immoren's often-dangerous roads and highways. He could be a villainous brute or a charming brigand of marked style and dash. Though seldom motivated by nobler intentions than the acquisition of wealth, some highwaymen make it a point of pride to target those most able to pay their rough tithe. Regardless of his motivations, the highwayman's life of crime has likely made him a skillful rogue adept at stalking and ambushing his targets and then quickly vanishing into the wilderness.

The character of a cloaked and hooded highwayman atop his treasured steed is a common subject of popular song and stories, but not all of them are such noble figures. Unscrupulous soldiers who have completed their service or have been discharged because of injury often find the life of highwayman an easy transition to make.

Playing a Highwayman: The Highwayman career is defined by a fast striking combat style. Whether riding down a victim or ambushing from a concealed position, the Highwayman excels at getting the drop on his opponents. Fast Draw and Prowl help a Highwayman to get that first strike, giving him many opponents to choose from when using the opportunistic Ambush ability. Highwayman is also a strong mounted career, and a starting Highwayman can explore the options of mounted combat without setting aside substantial coin for a horse. Highwaymen boast an expansive occupational skills list, further increasing their versatility. Starting players can pair the Highwayman career with a dedicated combat career like Pistoleer for additional options in battle, or with a more skill-based career such as Thief for non-combat specialization.

Experienced Highwaymen can evolve in a number of directions depending on party needs and player preference. They can learn to subdue foes with Waylay and Binding, become light horse experts with Light Cavalry and Expert Rider, or focus on maneuverability with Traceless Path and Swift Hunter.

INVESTIGATOR

PREREQUISITES: NONE

STARTING ABILITIES AND SKILLS	**Abilities:** Astute and Language (any) **Military Skills:** Hand Weapon 1 or Pistol 1 **Occupational Skills:** Detection 1, Forensic Science 1, Interrogation 1, Law 1, Medicine 1, and Sneak 1 **Special:** A character who chooses Investigator as one of his two starting careers gains the Hyper Perception Intellectual archetype benefit (p. 116).
STARTING ASSETS	100 gc

INVESTIGATOR ABILITIES	Anatomical Precision, Astute, Iron Will, Language, Prowl, Signal Language, Truth Reader
INVESTIGATOR CONNECTIONS	Connections (any)
INVESTIGATOR MILITARY SKILLS	Hand Weapon 2, Pistol 2, Unarmed Combat 2
INVESTIGATOR OCCUPATIONAL SKILLS	Cryptography 4, Deception 4, Etiquette 2, Forensic Science 4, General Skills 4, Interrogation 4, Law 4, Medicine 2, Negotiation 3, Research 4, Sneak 4, Streetwise 4

The investigator is a skilled detective adept in the techniques of deduction, criminology, and interrogation. He might be a watch inspector who uses his abilities to catch criminals and keep his city safe, a former inquisitor, or a member of a military intelligence-gathering organization who ferrets out the secrets of his nation's enemies within and without.

The cities and wilds of western Immoren conceal countless mysteries to be uncovered. Criminal conspiracies, ancient evils, and the plans of enemy generals are of interest to many individuals, and investigators have no lack of wealthy patrons who pay them to uncover nefarious agendas. Although investigators often serve as inspectors in the city watches of many large cities, freelance investigators who perform the same function for a fee are not uncommon.

Playing an Investigator: Nothing gets by a character with the Investigator career. The Hyper Perception benefit boosts all of his detection rolls, *and* he has two chances of success thanks to the Astute reroll. Coupling his investigative expertise with a varied stable of occupational skills marks the Investigator as a remarkable choice for social and investigative campaigns. While not one of the top combat careers, it's worth noting that starting as an Investigator is a great way to play a Mighty, Skilled, or Gifted character with some game play elements of the Intellectual archetype. A Gifted Gun Mage-Investigator, for example, has access to gunslinging spellcraft without sacrificing investigative expertise.

Experienced Investigators further hone their expertise in Detection and Research, and can eventually gain the Truth Reader ability, after which it becomes truly impossible to deceive the Veteran Investigator.

IRON FANG

STARTING ABILITIES, CONNECTIONS, AND SKILLS	**Special:** A character starting with the Iron Fang career must choose between Aristocrat, Military Officer, Soldier, or Warcaster for his second career. **Abilities:** Fast Rearm (Blasting Pike) and Specialization (Blasting Pike) **Connections:** Connections (Khadoran military) **Military Skills:** Great Weapon 1 and Shield 1 **Occupational Skills:** Command 1 and Survival 1
STARTING ASSETS	25 gc, blasting pike (with a spear head and ten blasting heads), Iron Fang full plate, shield

IRON FANG ABILITIES	Defensive Line, Fast Arm (Blasting Pike), Hyper Awareness, Load Bearing, Precision Strike, Relentless Charge, Rock Solid, Specialization (Blasting Pike), Swift Rider
IRON FANG CONNECTIONS	Connections (Khadoran military)
IRON FANG MILITARY SKILLS	Great Weapon 4, Lance 4, Shield 4, Unarmed Combat 3
IRON FANG OCCUPATIONAL SKILLS	Command 4, General Skills 4, Survival 2

The character is a trained Iron Fang, and belongs or has belonged to the mighty legions of Khador. His grueling training and battlefield experience have made him dauntless and inured to the hardships of battle. Skilled at formation fighting, the character is a master of the blasting pike and with it can deal catastrophic damage to his enemies.

Although the Iron Fang legions are a close-knit organization where most members would rather die than leave their brothers in arms, sometimes men do leave the legions for their own reasons. Those who do are seldom welcomed back. All the same, a man trained as an Iron Fang rarely wants for work. Their martial skill makes them highly attractive to mercenary companies across the Iron Kingdoms. Additionally, many ex-Iron Fangs are skilled battlefield leaders, and can be found in command of their own mercenary units. Additionally, the legions sometime grant leave to promising officers to settle their own affairs, though attempting to maintain a career as an adventurer while part of the Iron Fang legions is all but impossible in the long term.

Playing an Iron Fang: The Iron Fang career has far more specific requirements than most. It requires a specific race (human) *and* a specific country of origin (Khador), and it also can be combined only with a small handful of other careers at character creation. Though their equipment is very powerful, it is also very specific. These restrictions mark the Iron Fang as a rigorous choice, though the archetype selection remains wide open. The Iron Fang career definitely falls into the "combat-focused" end of the spectrum, though, so pair the Iron Fang career with the Aristocrat or Military Officer career for access to more occupational skill options if playing in a more socially oriented campaign.

From the start, Iron Fangs boast immense melee power and can quickly gain more maneuverability through Load Bearing and Relentless Charge. At the Veteran level, their leadership skills come to the forefront with abilities like Hyper Awareness and Rock Solid, both of which convey helpful bonuses to the Iron Fang's allies.

KNIGHT

PREREQUISITES: HUMAN OR IOSAN

STARTING ABILITIES, CONNECTIONS, AND SKILLS	Abilities: Cleave and Defender Connections: Connections (knightly order) Military Skills: Great Weapon 1, Hand Weapon 1, and Shield 1 Occupational Skills: Command 1, Etiquette 1, and Lore (knightly order) 1
STARTING ASSETS	100 gc

KNIGHT ABILITIES	Cavalry Charge, Cleave, Combat Rider, Defender, Defensive Line, Expert Rider, Iron Will, Load Bearing, Natural Leader, Precision Strike, Press the Attack, Relentless Charge, Ride-By Attack, Shield Slam
KNIGHT CONNECTIONS	Connections (knightly order)
KNIGHT MILITARY SKILLS	Great Weapon 4, Hand Weapon 4, Lance 4, Shield 4, Unarmed Combat 3
KNIGHT OCCUPATIONAL SKILLS	Command 4, Etiquette 2, General Skills 4, Law 2

Knights are proud and skilled combatants who fight for causes greater than themselves, often dedicated to a religious order, a sovereign, or a fellowship. The role of knights has evolved alongside warfare in the Iron Kingdoms, but all are trained in single combat and sworn to exacting codes of behavior. No commander can deny their strength of arms and conviction. A knight is skilled with the traditional weapons and armor of his order and has received training in battlefield command and basic diplomacy as well.

The knight follows a strict moral code of conduct that includes an overriding cause or directive. Freelance knights or those who have left their orders are not unknown, and these knights can be of any moral inclination. The term robber knight or robber baron is commonly applied to knights who have become criminals and are now knights in title only.

Playing a Knight: The Knight career is a versatile military career for melee-oriented characters. Whether wielding a great weapon two-handed or using a shield, whether mounted or on foot, a Knight is a close-combat powerhouse. Between Cleave and Defender, even a starting Knight has the possibility of making three attacks in a single round (four if he's Skilled). Knights can also gain high armor values with minimal penalties thanks to Load Bearing and a high Shield skill. Remember that Cleave is tied to Great Weapons, so weapons like the Caspian battleblade or war hammer are excellent choices for a Knight with shield.

As a Knight gains experience, he can specialize in mounted combat, defensive abilities, or a bit of both. For the Veteran shield-user Knight, it's hard to beat the combination of Shield Slam and Press the Attack. Put together, these abilities allow a knight to knock an opponent to the ground and continue attacking him.

MAGE HUNTER

STARTING ABILITIES, CONNECTIONS, AND SKILLS	**Abilities:** Arcane Assassin and Iron Will **Connections:** Connections (Retribution of Scyrah) **Military Skills:** Hand Weapon 1, and either Archery 1 or Crossbow 1 **Occupational Skills:** Climbing 1, Jumping 1, Sneak 1, and Tracking 1
STARTING ASSETS	75 gc

MAGE HUNTER ABILITIES	Arcane Assassin, Camouflage, Crackshot, Crossbowman, Fast Draw, Fast Reload, Iron Will, Mage Killer, Parry, Quick Work, Shadow Magic, Traceless Path
MAGE HUNTER CONNECTIONS	Connections (Retribution of Scyrah)
MAGE HUNTER MILITARY SKILLS	Archery 4, Crossbow 4, Hand Weapon 4, Thrown Weapon 2
MAGE HUNTER OCCUPATIONAL SKILLS	Deception 2, Disguise 2, General Skills 4, Rope Use 3, Sneak 4, Survival 2, Tracking 4

The mage hunter has devoted his life to hunting down and exterminating human sorcerers and arcanists. He, like many Iosans, believes the existence and use of human magic slowly drains the life from the remaining Iosan goddess Scyrah and was responsible for the disappearance of the remainder of their missing pantheon. Although he now likely operates with much autonomy, the mage hunter has received training from the Retribution of Scyrah in the deadly techniques of that sect. He can strike with lethal speed and accuracy, usually slaying his target in complete silence.

Mage hunters are dispatched to hunt human spellcasters. Many of these assassins operate in small bands, pursuing specific targets or objectives on behalf of the Retribution, working from safe houses scattered throughout western Immoren. Others choose to work unsupported, even taking up arms alongside adventurers or mercenaries in order to gather information or to get closer to otherwise difficult to reach targets.

Playing a Mage Hunter: The Mage Hunter has a powerful mix of melee and ranged aptitudes. The Arcane Assassin ability makes the Mage Hunter a serious threat to any character relying on arcane defenses and to Warcasters in particular. Thanks to Parry, it's also difficult to prevent a Mage Hunter from reaching his intended victim. The Mage Hunter career combines well with a broad variety of archetypes and other careers since it has a deep roster of powerful abilities and a useful selection of occupational skills to boot.

Though experienced Mage Hunters have a lot of potential growth through additional abilities and weapon expertise, the Mage

Killer ability is the real brass ring for Veteran Mage Hunters. It's one of the few abilities in the game that grants additional damage dice, guaranteeing that no spellcaster is safe from the Mage Hunter's bow or blade.

MAN-AT-ARMS

PREREQUISITES: NONE

STARTING ABILITIES AND SKILLS	**Abilities:** Defensive Line and Shield Guard **Military Skills:** Great Weapon 1 and Shield 1, and either Hand Weapon 1 or Pistol 1 **Occupational Skills:** Command 1 and Detection 1
STARTING ASSETS	100 gc

MAN-AT-ARMS ABILITIES	Bodyguard, Cleave, Defensive Line, Girded, Iron Will, Load Bearing, Retaliatory Strike, Set Defense, Shield Guard, Shield Slam, Specialization (Halberd), Specialization (Spear)
MAN-AT-ARMS CONNECTIONS	Connections (employer)
MAN-AT-ARMS MILITARY SKILLS	Great Weapon 4, Hand Weapon 3, Pistol 3, Shield 4, Unarmed Combat 3
MAN-AT-ARMS OCCUPATIONAL SKILLS	Command 3, Craft (metalworking) 2, General Skills 4

The man-at-arms is a highly skilled warrior who focuses on defense as well as devastating offense. He could be an ogrun *bokur*, attaching himself to an important Rhulic noble in order to prove his worth through martial skill, or he might be a guard, a watchman, or an aristocrat's bodyguard, defending his station or charge with strength and steel. The man-at-arms is accustomed to fighting with a wide variety of weapons, and favors melee weapons with considerable reach and great crushing or cleaving power.

The man-at-arms fills an important role in society, taking up sword or rifle in defense of his patrons. The Iron Kingdoms are home to many individuals in need of protection, whether they're aristocrats with vicious enemies or traveling arcanists and merchants who require the services of those with strong arms and sharp blades when traveling between cities.

Playing a Man-at-Arms: The Man-at-Arms career is a focused martial career with vast arrays of military skills and combat abilities. Though the career can be useful to players looking to bolster their melee damage output with Cleave and Retaliatory Strike or increase their combat options with Shield Slam, the real selling point of the Man-at-Arms is his unparalleled defensive capability. With Defensive Line, Girded, Set Defense, and the potential for Shield 4, it is tough for most enemies to break through the stalwart armor of a Man-at-Arms. From the Mighty

Knight-Man-at-Arms to the Gifted Man-at-Arms-Warcaster, this defensive specialist is a valued member of any party.

As he gains experience, the Man-at-Arms can quickly expand his offensive and defensive melee capabilities. At the Veteran level, a Man-at-Arms can take his party defense tactics to a whole new level with Bodyguard, allowing him limitless Shield Guard opportunities each round.

MILITARY OFFICER

STARTING ABILITIES AND SKILLS	**Abilities:** Battle Plan: Call to Action, Natural Leader, and Team Leader **Military Skills:** Hand Weapon 1 and either Great Weapon 1 or Pistol 1 **Occupational Skills:** Command 1, Medicine 1, and Navigation 1
STARTING ASSETS	100 gc and officer's uniform

MILITARY OFFICER ABILITIES	'Jack Marshal, Ace Commander, Battle Commander, Battle Plan: Call to Action, Battle Plan: Coordinated Strike, Battle Plan: Desperate Pace, Battle Plan: Go to Ground, Cavalry Charge, Defender, Drive: Assault, Drive: Pronto, Expert Rider, Good Breeding, Natural Leader, Port of Call, Ride-By Attack, Saddle Shot, Signal Language, Team Leader
MILITARY OFFICER CONNECTIONS	Connections (mercenary company or kingdom's military)
MILITARY OFFICER MILITARY SKILLS	Great Weapon 4, Hand Weapon 4, Pistol 4
MILITARY OFFICER OCCUPATIONAL SKILLS	Command 4, Cryptography 4, Etiquette 4, General Skills 4, Interrogation 4, Law 4, Medicine 4, Navigation 4, Oratory 4

The military officer is a highly skilled tactician and leader of men. He might be from a highly respected military family, groomed to lead other men in battle in one of the great national armies of the Iron Kingdoms. Conversely, he could be a down-to-earth mercenary who climbed the ranks through many years of hard work and persistence. Either way, the military officer is well versed in the skills necessary to command effectively on the battlefield, and he possesses high levels of martial prowess in melee or at range.

Most military officers learn the demands of rank in the standing armies of western Immoren. They must master the steely nerves required of those who lead men in battle. Mercenary groups and even criminal gangs are commonly led by self-styled captains, though few have the chops to truly lead. Those who do can command high wages for their skills on the field.

Playing a Military Officer: When a player is looking to create a character with strong leadership skills and a play style to match, the Military Officer career can't be beaten. With Natural Leader, a Battle Plan from the very start, and plenty of room for leadership growth, it's a perfect fit. The Team Leader ability, which is unique to the Military Officer, even allows him to give his feat points to others, ensuring that the team's resources can be brought to bear in an efficient manner. The Military Officer also has strong social skills, the ability to lead steamjacks in addition to men, and the potential for top-notch mounted combat.

The experienced Military Officer can find himself pulled in many directions at once but should focus on his strength: leadership. His numerous battle plans and high Command skill provide a natural path to the Veteran ability Battle Commander, allowing him to issue a Battle Plan every round without spending a feat point.

PIRATE

PREREQUISITES: NONE

STARTING ABILITIES AND SKILLS	Abilities: Gang, Steady, and Specialization (Cutlass) Military Skills: Hand Weapon 1, and either Pistol 1 or Thrown Weapon 1 Occupational Skills: Climbing 1, Intimidation 1, Sailing 1, and Swimming 1
STARTING ASSETS	75 gc

PIRATE ABILITIES	Binding, Disease Resistance, Gang, Gunfighter, Head-Butt, Languages, Port of Call, Quick Work, Specialization (Cutlass), Steady, Sucker!, Waylay
PIRATE CONNECTIONS	Connections (pirate crew)
PIRATE MILITARY SKILLS	Hand Weapon 3, Light Artillery 2, Pistol 3, Rifle 2, Thrown Weapon 3, Unarmed Combat 3
PIRATE OCCUPATIONAL SKILLS	Command 2, Deception 3, General Skills 4, Navigation 4, Negotiation 2, Rope Use 4, Sailing 4

Privateers, buccaneers, or pirates—their victims make no distinction—are raiders on the high seas or rivers of western Immoren. The pirate likely gained his skills and reputation as a crewmember on an infamous ship, or he might have once been part of a legitimate mercantile or naval force, serving with the Mercarian League or aboard a Cygnaran or Khadoran warship. The pirate is a deadly close-quarters combatant, and might have some experience with shipboard guns and heavy artillery.

Piracy is a fairly common occupation for sailors operating out of disreputable port cities along the coasts of Cygnar, Ord, or the notorious Scharde Islands. In some cases it is a legitimate pursuit, since many kingdoms issue letters of marque to the captains of fighting ships, granting these privateers leave to hunt and capture the ships of enemy nations or to combat pirates preying upon merchant ships.

Playing a Pirate: On the surface, the Pirate career is a close-in fighter with abilities and skills well suited to the open seas. Looking a bit deeper, however, his fighting style is one of dirty tricks. Head-Butt allows him to knock an opponent to the ground while Steady ensures he'll never fall prey to such tactics himself, Gang fighting tactics lets pirates team up to bring down tougher opponents, and the combination of Gunfighter and Quick Work means that his melee kills convert into free ranged attacks even if he's still engaged in melee. The Pirate career is sufficiently versatile that a whole party of Pirates is entirely possible and makes for an enjoyable theme. The Skilled Pirate-Pistoleer (a master gunner) and the Intellectual Military Officer-Pirate (captain) are just a few character possibilities for a pirate crew.

The experienced Pirate grows quickly in his dirty fighting style, culminating in the Veteran ability Sucker! No longer content to use his dirty tricks on enemies, a Pirate with Sucker! can throw his allies into harm's way to protect himself.

PISTOLEER

PREREQUISITES: NONE

STARTING ABILITIES AND SKILLS	**Abilities:** Fast Draw, Gunfighter, and Return Fire **Military Skills:** Pistol 1 **Occupational Skills:** Detection 1, Intimidation 1, and Sneak 1
STARTING ASSETS	50 gc, an ammo bandolier, and either a hand cannon (with ammunition for ten shots) or a pair of repeating pistols (each with one ammo wheel and ammunition for ten shots)

PISTOLEER ABILITIES	**Chain Attack:** Pin Down, Dodger, Fast Draw, Fast Reload, Gunfighter, Return Fire, Swift Hunter, Targeteer, Two-Weapon Fighting
PISTOLEER CONNECTIONS	—
PISTOLEER MILITARY SKILLS	Pistol 4
PISTOLEER OCCUPATIONAL SKILLS	Craft (gunsmithing) 4, General Skills 4, Sneak 3

The pistoleer deals in lead. He is a highly skilled gunman who relies solely on reflexes, skill, and trusty sidearm to take down his enemies. He might have acquired this skill through long years of practice both on and off the field, or he could have learned the fundamentals of shooting in the military or under the tutelage of another pistoleer. Although he might have picked up some skill with melee weapons, his combat abilities are focused on gunfighting.

Pistoleers often make their livings by serving as bodyguards and guns for hire, and their skills allow them to easily find employment as mercenaries. Some pistoleers barter their talents for position or the fruits of organized crime.

Playing a Pistoleer: The Pistoleer career is the epitome of a focused militant career. Practically devoid of military or occupational skills (except for general skills, of course), the Pistoleer does one thing very, very well: he shoots things . . . with pistols. Since he starts with the Gunfighter ability, a Pistoleer never has to worry about having a backup weapon when tied up in melee; his pistols still get the job done. Pistoleer characters should also strive to have a high DEF in order to trigger their Return Fire ability more frequently. The two different weapon options for a starting Pistoleer allow characters to fire more often with lower damage or fire less frequently but with more punch. Pistoleers rely heavily on their feat points for Run and Gun and Two-Fister (see p. 221), or extra quick actions used to reload.

The experienced Pistoleer follows the expected path of becoming ever more versatile and deadly with his pistols. Two-Weapon Fighting can eventually lead to the Veteran ability Chain Attack: Pin Down. This ability allows a Pistoleer to concentrate his fire on a particular target and drive him out of the action.

PRIEST

PREREQUISITES: HUMAN, GIFTED, WORSHIP OF MENOTH OR MORROW

STARTING ABILITIES, CONNECTIONS, SKILLS, AND SPELLS	**Special:** Choose a religion for the character to follow. The choices from this book are Menoth and Morrow. Future *Iron Kingdoms Full Metal Fantasy Roleplaying Game* books will include additional religions.

Priest of Menoth		**Priest of Morrow**	
Abilities:	Dispel	Abilities:	Empower
Connections (Menite temple)		Connections (Morrowan church)	
Military Skills:	Great Weapon 1 or Hand Weapon 1	Military Skills:	Great Weapon 1 or Hand Weapon 1
Occupational Skills:	Lore (Menite faith) 1 and Oratory 1	Occupational Skills:	Lore (Morrowan faith) 1 and Medicine 1
Spells:	Guided Blade, Ignite, and Immolation	Spells:	Blade of Radiance, Solovin's Boon, and True Sight

STARTING ASSETS	75 gc

PRIEST ABILITIES	Choir, Language, Natural Leader, Rallying Cry, University Education
PRIEST CONNECTIONS	Connections (character's church)
PRIEST MILITARY SKILLS	Great Weapon 3, Hand Weapon 3, Shield 2
PRIEST OCCUPATIONAL SKILLS	Command 2, Cryptography 2, Etiquette 4, General Skills 4, Law 4, Medicine 4, Negotiation 4, Oratory 4, Research 4
PRIEST SPELLS	Spells from the Priest spell list for the character's faith

A follower of one of the major faiths of Caen, the priest has devoted himself to a god or gods and commands divine magic in his deity's name. He could be a humble cleric or a militant priest, rooting out heretics with fire and steel.

The gods Morrow and Menoth receive the bulk of worship in the Iron Kingdoms, and the state religions of nations such as Cygnar and Khador center on the veneration of one or both deities. Priestly orders in the Iron Kingdoms range from the militant organizations, such as Morrow's battle chaplains and the various martial traditions in the Protectorate of Menoth, to those focused on healing the sick and spreading the faith to unbelievers.

Playing a Priest: The Priest career is really several careers in one. The Priests of Menoth and Morrow presented here represent two of the rich faiths present in the Iron Kingdoms— the two largest faiths of western Immoren. All Priests share a strong pool of occupational skills including the indispensible Medicine skill and numerous social skills like Negotiation and Oratory. Their spell lists differ dramatically, however, and lend a unique character to each priestly order. The various combat hymns and fiery incantations of the Menite Priest are markedly different from the spells of healing and holy judgment of the Morrowan Priest. Priests make a good pairing for melee-oriented careers like Knight or can focus on a high Arcane stat and versatile spell list by pairing with a Gifted-only career such as Arcanist.

Experienced Priests are most defined by the new additions to their spell options, but Natural Leader, increased Command skill, and the Veteran ability Rallying Cry can also make them inspiring party leaders.

RANGER

STARTING ABILITIES AND SKILLS	Abilities: Camouflage and Pathfinder Military Skills: Hand Weapon 1 and choose one other: Archery 1, Crossbow 1, Pistol 1, or Rifle 1 Occupational Skills: Detection 1, Sneak 1, Survival 1, and Tracking 1
STARTING ASSETS	75 gc

RANGER ABILITIES	Battle Plan: Go to Ground, Battle Plan: Reconnaissance, Battle Plan: Shadow, Camouflage, Disease Resistance, Fast Reload, Light Cavalry, Night Fighter, Pathfinder, Prowl, Saddle Shot, Signal Language, Swift Hunter, Swift Rider, Traceless Path
RANGER CONNECTIONS	—
RANGER MILITARY SKILLS	Archery 4, Crossbow 3, Hand Weapon 2, Pistol 2, Rifle 4, Thrown Weapon 4, Unarmed Combat 3
RANGER OCCUPATIONAL SKILLS	Command 3, Craft (any) 2, Cryptography 1, General Skills 4, Medicine 3, Navigation 4, Rope Use 4, Sneak 4, Survival 4, Tracking 4

The ranger is a skilled woodsman, hunter, and wilderness scout. He might be a member of a military organization such as the Cygnaran Reconnaissance Service or he could be a guide or hunter, leading others through the dangerous wilderness for a fee. The ranger is trained in a wide array of skills useful for surviving in the wilderness, including significant combat training in archery, firearms, and simple melee weapons.

Although rangers are common in the militaries of many Iron Kingdoms nations, where they serve as advance scouts and elite wilderness warriors, the same skill set can be found among hunters and freelance guides.

Playing a Ranger: The Ranger career is the path of the consummate woodsman. With the Pathfinder ability to traverse wooded regions with ease and the Camouflage ability to conceal him within them, players interested in playing an outdoor survivalist should strongly consider the Ranger career. Rangers exemplify a solid combat career as well as a versatile non-combat career, and they draw abilities from a broad range of talents. Ranger play styles range from the sniper with Night Fighter and Prowl, to the horseman with Light Cavalry and Saddle Shot, to the wilderness leader with Battle Plan: Go to Ground and Battle Plan: Shadow. Such directions can inform a player's selection of archetype and supporting career with combinations like Skilled Rifleman, Mighty Highwayman, and Intellectual Military Officer supporting vastly different styles of ranger.

The experienced Ranger has no lack of options and can begin to explore multiple different character directions. The Veteran abilities Battle Plan: Reconnaissance and Swift Hunter are exceptional for the guide-style Ranger and the sniper-style Ranger respectively.

RIFLEMAN

PREREQUISITES: NONE

STARTING ABILITIES AND SKILLS	Abilities: Crackshot, Dual Shot, and Marksman Military Skills: Rifle 1 Occupational Skills: Climbing 1, Detection 1, and Survival 1
STARTING ASSETS	50 gc, ammo bandolier, and a heavy rifle or a repeating long rifle (with powder and ammunition for ten shots)

RIFLEMAN ABILITIES	Crackshot, Dual Shot, Fast Reload, Marksman, Night Fighter, Return Fire, Saddle Shot, Sniper, Swift Hunter, Targeteer
RIFLEMAN CONNECTIONS	—
RIFLEMAN MILITARY SKILLS	Rifle 4
RIFLEMAN OCCUPATIONAL SKILLS	Craft (gunsmithing) 4, General Skills 4, Survival 3

The rifleman is a master of the long arm, and given the range from which he deals death, he is among the most feared of combatants. He could have been part of an elite military unit, or developed his skill as a result of inborn potential and practice. In addition to his lethal ability with a rifle, the character's skill set can also include abilities that aid him in spotting targets and moving into the best firing position, regardless of terrain.

Riflemen who have left military service often find employment as guns for hire, and their skills (along with the high cost of maintaining their weapons) demand a premium fee. Others might become involved in criminal organizations, gunning down rivals with a sniper's ruthless accuracy.

Playing a Rifleman: Much like the Pistoleer, the Rifleman narrowly focuses on his craft to the exclusion of all others, and he  has the tools to back up his long arm mastery. The abilities Dual Shot and Marksman are unique to the Rifleman and essentially provide two modes to his gunplay. He can forfeit movement to take an additional shot during one activation or forfeit movement to make his shots more accurate in another. The Crackshot and Night Fighter abilities grant this extraordinary sniper even more accuracy, while Fast Reload is an attractive option for heavy rifle users who need to perform frequent reloading. Riflemen lean toward the Skilled archetype, although that shouldn't constrain creative players. An Intellectual rifleman with Feat: Flawless Timing can operate from the fringes of a battle, always benefitting from his own Intellectual bonus and taking his shots at opportune moments.

An experienced Rifleman typically selects his skill advancements from his other career or careers, but he wants numerous Rifleman abilities. The Veteran ability Sniper is particularly useful for maximizing the first shot of each turn and is a great way to deal with heavily armored enemies.

SOLDIER

PREREQUISITES: NONE

STARTING ABILITIES AND SKILLS	**Abilities:** Find Cover and Sentry **Military Skills:** Choose two of the following: Hand Weapon 1, Pistol 1, Crossbow 1, Great Weapon 1, Rifle 1, Thrown Weapon 1 **Occupational Skills:** Detection 1, Driving 1, Medicine 1, Survival 1
STARTING ASSETS	**100 gc**
SOLDIER ABILITIES	'Jack Marshal, Cautious Advance, Cavalry Charge, Disease Resistance, Fast Reload, Find Cover, Grenadier, Hit the Deck!, Language, Ride-By Attack, Roll With It, Saddle Shot, Sentry
SOLDIER CONNECTIONS	Connections (kingdom military or mercenary company)
SOLDIER MILITARY SKILLS	Crossbow 3, Great Weapon 4, Light Artillery 3, Hand Weapon 3, Pistol 3, Rifle 4, Shield 2, Thrown Weapon 3, Unarmed Combat 3
SOLDIER OCCUPATIONAL SKILLS	Command 3, General Skills 4, Medicine 3, Navigation 2, Sneak 2, Survival 3

The soldier is a well-rounded fighter at home in nearly any battlefield situation. He could have received his training from a mercenary company or in one of the great national armies of the Iron Kingdoms, honing his talents with blades and firearms in regimented training camps of Cygnar or Khador. His potential breadth of skills reflects the wide array of military occupations that exist in the Iron Kingdoms, from heavy infantry armed with halberds and greatswords to crack teams of expert marksmen armed with long-range rifles. Additionally, most soldiers have at least rudimentary training in first aid, battlefield command, and basic survival.

Western Immoren has existed in a state of almost constant warfare for the last century, and there are more ex-soldiers in the Iron Kingdoms than those serving actively in organized militaries. Former soldiers find work as bodyguards, caravan guards, or join one of hundreds of mercenary companies that exist in nearly every major city in the Iron Kingdoms. Others, less concerned with the law, become brigands or join criminal organizations as hired muscle.

Playing a Soldier: Though a number of careers throughout this chapter include individuals who could be described as soldiers, the professional soldier is, at his heart, a survivor as well as a military man. The Soldier career boasts one of the broadest lists of military skills but also has plentiful battlefield survival abilities. His starting ability Find Cover can be augmented by Hit the Deck! and Roll With It to make the Soldier exceptionally difficult to pin down, and his unique Sentry ability allows him to respond immediately to new threats. The Soldier career fits smoothly with any archetype and with virtually any career and weapon selection. When looking to build a battle-hardened character with a strong theme from another career, it's hard to go wrong with the Soldier.

The experienced Soldier continuously advances his combat expertise as well as his survival-based occupational skills. Once reaching Veteran level, most Soldiers pick up the Cautious Advance ability, ensuring they are never out of cover and making them the consummate survivors.

SORCERER

PREREQUISITES: GIFTED, STARTING CAREER

STARTING ABILITIES, CONNECTIONS, SKILLS, AND SPELLS	Special: Choose the element the Sorcerer can manipulate: Fire, Ice, Stone, or Storm. Once chosen, the element does not change. Abilities are etermined by element. Spells are determined by element.		
	FIRE	**Abilities:** Immunity: Fire **Spells:** Fire Starter, Howling Flames, Wall of Fire	
	ICE	**Abilities:** Immunity: Cold **Spells:** Blizzard, Chiller, and Ice Bolt	
	STONE	**Spells:** Battering Ram, Solid Ground, and Stone Stance Stone sorcerers begin with +1 PHY and +1 to their racial maximum PHY at each level.	
	STORM	**Spells:** Razor Wind, Storm Tossed, and Wind Blast Storm sorcerers begin with +1 SPD and +1 to their racial maximum SPD at each level.	
	Military Skills: Choose one: Archery 1, Crossbow 1, or Hand Weapon 1		
	Occupational Skills: Detection 1 and Survival 1		
STARTING ASSETS	75 gc		

SORCERER ABILITIES	Camouflage, Dodger, Elemental Mastery, Immunity: Cold (Ice Sorcerer only), Immunity: Fire (Fire Sorcerer only), Traceless Path
SORCERER CONNECTIONS	—
SORCERER MILITARY SKILLS	Archery 3, Crossbow 3, Hand Weapon 3, Thrown Weapon 2, Unarmed Combat 2
SORCERER OCCUPATIONAL SKILLS	General Skills 4, Sneak 3, Survival 3
SORCERER SPELLS	Spells from the Sorcerer spell list of the character's chosen element

The sorcerer is a vessel for potent elemental magic. When he awakened to this frightening gift, he found himself with command over a primal element—fire, ice, stone, or wind. He has likely had no formal training in the use of his magic, and honed his abilities through painful trial and error. Sorcerers are shunned and hunted in some parts of the Iron Kingdoms, and his skill set might reflect the hardships he has encountered because of his sorcerous ability. As such, he could have picked up skills that allow him to avoid detection or escape his enemies.

Sorcery carries less of a stigma among non-humans, and races such as the Nyss and trollkin view these individuals as valued members of their communities. Human sorcerers have often endured persecution and might be labeled witches and heretics, particularly in remote areas.

Playing a Sorcerer: Like the Priest career, the Sorcerer career is multiple careers in one. Not only do the various elemental forces grant a Sorcerer different spell lists, but they also grant elemental immunities or stat increases. As far as other careers go, an Arcanist-Sorcerer can bathe the battlefield in frost or flame, but that's not the only option. Consider a Knight-Sorcerer of stone: After putting another level in the Knight's Shield skill and learning the Sorcerer's Stone Strength spell, he'll have +4 ARM from most attacks. Due to the intrinsic variety of the sorcerous paths, the Sorcerer career encompasses a wealth of possibilities.

Experienced Sorcerers have plenty of great spells to learn as well as access to abilities like Camouflage and Dodger that keep them safe from those who would hunt them down for their questionable gifts.

SPY

PREREQUISITES: NONE

STARTING ABILITIES, CONNECTIONS, AND SKILLS	Abilities: Battle Plan: Shadow, Cover Identity, and Language (choose one) Connections: Connections (intelligence network) Military Skills: Choose one: Hand Weapon 1, Pistol 1, or Thrown Weapon 1 Occupational Skills: Command 1, Deception 1, Detection 1, Disguise 1, and Sneak 1
STARTING ASSETS	100 gc and forged identity papers
SPY ABILITIES	Battle Plan: Shadow, Cover Identity, Iron Will, Language, Poison Resistance, Prowl, Signal Language, Truth Reader, Waylay
SPY CONNECTIONS	Connections (any)
SPY MILITARY SKILLS	Hand Weapon 3, Pistol 3, Thrown Weapon 3, Unarmed Combat 3
SPY OCCUPATIONAL SKILLS	Bribery 4, Command 3, Cryptography 4, Deception 4, Disguise 4, Escape Artist 4, Etiquette 4, Forgery 4, General Skills 4, Interrogation 4, Law 4, Lock Picking 2, Negotiation 4, Seduction 4, Sneak 4, Streetwise 4

The spy is an intelligencer, either a freelance operative or an agent of one of the Iron Kingdoms. He lives in a shady world of hidden truths and shifting alliances. His skill set includes numerous ways to gain information his nation or clients require, and he might be a master of diplomacy, skilled at seduction, well versed in brutal interrogation techniques, or all three. The spy is a fairly skilled combatant, as well, with the ability to fight his way out of situations he cannot avoid through other means.

In the Iron Kingdoms, nearly every nation and influential organization employs spies and intelligence gathering agents. Examples include the Cygnaran Reconnaissance Service, King Baird's network of informants in Ord, the Greylords Prikaz Chancellery in Khador, and groups such as Dargule's Mice that gather information for the Sancteum. Freelance groups, such as the mysterious Unseen Hand, work for anyone with the coin to pay for their services. Such groups offer a variety of covert services, from simple research to intelligence gathering by more direct means.

Playing a Spy: The Spy career has a very distinct role, so it might not be an optimal fit in every campaign type. In campaigns laden with intrigue, subterfuge, and investigation, the Spy's strengths really come to light. Spies have a truly impressive array of non-combat skills and can even gain a degree of competence with other skills thanks to Cover Identity. The free occupational skill from Cover Identity allows a Spy to better assist his allies with Medicine or even to dabble in rudimentary Alchemy. Paired with a strong combat career, a Spy can become a very well-rounded character with plenty of opportunities during narrative and combat encounters alike.

The experienced Spy has plenty of room for growth throughout his occupational skills and can eventually learn the Truth Reader ability. No matter how far he comes, there's also always room for another Cover Identity.

STORMBLADE

STARTING ABILITIES, CONNECTIONS, AND SKILLS	**Special:** A character starting with the Stormblade career must choose between Aristocrat, Knight, Man-at-Arms, Military Officer, Soldier, or Warcaster for his second career. **Abilities:** Blaster and Specialization (Storm Glaive) **Connections:** Connections (Cygnaran military) **Military Skills:** Great Weapon 1 **Occupational Skills:** Command 1, Detection 1, Etiquette 1
STARTING ASSETS	Storm Glaive and Storm Knight armor

STORMBLADE ABILITIES	'Jack Marshal, Blaster, Gunfighter, Load Bearing, Quick Work, Relentless Charge, Specialization (Storm Glaive)
STORMBLADE CONNECTIONS	Connections (Cygnaran military)
STORMBLADE MILITARY SKILLS	Great Weapon 4
STORMBLADE OCCUPATIONAL SKILLS	Command 4, Etiquette 2, General Skills 4, Medicine 2

The character is a knight of Cygnar chosen to serve in the elite fighting force known as the Stormblades. He combines ancient fighting traditions with state-of-the-art mechanikal weaponry, lighting up the battlefield with blasts of arcing electricity from his signature weapon, the Storm Glaive. In addition to his fighting skills, the Stormblade is also trained in battlefield command and the etiquette expected of a knight.

Stormblades fight for the armies of Cygnar but are, on occasion, given special dispensation to take leave of their brothers and pursue the interests of the crown elsewhere. In such instances, a Stormblade might seek out others skilled individuals to aid him on his quest. Stormblades also sometimes retire from the order completely to pursue their own interests. These individuals retain a host of useful battlefield skills and sometimes manage to hold on to their Storm Glaives.

Playing a Stormblade: The Stormblade is a specific and highly specialized career. He is a galvanic knight of Cygnar who wields the iconic storm glaive and wears heavy, electrically insulated armor. Stormblades are peerless with the powerful storm glaives, and their armor protects them from the shocks the weapons typically deliver to their wielders. A starting Stormblade's other career shapes his development. The Aristocrat-Stormblade is comfortable at court from Ceryl to Caspia, while the Man-at-Arms-Stormblade bravely fights to protect his allies.

The experienced Stormblade becomes more comfortable in his armor and can eventually learn to use the glaive's electrical blast after felling an enemy in melee combat.

THIEF

STARTING ABILITIES AND SKILLS	Abilities: Conniver and Dodger Military Skills: Hand Weapon 1 or Thrown Weapon 1 Occupational Skills: Bribery 1, Deception 1, Escape Artist 1, Lock Picking 2, Pickpocket 2, Sneak 1, and Streetwise 1
STARTING ASSETS	75 gc and thief's tools

THIEF ABILITIES	Appraise, Camouflage, Card Sharp, Conniver, Dodger, Fleet Foot, Get Away, Language (Five Cant), Parry, Prowl, Traceless Path
THIEF CONNECTIONS	Connections (criminal)
THIEF MILITARY SKILLS	Hand Weapon 3, Pistol 2, Thrown Weapon 3, Unarmed Combat 2
THIEF OCCUPATIONAL SKILLS	Bribery 4, Craft (any) 2, Deception 4, Disguise 4, Escape Artist 4, Etiquette 1, Forgery 4, General Skills 4, Law 2, Lock Picking 4, Negotiation 4, Pickpocket 4, Sneak 4, Streetwise 4

The thief is a skilled criminal adept at breaking and entering, pickpocketing, and any number of skills designed to relieve a target of his coin and valuables. The thief might be a member of an organized group, such as the criminal syndicates operating out of Five Fingers, or he could be a lone burglar, cutpurse, or con artist, hording his ill-gotten proceeds for himself. Although his focus lies elsewhere, the thief is likely skilled in the use of one or more easily concealable weapons.

Where there is wealth, there are thieves, and such rogues are common in all major cities in the Iron Kingdoms. Obviously, the more lawless the city, the greater the number of criminals, and many of the more prosperous thieves operate in areas such as war-torn Llael, Ord, and amid the crowded streets of Cygnar and Khador's great cities.

Playing a Thief: The Thief is one shady customer, and the Thief career is ideal for criminal characters. Whether he's a pickpocket, gambler, safecracker, forger, con artist, or enforcer, the thief has his criminal bases covered. The Thief's abilities reinforce his slippery nature with over half of the career abilities in some way helping him hide, dodge, escape, or otherwise evade threats he faces. This is not to say the Thief cannot hold his own in a fight, although a more offensively minded career helps him in such pursuits. Though there's nothing wrong with a Mighty, Intellectual, or Gifted Thief, the Skilled Thief is by far the most common thanks to archetype benefits such as Deft, Feat: Untouchable, and Preternatural Awareness.

The experienced Thief can hone his criminal skills as well as his ability to get away with it. The unique Veteran ability Get Away is worth particular mention, since it allows the speedy rogue to advance his full SPD when he dodges instead of advancing 2″.

TRENCHER

PREREQUISITES: HUMAN, OGRUN, OR TROLLKIN (CYGNARAN),
STARTING CAREER, AND RESTRICTED 2ND CAREER

STARTING ABILITIES, CONNECTIONS, AND SKILLS	Special: A character starting with the Trencher career must choose between Military Officer, Ranger, Rifleman, Soldier, or Warcaster for his second career. Abilities: Bayonet Charge and Dig In Connections: Connections (Cygnaran military) Military Skills: Great Weapon 1, Rifle 1, Thrown Weapon 1 Occupational Skills: Command 1 and Detection 1
STARTING ASSETS	25 gc, ammo bandolier, bayonet, entrenching spade, military rifle, 3 smoke grenades, and Trencher medium infantry armor

TRENCHER ABILITIES	'Jack Marshal, Anatomical Precision, Bayonet Charge, Bomber, Dig In, Fire in the Hole!, Grenadier, Hit the Deck!, Relentless Charge, Specialization (Bayonet)
TRENCHER CONNECTIONS	Connections (Cygnaran military)
TRENCHER MILITARY SKILLS	Great Weapon 3, Light Artillery 4, Hand Weapon 3, Pistol 3, Rifle 4, Thrown Weapon 4, Unarmed Combat 3
TRENCHER OCCUPATIONAL SKILLS	Command 3, General Skills 4, Interrogation 3, Medicine 3, Sneak 3, Survival 3

Trenchers are the hardy soldiers that form the backbone of the Cygnaran military. Sometimes called "grave diggers," they are the first Cygnarans onto the battlefield and often the last to leave. Especially trained for trench-to-trench fighting, these soldiers carry out numerous battlefield roles. The character might be a simple infantryman, trained in the rifle and bayonet, or he could have been part of a heavy weapons crew with the skills necessary to fire and maintain cannons and chain guns. The character has likely received training in other skills useful in combat, such as basic interrogation techniques, first aid, and wilderness survival.

It is not uncommon for Trenchers to become mercenaries once they leave the Cygnaran military. The skills learned on the battlefields of western Immoren are easily parleyed into sometimes lucrative positions in the more prominent mercenary companies, especially for Trenchers who received training in heavy weapons or learned the necessary skills to commanded warjacks in the field.

Playing a Trencher: Though not nearly as restrictive as the Iron Fang or Stormblade, the Trencher career is still far more focused than most when it comes to race, nationality, and starting career options. Of particular note is the fact that regardless of the other career, the Trencher is a predominantly combat character with fewer options in an investigative campaign or campaign of high intrigue. But when it comes to combat, a Trencher is a versatile character with numerous military skills and combat-related abilities. Skilled with rifle, bayonet, and grenades, a Trencher has several paths available to him from the Rifleman-Trencher's ranged expertise to the Trencher-Warcaster who charges into the heat of battle.

Experienced Trenchers continue on the path of combat survivalists or snipers but can also become real experts with grenades. The Veteran Bomber ability can join Fire in the Hole! and Grenadier leading to a real expert in maximizing the potential of explosives.

WARCASTER

STARTING ABILITIES, CONNECTIONS, SKILLS, AND SPELLS	Abilities: Bond Military Skills: Hand Weapon 1 and Pistol 1 Occupational Skills: Command 1 and Detection 1 Spells: Boundless Charge and Convection Special: Change the character's arcane tradition to focuser if he has another arcane career. A warcaster can boost only with mechanikal weapons they have bonded to.
STARTING ASSETS	Choose one of the following: suit of warcaster armor (light or medium), mechanika hand weapon, or a mechanika hand cannon (with ten rounds of ammunition). Mechanika weapons have housings of the chosen weapon, runeplates inscribed with the Bond rune, and are powered by alchemical capacitors. This item begins the game bonded to the warcaster.

WARCASTER ABILITIES	Bond, Field Marshal: Magical Attack, Field Marshal: Relentless Charge, Field Marshal: Shield Guard, Natural Leader
WARCASTER CONNECTIONS	Connections (kingdom or mercenary company)
WARCASTER MILITARY SKILLS	Great Weapon 3, Hand Weapon 3, Pistol 3, Unarmed Combat 2
WARCASTER OCCUPATIONAL SKILLS	Command 4, General Skills 4
WARCASTER SPELLS	Spells from the Warcaster spell list

The warcaster is a rare and powerful battle mage gifted with the ability to commune with and command the most devastating weapons of war in the Iron Kingdoms: warjacks. The character's ability to manipulate the forces of magic is intrinsic, but it is likely he learned to hone and shape it in one of the great military institutes responsible for warcaster training—such as Cygnar's Strategic Academy—or as an apprentice to a warcaster. The character is a mighty force on the battlefield and commands a versatile set of combat skills as well as lethal spells.

The military potency of each nation in the Iron Kingdoms is dependent on the strength and number of its warcasters to maintain power and fend of rivals. As such, nearly all warcasters have at some point served in the military. Freelance warcasters can be found among some of the greatest mercenary companies in western Immoren. Many of these free companies are led by one or more powerful warcasters. Those warcasters who eschew the discipline of employment in a standing army might be hampered by lessened access to the infrastructure necessary to maintain a stable of warjacks but many find they are compensated by the freedom to make great fortunes selling their services to the highest bidder.

Playing a Warcaster: The Warcaster could perhaps best be summarized by "limitless potential." Though the Warcaster has only one archetype choice (Gifted) and relatively short skill lists, the power of the Bond ability cannot be overstated and is always a good choice for a Warcaster. Bonded warcaster armor adds to a Warcaster's vitality and can be empowered to add to his ARM as well. Bonded warcaster weapons can use focus points to boost attack rolls, boost damage rolls, or even make additional attacks, and bonded steamjacks are the most powerful weapons in a party's arsenal. Virtually any other career can make a good pairing for Warcaster. From the deadly Cutthroat-Warcaster to the implacable Knight-Warcaster, almost nothing is off-limits.

Experienced Warcasters want an extra selection or two of the Bond ability, but they'll also want additional spells and abilities from their other career. Veteran and Epic-level Warcasters can also take field marshal abilities, granting their whole battlegroup additional abilities.

PLAN AHEAD!

It is a good idea to have a rough concept for your character before starting the character creation process. If you know your character is going to be some type of gunslinger, it's a good idea to spend advancement points increasing his Poise, since that impacts his accuracy with firearms. If your character is going to be an expert tracker, think about increasing Perception so his Detection rolls are more likely to succeed. If you want durability in combat, increase Physique, Speed, Agility, or Perception to increase your character's Defense and Armor.

There's also nothing wrong with going back and changing your mind along the way. It's all part of the fun of character creation!

STEP 4: INCREASE STATS

You now have 3 advancement points to spend on increasing your character's primary and secondary stats: Physique, Agility, Intellect, Speed, Strength, Poise, Prowess, Arcane (if the character has the Gifted archetype), or Perception. Increasing a stat by 1 costs 1 advancement point.

Remember that starting stat values are limited by your character's race and level. Unspent stat advancement points are lost.

FILLING OUT YOUR CHARACTER'S LIFE SPIRAL

Once you have increased your character's stats, you can fill out his life spiral. First, completely fill in the circles that you will not use—starting on the outside of the spiral working in—so that the number of available damage circles in each aspect are equal to the corresponding primary stat. Available damage circles should be split as evenly as possible across the two branches within each aspect. When your character takes damage during play, put a slash mark or x in the circles that take damage.

Will's human character started with an Intellect of 3, a Physique of 5, and an Agility of 3. During character creation he spent one of his advancement points to increase his character's Physique to 6. To set up his character's life spiral, he fills in circles so that 3 circles remain in the Intellect aspect, 6 circles remain in the Physique aspect, and 3 circles remain in the Agility aspect.

STEP 5: FINISHING TOUCHES

At this point, your character's creation is pretty much complete. There are just a couple loose ends to tie up before you can begin your character's adventures in the Iron Kingdoms: purchasing additional equipment and considering the teamwork of your character's party.

PURCHASE ADDITIONAL EQUIPMENT

Add up the money (in Cygnaran gold crowns) that each of your character's starting careers grants. Now it is time to spend that gold to prepare your character for the challenges he is likely to face while adventuring. Please refer to "Gear, Mechanika, and Alchemy" (p. 247) for descriptions and prices of what you can purchase.

Each character should purchase a weapon that matches one of the military skills he received from his chosen careers and some armor to protect him from the inevitable attacks he must endure. Savvy characters also make sure to pick up a ranged weapon whether they have the training for it or not. You never know when your character might find himself in a situation where his sword just won't reach an enemy in time.

After purchasing weapons and armor, use the remaining gold to buy ammunition for weapons and then purchase gear you think would be appropriate for your character. A gambling character might want to buy a deck of cards, or a priest might want a holy symbol of his faith, for example. It is also a good idea to hold onto some gold so that your character has some spending money once the game starts (he keeps all unspent gold).

All characters in the *Iron Kingdoms Full Metal Fantasy Roleplaying Game* are considered to possess a basic set of equipment that covers their essential day-to-day needs. This intrinsic equipment includes things like traveling clothes, utensils for eating, a canteen or water skin, ammo pouches, coin purses, and a pack. These ordinary items do not need to be listed and tracked on a character sheet, and they confer no game effects or bonuses.

COMPLETING AND USING THE CHARACTER SHEET

If you haven't done so already, print or photocopy the character sheet (p. 349) and write in the choices you have made about your character: stats, name, archetype, race, careers, skills, benefits, abilities, and so on. Write down the weapons and armor you purchased, determine your character's MAT and RAT with each weapon (p. 106), and note the SPD, DEF, and ARM modifiers of the armor your character wears. With those things settled, you can now calculate the derived stats of DEF, ARM, Initiative, Command Range, and Willpower.

The character sheet breaks down the calculations for determining those derived stats, so simply fill in the spaces and add up the totals. Similarly, the skills portion of the character sheet is designed for you to predetermine your character's total skill roll modifier to make gameplay run more smoothly. Fill in the stat that governs each skill, the level of the skill, and then the total. When you make skill rolls, add the total to the roll of the dice. We recommend listing a skill's parent stat in parentheses next to the name of the stat for ease of future reference.

The benefits and abilities portion of the character sheet has space for you to list your character's abilities and benefits and leave yourself a short reminder note of what the ability does. There is also room for a rulebook page reference to help you look up abilities during the game.

Write "Hero" in the space for your character's level unless your Game Master has decided to start all characters at a higher experience level. All characters start at Hero level. Then write '3' into the field for current feat points, and your character is ready to begin adventuring in the Iron Kingdoms!

TEAMWORK

Now that your character is complete, it's time to consider how he works with the other members of his adventuring party. Teamwork is essential to survival in the Iron Kingdoms. Characters in the game are exceptional people who are capable of tackling challenges and dangers that would be insurmountable to ordinary folk. Still, they do not face these challenges alone; to do so would be to invite almost certain death. Instead, these intrepid souls band together with others of common cause. Every character is the star of his own story, but together the group of players makes up an ensemble who must work together, especially in the heat of combat, if they are going to survive and prosper against the dangers they face.

The most successful groups of players take a few moments to discuss their battle plans before and during a fight. Taking a second to consider how to best engage the enemy, how to use cover, and which member of the group should attack which enemy gives a group a considerable edge, and the Game Master should encourage this sort of teamwork. Even the most ragtag and mismatched group of characters have access to synergies between themselves, but groups of characters created with some focus before the campaign begins can gain even greater advantage.

For example, a gun mage has access to deadly rune shots, but his most important attack in combat could be his Rune Shot: Earth Shaker that knocks down a group of enemies, setting them up for easy attacks from the rest of his party. A heavily armored knight or man-at-arms might not have the raw stopping power of warcasters, but can save the day by taking a hit that might fell one of his weaker comrades.

ADVENTURING COMPANIES

Adventuring companies represent groups of characters bound together for some purpose. The company provides a theme, special benefits, and a loose framework for a group of characters.

Creating an adventuring company is optional and can be done only with the Game Master's consent before the start of the game. Unless the Game Master mandates the use of a particular adventuring company, all the players have to agree to form a company. They then select one company concept for their characters. A group of characters gains the benefits of a single adventuring company; they cannot benefit from belonging to multiple adventuring companies.

If your gaming group decides to form an adventuring company, all of the player characters in the group must be members of the company and satisfy its membership requirements. Likewise, new characters joining the company must satisfy the membership requirements of the company.

Not every adventuring company concept is appropriate for every campaign and the Game Master is the final arbiter of which concepts, if any, are permitted his campaign. The Game Master might even choose to base an entire campaign on a given adventuring company concept. Players should feel free to expand upon the skeleton of the company concept they have chosen. Pirates should name their ship, criminal gangs should have a name for their crew, and so on. Such embellishments help you breathe life into your character and the organization of which he is a part.

If your adventuring company gives your character an ability he already has from one of his starting careers, choose a new ability from any of your character's careers.

ARCANE ORDER

The Iron Kingdoms are home to many guilds and orders that exist to promote the arcane arts and esoteric sciences. The characters belong to one such group. They might represent a small chapter house of a larger organization or be the sole members of a smaller order.

Requirements: Any character can belong to the company. The company must include at least one character with the Gifted archetype. Those with the Gifted archetype are full members of the organization with an equal vote on decisions pertaining to the good of the order (or chapter house). The players should decide among themselves who the nominal leader of the group is. Non-spellcasting characters are assumed to be guards and skilled experts in the employ of the order.

Benefits: The company begins the game with a small guild house that includes servants' quarters, stable, kitchen, great hall, meeting room, member bedchambers, guest rooms, an arcane library, and an alchemical workshop.

Each character created as a member of the company gains one additional occupational skill level in Lore (Arcane) and treats it as a career skill regardless of his careers.

Each Gifted character created as a member of the company also gains the Arcane Scholar ability (p. 157) at character creation (in addition to any other abilities granted by his career selections).

Each non-Gifted character created as a member of the company begins with the Shield Guard ability (p. 167).

INTREPID INVESTIGATORS

The pursuit of knowledge might be its own reward but like any pursuit, it is not earned without cost. The characters are a group of individuals seeking a greater understanding of the mysteries of western Immoren. They could be explorers, ghost hunters, tomb-robbing adventurers, or perhaps an expedition from Corvis University tasked with cataloguing the more unusual flora and fauna of the Thornwood Forest. In the Iron Kingdoms, many academics that spend time in the field learn their way around a pistol or sword, but few are unwilling to hire guards and assistants to accompany them on their sometimes-perilous research missions.

Requirements: Each member of the company must have at least one of the following careers: Alchemist, Arcane Mechanik, Arcanist, Aristocrat, Explorer, Investigator, Military Officer, Priest, or Spy.

Benefits: The company is able to seek funding for its activities through support from a major university, financial backers, or private donations. Each month the company gains 100 gc for upkeep and equipment that can be spent any way the players see fit.

Each character created as a member of the company can benefit from the starting Intellectual archetype bonus (+1 on attack and damage rolls while in an Intellectual character's command range) from up to two Intellectual characters simultaneously instead of just one.

LAW DOGS

The characters are professional bounty hunters who make their livings tracking the most dangerous criminals and army deserters. A good bounty hunter must be ready to go anywhere the trail leads him, and so the law dogs regularly traverse the Iron Kingdoms with little concern for national borders or boundaries. In the end, all that matters is getting their man.

Requirements: Each member of the company must have at least one of the following careers: Bounty Hunter, Highwayman, Investigator, Military Officer, Ranger, or Soldier.

Benefits: The characters in the company should be regularly presented with bounty opportunities. They are regarded as solid professionals by the various kingdoms and law enforcement agencies throughout western Immoren.

While pursuing a bounty, characters created as a member of the company gain +2 on non-combat skill rolls directly pursuant to capturing the target of their bounty and gain +2 on attack rolls against their bounty.

MERCENARY CHARTER

The characters represent a recognized mercenary company and possess a charter recognized by most nations and authorities in the Iron Kingdoms. The characters might be in the employ of a larger organization like the Steelheads Mercenary Company, or they could be the only members of their charter. They have an easier time negotiating work as sell-swords than those without a charter and are members of a well respected if sometimes brutish profession.

Requirements: Any character can belong to the company. The players in the group should designate one member of the company to be the captain. The captain then designates a lieutenant and a treasurer. Other members are sergeants.

Benefits: The captain gains the Natural Leader ability whether or not he meets the prerequisites.

Additionally, each character created as a member of the company begins with one additional occupational skill level in one of the following skills: Animal Handling, Command, Driving, Gambling, Interrogation, Medicine, Negotiation, or Riding.

OUTLAWS

Crime does pay, but sometimes in blood. This lesson is learned by criminals across the Iron Kingdoms, from the streets of Five Fingers to the vicious bratyas of the Korsk underworld to the feral gangs of the Cryxian port of Blackwater. The characters are members of a close-knit gang of criminals, ruffians, and thugs motivated by the promise of coin or blood for blood's sake.

Requirements: Each member of the company must have at least one of the following careers: Alchemist, Cutthroat, Duelist, Highwayman, Pistoleer, Rifleman, Sorcerer, Spy, or Thief. The players in the group should designate one member of the company to be the boss. The boss then designates an underboss.

Benefits: The company begins the game with a hideout watched over by a network of gang affiliates who keep an eye out for dangerous rivals and the law. When a threat is spotted, the gang is quickly alerted. The hideout itself consists of a meeting area, an administrative office, sleeping chambers, hidden cells, and a number of secret exits or hidden passages.

Each character created as a member of the company gains the Gang and Language (Five Cant) abilities in addition to any abilities granted by his careers.

PIRATES OF THE BROKEN COAST

The characters are pirates or privateers, the ranking officers of a small frigate. The characters might choose to be criminals of the sea, pillaging and looting the coasts of the Iron Kingdom either for their own purposes or even in the employ of the Cryxian Pirate Fleet. Or they might be recognized privateers bearing a letter of marque issued by the naval authorities of Cygnar, Khador, or Ord.

Requirements: Each member of the company must have at least one of the following careers: Cutthroat, Explorer, Military Officer, Pirate, or Thief. The players in the group should designate one member of the company to be the captain. The captain then designates a first mate.

Benefits: The company begins the game with a small pirate ship crewed by unwashed sea dogs. Known throughout the secret coves and smugglers dens throughout the Broken Coast, the crew can choose between dozens of safe ports to lie low or finish repairs.

The captain gains the Natural Leader ability whether or not he meets the prerequisites.

Each character created as a member of the company gains the Hit the Deck! ability.

SPY RING

The characters in the company are intelligencers employed by a kingdom, major organization, or private concern. They could be members of the Cygnaran Reconnaissance Service, agents of a noble house, or simply freelancers in the employ of the highest bidder. In any case, they are practiced professionals in the art of espionage and surveillance.

Requirements: Each member of the company must have at least one of the following careers: Aristocrat, Investigator, Ranger, Spy, or Thief.

Benefits: Although the characters are disavowed if captured, they can count on material assistance from their employers. Depending on the mission undertaken, the characters in the company can receive specialized equipment, access to safe houses, forged documents, uniforms, and so forth. Additionally, they can expect to call upon the intelligence resources of their employers before a given mission.

Additionally, each character created as a member of the company begins with either the Language ability or one additional occupational skill level in one of the following skills: Bribery, Climbing, Cryptography, Deception, Detection, Disguise, Escape Artist, Etiquette, Forensic Science, Forgery, Gambling, Interrogation, Intimidation, Jumping, Lock Picking, Negotiation, Pickpocket, Research, Riding, Rope Use, Seduction, Sneak, or Streetwise.

EXPERIENCE AND ADVANCEMENT

As your character performs notable deeds and overcomes dramatic obstacles, he earns Experience Points (XP). The total number of XP a character has earned is a measure of how accomplished he is and how practiced his skills have become. As a character's XP total increases, he gains the opportunity to increase his stats, learn new skills or increase existing ones, add additional archetype benefits, learn new abilities or spells, or even add new careers.

You track the total number of XP your character has earned on the character sheet. The advancement of XP is broken into tiers that represent a character's Experience Level. All characters begin at the Hero level. After accruing enough XP a character's level becomes Veteran, and after accruing even more his level becomes Epic. Your character's level determines the maximum allowable values for his stats as well as the maximum skill level for his skills. A Hero character can have skills up to level 2, a Veteran character can have skills up to level 3, and an Epic character can have skills up to level 4.

EARNING EXPERIENCE POINTS

Characters earn XP at the end of each game session (or at another interval if the Game Master sees fit). The Game Master determines how much XP each character earns when XP is awarded. Obviously, the more XP awarded, the faster characters will develop. The following guidelines should be used when awarding XP.

- **Play Award:** At the end of each game session, each character who participated in the session gains 1 XP. Thanks for playing!

- **Teamwork Award:** Players who work together tactically through a play session each gain 1 XP. This is, as usual, up to the Game Master's discretion, but making and executing a plan that utilizes the strengths of multiple characters and which requires thought and coordination should be rewarded with extra XP. Kicking in the door of a dockside warehouse and shooting all the gangsters inside is fine. It works. But sneaking under the warehouse to sabotage the structural base and fit it with cargo netting, impersonating a local official to get all the gangsters in the same place, then detonating charges with a scoped sniper rifle to destroy the floor and dump all the gangsters into the netting where the characters then negotiate the terms of the gangsters' surrender is a brilliant plan worthy of bonus XP.

- **Milestone Bonus:** When the characters in a party achieve a milestone in play, such as defeating a significant enemy, overcoming a great obstacle, or pushing the story forward in a major way, they are awarded with 1 XP. The Game Master determines when the characters achieve a milestone.

- **Conclusion:** At the end of a major storyline, the Game Master should award each participating character 1 – 3 XP depending on the scope of the story, the power level of the characters involved, and how fast he wishes the characters to advance.

CHARACTER ADVANCEMENT TABLE

HERO LEVEL

XP TOTAL	CHARACTER ADVANCEMENT
2	+ 2 occupational skills
4	+ 1 spell, ability, connection, or military skill
6	+ 1 stat
8	+ 2 occupational skills
10	+ 1 spell, ability, connection, or military skill
12	+ 1 archetype benefit
15	+ 1 stat
18	+ 2 occupational skills
21	+ 1 spell, ability, connection, or military skill
24	+ 1 stat
27	+ 2 occupational skills
30	+ 1 archetype benefit or + 1 career and + 2 occupational skills
33	+ 1 spell, ability, connection, or military skill
36	+ 1 stat
39	+ 2 occupational skills
42	+ 1 spell, ability, connection, or military skill
45	+ 1 stat

VETEREN LEVEL

XP TOTAL	CHARACTER ADVANCEMENT
50	+ 1 archetype benefit
55	+ 2 occupational skills
60	+ 1 spell, ability, connection, or military skill
65	+ 1 stat
70	+ 2 occupational skills
75	+ 1 spell, ability, connection, or military skill
80	+ 1 archetype benefit or + 1 career and + 2 occupational skills
85	+ 1 stat
90	+ 2 occupational skills
95	+ 1 spell, ability, connection, or military skill

EPIC LEVEL

XP TOTAL	CHARACTER ADVANCEMENT
100	+ 1 stat
105	+ 2 occupational skills
110	+ 1 archetype benefit or + 1 career and + 2 occupational skills
115	+ 1 spell, ability, connection, or military skill
120	+ 1 stat
125	+ 2 occupational skills
130	+ 1 spell, ability, connection, or military skill
135	+ 1 stat
140	+ 1 archetype benefit
145	+ 2 occupational skills
150	+ 1 spell, ability, connection, or military skill

+2 occupational skills – Choose two new occupational skills from any of your character's careers. Instead of adding a new skill, you can increase the level of an occupational skill your character already has by 1. If you choose to do this with both new occupational skills, you can increase the level of one skill by 2. Remember the skill level limits: A Hero character can have skills up to level 2, a Veteran character can have skills up to level 3, and an Epic character can have skills up to level 4.

+1 military skill – Choose a new military skill from any of your character's careers or increase the level of a military skill your character already has by 1.

+1 ability – Choose a new ability from any of your character's careers.

+1 connection – Choose a new connection from any of your character's careers.

+1 spell – Choose a new spell for your character to learn from one of his careers' spell lists. Remember, a character can have up to a number of spells equal to his INT x 2.

+1 stat – Increase one of your character's primary or secondary stats by 1. You cannot increase a stat beyond its maximum allowable value.

+1 archetype benefit – Choose another archetype benefit from your character's archetype.

+1 career – Add a new career to your character sheet. Your character does not gain any of the starting skills, abilities, connections, money, or equipment (those are for new characters only), but as he advances in level you can choose advancements from the new career.

CHARACTER ADVANCEMENT

As a character's XP total grows, he has the opportunity to enhance his talents and attributes. Character advancement takes place between game sessions. If a character is awarded enough XP to gain an advancement, he must select the advancement before the next game session. Advancements cannot be saved for later.

Refer to the Character Advancement Table on the next page to see what advancements are available to characters as their XP totals grow.

HIGH-LEVEL STARTING CHARACTERS

When playing in a campaign that chooses to start with experienced characters or when creating experienced NPCs (non-player characters), the following lists can be helpful to jump forward quickly in character advancement rather than taking things one step at a time.

From 0 XP to 25 XP, a character gains +6 occupational skills, +3 stats, +3 spells, abilities, connections, or military skills, and +1 archetype benefit. No stats can exceed Hero racial limits, and no skills can exceed level 2.

From 0 XP to 50 XP, a character gains +10 occupational skills, +5 stats, +5 spells, abilities, connections, or military skills, and +3 archetype benefits (1 of which can be substituted for +1 career and +2 occupational skills). No stats can exceed Hero racial limits, and no skills can exceed level 2.

From 50 XP to 75 XP, a character gains +4 occupational skills, +1 stat, and +2 spells, abilities, connections, or military skills. No stats can exceed Veteran racial limits, and no skills can exceed level 3.

From 50 XP to 100 XP, a character gains +6 occupational skills, +3 stats, +3 spells, abilities, connections, or military skills, and +1 archetype benefit (which can be substituted for +1 career and +2 occupational skills). Only one stat can exceed Veteran racial limits, and no skills can exceed level 3.

ABILITIES

Abilities are special capabilities that a character has access to as a result of his career choices. They can be learned only once and do not have levels of mastery. A character must have an ability in order to use it.

Specific ability rules override general rules whenever there is a conflict. For example, an ability that grants the use of another ability for a round does so regardless of whether or not the character meets the granted ability's prerequisites.

Prerequisite: Note that some abilities have prerequisites that must be met before the character can learn the ability.

ALL ABILITIES AT A GLANCE

'Jack Marshal
Ace Commander
Acrobatics
Advisor
Ambush
Anatomical Precision
Appraise
Arcane Assassin
Arcane Defenses
Arcane Engineer
Arcane Precision
Arcane Scholar
Astute
Backstab
Battle Commander
Battle Plan: Call to Action
Battle Plan: Coordinated Strike
Battle Plan: Desperate Pace
Battle Plan: Go to Ground
Battle Plan: Reconnaissance
Battle Plan: Shadow
Bayonet Charge
Big Game Hunter
Binding
Blaster
Blood Spiller
Bodge
Bodyguard
Bomber
Bond (bond slot)*
Brew Master
Camouflage
Card Sharp
Cautious Advance
Cavalry Charge
Chain Attack: Bleed Out
Chain Attack: Pin Down
Choir
Cleave
Combat Rider
Conniver
Cover Identity (identity)*
Crackshot
Craft Rune Shot
Crossbowman
Defender
Defensive Line
Dig In
Disease Resistance

Dispel
Dodger
Drive: Ancillary Attack
Drive: Assault
Drive: Off Road
Drive: Pronto
Dual Shot
Elemental Mastery
Empower
Expert Rider
Fast Cook
Fast Draw
Fast Rearm (weapon type)*
Fast Reload
Fell Call: Cacophony
Fell Call: Call of Defiance
Fell Call: Ground Shaker
Fell Call: Heroic Ballad
Fell Call: Reverberation
Fell Call: Signal Call
Fell Call: Sonic Blast
Field Alchemist
Field Marshal: Magical Attack
Field Marshal: Relentless Charge
Field Marshal: Shield Guard
Find Cover
Fire in the Hole!
Fleet Foot
Free Style
Gang
Get Away
Girded
Good Breeding
Great Power
Grenadier
Gunfighter
Head-Butt
Hit the Deck!
Hyper Awareness
Immunity: Cold
Immunity: Corrosion
Immunity: Electricity
Immunity: Fire
Inscribe Formulae
Iron Sentinel
Iron Will
Keen Eyed
Language (language)*
Legacy of Bragg

Light Cavalry
Load Bearing
Mage Killer
Marksman
Natural Leader
Night Fighter
Parry
Pathfinder
Poison Resistance
Port of Call
Precision Strike
Press the Attack
Privilege
Prowl
Pursuit
Quick Work
Rallying Cry
Relentless Charge
Resourceful
Retaliatory Strike
Return Fire
Ride-By Attack
Riposte
Rock Solid
Roll With It
Saddle Shot
Scrounge
Sentry
Set Defense
Shadow Magic
Shield Guard
Shield Slam
Signal Language
Sniper
Specialization (weapon type)*
Steady
Steamo
Sucker!
Swift Hunter
Swift Rider
Take Down
Targeteer
Team Leader
Traceless Path
Truth Reader
Tune Up
Two-Weapon Fighting
University Education
Waylay

*These abilities can be taken multiple times. See the ability description.

'JACK MARSHAL

Prerequisite: None

The character is skilled at instructing steamjacks to act. The 'jack marshal must know the cortex's native language to instruct it as well as the 'jack's cortex lock codes.

Bonded steamjacks (p. 323) cannot be affected by this ability.

For a complete description of how this ability is used, see "'Jack Marshals" (p. 322).

ACE COMMANDER

Prerequisite: 'Jack Marshal, Command 2

The character gains an extra quick action during each of his turns that can only be used to drive a 'jack.

ACROBATICS

Prerequisite: AGL 6

The character can advance through other characters if he has enough movement to move completely past their bases. The character also gains +3 on his Jumping skill rolls.

ADVISOR

Prerequisite: Command 2

While B2B (base-to-base, see p. 204) with this character, friendly characters gain +1 to their command range.

AMBUSH

Prerequisite: None

During the first round of an encounter, this character gains boosted attack and damage rolls against enemies that have not yet activated that encounter.

ANATOMICAL PRECISION

Prerequisite: None

When this character hits a living target with a melee attack but the damage roll fails to exceed the target's ARM, the target suffers d3 damage points instead of the damage rolled.

APPRAISE

Prerequisite: None

The character has a sharp eye and keen mind for detail, especially where monetary values are concerned. The character can judge the value of most fine goods with an inspection. Truly good fakes might require a Detection + INT roll to spot.

ARCANE ASSASSIN

Prerequisite: None

When making attacks, this character ignores focus points overboosting the target's Power Field and spell effects adding to its ARM or DEF.

ARCANE DEFENSES

Prerequisite: ARC 5

This character gains +3 ARM against magic attacks.

ARCANE ENGINEER

Prerequisite: Mechanikal Engineering 2

The character can reroll failed Mechanikal Engineering rolls. Each failed roll can be rerolled only once as a result of Arcane Engineer.

ARCANE PRECISION

Prerequisite: Detection 3

When this character forfeits his movement to aim with a ranged weapon, he ignores stealth that turn.

ARCANE SCHOLAR

Prerequisite: None

This character can have a number of spells equal to his INT x3, instead of the normal limit of INT x2.

ASTUTE

Prerequisite: Detection 1

The character can reroll failed Detection rolls. Each failed roll can be rerolled only once as a result of Astute.

BACKSTAB

Prerequisite: None

This character gains an additional die on his back strike damage rolls.

BATTLE COMMANDER

Prerequisite: Command 3

This character can use one battle plan during each of his turns without spending a feat point.

BATTLE PLAN: CALL TO ACTION

Prerequisite: Command 1

The character can spend 1 feat point to use Battle Plan: Call to Action. Using a battle plan is a quick action. When a character uses this battle plan, each friendly character in his command range who is under his command and is knocked down immediately stands up or goes prone.

BATTLE PLAN: COORDINATED STRIKE

Prerequisite: Command 1

The character can spend 1 feat point to use Battle Plan: Coordinated Strike during a surprise round (p. 201) before a battle. Using a battle plan is a quick action. When a character uses this battle plan, each friendly character in his command range can immediately make one attack. After these attacks, the surprise round ends and the characters are detected.

BATTLE PLAN: DESPERATE PACE

Prerequisite: Command 3

The character can spend 1 feat point to use Battle Plan: Desperate Pace. Using a battle plan is a quick action. When a character uses this battle plan, each friendly character who follows the character's orders gains +2″ movement for one round.

BATTLE PLAN: GO TO GROUND

Prerequisite: Command 2

The character can spend 1 feat point to use Battle Plan: Go to Ground. Using a battle plan is a quick action. When a character uses this battle plan, each friendly character who follows the character's orders gains cover, does not suffer blast damage, and does not block LOS until he moves, is placed, or is engaged.

BATTLE PLAN: RECONNAISSANCE

Prerequisite: Command 2, Survival 3

The character can spend 1 feat point to use Battle Plan: Reconnaissance. Using a battle plan is a quick action. When a character uses this battle plan, the character and each friendly character who starts his activation in his command range gains the Pathfinder ability. Battle Plan: Reconnaissance lasts for one round.

BATTLE PLAN: SHADOW

Prerequisite: Command 1

The character can spend 1 feat point to use Battle Plan: Shadow. Using a battle plan is a quick action. When a character uses this battle plan, each friendly character who follows the character's orders gains Prowl (p. 165) for one round.

BAYONET CHARGE

Prerequisite: None

When this character charges with a ranged weapon that has a bayonet, after moving but before making his charge attack, he can make one ranged attack targeting his charge target unless he was in melee with his charge target at the start of his turn. When resolving a Bayonet Charge ranged attack, the character does not suffer the target in melee attack roll penalty (see p. 212). If the target is not in melee range after the charging character moves, the character can make the Bayonet Charge ranged attack before his turn ends. A character making a Bayonet Charge must make his charge attack with a bayonet.

BIG GAME HUNTER

Prerequisite: Survival 1

A character with the Big Game Hunter ability has hunted more than his fair share of game in the wilds of Immoren. When a character with Big Game Hunter makes a melee or ranged attack against a natural animal or beast native to the wilds of Immoren, he gains a bonus on attack rolls equal to his Survival skill.

BINDING

Prerequisite: Rope Use 1

When the character ties up, manacles, or otherwise restrains another character with some form of restraints, add +3 to the skill roll difficulty for the bound character to escape.

BLASTER

Prerequisite: None

The character gains +2 to hit with electrical ranged attacks.

BLOOD SPILLER

Prerequisite: Hand Weapon 3

The character gains +2 on damage rolls against living characters.

BODGE

Prerequisite: Mechanikal Engineering 1

The character can make temporary repairs to a steamjack in the midst of combat. See the "Steamjacks" chapter (p. 299) for more details.

BODYGUARD

Prerequisite: Shield Guard, Shield 3

This character is not limited in the number of times he can use Shield Guard each round.

BOMBER

Prerequisite: Thrown Weapon 3

When this character's grenade ranged attack deviates, you can reroll the direction and/or distance of deviation. A roll can only be rerolled once as a result of Bomber.

BOND

Prerequisite: None

This ability can be taken more than once. Each time a character takes this ability he gains a bonding slot that can be used to bond with warcaster armor, a steamjack, or a mechanika weapon – one per slot.

- The character must bond to a steamjack to make it part of his battlegroup.

- He must bond to a mechanika weapon to spend focus points to boost attack and damage rolls and to make additional attacks with it.

- He must bond to warcaster armor to gain the benefits of its power field and overboosting.

To form a bond, a character must spend a full action touching the steamjack or object he intends to bond to. Forming a bond with a steamjack requires the warcaster to know its cortex's native language and the pass codes to any locks on its cortex. A character can break a bond at will in order to free up a slot to form another bond.

Bonded steamjacks are not affected by 'jack marshaling. A character cannot bond with a steamjack, mechanika weapon, or mechanika armor bonded to another character.

BREW MASTER

Prerequisite: Alchemy 2

The character can reroll failed Alchemy rolls. Each failed roll can be rerolled only once as a result of Brew Master.

CAMOUFLAGE

Prerequisite: None

The character gains an additional +2 DEF when benefiting from concealment or cover.

CARD SHARP

Prerequisite: Gambling 2

The character is skilled at manipulating his fortune at cards by the judicious application of legerdemain. He's a cheat. When the character uses this ability, he adds an extra die to his Gambling skill rolls and drops the lowest die result.

Anyone watching the character play when he uses this ability can make a Detection skill roll to catch the character in the act. The difficulty for this skill roll is equal to the cheating character's INT + AGL + Gambling skill.

CAUTIOUS ADVANCE

Prerequisite: Survival 3

The character gains one extra quick action each turn that can be used only to take cover.

CAVALRY CHARGE

Prerequisite: Riding 1

This character can make a cavalry charge (p. 214) while riding a mount designated as a warhorse.

CHAIN ATTACK: BLEED OUT

Prerequisite: Two-Weapon Fighting, Hand Weapon 3

If this character fights with two melee hand weapons and hits the same living target with both his initial attacks, after resolving the attacks he can immediately make one additional melee attack against his target. If the additional attack hits, it does not inflict damage but the target must forfeit either its movement or action on its next Activation Phase.

CHAIN ATTACK: PIN DOWN

Prerequisite: Two-Weapon Fighting, Pistol 3

If this character hits the same living target with initial attacks from two pistols, after resolving the attacks he can immediately make one additional ranged attack against that target ignoring ROF. If the additional attack hits, it does not inflict damage. Instead, the target hit can advance up to 2″, and it is then knocked down.

CHOIR

Prerequisite: ARC 4

A character gains a cumulative +1 on magic attack rolls for each other friendly character of his faith with this ability within 1″ of him.

CLEAVE

Prerequisite: Great Weapon 1

When this character incapacitates one or more enemies with a melee attack made with a great weapon during his turn, the character can make one additional melee attack immediately after the attack is resolved. A character can gain only one additional attack from Cleave each turn.

COMBAT RIDER

Prerequisite: Riding 1

While this character is riding a mount designated as a warhorse, the mount can make one impact attack against a target in its melee range if the mount and rider did not charge this turn.

CONNIVER

Prerequisite: Bribery 1, Deception 1

The character is well skilled in the arts of deception. The character can reroll failed Bribery and Deception-based social skill rolls. Each roll can be rerolled only once as a result of Conniver.

COVER IDENTITY

Prerequisite: Disguise 1

The character has an established cover identity with its own history, contacts, and criminal record (or lack thereof). The character's Disguise rolls while using his cover identity are automatically boosted. Choose a career for the cover identity. The character gains one occupational skill at level 1 from the cover identity's career. The cover identity must be reasonably believable. A gobber disguised as a trollkin fell caller won't fool anybody. This ability can be taken multiple times. Each time, it applies to a different cover identity.

CRACKSHOT

Prerequisite: None

The character can accurately track his target despite its attempts to take cover. When making a ranged or magic attack against a target that has concealment, cover, or elevation, this character gains +2 on the attack roll.

CRAFT RUNE SHOT

Prerequisite: None

The character can craft his own rune shot ammunition. Instead of paying 5 gc for each metal cartridge round of rune shot ammunition, a character with this ability and a rune shot casting kit can cast his own rounds, paying 1 gc for the powder, material to cast a rune bullet, and metal casing to press one round of rune shot ammunition. The character must inscribe the casing and bullet by hand. A character can craft up to five rune shot cartridges in an hour.

CROSSBOWMAN

Prerequisite: None

The character can reload a crossbow as a quick action instead of a full action.

DEFENDER

Prerequisite: None

Once per round, when a friendly character within this character's command range is hit with an enemy attack, immediately after the attack has been resolved this character can advance toward the enemy character, up to twelve feet (2″), and make one melee attack.

DEFENSIVE LINE

Prerequisite: None

While this character is B2B with one or more friendly characters, he gains +1 ARM. While the character is B2B with one or more friendly characters who also have this ability, the bonus increases to +2.

DIG IN

Prerequisite: None

While he has a spade in hand, this character can make a quick action to dig an improvised foxhole. Until he moves, is placed, goes prone, or is engaged, the character gains cover, does not suffer blast damage, and does not block line of sight. A character cannot use the Dig In ability during a turn in which he ran.

DISEASE RESISTANCE

Prerequisite: None

The character can make boosted rolls to resist disease and infection.

DISPEL

Prerequisite: None

When this character hits an enemy with a melee attack, he can spend 1 feat point to cause any upkeep spells on that enemy to immediately expire.

DODGER

Prerequisite: None

When this character is missed by an enemy attack, he can immediately advance up to 2″ after the attack is resolved unless was missed while advancing. He cannot be targeted by free strikes during this movement.

DRIVE: ANCILLARY ATTACK

Prerequisite: 'Jack Marshal

This character can make a quick action to use Drive: Ancillary Attack on a steamjack he controls. The steamjack immediately makes one normal melee or ranged attack.

DRIVE: ASSAULT

Prerequisite: 'Jack Marshal

This character can make a quick action to use Drive: Assault on a steamjack he controls. The steamjack charges during its turn this round without spending focus or being forced. As part of that charge, after moving but before making its charge attack, the steamjack can make one ranged attack targeting its charge target unless it was in melee with its charge target at the start of its turn. When resolving a Drive: Assault ranged attack, the steamjack does not suffer the penalty for a target in melee. If the target is not in melee range after the steamjack moves, the steamjack can make the Drive: Assault ranged attack before its turn ends.

DRIVE: OFF ROAD

Prerequisite: 'Jack Marshal

This character can make a quick action to use Drive: Off Road on a steamjack he controls. The steamjack gains the Pathfinder ability during its turn this round and must use its normal movement and combat action to charge or make a slam power attack during its turn this round.

DRIVE: PRONTO

Prerequisite: 'Jack Marshal

This character can make a quick action to use Drive: Pronto on a steamjack he controls. The steamjack immediately makes a full advance.

DUAL SHOT

Prerequisite: None

The character can forfeit his movement during his turn to make one additional ranged attack with a pistol or rifle.

ELEMENTAL MASTERY

Prerequisite: ARC 5

The sorcerer gains +1 on his attack and damage rolls when casting an offensive spell from his elemental spell list.

EMPOWER

Prerequisite: None

During this character's turn, while he is B2B with a non-incapacitated friendly character, this character can spend 1 feat point to cause the friendly character to regain d3+1 vitality points.

EXPERT RIDER

Prerequisite: Riding 2

The character can reroll failed Riding rolls. Each roll can be rerolled only once as a result of Expert Rider.

Additionally, provided the mount has not been knocked out, this character and his mount cannot be knocked down while this character is mounted.

FAST COOK

Prerequisite: Alchemy 2

The character has learned a number of time-saving shortcuts in the art of brewing potions and mixing alchemical substances. He can create alchemical items in half the normal time.

FAST DRAW

Prerequisite: None

A character with this skill gains +2 on initiative rolls. He also gains an additional quick action during his first turn of combat each encounter that can be used only to draw a weapon.

FAST REARM

Prerequisite: None

The character gains one extra quick action each turn that can be used only to rearm a weapon of the type noted, such as a blasting pike. A character can have this ability several times, each time with a different specified weapon.

FAST RELOAD

Prerequisite: None

The character gains one extra quick action each turn that can be used only to reload a ranged weapon.

FELL CALL: CACOPHONY

Prerequisite: Fell Calling 2

The character can use this call as a quick action. For one round, enemies cannot cast spells, use battle plans, or use drives while in this character's command range.

FELL CALL: CALL OF DEFIANCE

Prerequisite: Fell Calling 2

The character can use this call as a quick action. For one round, when a friendly trollkin character makes a Tough roll while in this character's command range, on a roll of 4, 5, or 6 the trollkin heals 1 vitality point and is knocked down.

FELL CALL: GROUND SHAKER

Prerequisite: Fell Calling 3

Once per turn, the character can use this call instead of attacking. The character then makes a RNG 10, AOE 5 fell call ranged attack that causes no damage. Targets hit are knocked down.

FELL CALL: HEROIC BALLAD

Prerequisite: Fell Calling 2

The character can use this call as a quick action. For the rest of the round, while in the Fell Caller's command range, friendly trollkin characters are fearless and gain +2 to melee attack rolls. Heroic Ballad lasts for one round.

FELL CALL: REVERBERATION

Prerequisite: Fell Calling 2

The character can use this call as a quick action. The character makes a RNG SP 6 ranged attack that causes no damage. The character uses his POI + Fell Calling skill for his attack rolls. Enemies hit are pushed d3″ directly away from this character. Move the enemy who was farthest away first.

FELL CALL: SIGNAL CALL

Prerequisite: Fell Calling 1

The character can use this call as a quick action. The character can unleash a call that can be heard for a number of miles equal to his Fell Caller skill.

FELL CALL: SONIC BLAST

Prerequisite: Fell Calling 2

Once per turn, the character can use this call instead of attacking. The character then makes a RNG SP 8, POW 12 ranged attack. The character uses his POI + Fell Calling skill for his attack rolls.

FIELD ALCHEMIST

Prerequisite: Alchemy 1

The character gains an additional quick action each turn that can be used only to create a field alchemy quick effect.

FIELD MARSHAL: MAGICAL ATTACK

Prerequisite: ARC 5

The warcaster can spend a focus point during his turn to use Field Marshal: Magical Attack. For one round, the weapons of characters in his battlegroup become magical weapons while in the warcaster's control area.

FIELD MARSHAL: RELENTLESS CHARGE

Prerequisite: ARC 5

The warcaster can spend a focus point during his turn to use Field Marshal: Relentless Charge. For one round, when a character in the warcaster's battlegroup begins a charge while in his control area, that character gains the Relentless Charge ability for his turn. (A character who already has Relentless Charge ignores penalties for rough terrain during an Activation Phase in which he charges.)

FIELD MARSHAL: SHIELD GUARD

Prerequisite: ARC 7

The warcaster can spend a focus point during his turn to use Field Marshal: Shield Guard. For one round, characters in his battlegroup gain the Shield Guard ability while in the Warcaster's control area. Once per turn, when a friendly character is directly hit by an attack while within 2″ of a character with Shield Guard, the character with Shield Guard can become the target of the attack and be automatically hit instead. A character cannot use Shield Guard if he is incorporeal, knocked down, or stationary.

FIND COVER

Prerequisite: None

At the start of combat before initiative is rolled, this character can immediately advance up to twelve feet (2″) and perform a quick action to take cover or go prone.

FIRE IN THE HOLE!

Prerequisite: Thrown Weapon 1

This character can make a grenade attack at the start of the Action Phase of his turn before moving or making his normal attacks. A character making a Fire in the Hole! attack must use his movement that turn to run or make a full advance.

FLEET FOOT

Prerequisite: SPD 7

When the character runs, he moves at SPD x 3.

FREE STYLE

Prerequisite: Alchemy 1

The character can improvise the ingredients in his alchemical compounds. This allows the character to attempt to make do without a specific ingredient. This requires an Alchemy skill roll with a target number equal to 10 plus the gc value of the ingredient.

This ability also allows the character to get by with less expensive versions of common alchemical ingredients, reducing the cost of his alchemical compounds by 1 gc each (to a minimum of 1 gc). Alchemical compounds brewed using this skill vary slightly in appearance or physical quality from items created by following time-tested recipes.

GANG

Prerequisite: None

When making a melee attack that targets an enemy in melee range of another friendly character, this character gains +1 to melee attack and melee damage rolls. When making a melee attack that targets an enemy in melee range of another friendly character who also has this ability, these bonuses increase to +2.

GET AWAY

Prerequisite: Dodger, Escape Artist 3

When the character is missed by an enemy attack at any time other than while advancing, instead of advancing up to 2″, the character can immediately make a full advance.

GIRDED

Prerequisite: Shield 2

While armed with a shield, this character does not suffer blast damage. Friendly characters B2B with this character do not suffer blast damage either.

GOOD BREEDING

Prerequisite: None

The character was raised in high society. He can reroll failed Etiquette rolls. Each roll can be rerolled only once as a result of Good Breeding.

GREAT POWER

Prerequisite: None

This character can upkeep one spell each turn without spending a focus point or gaining a fatigue point.

GRENADIER

Prerequisite: Thrown Weapon 1

The character gains an additional quick action each turn that can be used only to pull the pin on a grenade.

GUNFIGHTER

Prerequisite: None.

The character does not suffer a −4 penalty on ranged attack rolls with pistols or carbines while engaged.

HEAD-BUTT

Prerequisite: STR 5, Unarmed Combat 2

Instead of making a normal Unarmed Combat attack, this character can spend a feat point to make a head-butt attack. The character makes an unarmed melee attack roll against his target. If the attack hits, the target is knocked down and suffers a damage roll with a POW (Power) equal to the character's current STR. A character cannot head-butt a target with a larger base.

HIT THE DECK!

Prerequisite: None

The character is so accustomed to catastrophic explosions in his presence that he has developed the uncanny ability to hit the ground the second before he is affected by a blast. While prone, the character does not suffer damage from AOEs unless he is directly hit by the AOE. If the character is caught in an AOE that would cause blast damage but was not directly hit by the AOE, he goes prone but suffers no damage.

HYPER AWARENESS

Prerequisite: Command 3

While in this character's command range, friendly characters gain Circular Vision. (The front arc of a character with Circular Vision extends to 360°.)

IMMUNITY: COLD

Prerequisite: None

The character is immune to cold damage.

IMMUNITY: CORROSION

Prerequisite: None

The character is immune to corrosion damage.

IMMUNITY: ELECTRICITY

Prerequisite: None

The character is immune to electrical damage.

IMMUNITY: FIRE

Prerequisite: None

The character is immune to fire damage.

INSCRIBE FORMULAE

Prerequisite: Mechanikal Engineering 1

The character can inscribe runeplates. See "Mechanika" (p. 279).

IRON SENTINEL

Prerequisite: 'Jack Marshal, Command 3

The character has learned to position himself behind the steamjacks he commands to stay out of harm's way. While B2B with one or more steamjacks he commands, the character gains +2 ARM and cannot be knocked down.

IRON WILL

Prerequisite: None

The character can reroll failed Willpower rolls. Each roll can be rerolled only once as a result of Iron Will.

KEEN EYED

Prerequisite: None

The character can increase his effective range with a bow or rifle by twelve feet (2˝) and his extreme range by sixty feet (10˝).

LANGUAGE

Prerequisite: None

This ability can be taken multiple times. Each time a character takes this ability, he learns how to speak, read, and write a new language.

LANGUAGE – FIVE CANT

Five Cant is the language of the underworld that developed on the streets of Five Fingers. Though it is most commonly used in Ord and northern Cygnar, speakers can be found throughout criminal circles across the Iron Kingdoms. It has no written form.

LEGACY OF BRAGG

Prerequisite: Fell Calling 2

The character gains an additional quick action each turn that can be used only to make fell calls.

LIGHT CAVALRY

Prerequisite: Riding 2

If this character is riding a mount not designated as a warhorse, at the end of his turn he can advance up to 5˝.

LOAD BEARING

Prerequisite: STR 5

The character is well practiced at fighting while wearing heavy armor. Reduce the SPD and DEF penalties from the armor the character wears each by 1.

MAGE KILLER

Prerequisite: PER 6

This character gains an additional die on damage rolls against characters that can cast spells.

MARKSMAN

Prerequisite: None

The character can use quick actions and aim in the same round, but still has to forfeit his movement to gain the aiming bonus.

NATURAL LEADER

Prerequisite: Command 1

A character with Natural Leader increases his command range by 2″.

NIGHT FIGHTER

Prerequisite: None

The character is well versed in dispatching an opponent at a distance in the dark of night. When making a ranged or magic attack against a character with stealth or Prowl, this character automatically misses the target only if he is 8″ or farther away (instead of 5″ away).

PARRY

Prerequisite: None

While armed with a hand weapon, the character cannot be targeted by free strikes.

PATHFINDER

Prerequisite: Survival 1

The character can move over rough terrain without penalty.

POISON RESISTANCE

Prerequisite: None

The character gains boosted rolls to resist poisons and toxins.

PORT OF CALL

Prerequisite: Navigation 1

A character with Port of Call can always find his way home again. For each level of Navigation, a character can nominate one location he's visited more than once as a Port of Call. When traveling to a Port of Call and using the Navigation skill (p. 186), treat any results worse than "Arrive as planned" as "Arrive as planned."

PRECISION STRIKE

Prerequisite: None

When the character hits with a melee attack, he chooses the branch of the target's life spiral or the column of the target's damage grid that is hit, if applicable.

PRESS THE ATTACK

Prerequisite: Shield Slam, Shield 3

When this character slams an enemy, immediately after the slam is resolved this character can advance directly toward the slammed enemy up to the distance the slammed enemy was moved and then make a melee attack against that enemy.

PRIVILEGE

Prerequisite: None

Whether he was born into an ancient bloodline or a family that purchased status, this character is afforded the rights of a noble. He is immune to persecution for petty crimes and can be tried only by a court of his peers. Should he be found guilty of a high crime, he has the right to be executed in the style befitting a noble. Each kingdom has distinct benefits and obligations for those born of privilege. With a successful Etiquette skill roll, this character can demand hospitality and request aid from other nobles not at war with his kingdom. Additionally, the character gains +2 on social skill rolls when dealing with those beneath his station who recognize his status and respect the nobility.

HIGH COURTS

Those of high privilege are rarely arrested for petty crimes such as larceny or trespassing. Those of privilege are expected to defend themselves if attacked by inferiors and are rarely accused of assault if it is clear they did not instigate violence, even in cases where deaths have occurred. The degree to which privilege affords protection varies greatly from one region to another.

Though the character cannot be tried by a low court, that does not mean he can entirely escape justice. If he is found violating major laws of a kingdom, he can be held by the local law officers until he is taken prisoner by the knights of the kingdom or agents of a noble with dominion over the lands whose laws the character broke. He is then judged by the kingdom's nobles. Once high courts are convened, punishments for the guilty are severe.

PROWL

Prerequisite: Sneak 1

The character is virtually invisible while in the shadows or in terrain that grants a degree of concealment. The character gains stealth (p. 220) while within terrain that provides concealment, the AOE of a spell that provides concealment, or the AOE of a cloud effect.

PURSUIT

Prerequisite: Tracking 3

The character can spend 1 feat point during his turn to use this ability. When this ability is used, the character designates one enemy. For the rest of the encounter, when that enemy moves during his turn, immediately after the enemy ends his movement this character can make a full advance. A character can use this benefit only once per encounter unless the original subject of this ability is destroyed, at which point the character can spend a feat point to use this benefit on a new enemy.

QUICK WORK

Prerequisite: AGL 5

When this character kills one or more enemies with a melee attack during his combat action, immediately after that attack is resolved this character can make one ranged attack.

To make a ranged attack, the character's ranged weapon must be loaded.

RALLYING CRY

Prerequisite: Command 3

This character can spend a feat point to use Rallying Cry. For one round, this character's command range is doubled and friendly characters in his command range, including this character, become fearless (p. 224).

RELENTLESS CHARGE

Prerequisite: None

This character ignores penalties for rough terrain while charging.

RESOURCEFUL

Prerequisite: Mechanikal Engineering 3

This character can upkeep spells on steamjacks he controls without spending focus or gaining fatigue points.

RETALIATORY STRIKE

Prerequisite: PHY 7

When this character is hit by a melee attack made by an enemy at any time other than during his own turn, after the attack is resolved the character can spend 1 feat point to immediately make one normal melee attack against the enemy that hit him.

RETURN FIRE

Prerequisite: Fast Draw

Once per round when this character is missed by an enemy's ranged attack, immediately after the attack is resolved he can make one normal attack against the attacking enemy.

To make a ranged attack, the character's ranged weapon must be loaded.

RIDE-BY ATTACK

Prerequisite: Riding 2

While mounted, this character can combine his movement and action during his turn to make a Ride-By Attack. The character declares a Ride-By Attack at the start of his Activation Phase. He makes a full advance and can halt his movement at any point to make his attacks. After his attacks, he resumes his movement.

RIPOSTE

Prerequisite: None

Once per round when this character is missed by an enemy's melee attack, immediately after the attack is resolved he can make one normal attack against the attacking enemy.

To make a ranged attack, the character's ranged weapon must be loaded.

ROCK SOLID

Prerequisite: PHY 8

This character and friendly characters B2B with him cannot be knocked down. The character loses this ability while he is mounted.

ROLL WITH IT

Prerequisite: None

When the character would ordinarily be knocked down, he goes prone instead. The character loses this ability while he is mounted.

SADDLE SHOT

Prerequisite: Riding 1

This character does not suffer the firing from horseback penalty when making ranged attacks while mounted (see p. 214).

SCROUNGE

Prerequisite: None

The character is adept at finding hard to acquire or expensive replacement parts to repair steamjacks. Given a day to find the parts in a town or industrialized settlement, the character can find any part needed (or something close enough he can bodge it together). The character can purchase steamjack parts, weapons, and gear for half the normal price.

SENTRY

Prerequisite: None

Once per round when an enemy is placed in or moves into the line of sight of this character, this character can immediately make one attack, targeting that enemy.

SET DEFENSE

Prerequisite: Great Weapon 2

While this character is armed with a weapon that has reach, an enemy in this character's front arc suffers –2 on charge, slam power attack, and impact attack rolls against him.

SHADOW MAGIC

Prerequisite: Gifted, Sneak 2

When this character casts a spell, no spell runes appear and magically sensitive characters cannot sense the character's magic. A focuser with this ability cannot be detected by another focuser with the Magic Sensitivity archetype benefit.

SHIELD GUARD

Prerequisite: Shield 1

Once per turn, when a friendly character is directly hit by an attack while within 2″ of this character, this character can choose to be directly hit instead. This character cannot use Shield Guard if he is incorporeal, knocked down, prone, or stationary.

SHIELD SLAM

Prerequisite: STR 6

When this character charges while armed with a shield, instead of making a charge attack, he can spend a feat point to slam his target, making an attack roll with his shield. A character who slams another character with a larger base suffers –2 to this attack roll. The POW of the slam damage roll is equal to the STR of the attacking character plus the POW of the shield. The POW of collateral damage is equal to the STR of the attacking character.

SIGNAL LANGUAGE

Prerequisite: Cryptography 1

The character can spend time developing a coded signal language for use with his party using the same rules as creating a code. The language can convey simple messages or commands and has a Cryptography target number based on the target number used during the code's creation. The signal language can be taught to any character that has Intellect 3 or greater.

SNIPER

Prerequisite: Rifle 3

When this character forfeits his movement to aim during his turn, the character's first ranged attack that turn gains boosted damage.

SPECIALIZATION

Prerequisite: None

The character does not suffer attack roll penalties when attacking with a weapon of the type chosen, such as a blasting pike. A character can have this ability several times, each time choosing a different weapon.

STEADY

Prerequisite: None

This character cannot be knocked down. The character loses this ability while he is mounted.

STEAMO

Prerequisite: Mechanikal Engineering 2

The character can reroll failed Mechanikal Engineering rolls to repair or dismantle steamjacks. Each roll can be rerolled only once as a result of Steamo.

SUCKER!

Prerequisite: Intimidation 3

If this character is directly hit by an enemy ranged attack, he can choose a friendly living non-incorporeal character within 2″ of him to be directly hit instead. That character is automatically hit and suffers all damage and effects.

SWIFT HUNTER

Prerequisite: AGL 6

When this character incapacitates an enemy by using a normal ranged attack, immediately after the attack is resolved he can advance up to twelve feet (2″).

SWIFT RIDER

Prerequisite: None

While riding a mount, the character can move over rough terrain without penalty.

TAKE DOWN

Prerequisite: None.

This character can use Take Down anytime he incapacitates another character with an attack and while the incapacitated character is in this character's melee range. The incapacitated character regains 1 vitality point and is no longer incapacitated but is considered to be manacled, tied up, unconscious, or otherwise out of action for the rest of the encounter. Once the combat portion of the encounter has ended, the subject of the take down is at the mercy of the victors to be questioned or worse.

TARGETEER

Prerequisite: None

When the character hits with a ranged attack, he chooses the branch of the target's life spiral or the column of the target's damage grid that is hit, if applicable.

TEAM LEADER

Prerequisite: None

When this character gains a feat point, instead of keeping it himself he can give it to another character currently in his command range.

TRACELESS PATH

Prerequisite: Sneak 2

The character knows how to conceal his trail when moving over land. Though he can move at only half his usual rate of speed while using this ability, either on foot or horseback, anyone attempting to follow his trail has +3 added to his skill roll target number.

TRUTH READER

Prerequisite: Detection 3

The character automatically knows when someone is lying to him. Keep in mind that knowing someone is lying is different than discerning the truth.

TUNE UP

Prerequisite: Mechanikal Engineering 3

While B2B with a steamjack he controls, this character can spend a quick action to use Tune Up. During its turn this round, the steamjack gains either boosted attack or damage rolls.

TWO-WEAPON FIGHTING

Prerequisite: AGL 4

While fighting with a one-handed weapon or pistol in each hand, the character gains an additional attack for the second weapon. He suffers –2 on attacks rolls with the second weapon while doing so.

UNIVERSITY EDUCATION

Prerequisite: None

The character can reroll failed Lore and Research skill rolls. Each roll can be rerolled only once as a result of University Education.

WAYLAY

Prerequisite: None

When an attack made by this character has the chance to knock out a target, increase the target number for the Willpower roll to resist the knockout by 2.

CONNECTIONS

Connections represent associations, familial bonds, and networks of contacts. A character can have several different networks of connections, each relating to a different group, government, or society.

A character can use his connections to gain information, material aid, or assistance. The aid a character can reasonably request from his connections depends on the nature of the connection and the character's relationship with the connection. The character should be able to call on the hospitality of his home kriel or clan for information, a safe place to sleep, and a meal. From time to time he might even call on such a connection for monetary support or manpower.

The sort of aid given might be different if the character is a full member of the organization represented by the connection or if he is just a well-informed outsider. The character's relationship with the connection also determines what the connection expects in return. For example, a member of the Retribution of Scyrah can readily call on his contacts for intelligence and news of home, use of remote safe houses (for himself, not for non-member associates), and possibly for special gear and weapons. A non-member with connections to the Retribution would be able to set up meetings with agents of the group for tense meetings and exchanges of information. In this case the relationship is much more give-and-take with the expectation that all aid given will be returned.

A character might not trust his contact and might not be trusted in return. This lack of trust can be built up overtime or it can be inherent in the character's relationship with his connections from the inception. For example, though a character's criminal contacts might not have provided him with a concrete reason for concern yet, no one should completely trust those contacts. That is just the nature of the beast.

Depending on the demands a character puts on his connections, he might have to resort to diplomacy, negotiation, or bribery to get what he wants. In these cases, the player describes what his character is doing to coerce his connection into giving him more aid than the connection was initially willing to provide. Based on the tact taken, the Game Master determines the stat and skill for a social skill roll. Then the Game Master sets the target number for the roll. If the roll fails, the character does not get what he wants and risks straining his relationship with his connection. Even if he succeeds, there could be repercussions that arise from pushing his connection too far. He could owe the connection a favor, or his connection might become angry or distrusting and refuse to work with the character for some time.

When managing a character's connections, the Game Master should consider the needs and personality of the characters who make up the connection. What are they willing to give away? What remains hidden? What risks are put on the character's connections by aiding them? What do they have to lose? What do they want in return?

A character's connections can also be a great tool to jumpstart a scenario. Just as the character can ask things of his connections, his contacts might also come to him for help, information, or material aid. If the character refuses, there should be consequences, not the least of which is that his connections might refuse him any future aid until he makes good on his commitments and responsibilities.

The Game Master and the character's controller should take time to discuss the character's connections before the start of the game. Though a connection represents a web of contacts rather than one or two individuals, the player and Game Master should try to give the connection a face (or faces). The face of the connection is the NPC or NPCs the character most often meets with when he wishes to use his connection. The face could be a ranking shot caller, a discrete agent, a well-connected member of the organization, or just about anyone who has the influence to be considered the representative of the character's connection. Additional faces could be other NPCs affiliated with the character's connection or other additional contacts the character has the freedom to meet with. For example, if the character has a trollkin kriel as a connection, for him the face of the connection could be its chieftain or shaman, but he also knows a number of junior members he can press for information or request for aid in times of need.

Below are a few examples of possible connections and the potential support given by each.

Alchemical Order: The character can call upon the knowledge, resources, and talents of an alchemical order, such as the Order

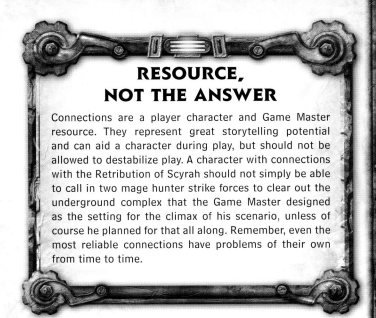

of the Golden Crucible. If the character is an alchemist, he is likely a member of the order. A member of an order can, at very least, expect access his order's labs and libraries and possibly a bed and meal. His friends and other traveling companions might not be as welcome.

Criminal: The character has contacts with the criminal underworld and organized crime. His connections are likely centered on a single city or criminal organization, but those contacts can to reach out to other organizations on the character's behalf. The character can always press his contacts for information, and he might also be able to use them to purchase or smuggle contraband, set up criminal enterprises, aid in entering or escaping locations unseen, dispose of goods or bodies, find safe hiding places, or for anything else that falls under the criminal purview. Such contacts are notoriously untrustworthy and complications abound. Greed and self interest are the surest motivators when dealing with these connections.

Dwarven Clan: The character has dealings with a dwarven clan. Though a member of the clan can expect to be treated like family, outsiders have a more business-like relationship with the clan. The clan is likely based in Rhul, possibly with smaller branches in Cygnar or Khador. The clan can provide information, especially pertaining to trade routes, business ventures, wartime developments, of news from Rhul. It can also provide a great deal of technical expertise and other means of support depending on the clan's holdings in the area where they are encountered.

Intelligence Network: The character has access to a vast spy network, such as the Cygnaran Reconnaissance Network, the Prikaz Chancellery, the Unseen Hand, or the Retribution of Scyrah. The character's relationship with the network should be discussed between the player and the Game Master. If he is a member of the group, the character can expect much greater access to information and material aid, but he has substantial responsibilities in return. He could be called upon the network to provide information and assistance at any time. If he betrays his organization or exposes its members, he will certainly be marked for death. More informal affiliates of an organization can be called upon for information and possibly support when the network's aims coincide with the character's actions. Such networks are proficient, professional, and ruthless. The spy game is no place for amateurs.

Knightly Order: The character has a connection to a knightly order. He could be a member of the order or an advocate for its causes. In either case, he can use this connection to gain information pertaining to the affairs of the order, its members, and its home kingdom. If the character is a member, he can also call on the resources of his order and can find a warm bed and a hot meal at his order's holdings. The character can also expect to have armor repaired and his mount groomed. From time to time, the character's order might call upon him to undertake tasks relating to his responsibilities as a knight of the order.

Kriel: The character has contact with a trollkin kriel. He could be a close friend or ally, or a member of the kriel. The kriel is either based at a village or urban settlement, or nomadic. With great numbers of trollkin having been uprooted by the recent wars, there are greater numbers of nomadic trollkin than ever before. The character can call upon the kriel for information relating to trollkin history, its home history, and the individual knowledge of the members of the tribe. Likely the kriel has little in the way of material support it can lend a character, but the kriel might provide warriors in times of need, especially if the kriel shares the character's interests in a given fight. What little the kriel has, it is likely to share with a friend. As a member of a kriel, a character could be called upon to aid the kriel in its most dire moments, especially if the character is a Fell Caller or has another important role in his kriel.

Magical Order (Arcanist or Gun Mage): The character is affiliated with an arcane order, such as the Greylords Covenant, the Fraternal Order of Wizardry, or the Militant Order of the Arcane Tempest. Many, but not all, orders are tied very closely to a given kingdom and membership in the order is limited to citizens of that kingdom in good standing. For example, the Gun Mages of the Arcane Tempest are members of Cygnar's military in addition to being members of the order. A character with a connection to an arcane order can call upon the order for information relating to the knowledge of the order, its current dealings, information pertaining to its members, and to its home kingdom. A character might also be able to call upon the services of the order in times of need. Members can expect to be welcomed into the order's chapter houses, fed, given access to the chapter's facilities and libraries, and possibly given a place to sleep.

Mechaniks Organization: The character has contact with a major mechanik's organization or firm such as the Khadoran Mechanik's Assembly, the Steam & Iron Workers' Union, Engines East, the Cygnaran Armory, or Black Anchor Heavy Industries. The character can utilize this connection to gather information pertaining to the organization, its projects, or its members. Members of the organization can expect to recruited

for work, given access to machine shops, and possibly be able to scrounge parts and scrap metal. Members of unions are required to pay their dues.

Military, Kingdom or Mercenary: The character has a connection with a mercenary company or with one of the kingdom's militaries. Most likely the character is or was a member of that military. Though he maintains contacts with the group, how he is perceived depends on his service record and the terms on which he left duty. A character can call upon his contacts to discover the details of given battles, gain intelligence on troop movements, learn about an aspect of the military, or gain access to its personnel. A character might be able to leverage his connections to get his hands on military gear or to request aid from former brothers in arms. This sort of aid usually comes at a high cost. If the character is an active member of the military, that complication adds its own issues and is sure to curtail the character's mobility and options for adventure.

Nobility: The character has connections to the nobility of a given kingdom or the members of a continent-spanning dynastic family. The character might even be a lesser nobleman in his own right. Whichever the case, the character has access to the halls of power. He can use these contacts to learn the secrets of the great families, the truths behind politics, or to gain access to the most powerful men in western Immoren. Such benefits are not without their cost. The nobility is vain, self-interested, jaded, and value appearances above all else. In addition to having to return favors, a character also has to be on his best behavior to maintain noble connections. A character who is crude, insulting, impolite, or impolitic can expect his connections to wither and die. Not only do the nobility not wish to aid an embarrassing ally, they do not wish to seem to be aiding that ally.

Pirate Crew: The character is either the member of a pirate crew or has a close connection to a crew, likely through its captain. The pirates can be called upon to provide information pertaining to ports of call, the strength of various navies, trade lanes, the best locations for plunder, hiding places along the coast, and all manner of lore pertaining ships and piracy. Pirates can be called up for transportation and possibly for help in a fight if there is plunder for the taking. Just remember that no one can trust a pirate.

Retribution of Scyrah: See Intelligence Network, above.

Religious Organization: The character has contact with one of the major religions of western Immoren. If the character is not a member of the church, this connection provides him with information only. If he is a member of the church, he can expect access to the organization's churches, libraries, and other holdings, and he can gain access to ranking members of the church. Should his actions be in the interests of the church, he can potentially expect even greater aid in times of need. Of course, should the character bring shame upon the church or fail in its central teachings, he might find himself ostracized and his access denied.

Wealthy Patrons: The character has a network of wealthy patrons that go out of their way to aid him in times of need. This network is made up of aristocrats, industrialists, and men of privilege who either believe in the character's work or see their connection to the character as a means of winning acclaim and sharing in his victories. The character can call upon his patrons for information relating to politics and trade and can call upon their financial support. The character's contacts expect to see a return on their investments. The character's associates might be willing to finance a dangerous sea voyage or treasure hunting expedition to isolated ruins, but only if they expect the plan to succeed. They might monitor the character's use of their money and even send observers along on his expeditions. The character is expected to give private and personal presentations regarding his adventures and findings, any artifacts he discovers are put on display for the pleasure of his patrons, and they take a stake in any financial rewards that spring from their investments. Additionally, the character's patrons expect him to maintain a degree of decorum and professionalism that does not besmirch their own reputations.

SKILLS

Skills represent knowledge, talents, and proficiencies that a character develops over time. A character's mastery in a skill is measured by its level. Each of the character's skills has a level between 1 and 4. Characters learn new skills and increase proficiency in existing skills through Character Advancement.

Military Skills are a character's weapons training. Some represent niche training in a very specific sort of weaponry such as the lance, whereas others embody training in an entire weapons group such as great weapons. Military skills can be used untrained.

Occupational Skills represent specialized training and non-combat proficiencies tied to a given career. Occupational skills encompass alchemy, forgery, mechanikal engineering, tracking, and much more. **General skills** are occupational skills available to every character regardless of his careers. General skills encompass climbing, gambling, riding, and other skills that a character has the potential to learn regardless of specialized career training.

A starting character at Hero level can develop a skill to level 2. Once a character reaches Veteran status (see "Character Advancement," p. 155), he can develop skills to level 3 as permitted by his careers. Once a character reaches Epic status, he can develop skills to level 4 as permitted by his careers.

The skills listed here are grouped into military skills and occupational skills. Each skill is also listed with its governing stat. This is the stat used when determining whether your skill roll to use the skill is successful or not (see "Skill Resolution Rolls," p. 198). Some skills have "social" as the governing stat. **Social skills** do not have a single defined stat that is always added when making die rolls, because the attribute used depends on the specific social situation at hand. When a character attempts to use a social skill, the Game Master determines which stat is most applicable based on the situation at hand and the character's approach to that situation.

USING SOCIAL SKILLS

The Game Master determines the best stat to use for social skills based on the way the character intends to use the skill. For example, if a hulking trollkin mercenary attempts to intimidate a thug with his obvious physical strength, his Game Master is likely to choose to have him add his STR to his Intimidate roll. Alternatively, a physically puny but cunning and well connected Kayazy aristocrat might be better served by attempting to intimidate that same thug with well-stated innuendo about his connections to people quite willing to do violence on his behalf. The aristocrat's Game Master would likely have the character use his PER to deduce the threat most likely to intimidate the thug.

In some cases the Game Master might inform the characters that one approach or another is inappropriate to the situation at hand. A congregation of Gatormen in the depths of the Bloodsmeath is unlikely to be impressed by any threats of later reprisal from a character's allies in Korsk, and the Game Master might decide that the only hope of successful intimidation relies on physical brawn, requiring a character to make an Intimidation roll using his STR.

As a further complication of social skill rolls, the target number can be impacted by the subject's disposition toward the character attempting the roll. If the subject has longstanding prejudices against the character, his organization, or his people, the target number might be higher than usual. If the subject looks favorably upon the character, or is interested in him for other reasons, the target number could be lowered.

Some complex social situations could require the character to make a series of skill rolls. A Khadoran spy, newly arrived in the Ordic city of Midfast and attempting to bribe the city guards to look the other way while he conducts his business, might first need to make a successful Deception roll to convince the guardsmen that he's not actually a spy or other threat to their nation before he can make his Bribery roll to achieve his real aim.

The Game Master is the final arbiter of what social skills are appropriate and necessary in any situation, and is encouraged to err on the side of engaging and creative roleplaying by his players whenever possible.

MILITARY SKILLS

A character knows how to properly handle, maintain, and clean the weapons he understands how to use.

ARCHERY (POISE)

Each level of this skill adds to the character's POI when making attacks with bows.

CROSSBOW (POISE)

Each level of this skill adds to the character's POI when making attacks with crossbows.

GREAT WEAPON (PROWESS)

Each level of this skill adds to the character's PRW when making attacks with great weapons. Some great weapons require two hands to wield. A character cannot wield more than one great weapon at a time.

HAND WEAPON (PROWESS)

Each level of this skill adds to the character's PRW when making attacks with melee hand weapons.

LANCE (PROWESS)

Each level of this skill adds to the character's PRW when making attacks with lance weapons. A character cannot wield another lance or great weapon while wielding a lance.

LIGHT ARTILLERY (POISE)

The character is knowledgeable in the operation, loading, and transport of light artillery weapons. Each level of this skill adds to the character's POI when making attacks with light artillery.

PISTOL (POISE)

Each level of this skill adds to the character's POI when making attacks with pistols.

RIFLE (POISE)

Each level of this skill adds to the character's POI when making attacks with rifles.

SHIELD (PROWESS)

Each level of this skill adds to the character's PRW when making attacks with a shield. Additionally, a character armed with a shield gains +1 ARM for each level of the Shield skill he has against attacks originating in his front arc. This bonus is not cumulative with additional shields.

THROWN WEAPON (PROWESS)

Each level of this skill adds to the character's PRW when making attacks with thrown weapons or slings.

UNARMED COMBAT (PROWESS)

Each level of this skill adds to the character's PRW when making attacks with his bare hands.

MILITARY SKILLS AT A GLANCE

Archery (Poise)

Crossbow (Poise)

Great Weapon (Prowess)

Hand Weapon (Prowess)

Lance (Prowess)

Light Artillery (Poise)

Pistol (Poise)

Rifle (Poise)

Shield (Prowess)

Thrown Weapon (Prowess)

Unarmed Combat (Prowess)

OCCUPATIONAL SKILLS

Each skill entry explains what the skill enables the character to do and describes the types of situations in which the skill would be useful. Each entry also covers the following categories:

Untrained Skill Use. Some skills cannot be used unless the character has at least one level in the skill. Others can be used without training. This section explains if the skill can be used without training and how players can do it.

Skill Rolls. This section tells players when and how they can use the skill and often includes one or more tables of results.

Assisted Skill Rolls. This section tells players if multiple characters can work together to achieve a better result.

Game Master Notes. The final section gives the Game Master information about the sort of non-player characters who have this skill, at what level, and how to resolve their skill use.

ALCHEMY (INTELLECT)

The science of alchemy is a practical and empirical pursuit in the Iron Kingdoms. Apothecaries, surgeons, mercenaries, and adventurers employ its fruits freely. A character with this skill has learned the basics of alchemy and can create simple alchemical compounds provided he has access to the proper materials and an alchemical lab.

Untrained Alchemy: A character cannot use this skill untrained. To a character unskilled in alchemy, its reagents are nothing more than dangerous unrecognizable substances.

OCCUPATIONAL SKILLS AT A GLANCE

Alchemy (Intellect)

Bribery (Social)

Command (Social)

Craft (Intellect)*

Cryptography (Intellect)

Deception (Social)

Disguise (Intellect)

Escape Artist (Agility)

Etiquette (Social)

Fell Calling (Poise)

Forensic Science (Intellect)

Forgery (Agility or Intellect)

Interrogation (Social)

Law (Intellect)

Lock Picking (Agility)

Mechanikal Engineering (Intellect)

Medicine (Intellect)

Navigation (Perception)

Negotiation (Social)

Oratory (Social)

Pickpocket (Agility)

Research (Intellect)

Rope Use (Agility)

Sailing (Intellect or Strength)

Seduction (Social)

Sneak (Agility)

Streetwise (Perception)

Survival (Perception)

Tracking (Perception)

GENERAL SKILLS

Animal Handling (Social)

Climbing (Agility)

Detection (Perception)

Driving (Agility)

Gambling (Perception)

Intimidation (Social)

Jumping (Physique)

Lore (Intellect)*

Riding (Agility)

Swimming (Strength)

*These skills can be taken multiple times. See the skill description.

Alchemy Rolls: To attempt an alchemical creation, make an INT + Alchemy roll against a target number set by the Game Master or the formula the character is trying to brew (see "Alchemy," p. 290).

Substance Identification: Characters with the Alchemy skill can identify chemical substances and their traits and sources of ingredients. The target number is variable based on the rarity of the substance and the alchemist's knowledge of it. Increase the target number by 2–4 for banned or illegal substances.

Alchemists gain +2 to identify any substance they have previously created or identified.

TARGET NUMBER	ALCHEMICAL SUBSTANCE BEING IDENTIFIED
10	Substance is common and openly available
11–14	Substance is uncommon and available in select markets
15–19	Substance is rare and difficult to purchase
20+	Substance is unique

Craft Alchemical Items: Alchemists can create a variety of useful alchemical equipment and weapons by brewing a complex recipe of ingredients. Alchemical items can be found on p. 293, and the formula for creating each item can be found in the item's description.

Field Alchemy: Alchemists can quickly brew a few simple recipes that create alchemical effects on the spot. See p. 296 for formulas and rules.

Ingredient Extraction: Characters with the Alchemy skill can extract alchemical ingredients from creatures both living and dead and gather them from their surrounding environments. From cutting out the adrenal gland of a burrow-mawg to siphoning mineral acid from deep cave pools, these ingredients can be sold for profit or brewed into useful alchemical items. A full list of basic alchemical ingredients can be found in the Alchemy rules (p. 290). Rules for extracting ingredients from creatures can be found in the entry for each creature.

Assisted Alchemy Rolls: One additional character trained in Alchemy can assist in an Alchemy skill roll. The character with the higher Alchemy modifier (INT + Alchemy level) makes the roll and adds 1 to the result of the die roll for each of his assistant's levels in Alchemy.

Game Master Notes: Alchemist shops can be found in nearly every major city in the Iron Kingdoms. Player characters frequently want to seek out alchemists to purchase restoratives, glues, acids, or blasting powder.

ANIMAL HANDLING (SOCIAL, GENERAL SKILL)

Steam and mechanika technology is used to simplify life in the prosperous urban areas of the Iron Kingdoms, but adventurers traveling outside the cities still come across numerous domesticated and wild animals. A character with this skill is comfortable around animals and can find ways of making them do what he wants.

Untrained Animal Handling: A character unskilled in Animal Handling can interact only with well-trained animals and have them perform according to their previous training.

Animal Handling Rolls: Characters with one or more levels of Animal Handling can attempt to urge an animal to perform an action it does not want to make or otherwise bend it to his will. This can allow him to bring a panicking horse under control or convince a pack of angry dogs that they don't want to attack him.

When your character makes an animal handling attempt, you make a roll using a stat determined by the Game Master and add your character's Animal Handling level. The following chart offers a sample range of target numbers.

TARGET NUMBER	ANIMAL BEING HANDLED
11 +	Trained animal unfamiliar with the character, or trained animal familiar with the player in a highly charged emotional state
13 +	Trained animal unfamiliar with the character in a highly charged emotional state
15 +	Wild animal
21 +	Wild animal attacking the character

Results of failing an Animal Handling roll are determined by the Game Master and should reflect the situation between the animal and the character. This could result in a panicking horse trampling the character, or a wild wolf that normally would have run from the party choosing to attack.

Assisted Animal Handling Rolls: One additional character trained in Animal Handling can assist in an Animal Handling roll. The character with the higher Animal Handling modifier (stat of the Game Master's choice + Animal Handling level) makes the roll and adds 1 to the result of the die roll for each of his assistant's levels in Animal Handling.

Game Master Notes: The stat chosen for this social skill should be based on the sort of animal handling taking place. Examples include STR-based Animal Handling rolls for extricating a panicked horse's leg from some fallen machinery, or a PER-based Animal Handling roll to notice a hidden injury irritating a wild dog.

Some creatures of the wilds of Immoren are immune to player character's persuasion. A rampaging Thornwood mauler is unlikely to be soothed by a few kind words no matter how skilled the animal handler.

BRIBERY (SOCIAL)

The character is a shrewd criminal negotiator capable of buying his way out of trouble (or deeper into trouble, as the situation dictates.) He knows whom to contact for underhanded favors and knows how to estimate the cost for specific bribes.

Untrained Bribery: A character unskilled in Bribery can attempt a bribe but runs a far greater risk of failure. Treat all bribe attempts by an untrained character as one degree less successful on the results table than for a character trained in Bribery.

Bribery Rolls: When your character makes a bribery attempt, you make a roll using a stat determined by the Game Master and add your character's Bribery level.

The following table offers guidelines for setting Bribery target numbers, but like many social skills, the exact situation in-game might suggest deviations from these general guidelines.

TARGET NUMBER	SITUATION
10	Simple request with no substantial risk or cost to the character accepting the bribe
+ 1–5	Complex request requiring additional time
+ 1–5	Costly request requiring additional expenses or favors
+ 1 to Impossible	Risky request that could get the character into trouble
+ 1 to Impossible	Attempting to bribe a character of particularly strong moral fiber
+ 1 to Impossible	Bribe considered low to laughable for the task at hand
−1 to −5	Leverage over the character to whom your character is offering the bribe
−1 to Automatic	Attempting to bribe an impressionable or downright corrupt character
−1 to Automatic	Bribe considered high or even exorbitant for the task at hand

For example, attempting to bribe a town guardsman into letting characters into a town's side gate would typically range from an 8 to a 14 depending on the guardsman's ethics, the bribe offered, and the risk he would incur by opening the door. Attempting to bribe a lord into assassinating his liege would be at least a 20 and could be an automatic failure depending on the lord's temperament.

Once the bribe's target number has been determined and the roll has been made, consult the table below to determine its effect.

ROLL RESULT	RESULTING ACTION
Fail by more than 10	Bribe accepted and player character reported to the authorities
Fail by more than 5	Bribe accepted but assigned task ignored or failed
Fail	Bribe rejected
Succeed	Bribe accepted and task completed, possibly with some difficulties and/or added expenses passed on to the player characters
Succeed by 5 or more	Bribe accepted and task completed flawlessly

Assisted Bribery Rolls: Though any number of characters can donate to the bribery offer, only one spokesman can negotiate the bribe itself. Bribery rolls cannot be assisted.

Game Master Notes: A player character trained in Bribery can serve as a helpful storytelling tool, but he can also become a detriment. Always give your players plenty of choices and options, but do not be afraid to substantially amp up the target number for a Bribery skill roll to keep a story on track. A giant well-planned battle through numerous levels of a dungeon is far more exciting for players in the long run than one Bribery skill roll with a corrupt guard.

CLIMBING (AGILITY, GENERAL SKILL)

The character knows how to climb sheer surfaces. Add this skill to the character's AGL when climbing.

Untrained Climbing: Characters untrained in Climbing can make Climbing rolls normally.

Climbing Rolls: When your character attempts to climb a surface, you make an AGL + Climbing roll against a target number set by the Game Master to determine if the roll is a success.

The following chart offers a sample range of target numbers.

TARGET NUMBER	SURFACE BEING CLIMBED
11	Vine covered cliff, trees with relatively low branches
13	Rough stone walls, weathered rocks, trees with high branches
15 +	Well made stone walls, weathered cliffs with overhangs
21 +	Ice cliffs, cave interiors

Assisted Climbing Rolls: Without specific equipment, Climbing rolls cannot be assisted. It is up to each individual character to climb or fall on his own.

With the proper ropes, harnesses, and climbing equipment in place, one character can hoist other characters up a wall, cliff, or other sheer surface. Note that this typically still means that one character needs to climb up successfully in order to help any others who wish to scale the same surface. When making Climbing rolls for characters being pulled from above, add half the lifting character's STR (rounding up) to the Climbing roll. If the lifting character is using an actual pulley system to hoist another character, add the lifting character's STR to the Climbing roll.

Game Master Notes: Weather can also be factored into the difficulty of a climb. Normally a character would have no trouble getting to the top of a ladder, but if that ladder is outside in a howling wind the task isn't so simple.

It is up to the Game Master whether the armor worn by the character imparts an added layer of difficulty to the challenge. A character's greatcoat might snag in the branches of a tree, or his armor could restrict his movement and make climbing a cliff more difficult.

COMMAND (SOCIAL)

The character has been trained to lead subordinates in the field.

Command Range: Every character has a command range in inches equal to his INT + Command skill.

Untrained Command: The Command skill cannot be used untrained. Characters have command ranges whether or not they have this skill.

Command Rolls: A character with the Command skill can issue directives to men under his command that they obey. When a player character is issued an order, the player determines how his character responds to the order. In the case of NPCs, the commanding character makes a roll to determine how his directives are received.

When your character makes a command attempt, you make a roll using a stat determined by the Game Master and add your character's Command level. The following chart offers some sample situations and target numbers. If the roll succeeds, the character's orders are followed.

TARGET NUMBER	SITUATION
No Roll	Issuing a command to a group of subordinates in a safe situation
11	Issuing a command to a group of subordinates that contradicts their training or seems to make no sense
13	Issuing a command to a group of subordinates in a dangerous situation
15 +	Ordering a group of subordinates to take a clearly unwise or unnecessarily hazardous course of action
17 +	Issuing a potentially suicidal order to a subordinate

At the Game Master's discretion, this roll can be modified based on the respect the men the character commands have for him. If he is well respected or if he leads by example, add +2 to his Command rolls. If he is poorly respected, the character could suffer a –1 to –3 penalty on his Command rolls.

Steadying Nerves: When confronted with an entity or situation that can cause fear, a character with the Command skill can attempt to steady his nerve and the nerve of those around him. Before Willpower rolls are made to resist fear, the character can make an INT + Command skill roll against a target number equal to the entity or situation's fear value. If the roll succeeds, the character and other friendly characters in his command range gain +2 on their Willpower rolls to resist the effects of fear for the rest of the encounter. This bonus is not cumulative.

Assisted Command Rolls: Attempting to take command in a given situation depends on an individual character's leadership ability. Command rolls cannot be assisted.

Game Master Notes: Command is an essential skill for both 'jack marshals and military commanders. Not only does it enhance a character's authority over subordinates, but it also extends the character's command range.

CRAFT (INTELLECT)

Craft skills enable a character to manufacture or repair items. When a player selects this skill, he must determine the specific type of items his character can craft. This skill can be taken multiple times, each with a different area of specialization. The recommended Craft skills for player characters are Craft (carpentry), Craft (gunsmithing), Craft (metalworking), and Craft (tanning). Skills like Craft (pottery), Craft (stoneworking), and Craft (tailoring) are also an option but are more common to non-player characters.

Untrained Craft: With adventure around every corner, it's unwise to put your character's life in the hands of an amateur armorer or weaponsmith. Leave crafting to the professionals. Characters may not attempt untrained Craft rolls.

Craft Rolls: Characters with one or more levels in Craft (carpentry) can keep the party's wooden weapons, shields, bows, and equipment in good repair and can produce new wooden items using the table below.

Characters with one or more levels in Craft (gunsmithing) can keep the party's pistols and rifles in good repair and can produce new guns and bullets using the table below.

Characters with one or more levels in Craft (metalworking) can keep the party's metal weapons, armor, and equipment in good repair and can produce new metal items using the table below.

Characters with one or more levels in Craft (tanning) can keep the party's leather armor, clothing, holsters, and equipment in good repair and can produce new leather items using the table below.

For other Craft skills, consult your Game Master for the types of items the character can produce or repair.

A character with this skill can produce items suitable for use and selling. A character can produce any item related to a craft skill he has, and using a craft skill requires one full day of work. After this time is spent, the character makes a Craft roll to determine the total value of goods he was able to produce that day. The entire day of work costs the character 1 gc. If he is making an item that has a value higher than what he produced in a day, his item is partially finished and he can complete it another day.

For example, Greg's character is crafting a great sword worth 20 gc using his Craft (metalworking) skill of 1. After the first full day of work, Greg makes an INT + Craft skill roll and gets an 11. Referencing the table below, he completes 5 gc worth of work. He now has 15 gc worth of work left to do to finish the great sword. After his second full day of work, he rolls high enough to complete 10 gc worth of work. He then has 5 gc worth of work left to do, which he easily completes on his third day of work. The character completes his item in three days, so it cost him 3 gc worth of materials, and now he has a sword worth 20 gc.

To make a Craft roll, make a INT + Craft roll against a target number set by the Game Master to determine if the roll is a success and compare it to the table below.

ROLL RESULT	COMMON ITEM
8 or less	No progress
9–12	5 gc x skill level
13–16	10 gc x skill level
17–20	15 gc x skill level
21 +	20 gc x skill level

Assisted Craft Rolls: One additional character trained in the appropriate Craft skill can assist in a Craft skill roll. The character with the higher Craft modifier (INT + Craft level) makes the roll and adds 1 to the result of the die roll for each of his assistant's levels in the appropriate Craft skill.

Game Master Notes: Non-player characters trained in crafting are common in towns throughout the Iron Kingdoms and offer their services to build or repair items.

CRYPTOGRAPHY (INTELLECT)

The character is well versed in writing, using, and breaking codes.

Untrained Cryptography: Without training in Cryptography, a character can break only the simplest of codes and then only those in his native language. A character must have the Cryptology skill to create his own codes.

Cryptography Rolls: When your character attempts to break a code, you make an INT + Cryptography roll against a target number set by the Game Master to determine if the roll is a success.

When setting the target number for Cryptography rolls, the Game Master should consider the complexity of the code, whether or not a coded document was written in a language the character knows, and the amount of time the character takes attempting to crack the code.

TARGET NUMBER	CRYPTOGRAPHY ROLL CIRCUMSTANCES
10 to 25 depending on complexity	Break a code
+8 difficulty	Unknown language (familiar alphabet)
+12 difficulty	Unknown language (foreign alphabet)
−1 difficulty per hour (max −4)	Spend several hours
−1 to −4 difficulty	Code style the character has seen before
−10 dificulty	Exact code the character has used before

When designing his own code, a character chooses how complicated the code is by setting his own target number. He then makes a skill roll against that target number. It takes a number of hours equal to the intended target number to design a code. If he succeeds, this is the target number for someone to break the code. If he fails, his code is either obvious and easily solved or is fundamentally flawed and unintelligible. In either case the character has to spend time reviewing his work to discover how it is flawed.

If a character reuses a code he has already developed, it takes a number of minutes to write a coded message equal to the code's difficulty target number instead of a number of hours.

Assisted Cryptography Rolls: When working as a team to break a code, the players must select one character to lead the codebreaking efforts. Each character makes an INT + Cryptography roll. For each character who had a result of 15 or higher, add 1 to the result of the character who led the codebreaking team.

Game Master Notes: Coded messages are common in the Iron Kingdoms for military, merchant, and criminal organizations. Such groups also have numerous individuals trained in creating and breaking coded messages they intercept.

DECEPTION (SOCIAL)

Various situations in the Iron Kingdoms can be shifted to your character's favor with the appropriate application of a falsehood. A character skilled in Deception can be a great asset to many adventuring parties.

Untrained Deception: A character unskilled in Deception can still attempt to weave a believable lie.

Deception Rolls: When your character tells a lie, you make a roll using a stat determined by the Game Master and add your character's Deception level.

When determining the target number for a Deception roll, consider the INT of the target of the character's deception and the scope of the lie. The following table can offer some guidelines for setting Deception target numbers, but like many social skills, the exact situation in-game might suggest deviations from these general guidelines.

TARGET NUMBER	SITUATION
Subject's INT + 6	Simple lie that a character would have no reason to mistrust
Subject's INT + 9	A complex lie told with an element of truth
Subject's INT + 12	Complex lie requiring multiple connected falsehoods

If a deceptive character has manufactured believable evidence to support his lies, the Game Master should reduce the target number by up to 3 depending on the quality and believability of the evidence.

If a character attempts to deceive a crowd, have him make a single roll as above, but increase the target number by up to 3 depending on the size of the crowd. Use the highest INT of a character in the crowd to determine the target number.

If the roll succeeds, the subject(s) of the roll believe the character's ruse. If the roll fails, the subject(s) do not believe the character's lies.

Assisted Deception Rolls: One additional character involved in the lie and trained in Deception can assist in a Deception skill roll. The character with the higher Deception modifier (stat of the Game Master's choice + Deception level) makes the roll and adds 1 to the result of the die roll for each of his assistant's levels in Deception.

Game Master Notes: The reaction of the character being lied to on a failed roll is entirely up to the Game Master. A rural guardsman might just tell the character to get out of town. Failing a Deception roll against vigilant border guards could turn into the beginning of a combat encounter.

DETECTION (PERCEPTION, GENERAL SKILL)

The Detection skill measures how refined the character's skills of observation are. Whether scoping out a dark corner to detect a hidden foe or combing the scene of a battle to discern the nature of the combatants, a keenly perceptive character can glean information hidden from less astute eyes.

Untrained Detection: All characters have some degree of detection capability based on their Perception stat. Detection can be used untrained without any penalties.

Detection vs. Sneak: The rules for using detection to spot a sneaking character are described in the Sneak skill (see p. 193).

Detection Rolls: When your character tries to spot something hidden, you make a PER + Detection roll against a target number set by the Game Master to determine if the check is a success.

Detection rolls are made in two distinct situations: to detect an unknown threat or to search for items or clues. When making a Detection roll to search an area, the Game Master should determine what can be discovered or spotted with a Detection roll and what requires a specific skill like Forensic Science or Tracking to find.

Unseen or hidden threats can be detected once they are within range. This range varies based on the nature of the threat. For example, a party of ambushing dregg could be spotted when their hiding place comes into visual range, while a dangerous environmental hazard such as quicksand might only be detectable once characters are almost on top of it. When the Game Master gives characters the chance to spot an unseen threat, those characters close enough to detect it are allowed to make the roll.

The following table gives some typical target numbers for Detection rolls.

TARGET NUMBER	SUBJECT OF THE DETECTION ROLL
Automatic success	Obvious details in plain sight or a clear threat on the horizon, such as an charging steamjack or mass of cavalry troops
12	Enemies lacking the Sneak skill lurking in the shadows
12 +	Hearing muffled cries in the distance
13 +	Detecting a hazy or unclear detail, such as movement in thick fog, animal scratches in a dark room, or hidden traps

The Game Master should keep in mind how different environments can affect a Detection roll. This can be reflected by shortening the detection range or by increasing the target number.

Assisted Detection Rolls: Detection rolls cannot be assisted. Depending on the position of player characters, more than one player might have the opportunity to successfully detect a threat to the party using the rules above.

Game Master Notes: Detection ranges and target numbers are situational, so always set them based on your best judgment. Is the area well lit or full of shadows? Is it quiet or noisy? Are there distractions such as innocent travelers or innocuous wildlife that would cause player characters to lower their guard? All these factors can help determine the target number for a given threat.

DISGUISE (INTELLECT)

The character is skilled in the art of disguise. He can utilize clothing and accessories to mask his true identity in order to gain access to restricted areas, avoid paying back a debt, or lay low rather than face criminal charges.

Untrained Disguise: A character unskilled in Disguise can attempt to create a simple disguise but automatically fail disguise attempts against characters who already know the disguised character.

Untrained characters can also wear a disguise created by a trained character. After at least one hour of instruction and practice with the disguise, an untrained character can use the disguise as if he were the trained character who created it.

Disguise Rolls: When a player character takes the time to create a disguise, he creates the target number for other characters to beat. Rather than making the Disguise roll himself, a player should tell the Game Master his INT + Disguise level, and then the Game Master makes the roll. The Game Master then informs the player how confident he is that he created a disguise to the best of his abilities: doubtful (2d6 roll of 2–5), confident (2d6 roll of 6–8), or very confident (2d6 roll of 9–12). Based on this information, the character can choose to craft a new disguise, but it takes additional time to do so. The Game Master uses the Disguise roll and the table below to determine the target number that other characters use to attempt to perceive the character beneath the disguise.

A character can create a disguise to look like a member of a group such as a town's militia or like a specific individual—such as Walter Shayworth, captain of the town militia—but it is more difficult to create a convincing disguise of an individual than a nameless face in the crowd.

Once a disguise is created, characters observing the disguised character can detect the disguise with a successful PER + Detection roll against the target number of the disguise. Characters gain a +2 bonus on this roll if they personally know the disguised character. Characters also gain a +4 bonus on the roll if the disguise is intended to be a specific individual and they personally know that individual.

DISGUISE'S TARGET NUMBER	DISGUISE CREATION CIRCUMSTANCES
2d6 + INT + Disguise level – 2	Create an impromptu disguise (taking fifteen minutes to one hour)
2d6 + INT + Disguise level	Create an average disguise (taking two hours to eight hours)
2d6 + INT + Disguise level + 2	Create an elaborate disguise (taking several days)
–4 modifier	Disguise representing a specific individual rather than a group
–2 modifier	Disguise created from improvised materials
–2 modifier	Disguised as a different race
–2 modifier	Disguised as a different gender
+ 2 modifier	Disguise created from plentiful clothing, equipment, and accessories
+ 4 modifier	Disguise created using the exact raiment, armor, and/or heraldry of the individual or group the disguise represents

Assisted Disguise Rolls: One additional character trained in Disguise can assist in creating a disguise. The Game Master uses whichever of the two characters' Disguise modifier is higher (INT + Disguise level) and adds 1 to the result of the die roll for each of the assistant's levels in Disguise.

Game Master Notes: NPCs can make use of the Disguise skill to deceive the player characters as well! A well-placed spy or thief can be a memorable adventure element that opens up entirely new plot arcs for your campaign.

DRIVING (AGILITY, GENERAL SKILL)

The character is skilled at driving carts and carriages. A character does not need to make a skill roll to use this skill unless he wishes to move particularly fast, needs to avoid an accidental collision, or otherwise performs a dangerous maneuver.

Untrained Driving: Characters untrained in Driving can make Driving rolls normally.

Driving Rolls: When your character attempts a tricky driving stunt, you make an AGL + Driving roll against a target number set by the Game Master to determine if the check is a success. The following table offers some guidelines for Driving target numbers.

TARGET NUMBER	SITUATION
11	A relatively safe road at a high rate of speed
13+	Rapidly moving out of the path of an individual or obstacle without hitting it
13+	A dangerous road (bridge, cliff, and the like) at a low rate of speed
15+	A dangerous road (bridge, cliff, and the like) at a high rate of speed
15+	Truly daring and dangerous stunt

The Game Master should determine what modifiers affect the roll. The following chart offers sample target number modifiers.

ROLL MODIFIER	SITUATION
−1 to −3	The character is holding onto something in addition to the reins
−2	The animals pulling the vehicle are skittish or excited
−2 to −4	The vehicle is damaged

Assisted Driving Rolls: Driving rolls cannot be assisted. Each individual character must drive a cart, buggy, or other vehicle on his own.

Game Master Notes: Driving rolls should be limited to situations of danger and risk. The results of a failed roll are adjudicated by the Game Master and should add to the excitement or danger of the situation. For example, the party has highjacked an armored cart and is in a race with multiple pursuers. If the driver of the cart fails a roll to pass a slower-moving cart on the road, it could slow the cart enough that the pursuers get within pistol range.

ESCAPE ARTIST (AGILITY)

The character is a skilled escape artist. He can contort his body to slip from virtually any bonds.

Untrained Escape Artist: Characters untrained in Escape Artist can make Escape Artist rolls normally. Instead of making a roll every five minutes, an untrained character can make a roll every thirty minutes. When an untrained character attempts to escape from knots tied by a character with the Rope Use skill, he suffers −2 on the escape artist roll.

Escape Artist Rolls: A character bound or chained struggles to escape his bonds when his captors aren't watching. Each Escape Artist roll represents five minutes of the character's time laboring to get free. Make an AGL + Escape Artist roll against a target number set by the Game Master to determine if the roll is a success.

Note that many escape attempts are impossible without a high AGL, the proper training, and a bit of luck (in the form of a feat point).

TARGET NUMBER	SITUATION
12	Character's hands bound by rope
15	Character's hands and feet bound by rope
20	Character hog-tied
see Rope Use skill	Character bound by someone trained in Rope Use
15	Character's hands or feet manacled
20	Character's hands and feet manacled
25	Character's neck chained into a metal collar
12–18 depending on container	Character trapped in a closet, coffin, crate, or other confined space.
22	Character is in the stocks
−1 to −4 modifier	Poor quality materials trapping the character
+ 1 to + 4 modifier	High quality materials trapping the character

Assisted Escape Artist Rolls: In general, a character who has assistance in escaping his bonds does not use the Escape Artist skill. Someone could be cutting the ropes binding his arms and legs or picking the lock holding his chains. That character might use a skill in breaking the character loose, but the bound character would not be using a skill.

A character uses the Escape Artist skill to contort his body or otherwise slip his bonds. Contorting one's body is not an activity that lends itself to receiving help.

Game Master Notes: Though they can attempt to escape every five minutes, player characters might have a tough time escaping from some bonds without using a feat point. Feel free to reduce the Escape Artist target numbers if your players are out of feat points when they're captured (unless, of course, you do not want them to have a chance of escape).

ETIQUETTE (SOCIAL)

Etiquette is the skill of comporting oneself in polite society, especially with regard to the disparate traditions of the various Iron Kingdoms. A character with this skill knows how to interact with the upper classes, as well as members of theocracy, foreign dignitaries, and heads of state. He is capable of speaking eloquently and has a refined knowledge of social protocol.

Untrained Etiquette: A character unskilled in Etiquette can attempt to make his way through the perils of high society but won't be as successful as a trained character. Treat all Etiquette attempts by an untrained character as one degree less successful on the results table than for a character trained in Etiquette.

Etiquette Rolls: An Etiquette skill roll should be required only when the character interacts with those high above his station, tries to cover up a social gaffe, takes part in an unfamiliar ceremony, or deals with foreign dignitaries.

When your character's etiquette is in question, roll 2d6 + the stat of the Game Master's choice + Etiquette level against a target number set by the Game Master to determine if the roll is a success. The following table offers guidelines for Etiquette target numbers, but like many social skills, the exact situation in-game might suggest deviations from these general guidelines.

TARGET NUMBER	SITUATION
No roll required	A casual situation with a character of equal standing
11–13	A formal interaction with a character of equal standing
14 +	A formal interaction with a character of higher standing
16 +	A formal interaction with a foreign character of higher standing

For example, a knight is attempting to formally greet a dignitary from a different order he has met on the road. The chance of offending the other knight should be low. That same knight attempting to interact with King Leto at a formal state function would have a much higher chance of making a mistake.

Once the target number has been determined and the roll has been made, consult the table below.

ROLL RESULT	RESULTING ACTION
Fail by more than 10	Character made an embarrassing mistake and would be best off excusing himself from the situation
Fail by more than 5	Character's misstep has the potential to cause insult and he must offer some sort of amends
Fail	Character made a minor gaffe
Succeed	Character comported himself well
Succeed by 5 or more	Character comported himself excellently and might draw the favorable attention of onlookers

Assisted Etiquette Rolls: One additional character involved in the situation and trained in Etiquette can assist in an Etiquette skill roll. The character with the higher Etiquette modifier (stat of the Game Master's choice + Etiquette level) makes the roll and adds 1 to the result of the die roll for each of his assistant's levels in Etiquette.

Game Master Notes: Players should not make Etiquette rolls unless there is a chance of their characters making a significant mistake. If a knight is invited to a social event at the palace, he should be able to get through the night without making a fool of himself. If a player pushes the boundaries of his character's social standing, though, it is the perfect time for an Etiquette roll. If that same knight decides he wants to start a conversation with King Leto about the Cygnaran government's treatment of trollkin, he runs the risk of losing any social standing he might have.

FELL CALLING (POISE)

The character is skilled at using his powerful voice to inspire his friends, or as a weapon against his enemies.

Each fell call is a separate ability. The text of the ability describes its effects and the type of action it requires. A character can perform only one fell call on his turn.

Untrained Fell Calling: Characters who are not Fell Callers cannot make fell calls. They sound downright ridiculous when they try.

Fell Calling Rolls: Some fell calls are attacks. A fell call attack follows all the other rules for ranged attacks (p. 211). The character's POI + Fell Calling level is added to the roll against a target's DEF number.

Assisted Fell Calling Rolls: It is very difficult for Fell Callers to coordinate their actions in the chaos of battle, so Fell Calling rolls cannot be assisted.

Game Master Notes: The Fell Caller is an important member of trollkin society and is highly regarded by his people. In addition to the unique abilities that this skill offers, Fell Callers are also expected to be the chroniclers and storytellers of their people.

FORENSIC SCIENCE (INTELLECT)

Forensic science is the application of deductive reasoning and scientific principles to reconstruct the events of a crime based on evidence left at a scene. A character with this skill is adept at determining a likely sequence of events, gathering clues to the identity of a perpetrator, and collecting physical evidence.

Untrained Forensic Science: Characters untrained in Forensic Science have no hope of making sense of the subtle details surrounding a crime scene. Forensic Science cannot be used untrained.

Forensic Science Rolls: When a character tries to reconstruct a crime or piece together a sequence of events from physical evidence, make a INT + Forensic Science roll against a target number set by the Game Master. The character can make one roll for every half hour he investigates the physical clues at the scene of a crime or other event that involves physical evidence. A true expert can even discover if evidence has been tampered with.

The following chart offers a sample range of target numbers.

TARGET NUMBER	SITUATION
11	A scene with very obvious evidence
14	A scene with good evidence
17	A scene with poor evidence
20	A scene with almost no evidence

The Game Master should determine what modifiers affect the target number. The following chart offers sample target number modifiers.

TARGET NUMBER	SITUATION
−1	Every full half hour the character spends studying the evidence
+1	Every six hours that have passed since the event
+1 to +3	The environment is not conducive to the survival of evidence
+1 to +5	The evidence was tampered with

Assisted Forensic Science Rolls: When actively searching a battlefield, crime scene, bookshelf, or any other area under the characters' detection as a group, the players must select one character to lead the search. Each character makes his own INT + Forensic Science roll. For each character who had a result of 15 or higher, add 1 to the result of the character who led the search.

Game Master Notes: A successful Forensic Science roll should reveal all the important information a character can learn from the clues available at the scene, but the actual amount of information available is up to the Game Master. The character should be able to construct a loose narrative of the events as they happened that can be gleaned from the evidence, but physical evidence rarely tells the whole story. For example, if a man has been shot in his home, perhaps the only evidence is the type of bullet and the discovery that there was no forced entry.

FORGERY (AGILITY OR INTELLECT)

The character is a skilled forger capable of creating fake documents or currency.

Untrained Forgery: Without the proper know-how and practice, forgeries attempted by untrained characters are unlikely to fool anyone. Forgery cannot be used untrained.

Forgery Rolls: In criminal circles, forgers are seen as true artists. Their work is subtle and carries greater risks than any act of mere petty theft, since the forger steals authority and imperils security. Forging state documents and currency is not as simple as making a flawless match of content. The forger must also consider paper weight and texture, ink, the particulars of signature, and a thousand other details. As a result, the forging of complex documents that come under significant scrutiny, such as writs of passage across border or banking documents, cannot be produced with less than a week's labor.

When a character takes the time to create a forgery, his player sets the target number for other characters to beat. The Game Master should make the roll, whether the forgery is created by an NPC or a player character. The roll is based on the character's AGL or INT (whichever is lower) + his Forgery level. After the roll, the Game Master informs the player how confident the character is that he created a forgery to the best of his abilities: doubtful (2d6 roll of 2–5), confident (2d6 roll of 6–8), or very confident (2d6 roll of 9–12). Based on this information, the character can choose to craft a new forgery or use the one he's made.

The following table presents common modifiers for this roll.

FORGERY ROLL MODIFIER	CHARACTER'S CIRCUMSTANCES
+ 2	Takes several extra days perfecting his work
−1	Lacks the perfectly matching materials to make his forgery, but the materials he has are very close
−3	Has to improvise one or more key materials
−5 to Impossible	Has to do with inappropriate materials
−3 +	In a rush and has to produce the forgery in half the normal time
−3 +	Lacks an original of a complex item he is forging and has to work from memory
Impossible	Attempting to produce a complex document without ever having seen the original

Forging a document can be as simple as taking a quill to a piece of parchment. Forging coinage requires certain skills and access to specific equipment. A character's levels in Craft (metalworking) are added to the target number for coins he forges. A character with access to a workshop adds +1 to the Forgery target number when making coins.

Once a forgery is created, characters interacting with it can detect if it is a fake with a successful PER + Detection roll against the forger's modified skill roll total. The Detection roll to spot a fake is modified by the following:

DETECTION ROLL MODIFIER	CHARACTER'S CIRCUMSTANCES
+ 2	Deals with similar items on a regular basis
+ 3	Actively compares the forgery to a genuine article
−2	Has never seen a genuine article and the forgery is not an obvious fake
−2 or more	Is distracted or nor looking closely at the forgery

Assisted Forgery Rolls: One additional character trained in Forgery can assist in a Forgery skill roll. The Game Master uses whichever of the two characters' Forgery modifier is higher (their lower stat between AGL and INT + Forgery level) and adds 1 to the result of the die roll for each of the assistant's levels in Forgery.

Game Master Notes: Forgery can provide interesting hooks for a campaign. The player characters might require official writs granting safe passage across a hostile border, or find themselves in need of a particular false document such as a last will and testament, property deed, or mercenary contract.

GAMBLING (PERCEPTION, GENERAL SKILL)

The character is skilled at gaining the upper hand in games of chance and sport. He relies on skill, knowledge and manipulation of the odds, a firm knowledge of the rules of the game, but most of all, he relies on his ability to read the other players' intentions and discern their tells.

Untrained Gambling: Gambling can be used untrained without any penalties.

Gambling Rolls: Characters use this skill when resolving a game of chance in which they are active participants. Each participant makes a PER + Gambling roll. The character with the highest total wins.

There are a number of modifiers that can complicate this roll. The Game Master determines which modifiers apply.

ROLL MODIFIER	CHARACTER'S SITUATION
+ 1	Familiar with most of the other people he is playing with
+ 1 to + 5	Cheating
−2	Desperate to win
−2	Distracted
−1 to −3	Intoxicated or sleep deprived
−1 to −3	Unfamiliar with the rules of the game

When a character cheats during the game, his player must explain the nature of the cheating to the Game Master. The character then makes an AGL + Deception roll with a target number equal to double the highest PER + Detection total of any of the characters playing. Add 1 to the target number for each player beyond two playing the game. If the character succeeds, his cheat is not spotted. If he fails, one or more other characters at the table spot the cheat.

Assisted Gambling Rolls: Characters who help each other when gambling are considered to be cheating. Cheating of this nature does not require the AGL + Deception roll described above. The player making the Gambling roll is the leader. Each character assisting makes a PER + Deception roll. For each character who had a result of 15 or higher, add 1 to the result of the leader's roll.

Game Master Notes: If an NPC character spots another character cheating, his reaction is entirely up to the Game Master. Some characters might make a loud commotion to draw attention to the cheat, while others keep the information to themselves, especially if they can use the cheater's actions to an advantage.

INTERROGATION (INTELLECT)

The character is skilled in the art of extracting information from those within his power. His methods might rely on a combination of threat, coercion, cajoling, mental cruelty, or torture. Often sleep and hunger deprivation are used to prepare a subject for interrogation.

Untrained Interrogation: Characters untrained in Interrogation can attempt to force information from an unwilling subject. When making an Interrogation roll against a character trained in interrogation, the untrained character suffers a –2 penalty on the Interrogation roll.

Interrogation Rolls: When your character tries to interrogate a subject, both he and his subject make rolls. The interrogator adds his Interrogation and INT to the roll. The subject adds his PHY and INT.

The Game Master should consider the mental and physical condition of the subject and possibly give him a –1 to 3 penalty to his roll based on that condition. If the interrogator's total is higher, he pries some sought-after piece of information from the subject. If the subject rolls higher, he can feed the interrogator false information. The subject's roll should be made without the interrogator knowing its outcome.

Assisted Interrogation Rolls: One additional character trained in Interrogation can assist in an Interrogation skill roll. The character with the higher Interrogation modifier (INT + Interrogation level) makes the roll and adds 1 to the result of the die roll for each of his assistant's levels in Interrogation.

Game Master Notes: The Game Master can make careful use of this skill during play as a means of advancing the story. It can be used to feed information and plot hooks to player characters, or it can provide antagonists with vital intelligence to alter their own plans. Relying on player use of this skill to pass along information can be difficult, especially if your players are the shoot-first kind.

INTIMIDATION (SOCIAL, GENERAL SKILL)

A character's Intimidation skill determines how threatening and fearsome the character is. He can use it to cow others into submission, get enemies to back down from a fight, or scare people out of his way.

Untrained Intimidation: Intimidation can be used untrained without any penalties.

Intimidation Rolls: When your character attempts to intimidate a target, you make a roll using a stat determined by the Game Master and add your character's Intimidation level. The stat used for the Intimidation roll should reflect the method of intimidation employed. If the character is threatening grievous bodily harm, Strength might be the most appropriate stat. If the character alludes to a vague threat to a business venture, Perception could be more appropriate.

The target number is determined by the difference between the selected stat + Intimidation level of the two parties.

TARGET NUMBER	SITUATION
11	Target's stat + Intimidation total is lower by 5 or more than that of the intimidating character
13	Target's stat + Intimidation total is lower by 3 or more than that of the intimidating character
15	Target's stat + Intimidation total is equal to or lower than that of the intimidating character
17	Target's stat + Intimidation total is higher than that of the intimidating character
19+	Target's stat + Intimidation total is higher by 3 or more than that of the intimidating character

The Game Master should modify this roll according to the circumstances at hand. If the intimidating character clearly has the upper hand or the character being intimidated has a specific reason to credit the intimidating character's threats, the target number could be reduced by –1 to –5 at the Game Master's discretion. If the character being intimidated clearly has the upper hand or has a reason to not believe the intimidating character's threats, the target number could be increased by 1 to 5, or it simply could be impossible to intimidate the character without more leverage.

The outcome of the intimidation is entirely up to the Game Master. The target of a successful intimidation might run cowering from the scene, or simply stand aside to let the party pass. If an intimidation roll is failed, the Game Master should come up with an appropriate response. Not all failed Intimidation rolls should start a fight.

Assisted Intimidation Rolls: As a social skill roll, Intimidation rolls fall largely to the discretion of the Game Master. Under the right circumstances, a Game Master might allow assisted Intimidation rolls. The Game Master should assign a modifier to the target number based on his assessment of what added leverage the other characters can apply to the situation.

Game Master Notes: Intimidation can be as much a story-telling tool as a character skill. A common shopkeep might fold to even the weakest intimidation attempt while the full force of a town's militia won't back down under any circumstances. Do not hesitate to set high or low target numbers for intimidation rolls as the circumstances warrant.

JUMPING (PHYSIQUE, GENERAL SKILL)

The character's athletic abilities allow him to hurl his body over obstacles and distances.

Untrained Jumping: Characters untrained in Jumping can make Jumping rolls normally.

Long Jumping Rolls: To determine the horizontal distance a character can jump, make a PHY + Jumping roll and consult the following chart. A character with the Bounding Leap archetype benefit adds six feet (1") to the distance he jumps.

A character who makes a full advance during his turn can jump as a full action. A character who runs during his turn can jump as a quick action. He is placed anywhere within the specified distance or height of his current location following the rules for Being Placed (p. 205).

RESULT	DISTANCE
8 or less	Three feet (.5″)
9 to 12	Six feet (1″)
13 to 14	Twelve feet (2″)
15 to 16	Fifteen feet (2.5″)
17 to 18	Eighteen feet (3″)
19 to 20	Twenty-one feet (3.5″)
21 +	Twenty-four feet (4″)

High Jumping Rolls: To determine how high a character can Jump, make a PHY + Jumping roll and consult the following chart. A character with the Bounding Leap archetype benefit adds two feet to how high he jumps.

A character can jump upward as a quick action.

RESULT	HEIGHT
8 or less	One foot
9 to 14	Two feet
15 to 20	Three feet
21 +	Four feet

Jumping Modifiers: The Game Master should determine what modifiers affect the roll. The following chart offers sample target number modifiers.

RESULT MODIFIER	SITUATION
+1	Every full twelve feet (2″) the character moves before attempting the jump, up to a maximum of thirty-six feet (6″)
+2	Character ran and jumped using a pole
−1 to −3	The environment is dangerous (icy, windy, or the like)
−2	The character's armor has a −1 DEF modifier
−4	The character's armor has a −2 or more DEF modifier
+2	The jump is from a higher surface to a lower surface

Falling: A character with the Jumping skill has learned how to fall more safely. He suffers no damage roll for a fall of eighteen feet (3″) or less. When falling more than eighteen feet (3″), one less die is added for each additional increment of eighteen feet (3″)

Assisted Jumping Rolls: Under the vast majority of circumstances, Jumping rolls cannot be assisted. Each individual character must jump or fall on his own.

Game Master Notes: In the rare case that players create some sort of lever, trampoline, or bizarre contrivance to allow for an assisted jumping skill check, the Game Master can increase the results of a success but should also increase the target number. It's far easier to control one's own legs than a bodged-together mass of planks and debris.

The Game Master can also rule that some jumps are simply too easy to fail or too difficult to possibly succeed.

LAW (INTELLECT)

The character is versed in the common laws of the Iron Kingdoms and the more specific laws of each individual kingdom. A character with the Law skill has a general awareness of all aspects of criminality and an understanding of how each crime is regarded throughout each kingdom.

Untrained Law: Without the proper cunning and background information, the law is a confusing morass of seemingly arbitrary rules and contradictions. Law cannot be used untrained.

Law Rolls: The character can give basic legal advice without a die roll. When a character needs to employ a finer point of law, make an INT + Law roll against a target number set by the Game Master to determine if the roll is a success. Putting together a simple legal defense or a case for prosecution requires a successful skill roll verses a target number of 11. Putting together a more serious case requires a successful skill roll against a target number of 13 or more.

Presenting a case in court is a complex matter. In addition to the strength of the character's case, the Game Master should also weigh the strength of the evidence presented, the quality of the witnesses, the severity of the crime, whose interests are at stake, and other matters. A contested INT + Law roll can be used to determine which character has the strongest argument. The character with the highest total makes the best case.

Assisted Law Rolls: When working as a team to solve a legal problem or create a case strategy, the players must select one character to lead the casework efforts. Each character makes his own INT + Law roll. For each character who had a result of 15 or higher, add 1 to the result of the character who led the team.

Game Master Notes: The laws of the Iron Kingdoms don't have a place in every campaign. A group of tomb hunters in the depths of the Thornwood seldom interacts with legal matters, but a criminal gang in a major city might need a character well versed in Law to get its members out of trouble on a regular basis.

LOCK PICKING (AGILITY)

The Lock Picking skill allows a character to attempt to open doors without the keys and safes without the combinations.

Untrained Lock Picking: Without the proper knowledge and practice, attempting to pick a lock might ruin the lock but is unlikely to open it. Lock Picking cannot be used untrained.

Lock Picking Rolls: Each attempt to pick a lock requires two minutes unless the character takes his time. When a character

needs to pick a lock, make a AGL + Lock Picking roll against a target number set by the Game Master to determine if the roll is a success. The Game Master decides how well made the lock or safe is. The following chart offers some sample target numbers.

TARGET NUMBER	OBJECT BEING OPENED
11	Low quality lock
12–15	Average-quality lock or low-quality safe
16–19	High quality lock or average-quality safe
20+	High quality safe

The Game Master also determines what modifiers affect the roll. The following chart offers sample target number modifiers.

TARGET NUMBER MODIFIER	SITUATION
–1	Every full half hour the character spends on the attempt (up to a maximum of three hours)
–2	The lock or safe is extremely common
+1 to +3	The object has been customized in some way

Assisted Lock Picking: Lock picking is not a team activity. Lock Picking rolls cannot be assisted.

Game Master Notes: Most common locks can be easily picked without much effort. Heist adventures that center around stealing something large can depend on Lock Picking as an important central challenge.

LORE (INTELLECT, GENERAL SKILL)

The character has spent a considerable amount of time studying a particular subject and can call on a wealth of useful information when that subject comes up.

This skill can be taken several times. Each time the character takes this skill he chooses the subject of his character's knowledge. Areas of knowledge include but are not limited to the following: ancient history, ghost lore, lore of a particular nation or people, lore of a particular religion, Urcaen lore, Infernal lore, and draconic lore.

Untrained Lore: Characters untrained in a particular topic can still attempt to remember information they have casually heard about that subject. What information a character can recall, if any, is up to the Game Master but should be limited to general knowledge the character could have picked up in his travels.

Lore Rolls: When a character uses this skill, make an INT + Lore roll. Compare the total rolled to the table below to discern what the character can recall on a particular subject related to his knowledge specialty.

RESULT	INFORMATION REMEMBERED
9 or less	Very general information
10 to 12	One additional piece of useful information
3 to 15	All but the most specific information pertaining to the subject
16 or more	All information available pertaining to the subject

If the information the character is attempting recall pertains to a particularly obscure subject, the Game Master could impose up to a –3 penalty on this roll. If the character recently researched the topic at hand or if it pertains to particularly common knowledge, the Game Master could grant up to a +3 bonus on this roll.

Assisted Lore Rolls: Multiple characters who have all studied the same subject can put their heads together to come up with useful information on the topic. The players must select one character to make the primary roll. Each other character then makes his own INT + Lore roll. For each other character who had a result of 15 or higher, add 1 to the result of the primary roll.

Game Master Notes: The amount of information that a Lore roll reveals is in the hands of the Game Master. The results on the table can be a detail the Game Master tells the players, or can determine how many questions the players can ask the Game Master about a subject.

Information known by a few individuals, such as the origin of Lord Toruk, is impossible to learn with a Lore roll. A character cannot attempt to make a roll to learn something unknowable.

MECHANIKAL ENGINEERING (INTELLECT)

Though the arcane arts are critical to modern warfare in the Iron Kingdoms, a foundation of advanced mathematics and physics underpins the technology of firearms, steamjacks, mechanika, and siege warfare. A character trained in mechanikal engineering understands how to build and repair mechanikal as well as ordinary mechanical devices.

Untrained Mechanikal Engineering: Without the proper background knowledge and problem-solving skills, attempting to repair a mechanikal device or manipulate one's surroundings using physics is likely to go horribly wrong. Mechanikal Engineering cannot be used untrained.

Mechanikal Engineering Rolls: Mechanikal Engineering rolls are made when a character attempts to assemble or create mechanika (p. 280) or when he repairs a steamjack (p. 319). The skill can also be used to understand or interact with problems of a scientific nature: for example, finding a way to salvage a warjack at the bottom of a ravine, or disarming an elaborate trap found in an Orgoth tomb.

It is worth noting that to actually create mechanika, a character also needs the Inscribe Formulae ability so he can inscribe mechanika runes, a key component of mechanikal devices.

When a character attempts to use this specialized skill, make an INT + Mechanikal Engineering roll against a target number set by the Game Master to determine if the roll is a success.

Assisted Mechanikal Engineering Rolls: When working as a team to determine how a machine works, fabricate a device, or perform major repairs, the players must select one character to lead the engineering efforts. Each character makes his own INT + Mechanikal Engineering roll. For each character who had a result of 15 or higher, add 1 to the result of the character who led the engineering team.

Game Master Notes: While leeway can be given for temporary and imperfect solutions, the degree to which a character can improvise mechanika with inadequate materials or tools is limited. Many mechanikal applications require advanced metallurgy, rare minerals, specialized equipment, or refined components. Being lucky with a high Mechanikal Engineering roll does not allow a mechanik in the wilderness to rebuild an arcanum grade cortex using nothing but a rusty spoon.

MEDICINE (INTELLECT)

The character is a skilled physician and can treat the injured.

Untrained Medicine: Characters untrained in the medical arts can attempt basic battlefield triage, but should leave the treatment of major injuries to the professionals. Medicine can be used untrained normally, but just because your character can use this skill untrained doesn't mean he should.

Medicine Rolls: When a character tries to heal the sick or wounded, make an INT+ Medicine roll against a target number determined by the action attempted.

RESULT	INFORMATION REMEMBERED
11 +	Diagnosing an common disease or poison
12	Setting a broken bone
14	Stabilizing a grievously injured character (p. 216)
15 +	Diagnosing an rare disease or poison

Slow Recovery Bonus: Badly injured characters can suffer from slow recovery (p. 216) in which they do not recover lost vitality points at the normal rate. If the character is treated daily by a character with the Medicine skill, the injured character regains an additional number of points each week equal to the treating character's Medicine skill.

Poison and Disease Treatment: When a friendly character is required to make a poison or disease resistance roll, at the Game Master's discretion, a player whose character has the Medicine skill can make an INT + Medicine skill roll to diagnose and treat the poison. The Game Master sets the target number for this roll based on how familiar the treating character is with the poison (see the table above for guidance). If the roll succeeds, the friendly character gains +2 on his roll to resist the effects.

Assisted Medicine Rolls: The Game Master determines if a Medicine roll can be assisted, and by how many players. Diagnosing a disease can be a group effort, but delicate surgery on a bullet wound must be done alone.

On rolls that allow assistance, the players must select one character to lead the effort. Each character makes his own INT + Medicine roll. For each character who had a result of 15 or higher, add 1 to the result of the character who led the medical team.

Game Master Notes: Practical medical knowledge can be vital to the survival of a party. Not only can it save character's lives, but a skilled medical practitioner can also aid in patching other characters back together and greatly shortening their recovery time after sustaining injuries. Additionally, the Medicine skill can be a great plot hook. Whole scenarios could be based on player characters rushing to reach and then treating a sick or injured NPC in a remote locale or in finding the proper cure to a lethal disease.

NAVIGATION (PERCEPTION)

The character is adept at using the stars and other natural indicators to determine his location.

Untrained Navigation: Without a skilled navigator, characters should stick to major highways or, better yet, take a train in order to avoid getting lost when traveling from one city or port to another. Navigation cannot be used untrained.

Navigation Rolls: Characters with one or more levels in Navigation can get from point A to point B whether or not they follow the most direct route. This might allow them to bypass tolls, highwaymen, checkpoints, or other undesirable interactions.

To make a Navigation roll, make a PER + Navigation roll against a target number set by the Game Master to determine if the roll is a success.

Results of "Encounter delays en route" are determined by the Game Master and should reflect the sort of travel being used. This could result in arriving substantially later than planned, piracy on the high seas, running into an unanticipated military patrol (which could be disastrous if transporting illegal goods), or even becoming helplessly lost.

Assisted Navigation Rolls: One additional character trained in Navigation can assist in a Navigation skill roll. The character with the higher Navigation modifier (PER + Navigation level) makes the roll and adds 1 to the result of the die roll for each of his assistant's levels in Navigation.

Game Master Notes: Non-player characters trained in Navigation frequently offer their services for a fee. Such characters can be found in most major cities and can become an important auxiliary for a successful mercenary group or smuggling ring.

ROLL RESULT	NOTABLE DESTINATION	OBSCURE DESTINATION
10 or less	Encounter delays en route	Encounter delays en route
11–12	Arrive 10% later	Encounter delays en route
13–14	Arrive as planned	Arrive 10% later
15–17	Arrive 10% earlier	Arrive as planned
18–20	Arrive 20% earlier	Arrive 10% earlier
21 +	Arrive 30% earlier	Arrive 20% earlier

NEGOTIATION (SOCIAL)

Negotiation is the peaceful resolution of a conflict. A character with Negotiation might try to haggle for a lower price with a shopkeeper or talk his way out of a potential fight with a Bog Trog tribe.

Untrained Negotiation: A character without levels in the Negotiation skill can attempt to settle disputes by talking his way out of them. He is not particularly adept at haggling, bartering, or negotiating the particulars of a deal. He can also perform any financial transaction at the basic level. These include purchasing items from shops for the listed prices in gold crowns, settling bounties or contracts, selling mint condition items to a vendor for up to half of their listed value, and selling used items back to a vendor for some lesser portion of that value based on the current quality of the item. The exact price of used items is set by the Game Master but never exceed half of the original retail price.

Negotiation Rolls: Characters with the Negotiation skill can use it when resolving any dispute or transaction the Game Master deems appropriate. It commonly applies to buying and selling goods, negotiating a contract, or talking one's way out of a fight. When your character makes a negotiation attempt, roll using a stat determined by the Game Master and add your character's Negotiation level.

When characters negotiate a non-financial dispute with an NPC, they must first determine what they want and what they are willing to offer. The Game Master then compares how generous the character's offer is with what the other party feels entitled to receive to determine a target number. The following table offers some guidelines for setting a target number.

TARGET NUMBER	CONDITION
Automatic success	Incredibly generous offer
11	Generous offer
13	Fair deal
15 +	Weak offer
19 + to impossible	Insultingly weak offer

If the other party the character is dealing with has reason not to trust the character, the Game Master might increase the target number by 1 to 5, depending on the depth of the other party's suspicions. If the other party has reason to trust the character, the target number could be lowered by 1 to 5.

Once the target number has been determined and the Negotiation roll made, reference the results on the chart below to determine the other party's response to the character.

ROLL	RESULT
Fail by 10 or more	Negotiations completely break down. No more time for talk.
Fail by more than 5	Failure. The character must both sweeten his offer and reduce his demands or he fails in his negotiations.
Fail	Failure. The character can sweeten his offer or reduce his demands and continue negotiations with another roll.
Success	The other party agrees to the character's terms.
Succeed by 5 or more	The other party agrees to the character's terms and feels very favorable toward the bargain. In this case the next time the character negotiates with this party, the target number for his Negotiation roll is decreased by 2.

Optionally, if the Game Master feels the party the character is dealing with is prone to deceit, he can make the roll himself in secret. In this case, a failed roll could result in the other party temporarily accepting the character's terms, only to betray him at some date in the future.

In the case of buying or selling goods, use the chart below, and a single roll to represents the character shopping around for the best deal and then settling on a price. Players must abide by the price negotiated by the roll and cannot simply roll again.

ROLL RESULT	PURCHASE PRICE	MAXIMUM RESALE	CONTRACT OFFER
10 or less	100%	50%	100%
11–12	95%	55%	105%
13–14	90%	60%	110%
15–17	85%	65%	115%
18–20	80%	70%	120%
21 +	75%	75%	125%

If negotiating against a character who is also trained in the Negotiation skill, use the following chart instead.

ROLL RESULT	PURCHASE PRICE	MAXIMUM RESALE	CONTRACT OFFER
Equal Result	100%	50%	100%
Win by up to 2	95%	55%	105%
Win by 3 to 4	90%	60%	110%
Win by 5 to 7	85%	65%	115%
Win by 7 to 10	80%	70%	120%
Win by more than 10	75%	75%	125%

Assisted Negotiation Rolls: One additional character trained in Negotiation can assist in a Negotiation skill roll. The character with the higher Negotiation modifier (stat chosen by the Game Master + Negotiation level) makes the roll and adds 1 to the result of the die roll for each of his assistant's levels in Negotiation.

Game Master Notes: Negotiation is separated from Bribery, Deception, and Intimidation in that both parties have something to offer, and a certain amount of trust is necessary from everyone involved. Just like player characters, non-player characters try to get the most out of a negotiation, but few have an exceptional mastery of the skill. Some organizations offering high-end contracts and merchants offering high-end goods employ skilled negotiators who have the Negotiation skill. Even highly skilled negotiators should have Negotiation 1 or Negotiation 2, but the most silver-tongued delegates in the Iron Kingdoms could have a Negotiation 3 or even a Negotiation 4.

When such a merchant or organization negotiates with a party of player characters, use the rules for opposed Negotiation rolls. When setting a price, if no member of the party has the Negotiation skill, adjust the price in the non-player character's favor by 5% per point of non-player character's Negotiation skill.

ORATORY (SOCIAL)

The character is a skilled public speaker capable of spurring a crowd to action or calming an angry mob.

Untrained Oratory: Characters untrained in Oratory do not have the ability to sway large groups of people with their words. Oratory cannot be used untrained.

Oratory Rolls: When your character makes an oratory attempt, you make a roll using a stat determined by the Game Master and add your character's Oratory level. The following chart offers a sample range of target numbers.

TARGET NUMBER	CROWD DYNAMIC
11 +	Convincing a crowd in a highly charged emotional state to do something it wants to do
14+	Convincing an indifferent crowd to do something it wants to do
17 +	Convincing an indifferent crowd to do something it isn't likely to do
21 +	Convincing a crowd in a highly charged emotional state to do something it isn't likely to do

The Game Master can apply any number of modifiers to the oratory roll. If there are other speakers attempting to pull the crowd in a different direction, the roll is harder. If the crowd in on the verge of acting, and just needs a few words of encouragement, the roll is easier.

Results of failing an Oratory roll depend on what the character was attempting to accomplish. The Game Master should determine an outcome that reflects the situation the crowd and the players are in. This could result in a panicking crowd becoming a violent mob or a crowd peacefully dispersing instead of rising up in revolt.

Assisted Oratory Rolls: Typically, Oratory rolls cannot be assisted. At the Game Master's discretion, up to one additional character trained in Oratory can assist in an Oratory skill roll by warming up the crowd or yelling affirmation. This grants a flat +1 bonus to the character making the Oratory skill roll. The words of the speaker carry the day.

Game Master Notes: Oratory isn't magic, and can't force people to do something that they absolutely don't want to do. If the player is standing on a street corner trying to incite rebellion in an area where few people disagree with the government, it should be impossible to succeed.

PICKPOCKET (AGILITY)

The character has nimble fingers and can relieve others of their personal belongs without their notice.

Untrained Pickpocket: Without the proper understanding and practice, attempting to lift a character's weapon or purse is likely to get the would-be pickpocket arrested or worse. Pickpocket cannot be used untrained.

Pickpocket Rolls: When a character attempts to relieve someone else of his belongings, make an AGL+ Pickpocket roll against a target number set by the Game Master to determine if the roll is a success. The following table can offer some guidelines for setting Pickpocket target numbers.

TARGET NUMBER	SITUATION
Subject's PER + 6	A crowded area where the mark frequently brushes against other passers by
Subject's PER + 9	A moderately populated area where the mark is unaware of the pickpocket's presence
Subject's PER + 12	A moderately populated area where the mark is aware of the pickpocket's presence

If a character is attempting to steal a relatively large item from the subject increase the target number by up to 3 depending on the size of the item. Likewise, if the subject of the Pickpocket roll has taken specific precautions to safe guard his possessions, such as tying or chaining the goods to himself or by employing false pockets, the target number could be increased. By the same token, the Pickpocket target number could be lowered if the mark is particularly distracted, inebriated, or otherwise inattentive.

Failure doesn't always have to mean that the attempt to pickpocket has failed, but it does means the thief was caught in the act. If the character fails a pickpocket roll, he can make a second roll against the same target number to determine if he managed to snatch the item anyway.

The reaction of the character who discovers he is being pickpocketed on a failed roll is entirely up to the Game Master. An elderly man might call out to the town watch, but a vigorous young man might give chase.

Assisted Pickpocket Rolls: One additional character trained in Pickpocket can assist in a Pickpocket skill roll by distracting the mark or bumping into him at an opportune time. The character with the higher Pickpocket modifier (AGL + Pickpocket level) makes the roll and adds 1 to the result of the die roll for each of his assistant's levels in Pickpocket.

Game Master Notes: Pickpocket can be a very useful skill, but the Game Master should be careful to not allow a player to depend on it too much. If a character continually returns to the same market square every time he needs an item, citizens should begin taking precautions against pickpocketing. If the crime spree continues, eventually the city watch will be called in to investigate.

character gains +2 to his roll. The character can also take additional time researching the subject. Add +1 to the roll for every two additional hours he spends, up to a limit of ten additional hours. If the library is incomplete or poorly organized the character might suffer a –1 to –5 penalty on this roll.

Assisted Research Rolls: When working as a team to research something, the players must select one character to lead the research efforts. Each character makes his own INT + Research roll. For each character who had a result of 15 or higher, add 1 to the result of the character who led the research team.

Game Master Notes: Characters researching an archive are limited in what they can learn by what is contained within an archive. To find a particularly comprehensive archive pertaining to an obscure subject, characters might have to travel to distant localities. And even then, if particular knowledge has been lost, purged, or hidden, they might not find what they seek.

RESEARCH (INTELLECT)

Given access to the proper archive a character with the research skill can find any available information.

Untrained Research: Characters untrained in Research can attempt Research skill rolls normally.

Research Rolls: A character with access to a library, set of records, or other trove of knowledge can research a subject pertaining to the information contained within the archive.

To use this skill, first declare what subject the character is researching. The character must then spend at least four hours researching the archive, after which his player can make an INT + Research roll and consult the following table.

RESULT	INFORMATION DISCOVERED
10 or less	Common knowledge pertaining to the subject
11 to 13	Common knowledge pertaining to the subject and one additional relevant piece of information
14 to 16	All but the most obscure knowledge pertaining to the subject
17 or more	Every detail knowledge pertaining to the subject covered by the library

A number of additional modifiers can be applied to this roll. If the archive the character is researching is particularly extensive, such as the library at the Corvis University, the

RIDING (AGILITY, GENERAL SKILL)

The character is a skilled rider capable of controlling his mount with unparalleled ease. In dangerous situations like the heat of battle, a trained rider's horse is a deadly weapon rather than a terrified beast as prone to injure its master as its enemies. A character does not need to make a skill roll to use this skill unless he wishes to make particularly dangerous maneuver or needs to avoid being thrown from his mount.

Untrained Riding: Characters untrained in Riding can make Riding rolls normally.

Riding Rolls: When a character attempts a particular stunt with a mount, make an AGL + Riding roll against a target number set by the Game Master to determine if the roll is a success. The following table offers some guidelines for Riding target numbers.

TARGET NUMBER	SITUATION
11	Calming a startled horse
11	Avoid being thrown from a startled or injured mount
13 +	Avoiding an accident while riding at high speeds across treacherous terrain
14	Avoid being thrown from an incapacitated mount
15 +	Performing a particularly dangerous stunt

The GM should determine what modifiers affect the roll. The following chart offers sample target number modifiers.

RESULT MODIFIER	SITUATION
−1 to −3	The character is holding onto something in addition to the reins
−2	The mount is or skittish or excited
−3	The mount has not been broken in
−3	The mount does not have tack

Assisted Riding Rolls: Riding rolls cannot be assisted. Each individual character must control his own mount.

Game Master Notes: Riding rolls should be called for only when the situation is dangerous, and failure should matter. For example, if a player wants to ride his horse onto a river ferry, he doesn't need to make a roll. If that same character is trying to jump his horse onto a ferry that has already left the dock, there is a definite chance of failing the jump and falling into the river.

ROPE USE (AGILITY)

The character understands the proper uses of various knots, and how to subdue others by tying them up.

Untrained Rope Use: Characters untrained in Rope Use can make Rope Use rolls normally.

Rope Use Rolls: When a character ties a knot that no one will be trying to escape from, such as for securing rigging before repelling down a cliff, no roll is necessary. When a character puts his skills to use to tie up a subject, the character must make an AGL + Rope Use roll. The total for this roll is the target number the subject uses if he attempts to escape from his bonds (see "Escape Artist," p. 179).

The following table offers some common modifiers to this roll.

ROLL MODIFIER	TECHNIQUE USED
0	Subject's hands bound by rope
+2	Subject's hands tied behind his back
+2	Subject's hands and feet bound by rope
+3	Subject hog-tied
−2	Character rushed the job to tie up the subject

Assisted Rope Use Rolls: Most Rope Use skill rolls are made by individuals but some situations, such as tying up a large animal, do allow for assisted rope use. When working as a team to tie up a captive, the players must select one character to lead the efforts. Each character makes his own AGL + Rope Use roll. For each character who had a result of 15 or higher, add 1 to the subject's Escape Artist target number.

Game Master Notes: Rope Use alone might not be enough to subdue some captives. If a character doesn't search his subject first, he could miss the fact that the subject has a knife in his boot that could be used to cut the ropes when no one is looking.

SAILING (INTELLECT OR STRENGTH)

The character understands the ins and outs of operating a ship. The character does not need to make a skill roll unless the weather is dangerous, he needs to avoid an accidental collision, or is otherwise performing a hazardous maneuver.

Untrained Sailing: Without the proper strength, skill, and understanding, a character is as likely to hinder any sailing efforts as to help them. Sailing cannot be used untrained.

Sailing Rolls: When a character needs to perform a difficult maneuver aboard ship, make a STR or INT (whichever is lower) + Sailing roll against a target number set by the Game Master to determine if the roll is a success. The following table offers some guidelines for Sailing target numbers.

TARGET NUMBER	SITUATION
13 +	Turning quickly or steering past an obstacle (reef, shipwreck, dangerous rocks, or other obstacle) at a high rate of speed without hitting it
15 +	Avoiding getting lost in a powerful storm
17 +	Truly daring and dangerous stunt

The Game Master should determine what modifiers affect the roll. The following chart offers sample target number modifiers.

RESULT MODIFIER	SITUATION
−1 to −3	Sailing in bad weather
−2 to −4	Ship is damaged

Assisted Sailing Rolls: When working as a team to sail a boat or ship, the players must select one character to captain their efforts. For each character trained in Sailing (including any non-player sailors), add 1 to the captain's result.

Note that many ships are impossible to sail successfully without a crew.

Game Master Notes: If the character is trying to out-sail an opponent, for example by lining up the ships to give his cannons a better shot, a contested roll should be used.

The results of a failed Sailing roll should match the situation, but the outcome can be variable. A failed roll to furl the sails during a storm can result in serious damage to the mast, or the ship might be blown miles off course.

SEDUCTION (SOCIAL)

Seduction is the ability to foster romantic attachment in another sexually compatible individual. A character skilled in the seductive arts can use such romantic entanglements to his advantage for information, wealth, or political favor.

Untrained Seduction: Seduction is an art that must be cultivated. While anyone can flirt, turning infatuation to gain is a skill. Seduction cannot be used untrained.

Seduction Rolls: When your character makes a seduction attempt, make a roll using a stat determined by the Game Master and add your character's Seduction level. The stat used for the Seduction roll should reflect the method of seduction employed. If the character is depending on physical qualities, PHY could be the most appropriate skill. If he is employing poetry to woo his target, INT is more appropriate.

The target number is determined by the difference between the selected stat + Seduction level of the two parties.

TARGET NUMBER	SITUATION
11	Target's stat + Seduction total is lower by 5 or more than that of the intimidating character
13	Target's stat + Seduction total is lower by 3 or more than that of the intimidating character
15	Target's stat + Seduction total is equal to or lower than that of the intimidating character
17	Target's stat + Seduction total is higher than that of the intimidating character
19+	Target's stat + Seduction total is higher by 3 or more than that of the intimidating character

The Game Master should modify this roll according to the circumstances at hand. If the subject of the seduction is attracted to the seducing character, the target number could be reduced by 1 to 3 at the Game Master's discretion. If the target is chaste or faithful to another, the target number should be increased by 2 or more. If the subject of the seduction has a lot to lose from an entanglement with the seducing character, increase the target number by an additional +2. If the subject is not attracted to the character, the target number could be increased by an additional +1 to +3. Some targets are simply impossible to seduce.

If a seduction roll fails, the Game Master should come up with an appropriate response.

If the seducer succeeds in his attempts, he can form an intimate relationship with the target of his advances, who is favorably disposed to him. Succeeding in leveraging his paramour's affections for more concrete gains can require fostering their relationship further, additional Seduction rolls, or a change in tactics.

Assisted Seduction Rolls: One additional character trained in Seduction can assist in a Seduction skill roll by acting as the other character's wingman. The character with the higher sexual compatibility (determined by the Game Master) makes the roll and adds 1 to the result of the die roll for each of his assistant's levels in Seduction.

Game Master Notes: Though the subject of the seducer's advances is favorably disposed to him in the short term, how these feelings hold up over time depends entirely on how the seduced character is treated. If the character is left feeling used or abandoned, short-term infatuation can easily turn to long-term hatred and disgust.

Seduction should be limited to situations where it is appropriate. For example, when trying to resolve an altercation with a band of farrow, seduction is not really an option.

SNEAK (AGILITY)

The Sneak skill measures how capable a character is at hiding and moving undetected. It can apply to many situations, whether trying to sneak past a sleeping troll or silently moving into striking range of a target.

Untrained Sneak: Characters untrained in Sneak can make Sneak rolls normally.

Sneak Rolls: Any time a character attempts to hide, move silently, or follow another creature without being detected, the Game Master should make an AGL + Sneak roll for the character.

Do not share the Sneak roll result with the character. Until the character ceases using Sneak, this is his passive number for detection. Any time a character using the Sneak skill enters the sensory range of another character, make a PER + Detection roll for the other character. If the detecting character beats the hidden character's Sneak roll, his presence is detected. Whether he is seen, heard, or noticed by another means depends on the circumstances in which the character was detected. It the detecting character fails to beat the sneaking character's roll, he is not detected.

If a character specifically uses his Detection skill in an attempt to spot a sneaking character in his presence, the two character make contested PER + Detection and AGL + Sneak rolls. If the detecting character wins, the sneaking character is spotted. If the sneaking character wins, he remains undetected and his AGL + Sneak roll total becomes his new passive number for detection.

MODIFIER	SITUATION
+ 1 to + 3	The detecting character is distracted
+ 2	The area is dimly lit
+ 5	The area is in complete darkness
+ 2	The area is noisy
−3	The sneaking character's armor has a −1 DEF modifier
−5	The sneaking character's armor has a −2 DEF modifier
−1 to −3	The sneaking character is carrying an activated piece of mechanika (depending on the brightness of the object or its obvious effect)

The use of the Sneak skill is dependent on situations in which the character can remain obfuscated. If he enters a brightly lit room clearly in view of a watchman, he is detected without a roll.

Various factors can be a help or a hindrance to a sneaking. The following chart offers some example modifiers that can be applied to either a character's Sneak roll or to his passive number for detection.

Assisted Sneak Rolls: Sneak rolls cannot be assisted, except by creating a distraction. Each individual character must sneak around the cities of western Immoren on his own.

Game Master Notes: This skill does not make someone invisible. If the character is trying to hide out in the open or in a surrounding that he stands out in, he is spotted. The Game Master should make it clear to the characters where sneaking is possible, and where it has no application.

STREETWISE (PERCEPTION)

The character understands the streets and the criminal underworld. He can find markets for stolen or illicit goods, set up meets, and steer clear of trouble and unwanted attention.

Untrained Streetwise: Without the proper background and insight, attempting to reach out to shady characters or make back-room deals is extremely dangerous. Characters cannot make untrained Streetwise skill rolls.

Streetwise Rolls: Streetwise can be used for reaching out to underworld contacts, for locating or selling stolen or illicit goods.

When a character attempts to arrange a meeting with underworld contacts or track down a market for item (buying or selling), make a PER + Streetwise roll against a target number set by the Game Master to determine if the roll is a success.

The following chart offers a sample range of target numbers.

TARGET NUMBER	ACTION
11	Escape casual notice on the streets or set up a meeting with a low ranking criminal the character does not personally know
13	Steer clear of criminals on the prowl for victims in a bad neighborhood
13 to 15	Find a market for a common illicit item or setting up a meeting with a mid-level criminal the character does not personally know
16 to 18	Find a market for an uncommon illicit item.
16 +	The sneaking character's armor has a −1 DEF modifier
19 +	Find a market for an extremely rare illicit item.

The Game Master can assign modifiers to the roll based on a number of factors including the activity of the city watch, the type of goods the character is seeking or is trying to sell, the character's standing with the local underworld elements, the character's appearance, how subtle or high profile the character is, and the success of any bribes the character has paid out to get what he wants.

Assisted Streetwise Rolls: When working as a team to pool contacts or seek out markets, the players must select one character to lead the effort. Each character makes his own PER + Streetwise roll. For each character who had a result of 13 or higher, add 1 to the result of the leader's roll.

Game Master Notes: The Streetwise roll to meet with an underworld contact or find a market for an item is only the beginning of the process. Once a character has arranged the meeting, it might be resolved with the Deception or Bribery skills. After the buyer is found for a stolen item, Negotiation could be used to conduct the transaction.

Some Streetwise rolls should be impossible. A group of adventurers new to town should not be able to easily set up a meeting with the boss of a major criminal organization without first jumping through some hoops.

SURVIVAL (PERCEPTION)

The character is versed in building shelter, keeping warm, foraging for food, and sustaining life in the wilds.

Untrained Survival: Characters untrained in Survival can sustain life in harsh conditions for limited periods of time. Instead of making Survival rolls, an untrained character uses the first row of the table below for the given environment.

Survival Rolls: Characters with one or more levels in Survival can use the skill while away from the creature comforts afforded by urban life in the Iron Kingdoms

When a character needs to depend on his survival skills, make a PER + Survival roll against a target number set by the Game Master and use the following chart to determine the degree of success.

ROLL RESULT	PLAINS / HILLS / FOREST / RIVERBANK	SWAMP / DESERT / MOUNTAINS / ISLAND	STORMLANDS / SHIP WRECKAGE
8 or less	3 days	1 day	4 hours
9–10	1 week	3 days	1 day
10–12	2 week	1 week	3 days
13–14	1 month	2 weeks	1 week
15–16	2 months	1 month	2 weeks
17–18	Indefinitely	2 months	1 month
19–20	Indefinitely	Indefinitely	2 months
21 +	Indefinitely	Indefinitely	Indefinitely

A character can also attempt to provide for other characters. When providing for one additional character, decrease the roll result by one row. When providing for a party of up to six individuals, decrease the roll result by two rows.

Assisted Survival Rolls: Any number of additional characters trained in Survival can assist in a Survival skill roll. The character with the highest Survival modifier (PER + Survival level) makes the roll and adds 1 to the result of the die roll for each of his assistants' levels in Survival. Remember to modify the result to account for the number of members the Survival roll encompasses.

Game Master Notes: Non-player characters might be trained to survive in wilder locales but rarely need to make such rolls.

Non-player characters well suited for wilderness survival should be assigned at least one level in Survival while only a true paragon survivalist should have Survival 4.

SWIMMING (STRENGTH, GENERAL SKILL)

The character is a skilled swimmer comfortable with being in the water.

Untrained Swimming: Characters untrained in Swimming can make Swimming checks normally.

Swimming Rolls: To determine the speed a character can swim, make a STR + Swimming roll and consult the following chart.

ROLL RESULT	RESULT
8 or less	The character cannot move and suffers d3 damage points from choking
9 to 10	The character can move six feet (1˝)
11 to 13	The character can move up to half his SPD
14 or more	The character can move at full SPD

The Game Master can apply modifiers to the character's Swimming roll based on the conditions the character is swimming in. The following chart offers sample target number modifiers.

RESULT MODIFIER	SITUATION
+1	The character is holding onto something buoyant
−1 to −3	The water is rough (stormy sea, fast currents, and so on)
−2	The character's armor has a −1 DEF modifier
−4	The character's armor has a −2 DEF modifier

Assisted Swimming Rolls: Swimming rolls cannot be assisted. Each individual character must sink or swim on his own.

Game Master Notes: The Game Master should consider the kinds of characters his party has built when presenting situations to them. It isn't very heroic for a group of knights in full plate mail to drown in a swift-flowing stream. If a character not well suited to swimming attempts it, failure should be a real danger.

TRACKING (PERCEPTION)

The character understands how to follow a quarry through the wilderness by the signs left by its passage. When a trail runs cold, he knows the steps to take to reacquire the quarry and continue the hunt.

Untrained Tracking: A character without the Tracking skill can follow obvious paths and visual clues, like a warjack's swath of destruction, clear tracks in fresh snow, or trails of fresh blood. Identifying tracks and tracking quarry overland are beyond the abilities of an unskilled tracker.

Tracking Rolls: When a character tracks his quarry, make a PER + Tracking roll against a target number set by the Game Master to determine if the roll is a success.

The Game Master should have a character using the Tracking skill make periodic rolls to ensure he does not lose the trail. These should be made at least once every twenty minutes and any time tracking conditions worsen, such as when the tracker's quarry crosses a river, enters an area of heavy traffic, or leaves a region of very easy tracking such as fresh snow.

The following table offers some guidelines for Tracking target numbers.

TARGET NUMBER	SITUATION
No roll necessary	Obvious trails of smeared blood, the tracks of a warjack, or heavy tracks in fresh snow—any trail an unskilled tracker could follow
11	Neat prints of a heavy animal, such as a bear or horse, over seldom traversed territory
13	Following fresh tracks of a man-sized or lighter animal over reasonably clear terrain
15 +	Following a old tracks over inhospitable terrain
20 +	Tracking a fugitive through busy city streets be tracks alone. This task should be all but impossible unless the prey is leaving some sort of unique trail that can be followed.

The Game Master should determine what modifiers affect the roll. Tracking requires careful attention to detail. A tracker moves very slowly while following all but the most difficult terrain. If a character is attempting to move quickly overland while using this skill, the Game Master should give him a substantial penalty on his roll.

The following chart offers sample target number modifiers.

RESULT MODIFIER	CONDITIONS
−1 to Impossible	The trail crosses a body of water
−1 to Impossible	The trail is washed out or obscured by the weather (heavy rain, snowstorm, and the like)
+1	The quarry has a limp or other distinguishing characteristic that makes its tracks stand out from other tracks
+1 to +3	The quarry is injured and bleeding
+1	The quarry is carrying something heavy

Identifying Tracks: A character with the Tracking skill can also identify tracks on sight. Heavy and obvious tracks, like those of a warjack, shoed horse, booted human, or wagon can be identified without a die roll. More common animal tracks can be identified with a successful PER + Tracking roll against a target number of 11. Less common or distinct tracks can be much more difficult to identify.

The character can also study tracks to learn details about the creature that made them. He can determine if the animal was moving particularly slowly, whether it is injured, if it has a heavy load, and so on. The Game Master should set a target number for the character's roll based on how old the tracks are, how familiar the character is with the animal that made them, and the specific information he is seeking.

Assisted Tracking Rolls: When working as a team to track their prey, the players must select one character to lead the tracking efforts. Each character makes his own PER + Tracking roll. For each character who has a result of 15 or higher, add 1 to the result of the character who led the tracking team.

Game Master Notes: Certain creatures make no effort to conceal their trails, while intelligent beings running to a hideout might take convoluted paths to throw off a tracker. With a high enough roll, a character can realize that the trail he is following is too obvious and could lead to a trap.

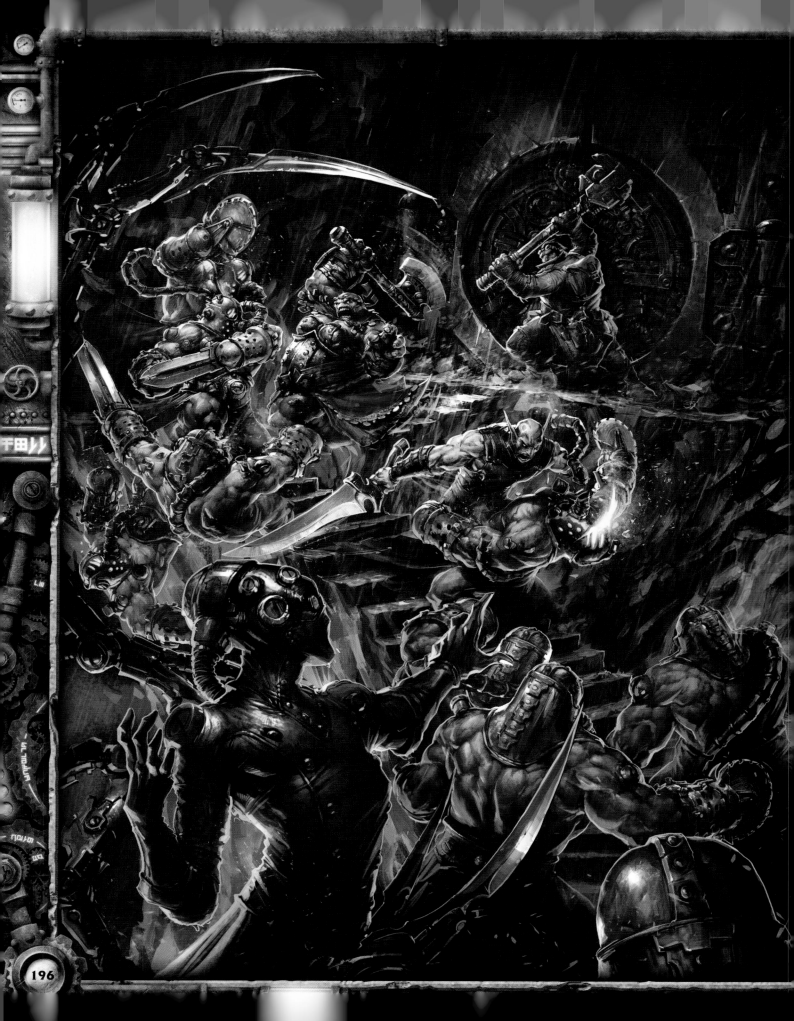

THE GAME

The rules for playing the *Iron Kingdoms Full Metal Fantasy Roleplaying Game* have been designed to be fast paced and action packed. There is a good deal of material presented here, but the core mechanics remain simple, easy to learn, and fun!

Before digging into the mechanics, it's important to cover a few basic concepts underlying everything in the game.

GAME MASTER FIAT

The rules provide guidelines for play. When a situation arises during play that is not covered by the rules, it is up to the Game Master to decide on the outcome. Because the role of the Game Master is to adjudicate the rules during the game, he is the ultimate authority on their interpretation.

MEASUREMENTS

Measurements in the *Iron Kingdoms Full Metal Fantasy Roleplaying Game* are listed in feet and in inches. Inches are used when playing out a battle on the tabletop using miniatures (see "Combat," p. 200). One inch on the tabletop equals six feet in scale.

CHARACTER CLASSIFICATIONS

Unless stated otherwise, all characters are considered to be **living**. Undead characters and steamjacks are not living characters.

DIE ROLLS

During the course of playing the game, you roll dice to determine the outcome of situations in which your character finds himself. Most often, when your character attempts an action for which the Game Master has determined there is a chance of failure, such as repairing a damaged warjack, scaling a sheer cliff face, or making an attack, you roll dice to determine the outcome of the action. You then compare the result of the roll to the target number set by the Game Master to see if the roll is successful.

The *Iron Kingdoms Full Metal Fantasy Roleplaying Game* uses six-sided dice, abbreviated d6, to determine the success of actions and to determine the amount of damage inflicted by attacks. Most rolls, such as skill rolls and damage rolls, require rolling two dice (abbreviated 2d6). Other events typically require rolling from one to four dice. Die rolls often have modifiers, which are expressed as + or – some quantity after the die roll notation. For example, melee attack rolls are described as "2d6 + PRW + military skill + weapon attack modifier." This means "roll two six-sided dice and add the attacking character's Prowess stat and the character's applicable military skill as well as the weapon's attack modifier to the result."

Some rules call for a character's stat or a die roll to be divided in half. For distance measurements, use the actual result after dividing the number in question. For everything else, always round a fractional result to the next highest whole number.

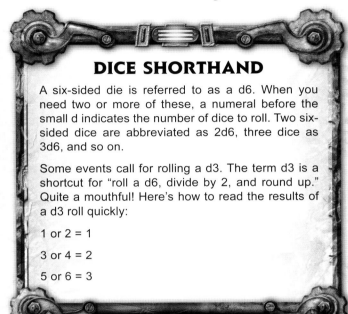

DICE SHORTHAND

A six-sided die is referred to as a d6. When you need two or more of these, a numeral before the small d indicates the number of dice to roll. Two six-sided dice are abbreviated as 2d6, three dice as 3d6, and so on.

Some events call for rolling a d3. The term d3 is a shortcut for "roll a d6, divide by 2, and round up." Quite a mouthful! Here's how to read the results of a d3 roll quickly:

1 or 2 = 1

3 or 4 = 2

5 or 6 = 3

ADDITIONAL DICE AND BOOSTED ROLLS

Sometimes a special ability or circumstance allows a character to roll an additional die. An additional die is a die added to the number of dice a character would ordinarily roll. For example, when a character makes a melee attack roll, he rolls 2d6 and adds his Prowess stat + his skill with the weapon and the weapon's attack modifier. If the character gains an additional die on this attack, he would roll 3d6 and add his PRW + skill with the weapon and the weapon's attack modifier.

A die roll can include multiple additional dice as long as each additional die comes from a different rule or ability.

Some effects grant characters boosted attack or damage rolls. Add one extra die to a boosted roll. Boosting must be declared before rolling any dice for the roll. Each skill, attack, or damage roll can be boosted only once, but a character can boost multiple rolls during his turn. When an attack affects several characters, the attack and damage rolls against each individual character must be boosted separately.

Example: A character who hits a target with a charge attack gains a boosted damage roll, meaning he adds an extra die to his damage roll. Because this roll is boosted, the character cannot boost the damage roll again to gain two extra dice on the roll (even if he has an ability that allows him to boost the roll). He can still take advantage of other circumstances that grant a non-boosted additional die.

CONTESTED ROLLS

If a character is attempting a task that another character directly and actively opposes, both characters make contested rolls. For example, to resolve two characters arm wrestling, they would make contested rolls. One character picking the pocket of another is not a contested roll.

Contested rolls do not have target numbers. Instead, each character makes a skill roll. The character with the highest total succeeds. If both characters have the same result, the roll is a draw and neither succeeds.

RULE PRIORITY

Unless otherwise specified, multiple instances of the same named effect on a character are not cumulative. If a character would be affected by a second instance of an effect, the second instance is not applied and does not change anything about the first instance, including its expiration. If the effect has a duration, this means it expires when the first applied effect expires. Multiple instances of the same named effect are not cumulative even when the effect comes from different sources. Furthermore, benefits and penalties with the same name coming from different sources overlap and are not cumulative.

Example: Simon's character casts the spell Ice Shield on Shona's character to grant her a +2 bonus on her ARM. If Ed's character also casts Ice Shield on Shona's character, she does not benefit from +4 to her ARM. She gets a bonus of +2.

On the other hand, effects, benefits, and penalties from differently named sources *are* cumulative with each other, even if they happen to apply the same modifier to a character.

Example: Brent's character casts Ice Shield on Will's steamjack to grant it a +2 bonus to its ARM. Darla then casts Fail Safe on Will's steamjack to grant it an additional +2 bonus to its ARM. Since the same effect comes from two sources with different names, their effects are cumulative. Will's steamjack now has a total bonus of +4 ARM.

Situations can occur where two special rules conflict. Use the following guidelines, in order, to resolve special rules interactions.

- If one rule specifically states its interaction with the other rule, follow it.
- Special rules stating that something "cannot" happen override rules stating that the same thing "can" or "must" happen. (Rules directing or describing actions or circumstances are treated as if they used "must." Examples include "Gain an additional die," "Knocked down characters stand up," and "This character gains cover.")

Example: Will's character has a rule stating he cannot be knocked down, but he is affected by something that states he is knocked down. Because the rules make no specific mention of each other, follow the second guideline above. Will's character is not knocked down.

SKILL RESOLUTION ROLLS

When a character uses a skill to perform an action that the Game Master determines has a reasonable chance of failure, the character must make a skill roll. To make a skill roll, roll 2d6 and add the result to a related stat and the level of the skill being used.

Skill Roll = 2d6 + Stat + Skill Level

When you have the result of the roll, compare it to the target number set by the Game Master. If the total is equal to or higher than the target number, the skill action succeeds. If it is less than the target number, the skill attempt fails.

EXAMPLE: *John's character uses his Detection skill to attempt to find a hidden enemy. Detection is a Perception skill, and the character has a PER of 4. His Detection skill level is 2. Therefore he adds 6 to the roll of two dice. John rolls two six-sided dice and gets an 8. He adds 6 to that for a total result of 14. The Game Master determined that the roll would have to be at least 13 to be successful, so the character successfully locates the enemy hiding in the shadows.*

If the skill can be used untrained, a character does not need to have levels in the skill in order to attempt to use it, but training in the skill grants a bonus on the roll and therefore makes success more likely. Some skills cannot be used untrained.

If the rules do not explicitly state what stats and skills are used for a particular action, the Game Master decides.

TARGET NUMBERS

If the rules do not define a target number for an action that a player wishes his character to perform, the Game Master sets the target number. The target number should be a reflection on the difficulty of the action being attempted. Very simple actions, in which there is little chance of failure, should succeed automatically. Actions with a moderate chance of failure should have a target number of 10–12. Complex actions should have a target number of 13–15, while truly difficult actions with a likely chance of failure could require a roll against 16 or more. There is no roll for actions the Game Master deems impossible. Such actions certainly end in failure.

A roll of all 1s on the dice is an automatic failure. A roll of all 6s on the dice is an automatic success unless you are rolling only one die. Some rolls also have critical effects that are triggered when a roll succeeds and any two dice used in the roll show the same number.

SETTING TARGET NUMBERS

TARGET NUMBER	TASK DIFFICULTY
No roll, automatic success	Simple
10–12	Moderate
13–15	Complex
16+	Difficult
No roll, automatic failure	Impossible

ATTRIBUTE RESOLUTION ROLLS

When a character attempts an action for which there is no applicable skill and the Game Master wants to use a roll to determine its success, the player makes an attribute roll. These function just like skill rolls except there is no skill value added to the roll. The Game Master determines the appropriate stat to use, and the player rolls 2d6, adds the stat, and compares it to the target difficulty number.

Below are some basic actions characters might attempt that would be governed by attribute rolls.

PHYSIQUE ROLLS

Physique rolls determine if a character resists the effects of a poison or avoids contracting a disease. The target difficulty should be based on the potency of the poison or the virility of the contagion. Note that the potency of poisons or contagions does not necessarily correlate to their effects. A disease that is fairly easy to resist can have extremely debilitating symptoms, while a potent poison might knock someone unconscious.

TARGET NUMBER	POISON AND DISEASE
11	Weak poison or disease
13	Typical poison or disease
16	Potent poison or virulent contagion
20	Extremely potent poison or virulent contagion

SPEED ROLLS

The most common use for Speed rolls is during a chase. When determining if a character can catch up to someone he is chasing, the target difficulty equals the fleeing character's SPD + 7.

STRENGTH ROLLS

Strength rolls are most commonly used when a character attempts to lift a heavy object. The following chart details how much a character can lift or carry. Dead Lift is how much weight a character can lift at one time if he does not intend to move with it. Carry is how much weight a character can comfortably carry for a long distance

CHARACTER'S SIZE	DEAD LIFT	CARRY
Small base – small stature	25 lb per point of Strength	12 lbs per point of Strength
Small base	50 lbs per point of Strength	20 lbs per point of Strength
Medium base	75 lbs per point of Strength	25 lbs per point of Strength
Medium base – huge stature	100 lbs per point of Strength	30 lbs per point of Strength
Large base	100 lbs per point of Strength	30 lbs per point of Strength

If a character attempts to dead lift a weight lower than his Dead Lift maximum, he does not need to make a STR roll; success is automatic. If a character attempts to lift a weight equal or greater than his Dead Lift maximum, he must succeed on a STR roll to lift the weight. The target number for the roll starts at 12 and is increased by 2 for every point of Strength it would require to equal the Dead Lift value of the weight.

Carrying a weight is considerably different from simply lifting it. The weight a character can carry over a long distance includes armor, weapons, and supplies. It is up to the Game Master to determine when the weight of objects carried factors into a game.

When characters attempt to lift large objects, the Game Master might permit multiple characters to work together. With sufficient added lifting capacity of additional characters, the target number of the Strength roll decreases, possibly even becoming an automatic success. If it is not an automatic success, the character with the highest STR makes the roll against the target number.

AGILITY ROLLS

Agility measures a character's nimbleness, balance, and reflexes, so Agility rolls can be used to determine if a character is quick enough to avoid a trap as it triggers or safely traverse the trusses in a building's roof. Feats of balance or reflexes vary dramatically in difficulty, but the target number guidelines above serve as a good starting point for a Game Master selecting an appropriate Agility roll target difficulty.

POISE ROLLS

Generally Poise rolls are made only when the character makes a ranged attack.

PROWESS ROLLS

Generally Prowess rolls are made only when the character makes a melee attack or a thrown weapon attack.

INTELLECT ROLLS

Use Intellect rolls to test a character's wits, knowledge, and deduction. Most Intellect rolls are covered by using skills. Solving most riddles falls under Cryptography since they are typically linguistic or numerical puzzles, and figuring out how to move an inert steamjack uses Mechanikal Engineering. For a wit-, knowledge-, or deduction-based situation that does not reasonably fall into any skill category, use an Intellect roll and use the target number guidelines to help set the difficulty.

When attempting to solve some problems or riddles, the Game Master might permit multiple characters to work together. The Game Master should adjust the target number to take into account the added brainpower of the participants, and then the character with the highest INT makes the roll against the target number.

ARCANE ROLLS

Generally Arcane rolls are made only when the character makes a magic attack.

PERCEPTION ROLLS

Use Perception rolls to test a character's attention to detail. Like Intellect rolls, many Perception rolls fall into defined skill categories. Putting clues together to progress an investigation is part of Forensic Science, for example, whereas noticing a predator's prints in the woods falls under Tracking, and noticing that a document is written on the wrong kind of paper to be a letter of marque is Detection. For a situation dealing with attention to detail that does not reasonably fall into any skill category, ask for a Perception roll and use the target numbers guidelines to help set the difficulty.

COMBAT

The action of the game takes place in the minds of the Game Master and the players until the start of combat, at which time play moves to the tabletop where player characters and their enemies are represented by 32 mm figures. The Game Master then draws or arranges the field on which the battle takes place, explains to the players what the battlefield represents, and places the models representing the characters, their allies, enemies, and any bystanders in the area. (See "Tools of the Trade," p. 339.)

Battles are conducted in a series of game rounds. During a game round, each character involved in the battle, including the player characters and their enemies, will take a turn. During his turn, a character can move and take one or more actions such as casting a spell, making an attack, drinking a potion, reloading a firearm, or repairing a warjack. The players describe the actions taken by their characters and the Game Master describes the actions of non-player characters. Once all the characters involved in the combat have taken their turns, the current game round ends. Game rounds continue until the fighting stops, often with the player characters standing over their vanquished foes.

ENHANCING GAMEPLAY WITH MODELS

The *Iron Kingdoms Full Metal Fantasy Roleplaying Game* provides a rich and immersive experience right out of the book, but these rules are designed so that you can dramatically enhance the tactical sequences of your sessions with the use of models. We produce a wide range of models for our tabletop miniatures games WARMACHINE and HORDES, featuring hundreds of unique, high quality sculpts. These models are perfect for use in the *Iron Kingdoms Full Metal Fantasy Roleplaying Game*. We also produce several classic models from the original Iron Kingdoms miniatures line suitable for use with these rules.

BASE SIZE

The physical size and mass of a character is reflected by his model's base size. There are four circular base sizes, categorized by their diameter: small bases (30 mm), medium bases (40 mm), large bases (50 mm), and huge bases (120 mm). Generally speaking, most human-sized characters have small bases, larger creatures and light steamjacks have medium bases, and very large creatures and heavy steamjacks have large bases.

BASE SIZE BY RACE

Humans, dwarves, gobbers, Iosans, and Nyss are represented by small-based models. Ogrun and trollkin are represented as medium-based models. Mounted characters are represented by large-based models.

FACING

A character's facing in battle is determined by his model's shoulder orientation. The 180° arc in the direction its shoulders face defines the character's front arc; the opposite 180° defines his back arc. You can also make two small marks on either side of your character's model's base to indicate where the front arc ends and the back arc begins instead of relying on the positioning of its shoulder.

A character's front arc determines its perspective of the battlefield. A character typically directs his actions, determines line of sight, and makes attacks through this arc. Likewise, a character is usually more vulnerable to attacks from his back arc due to a lack of awareness in that direction.

LINE OF SIGHT

Many situations such as charging and making attacks require a character to have line of sight (LOS) to his intended target. Simply put, having line of sight means a character can see another character.

The Game Master decides which characters have line of sight to each other. He should begin each encounter by describing the terrain and how it affects line of sight.

MEASURING DISTANCES ON THE TABLETOP

Measurements on the tabletop are measured in inches, with each tabletop inch equating to six feet.

Though the Game Master can measure any distance on the table for any reason, players do not have this luxury. When a player makes a measurement during the game, he cannot measure past the maximum range of the attack, ability, spell, or effect for which he is measuring.

When measuring the distance from a model representing a character on the tabletop, measure from the edge of the base. Similarly, when measuring the distance to a character, measure up to, but not past, the edge of that character's base. Thus, a character is within a given distance when the nearest edge of its base is within that distance, or equivalently, when any part of its base is within the given distance. If two characters are exactly a certain distance apart, they are within that distance of each other.

A character is completely within a given distance when its entire base is within that distance. Equivalently, a character is completely within a given distance when the farthest edge of its base is within that distance.

If characters' bases overlap, they are within 0″ of each other.

When determining the effects of a spell or ability that affects characters within a specified distance of a character, the effect is a circular area extending out from the base of the model representing the character and including the area under his base. Unless the spell or ability notes otherwise, that character is not considered to be within the distance himself.

THE GAME ROUND

The "round" is an abstraction of a very small amount of in-game time that allows the chaos of multiple characters attempting different actions all occurring at relatively the same time to be broken up in a reasonable manner so an outcome can be determined.

Once a battle starts, it is fought in a series of rounds. During each round, every character has a turn in the initiative order. The character whose turn it is, or the **active character**, must end his turn before the next character can begin his turn. Once all the characters involved in the combat have taken their turns, the current game round ends and a new one begins. Game rounds continue until the player characters defeat their enemies, escape the battle, or are defeated.

DETERMINING INITIATIVE

At the start of a battle, each character rolls 2d6 and adds his Initiative plus any applicable bonuses.

Players roll initiative for their characters and the Game Master rolls for the initiative of non-player characters.

If two or more characters end up with the same initiative values, they should roll off to determine who goes first, second, and so on.

Once all initiative values for the battle have been determined and ties decided, the Game Master (or a designated player)

THE SURPRISE ROUND

It is possible for a character or a group of characters to attempt to approach their enemies to catch them unaware. Such ambushes take the form of surprise rounds in which characters can move and act until they draw the attention of the enemy, at which time the surprise round immediately ends and the battle truly starts. Surprise requires the consent of the Game Master because he determines the awareness of NPCs and determines when surprise is gained and lost.

If the Game Master determines that a character or group of characters has the potential to surprise their enemies, the characters attempting surprise roll initiative and take turns in initiative order, moving and making attacks. Attacks made by a surprising character gain the back strike bonus (p. 209).

Each time a character attempting surprise moves, the Game Master should determine whether the character has been seen, heard, or otherwise detected. This might require the characters being surprised to make Detection rolls, or the Game Master can either assume that due to the movement, a character is automatically spotted or that there is no chance of detection. If the character is spotted, the Game Master must determine whether spotting the character initiates combat, such as in the case of enemies on high alert, or whether the enemy is unaware of the danger presented by the character and ignores him.

Likewise, after every attack or other action taken by a surprising character, the Game Master must decide if the action raises alarm among the enemy and starts combat. For example, a loud gunshot is certain to draw the attention of the enemy, while an instantly fatal crossbow bolt to the throat of a scout on the fringe of a group of enemies might occur without detection.

If a surprise round ends without discovery, a new surprise round begins. Once the enemy recognizes the surprising characters as a threat, the surprise round ends and the battle begins. When the surprising characters are discovered, the active character's turn immediately ends once his current action or movement is resolved. If the active character was in the midst of charge, slam, or trample movement when detected, he can resolve any resulting charge, slam, or trample attacks before his turn ends.

When the battle begins, initiative is immediately rerolled for all characters participating in the battle, including the formerly surprising characters. Actions held by surprising characters are lost.

should list out the combat sequence by character, from highest value rolled to lowest. A character's initiative does not change during a battle unless he holds his activation (see below). Characters take turns in this combat sequence for the duration of the battle. If a new character joins the battle, his initiative is rolled at the start of the next round, and he is inserted into the combat sequence at the appropriate time.

STEAMJACKS AND INITIATIVE

A steamjack activates during its controller's turn during the Activation Phase (see below). The steamjack can move and take its action either before or after its controller moves and takes his action.

HELD ACTIVATION

Instead of acting in initiative order, a character can choose to hold his activation to react to the round as it unfolds. A character choosing to hold his activation must still resolve the Maintenance and Control Phases (see below) of his turn in initiative order that round. Only the Activation Phase of his turn is delayed.

Effects that expire at the start of the character's turn still expire at the start of his turn, so effects' durations are not affected by held activations.

A character holding his activation can choose to take his turn after any other character's activation. If a character who is controlling steamjacks holds his activation, the steamjacks he controls must also wait to move and take their actions.

After a character has used his held activation, his initiative is moved to that position in the initiative order during following rounds.

If a character does not resolve his Activation Phase before it is his turn to activate again during the round after he held his activation, his initiative remains unchanged, but he has now effectively skipped one turn of activation.

EXAMPLE: *Cody's character is fourth in initiative order, and he is currently suffering from the Fire continuous effect. Cody wants to hold his activation until after Lyle casts Earthquake in an attempt to knock all the opponents down. Lyle is fifth in initiative order. When Cody's turn begins he rolls for his continuous effect during his Maintenance Phase. It does not expire, so his character takes a POW 12 damage roll. He then holds the activation portion of his turn. After Lyle has completed his turn, Cody performs his Activation Phase. He does not roll for the fire again since it was already resolved in his Maintenance Phase this round. The Game Master then moves Cody's name to the spot after Lyle in the initiative order. Cody now goes after Lyle in all following rounds. Cody can hold his activation again later in the encounter to move further down the initiative order, or Lyle could hold his activation in a future round until right after Cody, effectively reversing their activation order to the previous sequence.*

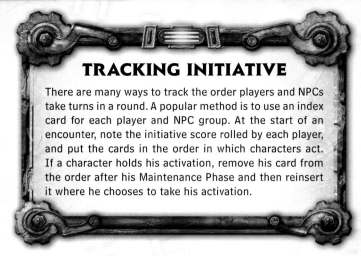

TRACKING INITIATIVE

There are many ways to track the order players and NPCs take turns in a round. A popular method is to use an index card for each player and NPC group. At the start of an encounter, note the initiative score rolled by each player, and put the cards in the order in which characters act. If a character holds his activation, remove his card from the order after his Maintenance Phase and then reinsert it where he chooses to take his activation.

ENDING AN ENCOUNTER

In many cases, it is immediately apparent when an encounter ends. When every character on one side of a battle has been incapacitated or destroyed while every character on the other side is still standing, the encounter is over. The Game Master can immediately stop tracking initiative, and the game can return to a narrative play style.

If the player characters are victorious but some of them are incapacitated at the time the last enemy falls, it might be necessary to continue tracking initiative and with the player characters taking turns as usual. This gives characters opportunities to stabilize their incapacitated comrades and often means the difference between life and death. Once all of the characters are either stabilized or dead, the encounter ends, and the Game Master can stop tracking initiative.

Another situation that might leave an encounter's conclusion unclear is the case of survivors on one side or the other attempting to flee combat. The Game Master resolves these situations on a case-by-case basis. If the last two surviving burrow-mawgs scamper into inaccessible cracks in a cave wall, it is probably time to end the encounter. If the last surviving caravan guard is running toward town to alert the authorities, it could be important to continue tracking initiative in the current combat. As with fleeing enemies, fleeing player characters should also be handled individually and the decision can be as story-driven as it is rule-driven. For some enemies, it is enough of a victory to drive off the player characters, but others might desire to eat their tasty, tasty flesh.

The Game Master determines when an encounter begins and ends.

EFFECTS LASTING ONE ROUND

An effect that begins on a character's turn and lasts for one round expires at the start of his next turn. If a character is destroyed, the effect lasts until the place in the initiative when he would have taken his next turn.

TURN STRUCTURE

Each character's turn consists of three phases: Maintenance, Control, and Activation.

MAINTENANCE PHASE

During the Maintenance Phase, perform the following steps in order:

1. The player checks for expiration of continuous effects on his character (see "Continuous Effects," below). After removing all expired continuous effects, resolve the effects of those that remain in play. Damage from multiple continuous effects is considered to happen all at once.

2. Any other effects that occur during the Maintenance Phase are resolved.

CONTROL PHASE

During the Control Phase, perform the following steps in order:

1. The player decides if he intends to upkeep spells. If the upkeep cost is not spent, the spell expires and its effects end immediately.

2. Any other effects that occur during the Control Phase are resolved.

ACTIVATION PHASE

During the Activation Phase a character can move and act. The type of actions a character can make might be limited by his choice of movement options. A character can make his actions before or after moving but cannot interrupt his movement to take an action.

MOVEMENT

When moving a character, measure from where the front of a character's base began the movement to where the front of the base is at the end of movement.

A character generally cannot move over another character's base. A character can move through friendly characters, however, provided he can move completely past the other character's base.

Advancing refers to any movement a character intentionally makes, rather than any movement caused by other effects such as being pushed or being slammed. A character can change his facing at any time during his advance, but when he moves he must always move in the direction he is facing. Changing facing by rotating in place does not cost any movement. A character who changes his facing is considered to have moved.

Terrain, spells, and other effects can modify a character's movement and/or his SPD by reducing or increasing it. Modifiers to movement apply only to the character's intentional

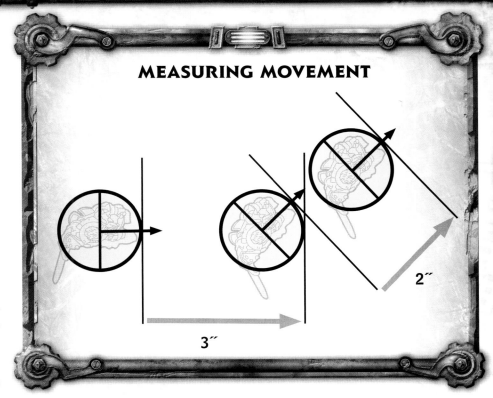

MEASURING MOVEMENT

3˝

2˝

movement, while modifiers to SPD apply whenever the character's SPD is used to determine the distance.

There are three basic types of movement that a character can make during his turn: full advance, run, and charge.

FULL ADVANCE

A character making a full advance moves up to his current speed (SPD) in inches.

RUN

A character who runs during his turn advances up to twice his current SPD in inches. A character who runs during his turn can make one quick action and cannot make attacks or full actions that turn. A running character cannot use his quick action to cast a spell. A character who forfeits his actions during a turn cannot run that turn.

CHARGE

A charging character rushes into melee and takes advantage of his momentum to make a powerful strike. A character who forfeits his actions during a turn cannot charge that turn.

At the time a character declares a charge, he must also declare which enemy he is charging. A character cannot charge a friendly character. The character must have line of sight to his charge target. The character then advances his SPD plus 3˝ toward his charge target, in a straight line. The charging character stops if he contacts any obstruction, such as another character or terrain he cannot move through. At the end of the charge movement, the charging character turns to face his target directly.

A character who ends his charge movement with his charge target in his melee range has made a successful charge. His first attack after charging must be against his charge target.

If the character charged at least 3″, his first attack was made with a melee weapon, and the attack hits, the damage roll is boosted. Attacks with ranged weapons do not gain boosted damage from charging. If a charging character moved less than 3″, the damage roll for his first attack is not boosted because he did not move far or fast enough to add sufficient momentum to his strike. His first attack must still be made against the charge target.

If a charging character ends his charge movement without his charge target in his melee range, then he has failed his charge. If a character makes a failed charge during his Activation Phase, his turn immediately ends.

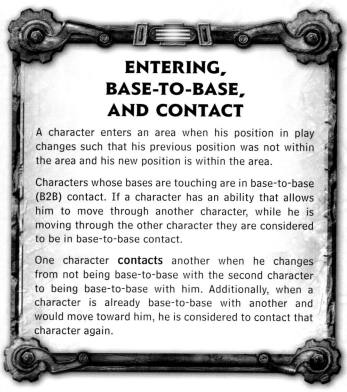

ENTERING, BASE-TO-BASE, AND CONTACT

A character enters an area when his position in play changes such that his previous position was not within the area and his new position is within the area.

Characters whose bases are touching are in base-to-base (B2B) contact. If a character has an ability that allows him to move through another character, while he is moving through the other character they are considered to be in base-to-base contact.

One character **contacts** another when he changes from not being base-to-base with the second character to being base-to-base with him. Additionally, when a character is already base-to-base with another and would move toward him, he is considered to contact that character again.

UNINTENTIONAL MOVEMENT

Characters can move without advancing as a result of being pushed or slammed, or from other effects. Determine the distance a character moves in this way by measuring the distance traveled by the edge of the character's base in the direction of the movement. Unless otherwise specified, a character's facing does not change when it moves unintentionally.

PUSHED

Sometimes characters are **pushed** as a result of an attack, ability, or spell. When a character is pushed, he is moved, but he is not considered to have advanced. Because the character is not considered to have advanced, he cannot be targeted by free strikes. A pushed character moves at half rate through rough terrain, suffers the effects of any hazards he moves through, and stops if he contacts an obstacle, obstruction, or another character.

A pushed character falls off elevated terrain if he ends the push movement with less than 1″ of ground under his base. See "Falling" below for detailed rules on determining damage from a fall.

SLAMMED

Sometimes characters are **slammed** as a result of an ability, spell, or attack. When a character is slammed, he is moved d6″ directly away from the point of origin of the slam, usually his attacker, and is then knocked down. If the slam was the result of a melee attack made by a character with a smaller base than the slammed character, the slammed character is slammed half the distance rolled. He then suffers slam damage as described in the ability, spell, or attack. A slammed character moves at half rate through rough terrain, suffers any damaging effects through which he passes, and stops if he contacts an obstacle, an obstruction, or a character with an equal or larger-sized base. A slammed character moves through characters with smaller bases than its own.

A character who is knocked down or prone cannot be slammed.

Add an additional die to the slam damage roll if the slammed character contacts an obstacle, an obstruction, or a character with an equal or larger-sized base.

A slammed character falls off elevated terrain if he ends the slam movement with less than 1″ of ground under his base. See "Falling" below for detailed rules on determining damage from a fall.

If a slammed character contacts another character with an equal-sized base or moves through a character with a smaller base, that second character is knocked down and suffers collateral damage. A character taking **collateral damage** suffers a damage roll as described in the ability, spell, or attack. Collateral damage cannot be boosted. A contacted character with a larger base than the slammed character does not suffer collateral damage and is not knocked down. Collateral damage is not considered to be damage from an attack or character. For example, an effect triggered by being "damaged by an enemy attack" would not trigger due to collateral damage.

THROWN

Sometimes characters are thrown as the result of an ability, spell, or attack. When a character is thrown, he is moved directly from the throw's point of origin in a straight line to the point of impact described in the ability, spell, or attack.

From this point, determine the thrown character's actual point of impact by rolling for deviation. Referencing the deviation rules (p. 212), roll a d6 for direction and a d3 for distance in

FALLING

A character who is slammed, thrown, pushed, or that otherwise moves off an elevated surface to another surface at least six feet (1″) lower falls. A **falling** character is knocked down and suffers a damage roll. A fall of up to eighteen feet (3″) causes a POW 10 damage roll. Add an additional die to the damage roll for every additional increment of eighteen feet (3″) the character falls, rounded up.

Fall Damage Roll = 2d6 + 10 + d6 for every eighteen feet (3″) of the fall after the first

Example: *A character falling eighteen feet (3″) suffers a damage roll of 2d6 + 10. One falling thirty feet (5″) suffers a damage roll of 3d6 + 10, and one falling forty-two feet (7″) suffers a damage roll of 4d6 + 10!*

If a falling character contacts a character with an equal or smaller-sized base, the contacted character is knocked down and suffers the same damage roll as the falling character. A contacted character with a larger base than the falling character does not suffer damage and is not knocked down.

BEING PLACED

Sometimes characters are placed in a new location as a result of an ability or spell. When a character is placed he is not considered to have moved or advanced. Because the character did not advance, he cannot be targeted by free strikes. There must be room for the character's base in the location his model is placed. A character cannot be placed in impassable terrain or with his base overlapping an obstacle, an obstruction, or another character's base.

ACTIONS

A character can act before or after his movement. A character cannot interrupt his movement to act.

A character does not have to make his actions all at once and can perform them in any order. For example, a character could make a ranged attack, reload, move, and make another attack. (For more on multiple attacks, see "Attacks," p. 207.)

There are three basic types of actions: quick, attack, and full.

During his turn a character can do one of the following:

1. Perform two quick actions.

2. Attack and perform one quick action.

3. Perform a full action.

Some abilities and benefits allow a character to make additional attacks or perform additional quick actions.

A character's choice of movement during his turn may impact his choice of actions that turn.

QUICK ACTIONS

Quick actions are simple and fast movements that a character can perform in addition to more complex actions, such as attacking. The quick actions that a character can perform include:

---

inches. The deviation distance cannot exceed half the distance between the thrown character and the intended point of impact.

The thrown character is moved directly from its current location in a straight line to the determined point of impact. A thrown character moves through characters with smaller bases during this movement without contacting them. Unlike when a character is slammed, rough terrain and obstacles do not affect this movement, but the thrown character still stops if he contacts an obstruction or a character with an equal or larger-sized base. The thrown character is then knocked down and suffers throw damage as described in the ability, spell, or attack. Add an additional die to the damage roll if the thrown character contacts an obstruction or a character with an equal or larger-sized base.

A thrown character falls off elevated terrain if he ends the thrown movement with less than 1″ of ground under his base. See "Falling" below for detailed rules on determining damage from a fall.

If a thrown character contacts another character with an equal-sized base, that character is knocked down and suffers collateral damage. A character taking **collateral damage** suffers a damage roll as described in the ability, spell, or attack. Collateral damage cannot be boosted. A contacted character with a larger base than the thrown character does not suffer collateral damage and is not knocked down. Collateral damage is not considered to be damage from an attack or character. For example, an effect triggered by being "damaged by an enemy attack" would not trigger due to collateral damage.

- Draw a weapon or item (including ammunition)

- Stow a weapon or item

- Reload a ranged weapon

- Pull a pin on a grenade

- Cast a spell

- Activate a runeplate

- Use a steamjack drive

- Use a skill or ability that requires a quick action

- Take cover or go prone

- Other fast, simple action at the Game Master's discretion

DRAW A WEAPON OR ITEM

A character can spend a quick action to draw a pistol from a holster, unsling a rifle, ready a shield, pull a sword from a sheath, or pull an item out of a pocket or pouch.

STOW A WEAPON OR ITEM

A character can spend a quick action to holster a pistol, sling a rifle or shield, sheath a sword, or put an item into a pocket or pouch. Dropping an item does not require any kind of action. Picking the item back up again requires a quick action. Some items might be damaged if dropped.

RELOAD A RANGED WEAPON

A character can spend a quick action to load a cartridge into a firearm, change an ammo wheel, or nock an arrow. Some weapons, such as crossbows and antiquated muzzle-loading firearms, take a full round to reload. The ammunition must be drawn from a pouch or pocket as a separate quick action. Various pieces of equipment, such as quivers and ammo bandoliers, enable a character to access ammunition quickly without the need to spend a quick action.

PULL A PIN

A character can spend a quick action to pull the pin on a grenade in advance of throwing it. Unless the grenade is slung on a grenadier's bandolier, drawing the grenade requires a separate quick action.

CAST A SPELL

On turns in which a character does not run, he can spend a quick action to cast a spell.

ACTIVATE A RUNEPLATE

A character can spend a quick action to toggle the runeplate activation switch on an item.

USE A DRIVE

A character with the 'Jack Marshal ability can spend a quick action to drive a steamjack he controls within his command range.

TAKE COVER

A character can spend a quick action to take cover while within six feet (1″) of a terrain feature that can either obscure his body or provide a solid barrier of protection. For one round, the character gains a DEF bonus from attacks made by characters on the other side of the terrain feature the character is taking cover behind. To consistently gain a bonus for taking cover, a character must make a taking cover quick action during each of his turns. The DEF bonus is determined by the nature of the terrain the character is taking cover behind.

Terrain not dense enough to block an attack but that makes it more difficult to see a character grants concealment. For example, low hedges or bushes might grant concealment. A character taking cover behind or within concealing terrain gains +2 DEF against ranged and magic attack rolls.

Terrain physically solid enough to block an attack grants solid cover. Examples include stone walls, giant boulders, and steamjack wrecks. A character taking cover behind a terrain feature that grants solid cover gains +4 DEF against ranged and magic attack rolls.

Taking cover provides no benefit against spray attacks.

A character taking cover behind a terrain feature that grants solid cover gains +2 DEF against melee attacks if the terrain feature is between the character and his attacker.

DEF bonuses from cover, concealment, and going prone are not cumulative. A character can claim only the best bonus he is eligible to receive.

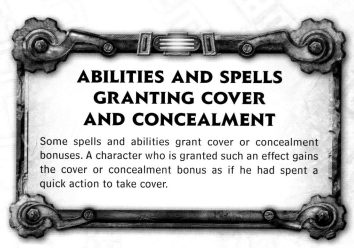

ABILITIES AND SPELLS GRANTING COVER AND CONCEALMENT

Some spells and abilities grant cover or concealment bonuses. A character who is granted such an effect gains the cover or concealment bonus as if he had spent a quick action to take cover.

GOING PRONE

A character can throw himself on the ground as a quick action to gain a DEF bonus from ranged and magic attacks. Once a character goes prone, he remains prone until he stands up.

While prone, the character gains +2 DEF against ranged and magic attacks, gains +4 ARM against blast damage, cannot run or charge, and when he makes a full advance he can move up to half his SPD in inches. Additionally, while prone the character suffers –2 on his melee attacks against characters who are not also prone. A character who is not prone that targets a prone character with a melee attack gains +2 on his attack roll.

A character cannot become knocked down while prone.

A prone character can stand up at the start of his turn. To stand up, a character must forfeit either his movement or his action that Activation Phase. A character who forfeits his action cannot perform quick or full actions, make attacks, or run that turn.

A character who forfeits his movement to stand can perform an action, but he cannot make attacks involving movement such as a slam. A character who forfeits his actions to stand can use his movement to make a full advance but cannot run or charge that turn.

The DEF bonuses from cover, concealment, and going prone are not cumulative. A character can claim only the best bonus he is eligible to receive.

FULL ACTIONS

The use of some skills requires a character's full attention during his turn. A character making a full action during his turn can move but cannot also perform a quick action or make an attack.

ATTACKS

A character who attacks during his turn can make one melee or ranged attack. Some abilities, benefits, and special rules allow a character to make additional melee or ranged attacks. Remember that spells, including magic attacks, are cast as quick actions.

A character who can make more than one melee or ranged attack during his turn can divide them among any eligible targets. Completely resolve each attack before making another attack.

When a character is granted more attacks as a result of an attack he made, he gains only one at a time. An attack can only ever grant one additional attack, though that additional attack can, in turn, grant another attack of its own, and so on. If two or more abilities would grant the character another attack as a result of making an attack, he chooses which ability to apply. The attack is then resolved using the rules for that ability.

An attack that allows a subsequent attack can grant only one such attack. Any single attack cannot grant more than one attack. If two or more abilities would grant the character another attack as a result of making a specified attack, he chooses which ability to apply. The attack is then resolved using the rules for that ability. Any subsequent attack can in turn generate its own additional attack.

ATTACKING

When a character makes an attack, his controller makes a roll to determine if the attack hits the intended target. If the attack hits, the character's controller then makes a damage roll to determine how much damage, if any, an attack deals. There are three main types of attacks: melee, ranged, and magic.

DECLARING A TARGET

When a character makes an attack, he can target anything or anyone in his line of sight (see "Line of Sight," p. 200). Unless a character has an ability, benefit, or special rule that says otherwise, he can declare attacks only against targets in his front arc.

MEASURING RANGE

After declaring the attack, measure to see if the target is within the range of the attack: melee range for melee attacks and a weapon or spell's RNG for a ranged or magic attack. Measure range from the edge of the attacking character's base to the maximum range of the attack. If the nearest edge of the target is within that distance, the target is in range.

If the target is in range, make an attack roll to determine if the attack hits. If the target is beyond range, the attack automatically misses. If an attack has an area of effect (AOE) and the target is out of range, the attack automatically misses, and its point of impact deviates from the point on the line to its declared target at a distance equal to its RNG. See "Area-of-Effect Attacks" (p. 212) for details on these attacks and deviation.

ATTACK ROLLS

An attack's success is determined by making an attack roll. The character rolls 2d6 and adds his character's appropriate stat and skill for the weapon used to make the attack.

Melee attack rolls use a character's PRW + military skill + weapon attack modifier. On the character sheet, this is abbreviated as MAT, the character's melee attack score with that weapon.

Most ranged attack rolls use a character's POI + military skill + weapon attack modifier. (Thrown weapon attacks use PRW + military skill + weapon attack modifier.) On the character sheet, this is abbreviated as RAT, the character's ranged attack score with that weapon.

Magic attack rolls use a character's Arcane stat.

Special rules and circumstances can further modify the attack roll by adding or removing dice and adding or subtracting values from the final result. A boost is an additional die added to the roll. A roll can be boosted only once.

A target is directly hit by an attack if the attack roll equals or exceeds the target's defense (DEF). If the attack roll is less than the target's DEF, the attack misses. A roll of all 1s on the dice is a miss. A roll of all 6s is a direct hit (see below) unless you are rolling only one die, regardless of the attacker's stat or the target's DEF. Sometimes a special rule causes an attack to hit automatically. Such automatic hits are also direct hits.

DIRECT HIT

A direct hit occurs when an attack hits the character it initially targeted as a result of a successful attack roll or a rule causing the attack to automatically hit. Characters caught in incidental effects, such as AOEs or effects that result from an initial direct hit, are not considered to suffer a direct hit. For example, a character targeted and hit by a Chain Lightning spell suffers a direct hit, but the characters hit by the lightning leaping from that target do not. This terminology comes into play primarily when adjudicating the additional effects of attacks such as AOEs, which often affect characters who were not the initial targets. See "Area-of-Effect Attacks" (p. 212).

ATTACKS THAT HIT OR MISS AUTOMATICALLY

Some special rules cause attacks to hit automatically or miss automatically. If a special rule causes an attack to hit automatically, you do not have to make an attack roll. If you do choose to make a roll (because you want to try for a critical hit, for example, see p. 219), the attack no longer hits automatically. If the attack roll fails, the attack misses.

If a special rule causes an attack to miss automatically, do not make an attack roll. The attack just misses.

If one rule causes an attack to hit automatically and one causes it to miss automatically, the automatic hit takes precedence over the automatic miss. For instance, an effect that allows attacks to hit automatically would override special rules such as stealth that would otherwise cause an attack to miss automatically.

REROLLS

Some characters have special abilities that enable them to reroll attack or damage rolls or that cause another character to reroll his attack or damage rolls. These rerolls occur before applying effects triggered by hitting/missing for attack rolls or by damaging/not damaging for damage rolls. The results of a reroll completely replace the results of the roll that was rerolled. For example, if a reroll causes a hit character to be missed, he is missed. If a reroll causes a missed character to be hit, he is hit. Multiple reroll effects can come into play on the same roll. Resolve them all before resolving any other effects dependent on hitting/missing or damaging/not damaging.

SWITCHING TARGETS

Some characters have the ability to cause another character to suffer a direct hit by an attack in their place. Others can cause themselves to suffer a direct hit by an attack in place of another character. Switching targets occurs immediately after a hit or a miss has been determined, including the resolution of all rerolls.

POINT OF ORIGIN

The point of origin of an effect or attack is the location or character from which the attack or effect originates. Typically this is the character causing the effect or making the attack, but not always. For example, when a warcaster channels a spell through an arc node, the arc node is the point of origin of the spell even though the warcaster is the character casting the spell. For attacks or effects that require line of sight to the target character, both line of sight and any attack roll modifiers that affect it (such as concealment) are checked from the point of origin of the attack. Range is also checked from the point of origin, including the placement of spray templates. Ignore the target in melee attack roll penalty when the point of origin of the magic attack is in melee with the character against which the attack roll is being made.

For most attacks, the origin of damage is the same as the point of origin of the attack. The origin of damage for a direct hit with an AOE attack is the attack's point of origin, but the origin of damage for any other damage caused by an AOE attack is the point of impact.

Finally, some non-AOE attacks have special rules that allow them to damage characters besides the attack's target. The origin of damage in those cases is the character or point from which you measure the range to other affected characters.

LINING UP THE SHOT

Channeled magic attacks can also gain the back strike bonus if the point of origin for the attack is completely in its target's back arc.

BACK STRIKE

A back strike is an attack made by a character completely in his target's back arc. For a character to receive the back strike bonus, the point of origin of the attack must have been in the target's back arc for the attacker's entire Activation Phase up to the moment of the attack. If the attack's point of origin

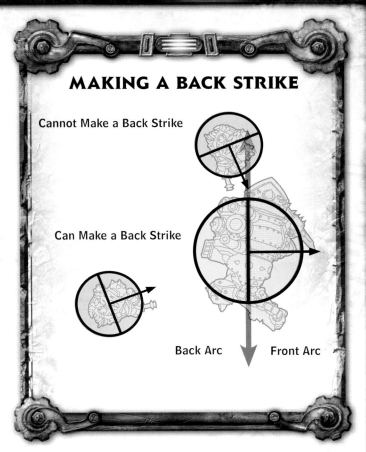

MAKING A BACK STRIKE

Cannot Make a Back Strike

Can Make a Back Strike

Back Arc   Front Arc

was in the target's front arc at any time during the attacking character's Activation Phase, the attacker does not receive this bonus. A character receives a back strike bonus only during his turn. A back strike grants a +2 bonus on the attack roll of any melee, ranged, or magic attack.

MELEE ATTACKS

Melee attacks include attacks made with fists, spears, swords, hammers, flails, saws, axes, and the like. A character can make melee attacks against any target in his melee range that is in his line of sight. A player can measure his character's melee range at anytime.

A melee weapon or unarmed attack has a melee range extending 0.5″ beyond the character's front arc for any type of melee attack. A weapon with Reach has a melee range of 2″. Some effects and special rules increase a weapon's melee range beyond this. A character's melee range is equal to the longest melee range of his usable melee attacks. A character who has a Reach weapon and another melee weapon in his hands can attack an opponent up to 2″ away with his Reach weapon, but his other weapon can be used only to attack targets within their normal 0.5″ melee range.

Melee Attack Roll = 2d6 + PRW + military skill + weapon attack modifier

ENGAGED

When a character has an enemy in his melee range and line of sight, he is engaging that character. When a character is either engaged or engaging, he is in melee.

FREE STRIKES

When an engaged character moves out of an enemy's melee range and/or line of sight, the enemy can immediately make a free strike against it just before the engaged character leaves his melee range and/or line of sight. The enemy character makes one normal melee attack with any melee weapon that has sufficient melee range to reach the moving character and gains a +2 bonus on his melee attack roll. If the attack hits, the damage roll is boosted. Free strikes cannot benefit from back strike bonuses.

UNARMED MELEE ATTACKS

Unarmed attacks include punches, kicks, and grapples. The unarmed combat rules also encompass attacks made with weapons such as knuckle dusters and the trench knife's skull crusher, since they are considered to be strikes made with the hands and feet.

KNOCKOUT STRIKE

A character making an unarmed melee attack can target his opponent's head in an attempt to knock him out. The attacker suffers –1 on his attack roll to land the aimed strike.

MELEE ATTACK MODIFIERS

The most common modifiers affecting a character's melee attack roll are summarized here for easy reference. Where necessary, additional detail can be found on the pages listed.

Attacker is not prone and attacking a prone target (p. 206): An attacker that is not prone who is attacking a prone target gains +2 on his attack roll.

Attacker prone and attacking a non-prone target (p. 206): If the attacker is prone and is attacking a target that is not prone he suffers –2 on his attack roll.

Back strike (p. 209): A back strike gains +2 to the attack roll.

Free strike (above): A free strike gains +2 to the attack roll and a boosted damage roll.

Knocked down target (p. 219): A melee attack against a knocked down character hits automatically.

Stationary target (p. 219): A melee attack against a stationary character hits automatically.

Target taking cover behind a terrain feature granting solid cover (see "Taking Cover," p. 206): A character who has taken cover behind a solid terrain feature between him and his attacker gains +2 DEF against melee attack rolls.

If the target suffers a knockout strike, he must make a Willpower roll against a target number equal to the attacker's STR + 7. If the target succeeds, he stays conscious. If he fails, he is knocked out (p. 219).

Only living characters can be knocked out.

Steamjacks and warbeasts can make knockout strikes as power attacks (p. 312).

GRAPPLE

Grappling represents an attempt to grab hold of and restrain a target. To grapple a target, the character must first hit it with an unarmed melee attack. If the attack hits, it causes no damage and the character enters a grapple with the target.

While maintaining a grapple, the grappling character has the option of restraining his target with both arms, or using one arm to continue to make attacks. While the grappling character is restraining his target with both arms, he can take no actions. The grappling character can release the target from the grapple at any time. A grappling character with multiple actions that maintains the grapple with one arm can take actions after a successful grapple. The grappling character can use attacks to punch, stab, bite, shoot, or make any other kind of attack against the grappled character the Game Master deems plausible.

During his turn, a grappled character can attempt to break free of a grapple instead of attacking. When the grappled character attempts to break free, both characters engaged in the grapple make contested STR + Unarmed Combat rolls. If the attacker is maintaining the grapple one-handed, the target gets +2 to his roll.

If the target of the grapple rolls a higher total than the attacker, he has broken free; otherwise, he remains held. If an attempt to break free from a grapple fails, the defender can use additional attacks to make more attempts to break free that turn.

While grappling or being grappled, characters suffer –5 DEF. Attacks made by characters engaged in a grapple targeting those not engaged in the grapple suffer a –3 penalty to hit.

Neither character can advance or be pushed while involved in a grapple. A grapple is broken automatically if any of the following conditions occur:

- An effect causes either character to move or be placed
- An effect knocks down either character
- An effect causes either character to become incorporeal
- An effect causes the attacker to become stationary
- Either character is incapacitated

Steamjacks, warbeasts, and characters lacking humanoid physiology cannot be grappled.

Steamjacks and warbeasts can make grapples as power attacks (p. 312).

PINNING ARMS

After successfully grappling a target, a character can attempt to pin the target's arms, keeping him from performing any actions or attacks with them until the grapple is broken. The grappling character can use a full action to attempt to pin his target's arms. The characters then make contested STR + Unarmed Combat rolls. If the attacker wins, the target's arms are pinned. If the target wins or it is a draw, his arms are not pinned though he remains grappled. Once the target's arms are pinned, the target cannot use his arms to take any action until the grapple is broken. An attacker who pins his target's arms must spend a full action to maintain the grapple until he releases the target's arms.

While the attacker is pinning his target's arms, the attacker is grappling the target with both arms.

RANGED ATTACKS

Ranged attacks include attacks made with weapons like bows, rifles, flamethrowers, crossbows, harpoon guns, mortars, and the like.

A character can make ranged attacks against any target in his weapon's range that is in his line of sight, subject to the targeting rules. A character making more than one ranged attack can divide his attacks among any eligible targets. A character in melee can make ranged attacks only against targets he is engaging.

Ranged Attack Roll = 2d6 + POI (or PRW for thrown weapon) + military skill + weapon attack modifier

RANGED ATTACK ROLL MODIFIERS

The most common modifiers affecting a character's ranged attack roll are summarized here for easy reference. Where necessary, additional detail can be found on the pages listed.

The DEF bonuses from cover, concealment, and going prone are not cumulative. A character can claim only the best bonus he is eligible to receive.

Aiming bonus: A character can forfeit his movement to gain an aiming bonus. The aiming bonus adds +2 to every ranged attack roll the character makes during that Activation Phase. This bonus does not apply to magic attack rolls. A character who gains the aiming bonus cannot make a quick action that turn.

Back strike (p. 209): A back strike gains +2 to the attack roll.

Cloud effect (p. 218): A character inside a cloud effect gains concealment.

Concealment (see "Taking Cover," p. 206): A character benefiting from concealment in relation to his attacker gains +2 DEF against ranged and magic attack rolls.

Elevated attacker: If the attacker is on terrain at least six feet (1″) higher than the target, he is an elevated attacker. When drawing line of sight from an elevated attacker, ignore intervening characters on terrain at least six feet (1″) lower than the attacker unless they are within six feet (1″) of the target. Additionally, ignore intervening characters within six feet (1″) of the target on terrain at least six feet (1″) lower than the attacker and have equal or smaller-sized bases than the attacker.

Elevated target: If the target is on terrain at least six feet (1″) higher than the attacker, he is an elevated target. When drawing line of sight to an elevated target, ignore intervening characters on terrain at least six feet (1″) lower than the target. An elevated target gains +2 DEF against ranged and magic attack rolls.

Engaged: An engaged character suffers a −4 penalty on his ranged attack rolls.

Firing from horseback (p. 214): A character making ranged or magic attacks while mounted suffers a −2 penalty on his attack rolls.

Knocked down target (p. 219): While knocked down, a character has his base DEF reduced to 5.

Prone target (p. 206): A prone character gains +2 DEF against ranged and magic attack rolls.

Solid cover (see "Taking Cover," p. 206): A character benefiting from solid cover in relation to his attacker gains +4 DEF against ranged and magic attack rolls.

Stationary target (p. 219): While stationary, a character has his base DEF reduced to 5.

Target in melee (p. 212): A ranged or magic attack roll against a target in melee suffers a −4 penalty. If the attack misses, it might hit a nearby character instead.

TARGETING A CHARACTER IN MELEE

A character targeting an enemy in melee combat with a ranged or a magic attack risks hitting another character participating in the combat, including friendly characters. In addition to any other attack modifiers, a ranged attack roll against a target in melee suffers a –4 penalty.

If the attack against the intended target misses and the target was in range, it might hit another combatant. If the target was not in range, the attack misses automatically and does not hit another combatant.

If the missed target was in range, the attacker must immediately reroll his attack against another character in that combat. When determining the attack's new target, the only characters considered to be in the same combat are those in melee with the attack's original target and any characters in melee with them. Any character meeting these criteria can become the new target. A character cannot become the new target if a special rule or effect prohibits him from being targeted by the attack or if the attacker's line of sight is completely blocked by obstructing terrain. Ignore intervening characters when determining a new target. If multiple characters in the combat are eligible targets, randomly determine which character becomes the new target (excluding the original target).

If the attack against the new target misses, it misses completely without the chance to hit any other characters.

An area-of-effect attack that misses a target in melee deviates normally instead of following these rules. Spray attack rolls that miss a character in melee do not follow these rules; they simply miss.

AREA-OF-EFFECT ATTACKS

An attack with an area of effect is referred to as an AOE attack. An area-of-effect attack, such as from an explosive spell or a gas cloud, hits every character in an area centered on his point of impact. The attack covers an area with a diameter equal to his area of effect (AOE). Templates for AOEs appear on p. 352.

An AOE attack follows all normal targeting rules. A successful attack roll indicates a direct hit on the intended target, which suffers a direct hit damage roll of 2d6 + the attack's POW. Center the AOE template over the point of impact—in the case of a direct hit, the center of the targeted character's base. Every other character with any part of his base covered by the AOE template is hit, but not directly hit, by the attack and suffers a blast damage roll of 2d6 + 1/2 POW of the attack. Make separate damage rolls against each character in the AOE; each roll must be boosted individually. An AOE attack's critical effect functions only on a direct hit, but every character under the template suffers the critical effect.

$$AOE\ Direct\ Damage\ Roll = 2d6 + POW$$

$$AOE\ Blast\ Damage\ Roll = 2d6 + 1/2\ POW$$

Prone characters gain +4 ARM against blast damage.

Any AOE attack targeting the ground automatically deviates.

An AOE attack that misses its target deviates a random direction and distance. An AOE attack declared against a target beyond its range (RNG) automatically misses, and its point of impact deviates from the point on the line from the attack's point of origin to its declared target at a distance equal to his RNG away from the attack's point of origin. An AOE attack that misses a target within its range deviates from the center of its intended target.

DAMAGE POINT OF ORIGIN

An AOE attack's point of impact determines the origin of damage and effects for characters within the AOE but not directly hit by the attack.

DEVIATION

When an AOE attack misses its target, determine its actual point of impact by rolling deviation. Referencing the deviation template (p. 352), roll a d6 to determine the direction the attack deviates. For example, a roll of 1 means the attack goes long and a roll of 4 means the attack lands short. Then roll another d6 to determine the deviation distance in inches. Determine the missed attack's actual point of impact by measuring the rolled distance from the original point of impact in the direction determined by the deviation roll. If the deviated point of impact would be off the table, reduce the deviation distance so the point of impact is on the edge of the table instead. If the intended target is beyond the weapon's RNG, determine deviation from the point on the line from the attack's point of origin to his declared target at a distance equal to his RNG.

If the target is within range of the attack, the point of impact does not deviate more than half the distance from the attack's point of origin to its intended target. If the target is not within range of the attack, the point of impact does not deviate more than half the RNG of the attack. Use the exact value for this maximum; do not round it. For instance, an attack made at a target 5˝ away from the attack's point of origin deviates

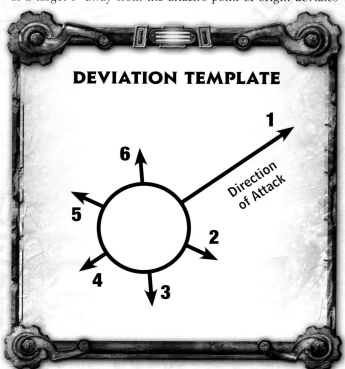

DEVIATION TEMPLATE

a maximum of 2.5″ even if the attacker rolls a 3, 4, 5, or 6 for deviation distance.

Terrain features, characters, or other effects do not block deviating AOE attacks. They always take effect at the determined point of impact.

Center the AOE template over the point of impact. Every character with any part of his base covered by the AOE template is hit, but not directly hit, by the attack and takes a blast damage roll. Deviating AOE attacks never cause direct hits even if the point of impact is on top of a character.

SPRAY ATTACKS

Spray attacks are attacks that use a spray template. Some weapons and spells, such as flamethrowers and the Frostbite spell, make spray attacks. This devastating short-ranged attack can potentially hit several characters. A spray uses the spray template and has a RNG of "SP 6," "SP 8," or "SP 10." Effects that modify RNG do not affect spray attacks. The spray template appears on p. 353.

When making a spray attack, center the spray template laterally over an eligible target with the narrow end of the template touching the nearest edge of the point of origin's base. The target itself need not be under the template. The targeting rules apply when choosing the attack's primary target. Every character with any part of his base covered by the appropriate section of the spray template can be hit by the attack.

Make separate attack rolls against each character under the template. Remember that each roll must be boosted individually. Spray attacks ignore concealment, cover, stealth, and intervening characters because the attack comes over, around, or in some cases through his protection.

A spray ranged or magic attack roll against a character in melee does not suffer a −4 penalty. A spray attack roll against a character in melee that misses is not rerolled against another character. It misses completely.

Terrain that obstructs line of sight blocks spray attacks. A character under the spray template cannot be hit by the attack if the attacker's line of sight to it is completely blocked by terrain.

Every character hit by a spray attack suffers a direct hit. Make separate damage rolls against each character hit.

MAGIC ATTACKS

A character can make magic attacks against any target in his spell's range that is in his line of sight, subject to the targeting rules. Magic attacks are similar to ranged attacks and follow most of the same rules, but they are not affected by rules that affect only ranged attacks. A magic attack roll does not suffer the target in melee attack roll penalty when the attacker is engaged in melee with the target. If such an attack misses and there are multiple characters in the combat, the attack can still hit another random character in the combat, excluding the attacker and the original target. For more information on magic attacks, see "Casting a Spell," p. 232.

Magic Attack Roll = 2d6 + ARC

MAGIC ATTACK ROLL MODIFIERS

The most common modifiers affecting a character's magic attack roll are summarized here for easy reference. Where necessary, additional detail can be found on the pages listed.

DEF bonus from cover, concealment, and going prone are not cumulative. A character can claim only the best bonus he is eligible to receive.

Back strike (p. 209): A back strike gains +2 to the attack roll.

Cloud effect (p. 218): A character inside a cloud effect gains concealment.

Concealment (see "Taking Cover," p. 206): A character benefiting from concealment in relation to his attacker gains +2 DEF against ranged and magic attack rolls.

Elevated attacker: If the attacker is on terrain at least six feet (1″) higher than the target, it is an elevated attacker. When drawing line of sight from an elevated attacker, ignore intervening characters on terrain at least six feet (1″) lower than the attacker unless they are within six feet (1″) of the target. Additionally, ignore intervening characters within six feet (1″) of the target on terrain at least six feet (1″) lower than the attacker and have equal or smaller-sized bases than the attacker.

Elevated target: If the target is on terrain at least six feet (1″) higher than the attacker, it is an elevated target. When drawing line of sight to an elevated target, ignore intervening characters on terrain at least six feet (1″) lower than the target. An elevated target gains +2 DEF against ranged and magic attack rolls.

Firing from horseback (p. 214): A character making ranged or magic attacks while mounted suffers a −2 penalty on his attack rolls.

Knocked down target (p. 219): While knocked down, a character has his base DEF reduced to 5.

Prone target (p. 206): A prone character gains +2 DEF against ranged and magic attack rolls.

Solid cover (see "Taking Cover," p. 206): A character benefiting from solid cover in relation to his attacker gains +4 DEF against ranged and magic attack rolls.

Stationary target (p. 219): While stationary, a character has his base DEF reduced to 5.

Target in melee (p. 212): A ranged or magic attack roll against a target in melee suffers a −4 penalty. Remember that a character making a magic attack while in melee with his target does not suffer this penalty. If the attack misses, it might hit a nearby character instead.

MOUNTED COMBAT

Mounted combat adds a number of options and complications to battle. While mounted, a character gains a number of benefits from his fast-moving steed. A mounted combatant also suffers from some unique vulnerabilities, since he must rely on both his mount's nerve and his own skill as a rider. Any time a mounted character attempts a dangerous maneuver or tries to evade a potentially hazardous obstacle, he must make an AGL + Riding skill roll to determine the success of his maneuver (p. 190).

A rider must also take into account his mount's stats and degree of training. Most mounts must be trained to wear armor and fight in battle. Without the proper training, a horse is unreceptive to its rider's commands. Though any horse that has been broken in can carry a rider, only one designated as a **warhorse** can execute **cavalry charges** and other complex maneuvers.

MOUNTING AND DISMOUNTING

A character must be B2B with his mount to get on its back. A character without the Riding skill must spend a full action to mount his steed. A character with the Riding skill can mount his horse as a quick action. When a character mounts his horse, remove his model from the table.

Whether trained or not, dismounting a steed is a quick action. When a character dismounts, place a model representing the character anywhere B2B with the mount. The character's player chooses where the model is placed.

TALL IN THE SADDLE

Mounted characters can ignore characters with bases smaller than their own when making melee attacks.

FIRING FROM HORSEBACK

A character making ranged or magic attacks while mounted suffers a –2 penalty on his attack rolls.

MOUNT ATTACKS

Some mounts can make attacks. Mounts with attacks have a 0.5″ melee range.

Attacks made by a mount are melee attacks and are resolved using the rider's PRW + Riding skill. If the attack hits, use the mount's STR and the POW of the attack. A mount's attack and damage rolls cannot be boosted.

A mount designated as a warhorse can make impact attacks as part of a cavalry charge (see below).

CAVALRY CHARGE

A character must have the Cavalry Charge ability and be riding a mount designated as a warhorse to charge while mounted.

When declaring a charge target, a character who can charge while mounted ignores other characters with bases smaller than his own.

If a charging mounted character contacts another character during his movement and has moved at least 3″, he stops and makes **impact attacks** against all characters in the mount's melee range. Impact attacks are made using the mount attack rules above and are considered to be simultaneous. After resolving the impact attacks, the charging character resumes his charge movement. He cannot make further impact attacks during this charge. If the charging character did not move at least 3″ before contacting another character, he does not make any impact attacks and must stop his movement at that point. If the character's charge target is not in melee at the end of the charge movement, the charge fails. If the charge target is the first character contacted by the charging character, the charging character can still make an impact attack against him.

A mounted character gains +2 to his charge attack rolls. Impact attacks do not receive this bonus.

SPD, DEF, AND TARGETING A MOUNTED CHARACTER

While mounted, the character uses the SPD of his mount instead of his own.

When determining the DEF of a mounted character, use the character's DEF –4. Add +1 to the mounted character's DEF for each level of the Riding skill he possess.

When a mounted character is hit by an attack, roll a d6 to determine whether the mount or the rider is actually hit.

If the attacker is on foot, on a roll of 1–4, the mount is hit. On a 5 or 6, the rider is hit.

If the attacker is also mounted, on a roll of 1–3, the mount is hit.

On a 4–6, the rider is hit.

A character attacking a mounted character can also choose to specifically target the mount or rider. A character targeting the rider suffers –2 to hit. A character targeting the mount has no modifier on his attack roll.

BEING THROWN FROM THE SADDLE

Occasionally a mounted character risks being thrown from the saddle, such as when a mount is incapacitated, when his mount is startled or injured, or when the character fails a critical riding roll and the Game Master decides the character is thrown.

Any time his mount suffers 3 or more points of damage from an attack or other effect, the rider must make an AGL + Riding skill roll against a target number of 11 to keep from being thrown. If he succeeds, he stays on. If he fails, he is thrown.

When a character's mount is incapacitated, he is automatically thrown.

When a character is thrown, he must make an AGL+ Jumping roll against a target number of 14 to determine if he can control his fall or maneuver himself from harm.

If he succeeds, place a model representing the character anywhere B2B with the mount. The character's player chooses where the model is placed.

If he fails, the exact effect of being thrown depends on whether his horse was incapacitated or not. If the horse was not incapacitated, the rider is thrown d3″ directly from the horse, is knocked down, and suffers a POW 12 damage roll.

If the mount was incapacitated, roll a d6 to determine the character's fate. On the roll of 1–4, he is thrown as above. On the roll of 5–6, he is pinned beneath the steed. A pinned character is knocked down, suffers a POW 12 damage roll, and cannot move until he succeeds in a STR + AGL roll against a target number of 14. Roll at the start of each of the character's Activation Phases. If the roll succeeds, the character gets free. If the roll fails, he remains pinned and cannot move or take an action.

In any case, place a model on the table to represent the thrown character.

KNOCKDOWN, KNOCKOUT, AND COVER WHILE MOUNTED

When a mounted character is knocked down he must make an AGL + Riding skill roll against a target number of 14 to remain mounted. If the character succeeds, he suffers the effects of being knocked down, but remains on his mount. If the roll fails, the character is thrown and his mount is knocked down.

When a character is knocked out while mounted, he tumbles from the saddle to the ground. The Game Master should place a model representing the character on the table B2B with his mount. The character suffers an additional POW 10 damage roll from his fall.

A character cannot take cover or go prone while mounted. A character still gains concealment or cover from spells and other sources normally.

DAMAGE

Characters can take a fair amount of damage before they fall in combat. The amount of damage a character can take is based on his primary stats.

The amount of damage inflicted by an attack or other damage causing effect is determined by making a damage roll. In the case of ranged, magic, and most other damaging effects, roll 2d6 and add the Power (POW) of the attack. In the case of melee attacks, roll 2d6 and add the POW + STR of the attacking character. A boosted damage roll adds an additional die to this roll. Special rules for certain circumstances might modify the damage roll as well.

$$Damage\ Roll = 2d6 + POW\ (+ STR\ if\ melee)$$

Compare this total against the ARM of the character suffering the damage. That character takes 1 damage point for every point that the damage roll exceeds his ARM.

A weapon or attack with POW "—" does not cause damage.

LIFE SPIRALS

Characters have life spirals consisting of six branches grouped into three aspects that correspond with their primary stats: Physique, Prowess, and Intellect. Each aspect has a number of vitality points equal to its primary stats' value. Vitality represents a character's capacity for suffering bruises, scrapes, cuts, close calls, and the battered nerves that come from combat. When a character runs out of vitality on his life spiral, he finally succumbs to the punishment his body is taking and becomes disabled (next page).

When a character suffers damage, roll a d6 to determine which branch of his life spiral takes the damage. Starting with the outermost unmarked vitality point in that branch and working inward, mark one vitality point per damage point taken. Once a branch is full, continue recording damage in the next branch clockwise that contains an unmarked vitality point. Continue filling branches as required until every damage point taken has been recorded.

CRIPPLED ASPECTS

While all of a character's vitality points are filled in on a particular aspect as the result of damage, he suffers the effects of a crippled aspect.

The effects of losing an aspect are as follows:

Crippled Physique: The character suffers –2 STR.

Crippled Agility: The character suffers –2 on his attack rolls.

Crippled Intellect: The character suffers –2 DEF. Additionally, the character cannot upkeep spells.

DISABLED, INCAPACITATED, AND DESTROYED

A character is disabled when all of his vitality points are marked. When a character is disabled, immediately resolve any effects triggered by being disabled. A character cannot suffer more damage than he has vitality points (or damage boxes in the case of a steamjack). If a character regains 1 or more vitality points, he is no longer disabled. If an effect causes a character to regain a vitality point or otherwise cease being disabled, such as by healing a vitality point from a successful Tough roll, do not resolve any more effects triggered by the character being disabled.

After resolving any effects triggered by being disabled, if the character is still disabled he is considered to be incapacitated. An incapacitated character lacks any capacity to act, has no command range, and immediately suffers a roll on the Injury Table below.

After resolving incapacitated effects, at the Game Master's discretion less significant NPCs are considered destroyed and are removed from the table.

DEATH AND LONG-TERM INJURIES

When a character is incapacitated, he suffers extensive and potentially fatal injuries. While the loss of vitality represents physical wear and tear and reserves of energy, injuries are potentially mortal wounds that can cripple or outright kill a character.

Immediately after a character is incapacitated, roll on the injury table to determine the extent of his injuries.

Each time a character is incapacitated, roll once on the Injury Table to determine his long-term injury.

STABILIZING GRIEVOUSLY INJURED CHARACTERS

Some injuries are so dreadful that they require immediate medical attention to save the injured character's life. Unless the character is stabilized within a number of rounds equal to his PHY, he dies. Stabilizing a wound requires the treating

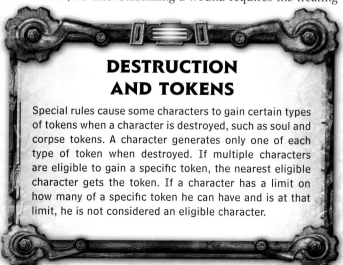

DESTRUCTION AND TOKENS

Special rules cause some characters to gain certain types of tokens when a character is destroyed, such as soul and corpse tokens. A character generates only one of each type of token when destroyed. If multiple characters are eligible to gain a specific token, the nearest eligible character gets the token. If a character has a limit on how many of a specific token he can have and is at that limit, he is not considered an eligible character.

character to be B2B with the injured character and spend a full action treating his wounds. The treating character then makes an INT + Medicine skill roll against a target number of 14. If the roll succeeds, the injured character is stabilized. If the roll fails, the treating character can attempt the roll again on his next turn unless the injured character dies before then.

SLOW RECOVERY

Characters who suffer serious injuries require some time to heal. It is recommended that a character suffering such a wound receive plenty of bed rest until fully mended.

A character suffering a slow recovery does not regain lost vitality points at the normal rate and cannot spend feat points to recover lost vitality. Instead, after the encounter in which the character was injured, he regains only 1 vitality point. He regains an additional 1 vitality point after each week. If he is treated daily by a character with the Medicine skill, the injured character regains an additional number of points each week equal to the treating character's Medicine skill level. Once he has regained all of his lost vitality, the character no longer suffers from slow recovery.

CONCUSSED

A concussed character has been badly stunned and comes to his senses only over time or once he has been brought back to his senses by another character. The concussed character automatically returns to his senses if he is given a dose of simple stimulant (p. 296) or if another character B2B with him spends a full action bringing him out of his concussed state. When the character comes out of his concussed state he regains 1 vitality point and is no longer incapacitated.

If the character does not receive aid from another character during combat, he comes out his concussed state quickly after the end of the encounter and recovers vitality normally.

RECOVERY AND REGAINING VITALITY

When a character regains vitality, remove the damage from anywhere on the character's life spiral. Remember, if a character regains vitality damage while disabled, he is no longer disabled.

After a short rest following an encounter, a character automatically regains a number of vitality points equal to his PHY.

Characters who have suffered damage continue to recover over time. A character regains 1 vitality point each hour for the first three hours after being injured. After that he regains 1 Vitality point every six hours until he has regained all of his vitality points.

INJURY TABLE

3D6	RESULT
3	**Dead** – The character dies as a result of his wounds. He is destroyed. At the Game Master's discretion, the character either died immediately as a result of his wounds or can gasp out a few last words before succumbing to his injuries.
4	**Critical Injuries** – The character is critically injured. Helpless and unable to take any action, he is rapidly losing blood and is certain to die unless he receives immediate medical attention. The character is **grievously injured** and if he is not **stabilized** within a number of rounds equal to his PHY, he dies. A stabilized character remains incapacitated throughout the battle. If the character survives, he does not recover lost vitality at the normal rate and instead suffers a **slow recovery**.
5	**Broken Limb** – The character has suffered a broken arm or leg. Roll a d6. On the roll of 1–3, the character has broken an arm. On the roll of 4–6, he has broken a leg. Though incapacitated, the character can spend 1 feat point to move and take actions during his turn. That turn he is not considered to be incapacitated. The character loses one quick action each turn in additional to any other penalties for lost aspects.
	The character cannot recover lost vitality points until his limb has been set. Setting a limb cannot be done in combat. Setting the character's limb requires a treating character to spend twenty minutes setting the break followed by a successful INT + Medicine skill roll against a target number of 12. If the roll fails, the character can try again after spending another ten minutes setting the limb.
	Once the limb has been set, the injured character immediately regains his PHY in lost vitality points and is no longer incapacitated. The limb itself takes another 20 + 2d6 days to fully heal. During this time, a character with a broken arm cannot use that arm and loses one quick action each turn. A character with a broken leg suffers −2 SPD, DEF, and Initiative until the leg fully heals.
6–8	**Spitting Blood** – The character has suffered a life threatening injury and is rapidly bleeding out. Unless he receives immediate medical attention, he is certain to die. Though incapacitated, the character can spend 1 feat point to move and take actions during his turn. That turn he is not considered to be incapacitated. The character suffers the penalties for his lost aspects and loses one quick action each turn.
	The character is **grievously injured** and if he is not **stabilized** within a number of rounds equal to his PHY, he dies. A stabilized character immediately regains 1 lost vitality point and is no longer incapacitated.
9	**Battered** – The character has suffered a traumatic injury that has left him **concussed** and badly beaten.
	Until the character recovers all of his lost vitality points, he suffers −2 PHY and SPD in addition to his other wound penalties.
10–11	**Concussed** – The character has been badly battered and dazed. He is **concussed** but has otherwise suffered no long-term injuries.
12	**Battle Scars** – The character has suffered an injury that has left him concussed and badly scarred.
	In addition to suffering the effects of being concussed, the character has also suffered a permanent disfigurement to his face and body. As a result of this disfigurement, the character suffers −1 on social skill rolls in which his scars would frighten or disgust the subject of the character's skill attempt. The character gains +1 on Intimidation skill rolls against anyone who can see his scars.
13–15	**Spitting Blood** – The character has suffered a life threatening injury and is rapidly bleeding out. Unless he receives immediate medical attention, he is certain to die. Though incapacitated, the character can spend 1 feat point to move and take actions during his turn. That turn he is not considered to be incapacitated. The character suffers the penalties for his lost aspects and loses one quick action each turn.
	The character is **grievously injured** and if he is not **stabilized** within a number of rounds equal to his PHY, he dies. A stabilized character immediately regains 1 lost vitality point and is no longer incapacitated.
16	**Lost Eye** – The attack destroys one of the character's eyes and also leaves him **concussed** from the attack.
	In addition to the effects of being concussed, one of the character's eyes has been lost or ruined as a result of the damage he has suffered, determine which randomly. The character permanently suffers a −1 penalty on ranged attacks rolls and on sight-based PER rolls.
17	**Critical Injuries** – The character is critically injured. Helpless and unable to take any action, he is rapidly losing blood and is certain to die unless he receives immediate medical attention. The character is **grievously injured** and if he is not **stabilized** within a number of rounds equal to his PHY, he dies. A stabilized character remains incapacitated throughout the battle. If the character survives, he does not recover lost vitality at the normal rate and instead suffer a **slow recovery**.
18	**Lost Limb** – One of the character's limbs has been severed or otherwise completely destroyed. Roll a d6. On the roll of 1–3, the character has lost an arm. On the roll of 4–6, he has lost a leg. There is no chance to save the limb, and if the character does not receive immediate medical attention he is certain to die. Suffering shock and crippling blood loss, the character can do nothing. The character is **grievously injured** and if he is not **stabilized** (see below) within a number of rounds equal to his PHY, he dies. Once stabilized, the character remains incapacitated throughout the battle.
	If the character survives, he does not recover lost vitality at the normal rate and instead suffer a **slow recovery**.
	A character with a missing leg suffers a permanent −2 SPD and his racial SPD maximum is likewise reduced by 2. The character can offset some of the effects of lost leg with a prosthetic limb.
	In addition to losing the use of his missing limb, a character with a missing arm also loses one quick action each turn.

SPECIAL EFFECTS

Some attacks cause special effects in addition to causing damage. Additionally, some spells and actions can put special effects into play.

CLOUD EFFECTS

A **cloud effect** produces an area of dense smoke, magical darkness, thick mists, or the like that remains in play for a specified length of time. Use an AOE template of the appropriate diameter to represent the cloud. Every character with any part of its base covered by the cloud's template is within the cloud and susceptible to its effects.

In addition to being affected by a cloud's special rules, a character inside a cloud effect gains concealment (see "Taking Cover," p. 206) whether he took cover or not. The cloud effect does not block line of sight from characters within it to those outside of it, but it completely obstructs line of sight from characters outside of it to anything beyond it. A character can see into or out of a cloud effect but not through one.

CONTINUOUS EFFECTS

Some attacks cause continuous effects in addition to causing damage. Continuous effects remain on a character and have the potential to damage or affect him in some other way on subsequent turns. A character can have multiple continuous effects on him of different types at the same time, but can have only one of each continuous effect type on him at a time.

Continuous effects have a chance of expiring each round. Check for expiration of continuous effects at the start of the affected character's Maintenance Phase each turn.

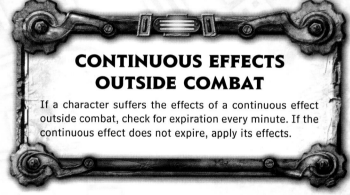

CONTINUOUS EFFECTS OUTSIDE COMBAT

If a character suffers the effects of a continuous effect outside combat, check for expiration every minute. If the continuous effect does not expire, apply its effects.

To check for the expiration, roll a d6. If the result is a 1 or 2, the continuous effect immediately expires without further effect. On a roll of 3, 4, 5, or 6 the continuous effect remains in play. After rolling for expiration for all of the continuous effects affecting a character, apply the effects of all continuous effects that remain on him simultaneously.

Some common continuous effects are described below:

- **Corrosion** – A character suffering the Corrosion continuous effect is slowly eroded as if by acid or another noxious substance. Corrosion does d3 damage point each turn to the affected character at the start of each of his Maintenance Phases unless it expires. Characters with Immunity: Corrosion never suffer this continuous effect.

- **Fire** – A character suffering the Fire continuous effect is on fire. A character on fire suffers a POW 12 fire damage roll at the start of each of his Maintenance Phases unless it expires. Characters with Immunity: Fire never suffer this continuous effect.

CRITICAL HIT

A critical hit occurs if any two dice in the attack roll show the same number and the attack hits. As a result of a critical hit, some attacks cause **critical effects** in addition to causing damage. The target suffers the special effect even if it takes no damage from the damage roll. An AOE attack's critical effect functions only on a direct hit, but every character under the template suffers the critical effect.

- **Critical Corrosion** - Critical Corrosion is a critical effect that causes characters hit by the attack to suffer the Corrosion continuous effect on a critical hit.

- **Critical Fire** - Critical Fire is a critical effect that causes characters hit by the attack to suffer the Fire continuous effect on a critical hit.

DAMAGE TYPES AND IMMUNITIES

Some weapons and spells inflict a specific **damage type** that might affect some characters differently than others. When a damage type is referenced in text, it is described as an "X damage roll." For example, a damage roll that causes electrical damage is described as an "electrical damage roll."

A character with an **immunity** to a certain damage type does not take damage of that type. An immunity is a special protection from some types of damage and effects. A character never suffers damage from a damage type to which he is immune.

A single attack can inflict damage of several damage types. If a character is immune to any of those types, he does not suffer damage from the attack. A character who is immune to damage from an attack can still suffer other effects from the attack.

Some damage types are identified by their attack type. For example, damage caused by a ranged attack might be referred to as "ranged attack damage."

KNOCKDOWN

Some attacks and special rules cause a character to be **knocked down**. While knocked down a character cannot move, perform actions, make attacks, cast spells, or be used to channel a spell and does not have a melee range. A knocked down character does not engage other characters and cannot be engaged by them. As a consequence, a character is never in melee with a knocked down character. A melee attack roll against a knocked down character automatically hits. A knocked down character has a base DEF of 5. A knocked down character does not block line of sight. He can be ignored for targeting purposes.

A knocked down character can stand up or go prone (p. 206) at the start of his next turn. A character cannot become knocked down while it is knocked down. To stand up, a character must forfeit either his movement or his actions that turn.

A character who forfeits his movement to stand can still perform actions that turn, but he cannot make attacks involving movement such as a slam.

A character who forfeits his actions cannot make quick actions, attacks, or full actions. Additionally, a character who forfeits its actions to stand can use his movement to make a full advance but not to run or charge that turn.

A character can go prone at the start of his turn without forfeiting either his movement or his actions.

When a character stands or goes prone, he ceases to be knocked down.

KNOCKOUT

When a character is knocked out, he is knocked down and his upkeep spells expire. The character is knocked down even if he has an ability that says he cannot be knocked down.

While knocked out, a character cannot allocate focus, take actions, make attacks, move, and must forfeit the Activation Phases of his turns.

At the start of each of his turns, a knocked out character can make a WIL roll against a target number 14 to regain consciousness. If he fails, he remains knocked out. If he succeeds, he is no longer knocked out and can act normally that turn though he is still knocked down.

Only living characters can be knocked out.

MAGICAL WEAPONS

A magical weapon can damage and affect characters with the Incorporeal ability. Attacks made with magical weapons are not magic attacks. Magical ranged weapons make ranged attacks. Magical melee weapons make melee attacks.

STATIONARY

A **stationary character** cannot activate. A stationary character does not have a melee range. A stationary character does not engage other characters nor can other characters engage a stationary character. A character is never in melee with a stationary character. A stationary character cannot advance, perform actions, make attacks, or cast spells.

A melee attack roll against a stationary character automatically hits. A stationary character has a base DEF of 5.

CONSTRUCT

Not all characters in the Iron Kingdoms are made of flesh and blood. A construct character is not living, and automatically passes any Willpower rolls that do not specifically reference construct characters.

INCORPOREAL

An incorporeal character can move through rough terrain and obstacles without penalty. He can move through obstructions and other characters if he has enough movement to move completely past them. Other characters, including slammed, pushed, or thrown models, can move through an incorporeal character without effect if they have enough movement to move completely past him. An incorporeal character does not count as intervening. Blessed weapons affect an incorporeal character normally. Spells, animi, and magical weapons can

GAINING FEAT POINTS

A character gains a feat point when one of the following conditions occurs.

- Incapacitates or destroys an enemy with an attack: A character gains 1 feat point for each enemy character he incapacitates or destroys an enemy with an attack. In the case of a particularly powerful enemy, the Game Master can award more than 1 feat point to a character or award 1 feat point to each character who helped defeat the enemy. Likewise, a Game Master can choose to award no feat points if the enemy destroyed was particularly weak or helpless.

- Critical success on a skill or attack roll: A character who rolls a critical hit on a skill or attack roll in which he rolled two or more dice gains a feat point.

- Game Master award: The Game Master can award feat points to characters for achieving milestones in play or as a reward for particularly inventive or heroic actions, and/or excellent role playing.

A character can never have more than three feat points. If he already has three feat points and gains another, the additional feat point is lost.

FEATS

Feat points are a resource that can be spent to accomplish any of a number of feats. Any character can take advantage of common feats listed below, and there are also a number of abilities and archetype benefits that require the expenditure of a feat point to use.

damage an incorporeal character but roll one fewer die on damage rolls. No other weapons can damage the incorporeal character. Incorporeal characters are immune to continuous effects and cannot be moved by a slam.

STEALTH

A character with stealth is extremely difficult to spot and target. Non-spray ranged and magic attacks declared against a character with stealth when the point of origin for the attack is more than thirty feet (5″) away automatically miss. A character with stealth is not an intervening model when determining line of sight from a character greater than thirty feet (5″) away.

UNDEAD

The line between life and death in the Iron Kingdoms can sometimes be blurred. There are numerous spells and artifacts that can return the dead to a semblance of life. An undead character is not considered living and automatically passes any Willpower rolls that do not specifically reference undead characters.

FEAT POINTS

Feat points represent a character's luck and raw heroic potential. They can enable him to reroll failed skill rolls, shake the effects of knockdown or continuous effects, or use any one of a number of special archetype benefits. Feat points are gained and spent regularly throughout play.

Generally only player characters gain feat points.

A character can have up to three feat points at any time and starts each session with three points.

AWARDING FEAT POINTS

The awarding of feat points is completely at the discretion of the Game Master. The rules above are merely guidelines. The Game Master should not award feat points to characters who are attempting to game the system, such as by making repeated Lore skill rolls for the express purpose of picking up extra feat points.

It is worth keeping in mind that these points are expected to be regularly earned and spent throughout play and that they are a resource characters need to fuel their abilities. Being too stingy with feat points has a stifling effect on the game.

A character can spend as many feat points during his turn as he wishes.

Any character can spend a feat point to use one of the following feats:

- Boost Non-Attack Skill Roll – A character can spend a feat point to boost a non-attack skill roll. A character can use this feat only to boost a skill roll if he has at least one level of the skill used for the roll.

- Heroic Dodge – A character can spend a feat point to suffer only half the damage from an attack, rounded up. The feat point is spent after the damage roll has been made.

- Make a Quick Action – A character can spend a feat point during his Activation Phase to make an additional quick action.

- Parry – A character can spend a feat point during his turn to keep from being targeted by free strikes that turn.

- Relentless Charge – A character can spend a feat point during a turn in which he charges. While charging that turn the character can move over rough terrain without penalty.

- Reroll Failed Attack, Skill, or Willpower Roll – A character can spend a feat point to reroll a failed attack, skill, or Willpower roll. A character can continue to reroll the same failed roll as long as he has feat points to spend.

- Run and Gun – When a character makes a full advance during his turn, he can spend a feat point to move up to 2x his SPD in inches instead of his SPD as normal.

- Shake Continuous Effect – A character can spend a feat point at the start of his turn to shake a continuous effect. When the character shakes the continuous effect, it immediately expires.

- Shake Knockdown – A character can spend a feat point to shake knockdown at the start of his turn. When the character shakes knockdown he immediately stands up.

- Shake Stationary – If a character is stationary, he can spend a feat point at the start of his turn to cause the stationary status to expire.

- Sprint – A character can spend a feat point during a turn in which he incapacitated or destroyed one or more enemy characters with a melee attack. At the end of the character's turn, he can make a full advance.

- Two-Fister – A character with a weapon in each hand can spend a feat point during his turn to attack once with the weapon in each of his hands without an attack roll penalty as if he had the Two-Weapon Fighting ability (p. 168) and the Ambidextrous Skilled archetype ability (p. 117).

- Walk it Off – A character can spend a feat point during his turn to immediately regain d3+1 vitality points. If a character suffers damage during his turn, the damage must be resolved before a character can use this feat. An incapacitated character cannot use Walk it Off.

TERRAIN

There are times when physical obstacles make getting from one place to another in the middle of a battle more difficult, and different sorts of terrain can have varying impact on battle. Terrain can put pressure on the players to reach an entrenched enemy firing on them or give them the chance to hunker down and weather an attack that might otherwise be overwhelming. Making use of a variety of terrain can make even a simple skirmish more tactically interesting.

TERRAIN TYPES

A countless variety of terrain is found in western Immoren, from simple terrain such as hilly grasslands and cobblestone city streets to more challenging terrain such as jagged rockslides and snowy cliffs. In the game, terrain breaks down into three categories: open, rough, and difficult.

OPEN TERRAIN

Open terrain is any ground that does not present challenge or hassle to traverse. Characters move at their full movement rate when travelling through open terrain and can perform actions normally. Examples include grassy plains, barren fields, flat rooftops, dirt roads, gently sloped hillsides, city streets, elevated walkways, sparse forests with little ground cover, and paved surfaces.

ROUGH TERRAIN

Rough terrain is any ground that presents enough of a challenge to slow characters down. As long as any part of his base is in rough terrain, a character moves at half rate through rough terrain. Though a character's movement is slowed in rough terrain, he can still perform actions normally. Rough terrain can take many forms, and it is up to the Game Master to determine when terrain is rough. Some examples include thick brush, jagged rockslides, murky bogs, rain-slicked muddy hills, shallow water, and deep snow.

DIFFICULT TERRAIN

Difficult terrain is so demanding that a character can do nothing else while traversing it. Characters do not use their normal movement to travel through difficult terrain. Instead they must use their skills, equipment, and teamwork. Examples of difficult terrain include cliff faces, oceans, vertical walls, and lava. The Game Master determines when terrain is difficult and what skills can be used to pass it as well as which actions the characters can still perform while engaged in crossing it.

EXAMPLE: *A group of characters must cross a section of fast-moving river rapids, and the Game Master determines the terrain is difficult. He then determines that any character attempting to swim across makes Swim rolls with a −3 penalty. A rope connects trees on either side of the river, and the Game Master determines that characters can climb across with a target number of 13 for Climb rolls.*

TERRAIN FEATURES

Terrain features can be either natural or man-made objects that affect how characters move and fight across the ground they traverse. Terrain features are virtually limitless in their variety, and they vary by how they affect movement, the type of protection they afford, and any adverse effects they cause. The Game Master decides what qualifies as a terrain feature and how it impacts character movement and combat.

OBSTACLES

An **obstacle** is any terrain feature of waist height that the Game Master determines is durable enough to afford protection. Characters can use obstacles as cover (see "Taking Cover, p. 206) from incoming attacks.

Obstacles are low enough that they can be climbed upon or, in some cases, easily crossed. An obstacle must be at least three feet (.5″) thick, such as a raised platform or the sides of a ziggurat, in order for a character to climb atop and stand on it.

An advancing character suffers a movement penalty when he climbs atop an obstacle. Once the character has contacted the obstacle, he needs to spend 2″ of his movement to climb up. A character cannot climb an obstacle if he does not have at least 2″ of movement remaining. Place a character who climbs an obstacle on top of it with the front of the character's base making only 1″ of forward progress. Once atop an obstacle, the character can continue with the remainder of his movement. Remember that a charging character cannot pay this movement penalty, cannot climb an obstacle, and ends his movement upon contact with the obstacle.

A moving character can descend an obstacle without penalty.

LINEAR OBSTACLES

An obstacle less than three feet (.5″) thick, such as a wall or hedge, is a **linear obstacle**. A non-charging advancing character can cross a linear obstacle at no penalty as long as the character can move completely past it. Otherwise the character must stop short of the linear obstacle. A character cannot partially cross, climb atop, or stand atop a linear obstacle.

OBSTRUCTIONS

An **obstruction** is a terrain feature taller than waist height, such as a high wall or a gigantic boulder. A character cannot move through or climb an obstruction. Like an obstacle, obstructions can provide cover from attacks (see "Taking Cover, p. 206).

FORESTS

A typical **forest** has many trees and dense underbrush, but any terrain feature that hinders movement and makes a character inside it difficult to see can also be designated a forest. A forest is rough terrain and provides concealment to a character with any part of its base inside the forest's perimeter.

When drawing line of sight to or from a point within a forest, the line of sight can pass through up to eighteen feet (3″) of forest without being blocked, but anything more blocks it.

HILLS

A **hill** is a terrain feature with a gentle rise or drop in elevation. A hill might be open or rough terrain depending on the ground's nature.

WATER

Depending on its nature, **water** can be hazardous to both men and steamjacks. Water is classified either as shallow or deep relative to the character crossing it. What would be considered shallow water to a massive ogrun would be deep water to a diminutive gobber.

SHALLOW WATER

A body of water is considered shallow water when it has a depth of at least knee height. Shallow water is not deep enough to swim in and counts as rough terrain for movement.

A steamjack knocked down while in shallow water has its furnace extinguished and goes inert. The steamjack cannot be reactivated until it is stood up or otherwise removed from the water, its furnace thoroughly dried, and its heart fire restarted.

DEEP WATER

A body of water is considered deep water if it has a depth of at least waist height.

A steamjack knocked down while in deep water has its furnace extinguished and goes inert. Furthermore, inert warjacks in deep water are completely waterlogged and extremely difficult to move without heavy equipment.

A character cannot begin a charge or run while in deep water. Characters in water deeper than shoulder height must make Swim rolls to move. Characters attempting to move without swimming do so at a quarter of their normal movement rate. Characters in deep water cannot cast spells, perform actions, or attack.

A character in deep water has his DEF reduced to 7.

DAMAGING INANIMATE OBJECTS AND STRUCTURES

Sometimes blasting a door off its hinges is a more effective route of entry than using the doorknob. Characters wishing to destroy an inanimate object have to overcome its ARM and inflict a number of points equal to its damage capacity to destroy the object.

Inanimate objects are automatically hit by melee attacks and have DEF 5 against ranged and magic attacks.

The Game Master is encouraged to be realistic about what sorts of damage can be effective on certain materials and how effective the methods of delivery are. For example, a knife blade is effective for cutting and damaging rope, but blunt force trauma such as a fist or hammer against a rope is likely to be ineffective. Fire is particularly effective against products made of wood or paper but might be useless against stone.

Inanimate objects suffer blast damage and collateral damage.

Items worn or carried by characters must be specifically targeted by characters in order to be affected by any attack.

Spells cause damage to inanimate objects. Ignore any other effects of a spell when used to target an inanimate object.

STRUCTURES

Inanimate objects of significant size, such as buildings or bridges, are known as structures. Structures are hit automatically by all forms of attacks. Due to their great size and structural integrity, not all attacks are effective against structures. Bullets and arrows are sufficient to shatter a glass bottle, but against very large inanimate objects such as structures, small caliber and traditional ranged weapons such as handguns, rifles, and crossbows are all but useless, effectively putting small holes or dents in buildings rather than destroying them outright.

Melee attacks and magic attacks can damage structures normally. Ranged weapons with an AOE, that cause fire damage or corrosion damage, or are POW 14 or greater can damage a structure.

APPLYING DAMAGE TO OBJECTS

An inanimate object can suffer only so much damage before being destroyed. Every inanimate object has an Armor (ARM) stat and damage capacity corresponding to its composition. See the table below for details.

Structures are destroyed in sections. Each section is roughly six feet wide (1˝). The amount of damage each section can take before being penetrated or otherwise collapsing is based on the material it is constructed from. A wooden or brick structure can typically take 10 points of damage to a section before that section is compromised. A section of a stone or iron structure can take 20 points before collapsing. A steel structure can take 25 points per section.

For mixed-composition structures, ARM values might vary from location to location. Assign damage capacity of mixed-composition structures proportionally. The following table assumes that the method of destruction being used is effective against that type of material.

INANIMATE OBJECT DAMAGE TABLE

MATERIAL TYPE	ARM	DAMAGE CAPACITY (POINTS PER INCH)
Rope	8	1
Glass	12	1
Wood	14	10
Reinforced Wood	16	10
Brick	16	10
Stone	18	20
Iron	20	20
Steel	22	25

EXAMPLE: *A wooden door in an otherwise stone building would have ARM 14 and could take 10 points of damage before being destroyed while each 1˝ section stone wall around it would have ARM 18 and be able to suffer 20 points of damage before being compromised.*

The Game Master is encouraged to increase the damage capacity of objects and structures if they are particularly dense. For example, a three foot section of stone wall has substantially more damage boxes than a one foot thick section of wall.

A structure collapses once half of its sections have been destroyed. When a structure collapses, it becomes a ruin. A ruin is rough terrain and provides solid cover to a character with any part of its base inside the ruin's perimeter.

A character inside the structure when it collapses suffers a damage roll with POW equal to the structure's ARM times the number of levels in the structure, after which the character is knocked down.

ANXIETY, FEAR, AND TERROR

The Iron Kingdoms are filled with dangers and mysteries that can unnerve even the most veteran of adventurers. The death of an ally or the sight of friends routing can be every bit as horrifying as that of the blighted, dragon-spawned horrors or the haunted tombs of the fiendish Orgoth.

When confronted by a terrifying entity or a sight or situation so terrible it sends the sane mind reeling, a character must make a Willpower roll to resist the effects of fear. Player characters might be hardened warriors well used to the horrors of combat, but from time to time even the most stalwart heroes witness something that causes their blood to run cold. Horrifying situations include, but are not limited to, witnessing a friend be devoured by a rampaging beast, encountering the sight of slaughter, or seeing the dead rise to hungrily charge the living.

Some types of NPCs have a chance to lose their nerve if their leader dies or the tide of battle dramatically turns on them.

When a character must make a roll to resist the effects of fear, he makes a 2d6 + Willpower roll against either a target number either determined by the Game Master or the ability causing the fear.

TERRIFYING ENTITIES

When a character comes face to face with an entity with the Terror ability, he must make a Willpower roll to resist the effects of fear. The target number for this roll is set by the rules of the creature causing the terror.

The Terror ability has a number set in brackets. The bracketed number is the target number for rolls to resist the fear generated by the creature. For example, a character confronted by a creature with Terror [12] has to make a Willpower roll against a target number of 12 to resist the effects of terror created by the creature.

When characters are confronted by several terrifying entities simultaneously, each makes only one roll against the highest terror target number among the entities present.

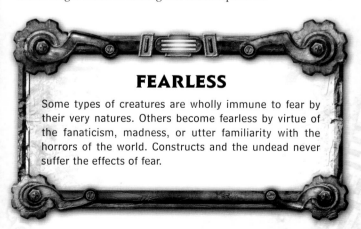

FEARLESS

Some types of creatures are wholly immune to fear by their very natures. Others become fearless by virtue of the fanaticism, madness, or utter familiarity with the horrors of the world. Constructs and the undead never suffer the effects of fear.

SITUATIONAL FEAR

A number of horrific situations might cause a character to make a fear roll. The Game Master determines when a situational fear roll is required. The following table lists possible causes for situational fear rolls and lists suggested target numbers for resisting those rolls.

TARGET NUMBER	FEAR EVENT
12	Horrific noises haunting the night
14	Encountering the sight of recent slaughter
15	Witnessing a particularly gruesome murder
16	Witnessing an ally consumed alive by a rampaging beast
16	Witnessing the dead rise and turn on the living

EFFECTS OF FEAR

A character is not simply afraid or not afraid. Fear ranges from a subtle, nuanced experience that heightens the senses and energizes the muscles for a flight-or-fight response to a mind-numbing blind panic.

Fear has three degrees: **Unaffected**, **Anxiety**, and **Panic**.

A character who succeeds in his initial Willpower roll to resist fear is **Unaffected**. A character unaffected by fear does not make another roll that encounter to resist fear unless he either witnesses a sight more terrible than the one that provoked his initial fear roll or he encounters an entity with a higher terror target number than the one that provoked his initial fear roll.

A character who failed his initial fear roll suffers **Anxiety**. While suffering Anxiety, the character gains +1 STR but suffers –1 on skill rolls, including attacks. The character cannot intentionally move toward the terror-causing sight or an entity with the Terror ability.

At the start of his next turn, the character must make another Willpower roll to resist the grip of fear if he is still in the presence of the source of his terror. If he succeeds, he becomes Unaffected. If he fails, the character suffers Panic. While suffering Panic, the character suffers –2 on skill rolls, including attacks. The character cannot intentionally move toward the terror causing sight or an entity with the Terror ability.

A character suffering **Panic** must make another Willpower roll to resist fear at the start of his next turn if he is still in the presence of the source of his terror. If he succeeds, he becomes Unaffected. If he fails, he must run away from the source of his terror, including all terrifying entities in his presence. If he cannot flee, he suffers hysterical paralysis and cannot move or take any actions. At the start of each of the character's Maintenance Phases he can make another roll to right his terror. If he succeeds, the character regains control over himself and becomes Unaffected. Otherwise, he keeps running.

LIGHT AND DARKNESS

Most conflicts in the Iron Kingdoms still occur in the light of day or well-lit urban environs, but player characters often find cause to skulk about in darkened streets, explore lightless crypts, or infiltrate an enemy camp under cover of darkness.

In bright light conditions such as sunlight or a well-lit room, characters follow all the standard rules for combat, detection, and sneaking. Bright light does not provide any bonuses or penalties. It is the assumed condition for most attacks and skill checks.

In dim light such as the light of a full moon or a few candles, most characters find it more difficult to attack or detect others but easier to hide from their foes. Characters in dim light gain concealment, granting them +2 DEF against ranged and magic attack rolls. Note that some spells (such as True Sight) and some attacks (like spray attacks) ignore the concealment bonus.

Characters in dim light conditions gain a +2 bonus on Sneak rolls.

In the complete darkness of a moonless night or pitch-black chamber, it is even more difficult to see a target and even easier to hide. Characters in complete darkness gain concealment and stealth, meaning that nearby enemies have a more difficult time hitting them with ranged or magic attacks and more distant enemies are guaranteed to miss them entirely.

Characters in complete darkness gain a +5 bonus on Sneak rolls.

Characters are likely to choose to carry their own light source, whether it's a pitch-smeared torch or an alchemical device.

Some light sources provide dim light while others provide bright light nearby and dim light farther away. Some of the more common light sources are listed below.

LIGHT SOURCE	BRIGHT LIGHT	DIM LIGHT	COMPLETE DARKNESS
Steam engine furnace	N/A	6 feet (1″)	> 6 feet
Runes of a spell being cast	N/A	12 feet (2″)	> 12 feet
Candle	N/A	24 feet (4″)	> 24 feet
Torchlight	18 feet (3″)	36 feet (6″)	> 36 feet
Campfire	18 feet (3″)	36 feet (6″)	> 36 feet
Alchemical torchlight	24 feet (4″)	48 feet (8″)	> 48 feet
Lantern	24 feet (4″)	48 feet (8″)	> 48 feet
Daylight or Light in the Darkness spell	36 feet (6″)	72 feet (12″)	> 72 feet
Mechanika lantern or mechanika light runeplate	36 feet (6″)	72 feet (12″)	> 72 feet

Game Masters should feel free to alter these distances based on various atmospheric conditions. High winds, storms, belching smoke, or falling ash could all serve to reduce the range of the characters' light sources.

MAGIC

At its most fundamental, magic is a supernatural energy and medium that can be manipulated to affect the underlying fabric of reality by an effort of will. The world of Caen normally exists in a state of stability and natural law, where matter and energy follow predictable and otherwise inviolable patterns. Magic allows those who master its principles to defy or bend natural law, whether subtly or overtly, creating causality that would not be possible without the manifestation of the arcane. Practitioners of magic have at their disposal tremendously useful but also singularly dangerous forces.

Some would say this is the power of the gods made manifest—a way mortals can perceive and affect the weft and weave that is the ineffable essence of reality. Many arcanists view it rather as a natural force that has its own strict laws, limits, and predictable interactions that are simply not yet fully understood. Some practitioners make it their life's work to add to the understanding of these powers and pass this lore to their peers. For others, magic is purely an outpouring of one's own will and is wielded intuitively like a weapon. Mortal minds find it difficult to control the vast and dangerous energies required to shape reality, but a very few reach levels of power that blur the line between mortal and divine.

Producing magic requires the ability to tap into a source of this supernatural energy and shape it by mentally visualizing and manipulating formulae comprised of mystical runes. It is by these runes that magical effects become fixed, their energies lying dormant but ready. Once an arcanist is satisfied with his formulae, he activates the runes to trigger the release of energy, by which the spell is completed and the magic invoked. For those practiced in these arts, this entire sequence takes mere seconds.

In order to accomplish this exploit, one must have the special Gift to see and shape mystical runes. This is sometimes described as an unlocked talent inherent to fully awakened immortal souls. This Gift can be found in humans, dwarves, elves, trollkin, and some other races, but remains dormant and unharnessed by most. Humanity has had a complex relationship with this talent, as for most of recorded history only priests could manifest magic. This changed during the Orgoth Rebellion, and as the ability became more widespread it also began to appear unpredictably in young individuals.

Those who spontaneously manifest arcane potential and develop this power without formal training are known as sorcerers. They still use mystical formulae when working magic, but their runes are less distinct and their formulae less precise and complex. The power of sorcerers is linked to a particular elemental affinity, such that the magic they can summon gives them power over rock and stone and manifests as blazing fire, flashes of lightning, or freezing winds.

Such natural aptitude is rare and has historically been met with fear and persecution in the Iron Kingdoms. This was exacerbated by incidents wherein incautious sorcerers unleashed destruction through unrestrained manifestations of elemental powers. Numerous organized efforts have cropped up over the years seeking to find and eliminate sorcerers. In the present day, sorcerers are no longer universally loathed and feared, but they are still seen as potentially dangerous. In many regions sorcerers are encouraged to seek formal training so their powers can be put to productive ends, such as within a kingdom's military.

MAGIC OF THE DIVINE

Since before written history there have been those who invoke magic through faith: priests and shamans. These spiritual leaders mix prayer and formulae to create magic through small miracles they credit to their divine patron. The greatest priests occasionally manifest miracles sent directly from the gods, and these serve as a tangible reminder that higher beings are watching and intervening in the world through their mortal intermediaries.

Most arcane scholars and theologians believe divine magic flows from the connection between the immortal soul and Urcaen, serving as a bridge for the energies of the gods. Others insist faith has inherent power and that truly divine energies are present only for the rarest and most spectacular miracles. Though the source of a faith caster's magic differs from that of secular arcanists, the fundamentals of how it is wielded are not dissimilar. Some faith casters rely on the force of their will to summon magic appropriate to their faith, whereas others tap into their powers with effortless ease or facilitate their magic by a connection to living beasts. All must still manipulate the mystical runes and formulae that allow magic to shape reality.

Faith casters rarely possess a deeper understanding of the complex rules by which magic functions and manifest magic strongly associated with the attributes of their divine patron. They sacrifice some flexibility to stand as an unwavering mortal conduit for the power of their god on Caen. In compensation, those who are truly faithful and become favored might be granted access to miracles beyond the power of scholarly arcanists.

Gifted individuals with any degree of instruction are deemed arcanists, even if their occult education is limited to the self-directed study of tomes. Arcanists make systematic efforts to understand and improve their control over magic. Some sorcerers pursue formal arcane study after realizing the limits of intuition, and join the ranks of the educated. Many of the most successful arcanists began their careers as sorcerers and eventually learned to temper and amplify their natural power through diligent study.

By empowering runes and unleashing this power in a controlled fashion, an infinite variety of magical effects are theoretically possible. That said, not all who practice magic are on equal footing. Access to the wellspring of magic varies and is manifested in different ways, analogous to how water can be gathered. For practitioners called will weavers, accumulating magical energy is a laborious process requiring exertion, like pumping water from a deep well, while those called focusers have access to a steady and constant flow like a man standing beside a river or a fountain. Some readily see mystical runes and effortlessly shape them, but others require a lifetime of careful study to apply these forces without risking destruction. Although there are a variety of traditions by which magic can be shaped, the underlying power is the same.

ARCANE TRADITIONS

All spellcasters belong to an arcane tradition that determines how their magic works in play. This book explores two, will weavers and focusers. Other arcane traditions will be explored in future products, such as harnessers (warlocks).

Most sorcerers and arcanists are **will weavers**, who rely on their own physical stamina and the force of their mental will to summon and direct arcane energy. This process can be incredibly taxing to the arcanist's body and mind but allows for the subtle weaving of intricate formulae. For these practitioners, siphoning mystical energy from its source requires concentration and fortitude. The greater the magical power called upon by the will weaver, the greater the risk as he pushes himself to exhaustion.

Some will weavers learn to augment their powers through engineering by mastering mechanika or studying alchemy, both invaluable skills. An exceptional few rise to the upper echelons of powerful arcane societies and gain access to formidable occult secrets and techniques. By tapping into their reserves, these masters of magic can become living arsenals of arcane power, aiding their allies by bending reality to suit their needs.

Rarer still are **focusers**, those for whom access to the flow of magical energy is instinctive and constant. Focusers tap into the magical forces both within the depths of their souls as well as all around them, acting as natural conduits. A focuser must still practice and train to refine their powers, but access to these energies comes unbidden.

Once a focuser becomes aware of the arcane energies flowing through him and can recognize the runes and formulae underlying reality, he is irrevocably changed. Arcane energy

RUNES AND FORMULAE

Harnessing power that can ignore the laws of nature or be transformed into tremendous surges of awe-inspiring elemental force is not a subtle or invisible practice. Although their techniques of summoning and shaping magic varies, all casters work through runes and formulae and these become visible to those around them when a spell is cast.

The exact shape and color spectrum of these runes varies by a caster's background and training, although there are fundamental sigils shared by many groups. For example, all modern human arcane orders draw from the same foundation, based on sigils developed during the early rebellion against the Orgoth. A caster inherits the runic forms of his source material, whether from a tutor or tome of recorded lore. Untrained sorcerers have less distinct runes and simpler formulae for this reason, pouring raw power into their sigils to make up for a lack of finesse. Sorcerer runes are closely aligned with their elemental affinity, being a more limited vocabulary describing manifestations of fire, ice, lightning, or earth. Some arcanists learn to customize the manifestations of their runes, but this requires considerable practice.

When an arcanist casts a spell, glowing runes depicting a tangible manifestation of formulae appear briefly surrounding his person, in a size and scope relative to the power being invoked. Less potent spells are prefigured by circles of runes around the caster's hand or an item used as a point of focus, such as a weapon. Larger effects result in concentric rings of runes around the caster's body, sometimes at waist height, at the shoulders, or around the head. If a spell is affecting someone else nearby, runes briefly manifest around that person as well.

To most people these glowing runes are indistinct and quickly forgotten manifestations of magic, with no meaning other than as an ominous sign of gathered supernatural forces. For other arcanists, it is possible to anticipate the scope and nature of the magic being gathered by witnessing the runes, an aptitude that can provide a tremendous tactical advantage. While bright, the appearance of these runes is too brief and focused to be utilized as a source of light, although they certainly draw attention to a caster in a dark place.

Casters involved in clandestine activities sometimes develop the ability to mask these runic formulae. Runes must always manifest for magic to function, but a skilled practitioner can change the hue and minimize the size and intensity to the point that they are all but unnoticeable. Certain spells specifically designed to augment stealth include these techniques as part of their casting.

is not an abstraction to the focuser, but as inseparable from his being as the blood in his veins. This enables him to extend his will into the environment in unique ways, augmenting his actions and easily tapping into mechanikal devices. Though a focuser has certain advantages over a will weaver, they do not have the same ability to plumb their inner reserves. A focuser's flow of magic is even and steady, but it can also be temporarily depleted and require time to replenish.

Compared to a focuser, a will weaver has a less finite supply of magic at any given moment. Drawing on magic requires more effort, but a skilled will weaver can push beyond his limits for special exertions. A will weaver has a deeper understanding of the fundamentals of the arcane and is practiced in fully exploiting that power.

DETERMINING YOUR CHARACTER'S TRADITION

A character's tradition determines the rules he uses when spell casting. All characters with the Gifted archetype begin the game with an arcane tradition. Once determined, a character's arcane tradition does not change.

Unless your character begins the game with the Warcaster career, his tradition is will weaver. Characters with the Warcaster career have the focuser tradition.

WILL WEAVERS

Will weavers rely on their force of will to summon and harness arcane energy. They do this by calling upon arcane formulae, often through some combination of thinking it, reciting it, and reading it. The mental formulation is the most important aspect, where the will is invested in the visualized image of the runes, but complex formulae are difficult to maintain perfectly in the mind without assistance. Most arcane practitioners utilize a variety of techniques to create mnemonic associations, and this can include the chanting of rote phrases, performing sequences of gestures, and complex written passages and diagrams. Many of these techniques are not strictly necessary to complete a spell, but arcanists find it easiest to perform magic by keeping to techniques they have repeatedly practiced, thereby entering into a meditative state.

As a will weaver works his magic, he generates fatigue points. Fatigue represents the mental toll of bending arcane forces to the spellcaster's will. A will weaver who operates within the limits of his capabilities runs little risk of overexerting himself, but one who pushes himself to the limit risks exhaustion, becoming unable to cast spells until taking a respite.

A will weaver can call upon his magic to cast and upkeep spells and to boost magical attack and magical damage rolls. As he does so, the will weaver generates fatigue points. Provided the will weaver does not exceed his ARC in fatigue points, nothing happens. If the character exceeds his ARC in fatigue points, he must make a fatigue roll to determine if he becomes exhausted. A will weaver cannot exceed double his ARC in fatigue points as a result of casting, upkeeping, or boosting spells.

GAINING FATIGUE POINTS

A will weaver can gain fatigue points to:

- Upkeep a Spell – A will weaver gains 1 fatigue point for each spell he upkeeps during each Control Phase.

- Cast a Spell – When a will weaver casts a spell, he gains a number of fatigue points equal to the COST of the spell.

- Boost a Magic Attack or Magic Damage Roll – Each time a will weaver boosts a magic attack or magic damage roll, he gains 1 fatigue point. Boosting must be declared before rolling any dice for the roll. Remember, a single roll can be boosted only once, but a will weaver can boost as many different rolls as he can afford.

- Increase the Range of a Spell – A will weaver can gain 1 fatigue point to increase the RNG of a spell by thirty feet (5″). Each spell cast can have its RNG extended only once as a result of gaining fatigue. Spells with a RNG of CTRL or SP cannot be affected in this way.

REMOVING FATIGUE POINTS

Will weavers remove a number of fatigue points equal to their ARC each Maintenance Phase.

FATIGUE ROLLS AND EXHAUSTION

If his fatigue points exceed his ARC, a will weaver must make a fatigue roll immediately after resolving each spell he casts. To make a fatigue roll, roll 2d6. If the total is equal to or over the number of fatigue points the will weaver currently has, nothing happens. If the total is less than the number of fatigue points the character has, he becomes exhausted.

When a character becomes exhausted his turn immediately ends and he cannot cast spells during the next round.

FOCUSERS

Focusers are able to tap into and manipulate the ambient arcane energy that permeates the world around them. The ability to extend one's mind into the environment to shape latent energies also allows focusers to connect with mechanika and affect these complex devices at a distance. This enables focusers to meld their minds with the inner workings of the cortexes within steamjacks. It is for this reason that only focusers have the potential to become warcasters.

For a warcaster to harness and channel his will into both steamjacks and other advanced mechanikal tools properly, he must spend some time attuning themselves to these items. By a concentrated exertion of mental effort, the focuser creates a lasting and unique bond with the mechanikal conduits of his most vital tools, and through this bond his energy can flow more easily (see the Bond ability, p. 158).

By these bonds, a focuser can empower warcaster armor to receive his arcane energy, wield mechanikal weapons to deadly effect, and use 'jacks as extensions of his will. Together these qualities have allowed warcasters to become unparalleled masters of the modern battlefield.

A focuser's arcane energy takes the form of focus points that he can allocate to the steamjacks he controls or spend to cast and upkeep spells, make additional attacks, or boost attack and damage rolls.

During the Control Phase of each round, a focuser receives a number of focus points equal to his Arcane stat. Unlike will weavers, who gain fatigue points as a result of casting spells or otherwise using their arcane powers, focusers spend the focus points they receive to work their magic.

A focuser can spend focus points to:

- Upkeep Spells – A focuser must spend 1 focus point for each spell he upkeeps during each Control Phase.

- Casting a Spell – When a focuser casts a spell, he must spend a number of focus points equal to the COST of the spell.

- Boost Attack and Damage Rolls – A focuser can spend focus points to boost magic attack and magic damage rolls. A focuser can also spend focus points to boost attack and damage rolls with a mechanika weapon he is bonded to. Each time a focuser boosts an attack or damage roll, he must spend 1 focus point. Boosting must be declared before rolling any dice for the roll. Remember, a single roll can be boosted only once, but a focuser can boost as many different rolls as he can afford.

- Make an Additional Attack – A focuser can spend focus to make additional melee or ranged attacks with a mechanika weapon he is bonded to during his turn. The focuser can make one additional attack for each focus point he spends.

- Allocate to Steamjacks – A focuser can allocate up to 3 focus points to each steamjack in his battlegroup in his control area. For full rules on how focusers interact with steamjacks, see pp. 321–324.

Unless otherwise stated, a character can spend focus points only during his turn.

REMOVING FOCUS POINTS

Remove all focus points from the focuser and the steamjacks in his battlegroup at the start of each of the focuser's Maintenance Phases.

GUN MAGES AND RUNE SHOT SPELLS

Gun mages are arcanists who channel their magic through special rune cast bullets. Gun mage is not a tradition, and a gun mage can be either a will weaver or a focuser (if he also has the Warcaster career). A gun mage works his magic through specially crafted weapons called magelocks that fire magically imbued rune shots.

RUNE SHOT SPELLS

Rune shots are specially crafted bullets designed to harness the arcane energies of a gun mage. Many gun mage spells are defined as rune shots. These spells are cast onto the ammunition round before the gun mage fires it, thus charging the round with arcane energy.

WARCASTER ARMOR

Warcaster armor is among the most advanced mechanika ever developed. In addition to providing physical protection in the form of masterwork armor, warcaster armor also integrates an arcane turbine, a highly efficient and advanced steam engine fueled by coal and designed to tap into and transform the focuser's arcane power into a protective field. The steam engine driving the arcane turbine is required to power small internal mechanisms, the negligible weight of which allows the turbine to run for many hours on a very small quantity of coal. The heart of the turbine is a complex series of wire-coiled wheels spinning inside a thinly layered metal lattice, all constructed of arcane-sensitive alloys. When worn by a focuser who has bonded to the armor, the turbine powers a protective field of force around the warcaster that also helps negate the encumbrance of the armor. This field absorbs damage that would otherwise be sustained by the focuser and can be replenished by redirecting the focuser's arcane power to the field. The focuser can also temporarily enhance the field's protective qualities by using focus to overboost the field.

A full description of warcaster armor can be found on p. 289.

Rune shot spells must be cast the turn they take effect and affect only the character's next shot with his magelock. If the character casts a rune shot spell and does not make an attack, the spell expires at the end of the turn. Unlike other spells, casting a rune shot spell does not require a quick action and any number of rune shot spells can be cast on a single shot. Although the gun mage can empower a single round with multiple spells, he can empower each round with the same spell only once and can empower each round only with a single rune shot spell that has an AOE.

A target directly hit by a rune shot attack suffers the effects of the ranged attack along with any spell effects the shot was empowered with.

CONTROL AREA

Gifted characters, both will weavers and focusers, have **control areas**. A control area is a circular area centered on the character with a radius that extends out from the edge of his base equal to his ARC x twelve feet (or twice his Arcane stat in tabletop inches). A character is always considered to be in his own control area. When a special rule changes a character's ARC stat, his control area changes accordingly. Some spells use the control area, noted as "CTRL," as their range or area of effect.

A character can measure his control area at any time, measuring the distance from himself to any point within his control area.

SPELLS

Some characters have the ability to cast spells during their turns. Will weavers cast spells by generating fatigue points. Focusers cast spells by paying the spell's COST in focus points. A spell can be cast multiple times per Activation Phase, but its COST must be paid each time.

With the exception of gun mage rune shot spells that do not require the expenditure of an action to cast, spells are cast as quick actions. A character cannot cast a spell during a turn in which he runs.

When a spell is cast, resolve its effects immediately.

STEAMJACKS AND CONTROL AREA

A steamjack must be in its controlling warcaster's control area to receive focus points from the warcaster or to channel spells.

A spell's point of origin is the character casting the spell or the character through which the spell is channeled (see "Channeling," p. 233). Unless noted otherwise, spells that target a character other than the casting character or the character channeling the spell require line of sight to their targets.

LEARNING SPELLS

Not all spells are available to every character. The spells a character can learn are determined by his career's spell list (pp. 234–236). A character can learn spells from any of his career lists.

A character can know a maximum number of spells equal to his INT x2.

SPELL STATISTICS

A spell is defined by the following six statistics:

COST – The cost of the spell. This is either the number of fatigue points a will weaver gains from casting the spell or the number of focus points a focuser spends to cast the spell.

RNG (Range) – The maximum distance in inches from the spell's point of origin to its target. A RNG of "SELF" indicates the spell can be cast only on the character casting it. A RNG of "CTRL" indicates the spell uses the spellcaster's control area as its range.

RANGE REMINDER

Remember that a single inch on the tabletop is the equivalent of six feet.

AOE (Area of Effect) – The diameter in inches of the template an AOE spell uses for its effects. When casting an AOE spell, center the template on the determined point of impact. A character with any part of his base covered by the template potentially suffers the spell's effects. See p. 212 for details on AOE attacks. Templates for AOEs appear on p. 352. A spell with an AOE of "CTRL" is centered on the spellcaster and affects characters in his control area.

POW (Power) – The base amount of damage a spell inflicts. The POW forms the basis of the spell's damage roll. A spell with POW "—" does not cause a damage roll.

UP (Upkeep) (Yes/No) – Determines whether the spell can be upkept. An upkeep spell remains in play if the character who cast it pays the upkeep to maintain it during the Control Phase. Will weavers gain 1 fatigue point for each upkeep spell they keep in play. Focusers must spend 1 focus point for each spell they keep in play.

OFF (Offensive) (Yes/No) – Whether the spell is offensive. An offensive spell requires a successful magic attack roll to hit its target. If the attack roll fails, the attack misses and, unless it is an AOE spell, has no effect. A failed attack roll for an offensive spell with an area of effect deviates.

If a stat is listed as "*" the spell does not use the stat in a normal way and contains special rules relating to that aspect of the spell.

EXAMPLE: *A spell that has an AOE but does not use one of the standard 3", 4", or 5" templates would have "*" as its AOE stat and include rules explaining how its AOE is measured.*

CASTING A SPELL

To cast a spell, a character must first pay its COST. For will weavers, this means gaining a number of fatigue points equal to the cost of the spell. For focusers, this means spending a number of focus points equal to the cost of the spell. If the spell is an upkeep spell, any other instances of that spell currently in play that were cast by the caster immediately expire. Next, declare the target. A spell can target any character in the caster's line of sight (see "Line of Sight," p. 200) subject to the targeting rules. Non-offensive spells with a numeric RNG can also target the point of origin of the spell.

Certain rules and effects create situations that specifically prevent a character from being targeted. A character who cannot be targeted by an attack still suffers its effects if inside the attack's AOE. Other rules and effects, such as stealth, might cause an attack to miss automatically but they do not prevent the character from being targeted by the attack. An offensive spell cannot target its point of origin.

MEASURING RANGE

After declaring the target of the spell, measure to see if the target is within the range (RNG) of the spell. Measure range from the edge of the point of origin's base to the target up to the maximum range of the spell. If the nearest edge of the target character's base is within the maximum range of the spell, the target is in range. If the target is in range and the spell is non-offensive, the spell immediately takes effect. If the target is in range and the spell is offensive, make a magic attack roll to see if it hits.

If the target is beyond maximum range, a non-offensive spell does not take effect and an offensive spell automatically misses. If a magic attack has an area of effect (AOE) and the attack's target is out of range, it automatically misses, and its point of impact deviates from the point on the line to its declared target at a distance equal to its RNG. See "Area-of-Effect (AOE) Attacks" on p. 212 for details on these attacks and deviation.

OFFENSIVE SPELLS AND MAGIC ATTACK ROLLS

An offensive spell is a magic attack that requires the spellcaster to succeed in a magic attack roll to hit its target. Magic attacks are similar to ranged attacks and follow most of the same rules.

Determine a magic attack's success by making a magic attack roll. Roll 2d6 and add the attacking character's ARC. Roll an additional die if the roll is boosted. Special rules and certain circumstances might modify the attack roll as well.

MAGIC ATTACK ROLL = 2D6 + ARC

A character is directly hit if the attack roll equals or exceeds his DEF. If the attack roll is less than the target's DEF, it misses. A roll of all 1s on the dice causes an automatic miss. A roll of all 6s is a direct hit unless you are rolling only one die, regardless of the target's DEF.

Sometimes a special rule causes an attack to hit automatically. Such automatic hits are also direct hits.

A magic attack roll does not suffer the target in melee attack roll penalty when the attacker is in melee with the target. If such an attack misses and there are multiple characters in the combat, the attack can still hit another random character in the combat, excluding the attacker and the original target. Resolve these situations following the rules in "Targeting a Character in Melee" on p. 212 and "Spell Targeting" below. An AOE spell that misses in this situation deviates normally.

The same modifiers that affect ranged attack rolls also affect magic attack rolls. See p. 211 for the complete list.

SPELL TARGETING

Many spells can be cast only on certain types of characters, such as steamjacks or enemies. Such restrictions are noted in a spell's description. To abbreviate these targeting restrictions, when a spell's description mentions an effect against a "target something," the spell can be cast only on that type of character.

Example: The Fail Safe spell states, "Target steamjack gains +2 ARM and does not suffer the effects of crippled systems." This spell can only target a steamjack.

When using an offensive spell to attack a structure, ignore its targeting restrictions.

When an offensive spell targeting a character in melee misses, ignore its targeting restrictions when determining which characters in the combat might be hit instead. If the new target is an invalid one for the spell, the spell has no further effect. (See "Targeting a Character in Melee" on p. 212 and "Offensive Spells and Magic Attacks" above for details on resolving a magic attack against a character in melee.) An AOE spell that misses deviates normally instead.

Example: A sorcerer attempts to cast the Freezing Grip spell on a farrow chieftain in melee with a town watchman who is himself in melee with two other farrow. There are four characters in the combat. If the sorcerer misses, determine which of the other three characters might be hit by the spell as usual. The sorcerer is not worried about hitting the town watchmen by mistake because the watchmen currently have Immunity: Cold. If the attack missed the farrow chieftain and hits one of the town watchmen instead, the spell has no effect.

UPKEEP SPELLS

Upkeep spells can be kept in play from round to round. During the Control Phase, a will weaver gains 1 fatigue point for each upkeep spell he keeps in play and a warcaster must pay 1 focus point for each upkeep spell he keeps in play. A character can maintain an upkeep spell even if the spell's effects are outside his control area, up to a distance of his ARC x 10". If an upkeep spell is not maintained during the Control Phase, the spell immediately expires.

A character can have only one instance of each specific upkeep spell in play at a time, but he can maintain any number of different upkeep spells simultaneously if he pays the cost to do so. A character can have only one offensive and one non-offensive upkeep spell on him at a time. If another upkeep spell of a type already affecting the character is cast on that character, the older upkeep spell expires and is replaced by the newly cast one when the affected character is hit by the spell.

A character can recast any of his upkeep spells already in play. If this happens, the spell's previous casting immediately expires when the COST of the new casting is paid.

Pay particular attention to this restriction when casting upkeep spells with a target of "SELF."

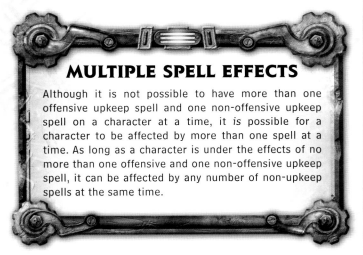

MULTIPLE SPELL EFFECTS

Although it is not possible to have more than one offensive upkeep spell and one non-offensive upkeep spell on a character at a time, it *is* possible for a character to be affected by more than one spell at a time. As long as a character is under the effects of no more than one offensive and one non-offensive upkeep spell, it can be affected by any number of non-upkeep spells at the same time.

UPKEEPING SPELLS OUTSIDE OF COMBAT

A character can upkeep a number of spells equal to his ARC outside of combat.

SPELLCASTER DEATH

If a spellcaster is destroyed or removed from play, his upkeep spells and any spells that would have expired at the start of his next turn immediately expire.

CHANNELING

Some characters and equipment, known as channelers, can act as passive relays for spells and thereby extend their effective range. Each channeler has a number of rules that determine how it can be used. A channeler must be in a spellcaster's control area for the spellcaster to cast spells through the channeler.

A spellcaster channeling a spell is still the attacker and is considered to be the character casting the spell, but the channeler becomes the spell's point of origin. This means

that eligible targets and the spell's range are measured from the channeler and that the channeler must have line of sight to the spell's target. Channeling a spell does not require the spellcaster to have line of sight to either the channeler or the spell's target. There is no additional cost for channeling a spell.

A channeler engaged by an enemy cannot channel spells. A stationary channeler can channel spells, but one that is knocked down cannot. A channeler can be the target of a non-offensive spell it channels, but a spell with a RNG of "SELF" cannot be channeled. A channeler cannot be the target of an offensive spell channeled through it.

Make a magic attack roll for a channeled offensive spell normally. The spellcaster can boost die rolls or otherwise enhance the spell normally.

Remember, the channeler is just a relay. Being used to channel a spell is a passive effect that occurs during a spellcaster's turn and has no impact on the channeler's own turn.

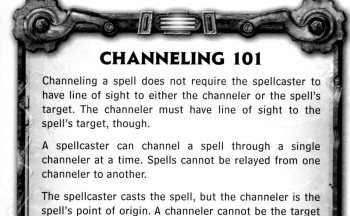

CHANNELING 101

Channeling a spell does not require the spellcaster to have line of sight to either the channeler or the spell's target. The channeler must have line of sight to the spell's target, though.

A spellcaster can channel a spell through a single channeler at a time. Spells cannot be relayed from one channeler to another.

The spellcaster casts the spell, but the channeler is the spell's point of origin. A channeler cannot be the target of an offensive spell channeled through it.

STEAMJACK ARC NODES

Steamjacks are sometimes equipped with arc nodes that allow focusers controlling them to cast spells through them. A warcaster can channel spells through any steamjack in his battlegroup with an arc node that is also within his control area. Focus points allocated to a steamjack with an arc node cannot be used to pay the spell's COST or boost its rolls.

SPELL LISTS

Spell lists are divided by career and COST.

ARCANE MECHANIK SPELLS

Arcane Mechaniks can learn spells from the following lists.

COST 1	Jackhammer, Jump Start, Locomotion, Power Booster, Protection from Electricity, Return Fire, Short Out
COST 2	Arcantrik Bolt, Electrify, Fortify, Polarity Shield, Positive Charge, Redline, Refuge, Temper Metal
COST 3	Broadside, Electrical Blast, Fail Safe, Force Field, Full Throttle, Grind, Guided Fire, Iron Aggression, Superiority
COST 4	Black Out, Tide of Steel, Voltaic Lock

ARCANIST SPELLS

Arcanists can learn spells from the following lists.

COST 1	Arcane Strike, Blizzard, Fire Starter, Guided Blade, Influence, Light in the Darkness, Protection from Cold, Protection from Corrosion, Protection from Electricity, Protection from Fire, Storm Tossed
COST 2	Arcane Bolt, Ashen Cloud, Aura of Protection, Banishing Ward, Celerity, Foxhole, Hand of Fate, Howling Flames, Icy Grip, Occultation, Rock Wall, Telekinesis, True Sight, Vision, Wind Blast
COST 3	Fog of War, Force Field, Hex Blast, Inhospitable Ground, Lightning Tendrils, Mirage, Rift, Rock Hammer, Zephyr
COST 4	Force Hammer, Overmind, Tempest

GUN MAGE SPELLS

Gun Mages can learn spells from the following lists.

COST 1	Return Fire, Rune Shot: Accuracy, Rune shot: Black Penny, Rune Shot: Brutal, Rune Shot: Iron Rot, Rune Shot: Molten Shot, Rune Shot: Silencer, Rune Shot: Spontaneous Combustion, Rune Shot: Thunderbolt
COST 2	Fire Group, Heightened Reflexes, Refuge, Rune Shot: Fire Beacon, Rune Shot: Shadow Fire, Rune Shot: Trick Shot, Snipe, True Sight
COST 3	Guided Fire, Rune Shot: Detonator, Rune Shot: Earth Shaker, Rune Shot: Phantom Seeker, Rune Shot: Spell Cracker
COST 4	Rune Shot: Freeze Fire, Rune Shot: Heart Stopper, Rune Shot: Momentum

PRIEST SPELLS

Priests can learn spells from their god's spell lists.

PRIEST OF MENOTH

COST 1	Flames of Wrath, Guided Blade, Influence, Protection from Fire
COST 2	Ashen Cloud, Banishing Ward, Hymn of Battle, Hymn of Passage, Ignite, Immolation, Righteous Flames, Vision, Wall of Fire
COST 3	Cleansing Fire, Crevasse, Crusaders Call, Hex Blast, Lamentation, Purification, True Path
COST 4	Ashes to Ashes, Blazing Effigy, Hymn of Shielding

PRIEST OF MORROW

COST 1	Blessing of Health, Guided Blade, Light in the Darkness, Solovin's Boon
COST 2	Aura of Protection, Banishing Ward, Blade of Radiance, Blessings of War, Eyes of Truth, Hand of Fate, Shield of Faith, Triage, True Sight
COST 3	Blessing of Morrow, Crusader's Call, Daylight, Prayer of Guidance, Sanguine Blessing, Sunburst, True Path
COST 4	Force of Faith, Heal, Star Fire

SORCERER SPELLS

When a character becomes a sorcerer, he chooses an elemental spell list. The character can learn spells from his elemental list. Once selected, his element cannot change.

FIRE

COST 1	Fire Starter, Flames of Wrath, Protection from Fire
COST 2	Ashen Cloud, Extinguisher, Howling Flames, Ignite, Immolation, Wall of Fire
COST 3	Barrier of Flames, Cleansing Fire, Flare, Fuel the Flames, Inferno
COST 4	Ashes to Ashes, Blazing Effigy, Sea of Fire

ICE

COST 1	Blizzard, Ice Shield, Protection from Cold
COST 2	Chiller, Frostbite, Ice Bolt, Icy Grip, Shatter Storm, Staying Winter's Hand
COST 3	Brittle Frost, Deep Freeze, Frozen Ground, Hoarfrost, Winter Storm
COST 4	Freezing Grip, Freezing Mist, White Out

STONE

COST 1	Earth's Cradle, Entangle, Stone Stance
COST 2	Battering Ram, Fortify, Fox Hole, Rock Wall, Solid Ground, Stone Strength
COST 3	Crevasse, Earthquake, Inhospitable Ground, Rift, Rock Hammer
COST 4	Earthsplitter, Obliteration, Shock Wave

STORM

COST 1	Fair Winds, Storm Tossed, Wind Strike
COST 2	Boundless Charge, Celerity, Razor Wind, Telekinesis, Wind Blast, Wings of Air
COST 3	Chain Lightning, Deceleration, Fog of War, Lightning Tendrils, Zephyr
COST 4	Raging Winds, Tempest, Tornado

WARCASTER SPELLS

Warcasters can learn spells from the following list:

COST 1	Arcane Strike, Jump Start, Return Fire
COST 2	Arcane Bolt, Aura of Protection, Battering Ram, Boundless Charge, Convection, Fortify, Foxhole, Redline, Refuge, Snipe, Temper Metal, Transference
COST 3	Awareness, Batten Down the Hatches, Eliminator, Fail Safe, Grind, Guided Fire, Iron Aggression, Rift, Superiority
COST 4	Force Hammer, Obliteration, Tide of Steel

SPELL DESCRIPTIONS

	COST	RNG	AOE	POW	UP	OFF
ARCANE BOLT	2	12	—	11	NO	YES

Magical bolts of energy streak toward the target.

	COST	RNG	AOE	POW	UP	OFF
ARCANE STRIKE	1	8	—	8	NO	YES

An arcane force blasts toward the target.

	COST	RNG	AOE	POW	UP	OFF
ARCANTRIK BOLT	2	10	—	12	NO	YES

A steamjack damaged by this attack becomes stationary for one round.

	COST	RNG	AOE	POW	UP	OFF
ASHEN CLOUD	2	CTRL	3	—	YES	NO

Place a 3″ AOE cloud effect anywhere completely in the spellcaster's control area. Characters without Immunity: Fire suffer –2 on attack rolls while within the AOE.

	COST	RNG	AOE	POW	UP	OFF
ASHES TO ASHES	4	8	•	10	NO	YES

If target character is hit, he and d6 of the nearest enemies within 5″ of the target suffer a POW 10 fire damage roll.

	COST	RNG	AOE	POW	UP	OFF
AURA OF PROTECTION	2	SELF	CTRL	—	YES	NO

While in the spellcaster's control area, friendly characters gain +2 ARM.

	COST	RNG	AOE	POW	UP	OFF
AWARENESS	3	SELF	CTRL	—	NO	NO

While in the spellcaster's control area, the front arcs of characters in his battlegroup are extended to 360°. When determining LOS, those characters ignore cloud effects, forests, and intervening characters. Awareness lasts for one round.

	COST	RNG	AOE	POW	UP	OFF
BANISHING WARD	2	6	—	—	YES	NO

Enemy upkeep spells on the targeted friendly character expire. The affected character cannot be targeted by enemy spells or animi.

ANIMI

The term "animi" refers to the spell-like abilities of warbeasts. Warbeasts and animi will be explained in depth in future Full Metal Fantasy books.

	COST	RNG	AOE	POW	UP	OFF
BARRIER OF FLAMES	3	SELF	CTRL	—	NO	NO

Friendly characters in the spellcaster's control area gain +1 DEF. When a friendly character is hit by a melee attack while in the spellcaster's control area, the attacker suffers the Fire continuous effect. Barrier of Flames lasts for one round.

	COST	RNG	AOE	POW	UP	OFF
BATTERING RAM	2	6	—	12	NO	YES

When a character is hit by Battering Ram, he can be pushed 3" directly away from the spell's point of origin.

	COST	RNG	AOE	POW	UP	OFF
BATTEN DOWN THE HATCHES	3	SELF	CTRL	—	NO	NO

While in the spellcaster's control area, characters in his battlegroup cannot be knocked down and gain +3 ARM but suffer −2 DEF. Batten Down the Hatches lasts for one round.

	COST	RNG	AOE	POW	UP	OFF
BLACK OUT	4	SELF	CTRL	—	NO	NO

Mechanika devices in the possession of enemy characters in the spellcaster's control area immediately deactivate. If an enemy enters the spellcaster's control area, mechanika devices in his possession immediately deactivate. While in the spellcaster's control area, enemy characters cannot activate mechanika devices. Black Out has no effect on steamjacks or mechanika armor. Black Out lasts for one round.

	COST	RNG	AOE	POW	UP	OFF
BLADE OF RADIANCE	2	10	—	10	NO	YES

Infernal and Undead characters hit by this spell suffer an additional die of damage.

	COST	RNG	AOE	POW	UP	OFF
BLAZING EFFIGY	4	SELF	*	14	NO	NO

Enemies within 2" of the targeted friendly character suffer a POW 14 fire damage roll.

	COST	RNG	AOE	POW	UP	OFF
BLESSING OF HEALTH	1	6	—	—	YES	NO

Target character gains +3 on PHY rolls to resist poison, disease, and infection. Additionally, if the affected character is currently suffering from the effects of a poison, he immediately makes a PHY roll against the toxin rating of the poison. If the roll succeeds, the effects of the poison immediately expire.

	COST	RNG	AOE	POW	UP	OFF
BLESSING OF MORROW	3	SELF	CTRL	—	YES	NO

While in the spellcaster's control area, friendly living characters do not suffer the effects of lost aspects.

	COST	RNG	AOE	POW	UP	OFF
BLESSINGS OF WAR	2	6	—	—	YES	NO

Target character's weapons gains Blessed. (When making an attack with a weapon with Blessed, ignore spell effects that add to the attacking character's ARM or DEF.)

	COST	RNG	AOE	POW	UP	OFF
BLIZZARD	1	6	—	—	NO	NO

Center a 3" AOE cloud effect on target character. The AOE remains centered on the character. If the target character is destroyed, remove the AOE from play. Blizzard lasts for one round.

	COST	RNG	AOE	POW	UP	OFF
BRITTLE FROST	3	8	—	—	YES	YES

The next time target enemy suffers damage, halve its base ARM when calculating damage from the damage roll. After applying this damage, Brittle Frost expires.

	COST	RNG	AOE	POW	UP	OFF
BOUNDLESS CHARGE	2	6	—	—	NO	NO

During his turn, target character can charge without spending focus or being forced and gains +2" movement and Pathfinder when it charges. Boundless Charge lasts for one round.

	COST	RNG	AOE	POW	UP	OFF
BROADSIDE	3	SELF	CTRL	—	NO	NO

The spellcaster and steamjacks under the spellcaster's control currently in his control area can immediately make one normal ranged attack. Broadside can be cast only once per turn.

	COST	RNG	AOE	POW	UP	OFF
CELERITY	2	6	—	—	YES	NO

Target character gains one additional quick action during each of his turns.

	COST	RNG	AOE	POW	UP	OFF
CHAIN LIGHTNING	3	10	—	10	NO	YES

A character hit by Chain Lightning suffers a POW 10 electrical damage roll, and lightning arcs from that character to d6 consecutive additional characters. The lightning arcs to the nearest character it has not already arced to within 4" of the last model it arced to, ignoring the spellcaster. Each character the lightning arcs to suffers a POW 10 electrical damage roll.

	COST	RNG	AOE	POW	UP	OFF
CHILLER	2	6	—	—	YES	NO

While within 2" of the targeted friendly character, enemy characters suffer −2 DEF unless they have Immunity: Cold.

	COST	RNG	AOE	POW	UP	OFF
CLEANSING FIRE	3	8	3	14	NO	YES

Cleansing Fire causes fire damage. On a critical hit, characters hit suffer the Fire continuous effect.

	COST	RNG	AOE	POW	UP	OFF
CONVECTION	2	10	—	12	NO	YES

When Convection destroys a living character, you can allocate 1 focus point to a steamjack in the spellcaster's battlegroup that is in his control area.

	COST	RNG	AOE	POW	UP	OFF
CREVASSE	3	8	—	12	NO	YES

If Crevasse incapacitates its original target, you can make a SP 6 attack using the incapacitated character as the attack's point of origin. Characters hit suffer a POW 12 magic damage roll.

	COST	RNG	AOE	POW	UP	OFF
CRUSADER'S CALL	3	SELF	CTRL	—	NO	NO

Friendly characters beginning a charge while in the spellcaster's control area gain +2″ movement. Crusader's Call lasts for one round.

	COST	RNG	AOE	POW	UP	OFF
DAYLIGHT	3	SELF	CTRL	—	NO	NO

While in the spellcaster's control area, Infernal and Undead characters suffer –3 DEF and ARM. Additionally, the area around the spellcaster glows with enough light for anyone in his control area to see in darkness (p. 225). Daylight lasts for one round.

	COST	RNG	AOE	POW	UP	OFF
DECELERATION	3	SELF	CTRL	—	NO	NO

While in the spellcaster's control area, friendly characters gain +2 DEF and ARM against ranged attacks. Deceleration lasts for one round.

	COST	RNG	AOE	POW	UP	OFF
DEEP FREEZE	3	SELF	—	—	NO	NO

Characters within 2″ of the spellcaster suffer a POW 12 cold damage roll. Characters damaged by this spell cannot run, charge, or make power attacks for one round.

	COST	RNG	AOE	POW	UP	OFF
EARTHQUAKE	3	10	5	—	NO	YES

Characters in the AOE are knocked down.

	COST	RNG	AOE	POW	UP	OFF
EARTH'S CRADLE	1	SELF	—	—	YES	NO

The spellcaster gains cover, does not suffer blast damage, and does not block LOS. Earth's Cradle expires if this character moves, is placed, or is engaged.

	COST	RNG	AOE	POW	UP	OFF
EARTHSPLITTER	4	10	3	14	NO	YES

Characters hit suffer a POW 14 fire damage roll. The AOE is a cloud effect that remains in play for one round. Characters entering or ending their turn in the AOE suffer an unboostable POW 14 fire damage roll.

	COST	RNG	AOE	POW	UP	OFF
ELECTRICAL BLAST	3	8	3	13	NO	YES

Electrical Blast causes electrical damage. Steamjacks damaged by Electrical Blast suffer Disruption. (A steamjack suffering Disruption loses its focus points and cannot be allocated focus or channel spells for one round).

	COST	RNG	AOE	POW	UP	OFF
ELECTRIFY	2	6	—	—	YES	NO

If target character is hit by a melee attack, after the attack is resolved the attacker is pushed d3″ directly away from the affected character and suffers an unboostable POW 14 electrical damage roll, then Electrify expires.

	COST	RNG	AOE	POW	UP	OFF
ELIMINATOR	3	8	3	13	NO	YES

Immediately after this attack is resolved, the spellcaster can advance up to 2″ for each enemy incapacitated by the attack.

	COST	RNG	AOE	POW	UP	OFF
ENTANGLE	1	8	—	—	NO	YES

Target character suffers –1 SPD and cannot run or charge for one round.

	COST	RNG	AOE	POW	UP	OFF
EYES OF TRUTH	2	SELF	—	—	YES	NO

This character's PER rolls are boosted. Additionally, the target number for Deception rolls against this character is increased by 3.

	COST	RNG	AOE	POW	UP	OFF
EXTINGUISHER	2	SELF	CTRL	—	NO	NO

Fire continuous effects in the spellcaster's control area immediately expire.

	COST	RNG	AOE	POW	UP	OFF
FAIL SAFE	3	6	—	—	YES	NO

Target steamjack gains +2 ARM and does not suffer the effects of crippled systems.

	COST	RNG	AOE	POW	UP	OFF
FAIR WINDS	1	SELF	—	—	NO	NO

The spellcaster gains +1 SPD this turn.

	COST	RNG	AOE	POW	UP	OFF
FIRE GROUP	2	SELF	CTRL	—	NO	NO

While in the spellcaster's control area, his weapons and the ranged weapons of steamjacks under his control gain +2 RNG. Fire Group lasts for one round.

	COST	RNG	AOE	POW	UP	OFF
FIRE STARTER	1	8	—	—	NO	•

The spellcaster starts a small fire within the range of the spell and in line of sight. This spell can be used to target an enemy, in which case it requires an attack roll. If the enemy is hit, he suffers the Fire continuous effect.

	COST	RNG	AOE	POW	UP	OFF
FLAMES OF WRATH	1	6	—	—	NO	NO

When target character incapacitates an enemy with a melee attack, enemy characters within 1″ of the incapacitated character suffer the Fire continuous effect. Flames of Wrath lasts for one round.

	COST	RNG	AOE	POW	UP	OFF
FLARE	3	SELF	CTRL	—	NO	NO

Enemies in the spellcaster's control area suffering the Fire continuous effect immediately suffer an additional unboostable POW 12 fire damage roll. This spell can be cast only once per turn.

	COST	RNG	AOE	POW	UP	OFF
FOG OF WAR	3	SELF	CTRL	—	YES	NO

Characters gain concealment while in the spellcaster's control area.

	COST	RNG	AOE	POW	UP	OFF
FORCE FIELD	3	SELF	CTRL	—	YES	NO

The spellcaster does not suffer blast or collateral damage and cannot be knocked down. When an enemy AOE ranged attack deviates from a point in the spellcaster's control area, after the deviation distance is rolled the spellcaster's player chooses the deviation direction.

	COST	RNG	AOE	POW	UP	OFF
FORCE HAMMER	4	10	—	12	NO	YES

If Force Hammer hits a non-incorporeal target, instead of suffering a normal damage roll, that target is slammed d6" directly away from the spell's point of origin regardless of its base size and suffers a POW 12 damage roll. Collateral damage from this slam is POW 12.

	COST	RNG	AOE	POW	UP	OFF
FORCE OF FAITH	4	SELF	CTRL	—	NO	NO

Enemies currently in the spellcaster's control area are immediately pushed d6" directly away from the spellcaster in the order he chooses.

	COST	RNG	AOE	POW	UP	OFF
FORTIFY	2	6	—	—	YES	NO

Target steamjack under the spellcaster's control gains +2 ARM. The affected steamjack and any friendly character B2B with it cannot be knocked down, pushed, or slammed.

	COST	RNG	AOE	POW	UP	OFF
FOXHOLE	2	CTRL	5	—	YES	NO

Place a 5" AOE anywhere completely in the spellcaster's control area. Characters completely in the AOE have cover and do not suffer blast damage. When drawing LOS to a character not completely within the AOE, ignore intervening characters completely within the AOE.

	COST	RNG	AOE	POW	UP	OFF
FREEZING GRIP	4	8	—	—	NO	YES

Target character hit becomes stationary for one round unless the target has Immunity: Cold.

	COST	RNG	AOE	POW	UP	OFF
FREEZING MIST	4	SELF	*	—	NO	NO

While in the spellcaster's control area, enemy characters without Immunity: Cold suffer −2 SPD and DEF. Freezing Mist lasts for one round.

	COST	RNG	AOE	POW	UP	OFF
FROZEN GROUND	3	SELF	—	—	NO	NO

Enemies that move more than 2" and end their movement in the spellcaster's control area are knocked down at the end of their movement. Frozen Ground lasts for one round.

	COST	RNG	AOE	POW	UP	OFF
FROSTBITE	2	SP8	—	12	NO	YES

Frostbite causes cold damage.

	COST	RNG	AOE	POW	UP	OFF
FUEL THE FLAMES	3	SELF	CTRL	—	YES	NO

Fire continuous effects on enemies in the spellcaster's control area never expire.

	COST	RNG	AOE	POW	UP	OFF
FULL THROTTLE	3	SELF	CTRL	—	NO	NO

Steamjacks under the spellcaster's control beginning their turns in his control area can run, charge, or make slam or trample power attacks without spending focus or being driven that activation. The spellcaster and steamjacks under the spellcaster's control in his control area gain boosted melee attack rolls. Full Throttle lasts for one turn.

	COST	RNG	AOE	POW	UP	OFF
GRIND	3	10	—	14	NO	YES

When a steamjack is hit by Grind, it suffers 1 damage point to its first available Movement system box.

	COST	RNG	AOE	POW	UP	OFF
GUIDED BLADE	1	6	—	—	NO	NO

Target friendly character gains +1 on his melee attack rolls and his melee weapons gain Magical Weapon. Guided Blade lasts for one round.

	COST	RNG	AOE	POW	UP	OFF
GUIDED FIRE	3	SELF	CTRL	—	NO	NO

The spellcaster and steamjacks under the spellcaster's control in his control area gain boosted ranged attack rolls. Guided Fire lasts until for one round.

	COST	RNG	AOE	POW	UP	OFF
HAND OF FATE	2	6	—	—	YES	NO

Target character gains an additional die on attack and damage rolls. Discard the low die in each roll.

	COST	RNG	AOE	POW	UP	OFF
HEAL	4	•	—	—	NO	NO

Target friendly incapacitated character B2B with the spellcaster is no longer incapacitated and regains 1 vitality point in each aspect. The character no longer suffers from the results of his most recent roll on the Injury Table (p. 217). The target character becomes knocked down. Each time a character is targeted by this spell make a d6 roll on the Price of Healing Table below, adding +1 to the roll for each time the character has been targeted by this spell after the first time.

	COST	RNG	AOE	POW	UP	OFF
HEIGHTENED REFLEXES	2	6	—	—	YES	NO

Target character cannot be knocked down or made stationary.

	COST	RNG	AOE	POW	UP	OFF
HEX BLAST	3	10	3	13	NO	YES

Upkeep spells and animi on the character directly hit by Hex Blast immediately expire.

	COST	RNG	AOE	POW	UP	OFF
HOARFROST	3	8	3	14	NO	YES

Hoarfrost causes cold damage. On a critical hit, the characters hit become stationary for one round unless they have Immunity: Cold.

	COST	RNG	AOE	POW	UP	OFF
HOWLING FLAMES	2	SP8	—	10	NO	YES

Howling Flames causes fire damage. On a critical hit, the character hit suffers the Fire continuous effect.

	COST	RNG	AOE	POW	UP	OFF
HYMN OF BATTLE	2	6	—	—	NO	NO

Target steamjack gains +2 on attack and damage rolls. Hymn of Battle lasts for one round.

HEALING

True healing is not a natural aspect of magic; knitting living flesh and organs is a complex and difficult endeavor better served by surgeons or allowing a body to rest and recover. Mystical restoration is possible only through a manifestation of divine energy, which makes all healing a minor miracle. Such miracles carry risk and inflict a toll on the body, whether as temporary weakness or, in the case of repeated healing, permanent marks or impairment.

PRICE OF HEALING

ROLL	RESULT
1–3	The character suffers no side effect from the healing.
4–5	**Temporary Affliction** – The character suffers from a mild and temporary side effect of the healing. He might take ill with a fever, feel extraordinarily tired, or suffer some other mild affliction. As a result, the character suffers −1 STR and ARM for the next 2d6 hours.
6	**Exhaustion** – The character is utterly exhausted by his ordeal. He suffers −3 to all INT and PER rolls until he has slept for at least eight hours.
7	**Dumb** – The character was temporarily struck dumb as a side effect of the healing. He cannot speak for the next 2d6 hours.
8	**Marked** – The rigors of healing have left their mark upon the character. His hair prematurely turns gray, dark circles appear around his eyes, or his features wrinkle with age. In any case, these changes are permanent.
9 +	**Broken** – Though his body was healed, it was healed imperfectly. One of the following stats, chosen by the affected character, is permanently reduced by 1: AGL, PHY, POI, PRW, SPD, or STR.

	COST	RNG	AOE	POW	UP	OFF
HYMN OF PASSAGE	2	6	—	—	NO	NO

Target steamjack cannot be targeted by non-magical ranged attacks. Hymn of Passage lasts for one round.

	COST	RNG	AOE	POW	UP	OFF
HYMN OF SHIELDING	4	SELF	CTRL	—	NO	NO

While in this character's control area, friendly characters cannot be targeted by enemy spells. Hymn of Shielding lasts for one round.

	COST	RNG	AOE	POW	UP	OFF
ICE BOLT	2	10	—	12	NO	YES

Ice Bolt causes cold damage. On a critical hit, the character hit become stationary for one round unless he has Immunity: Cold.

	COST	RNG	AOE	POW	UP	OFF
ICE SHIELD	1	6	—	—	YES	NO

Target character gains +2 ARM. Ice Shield immediately expires if the affected character moves or is damaged.

	COST	RNG	AOE	POW	UP	OFF
ICY GRIP	2	8	—	—	YES	YES

Target character without Immunity: Cold suffers –2 DEF and cannot run or make power attacks.

	COST	RNG	AOE	POW	UP	OFF
IGNITE	2	6	—	—	YES	NO

Target character gains +2 on melee attack damage rolls. The affected character gains Critical Fire on his normal melee attacks.

	COST	RNG	AOE	POW	UP	OFF
IMMOLATION	2	8	—	12	NO	YES

Immolation causes fire damage. On a critical hit, the character hit suffers the Fire continuous effect.

	COST	RNG	AOE	POW	UP	OFF
INFERNO	3	10	3	12	NO	YES

All characters hit suffer a POW 12 fire damage roll. The AOE remains in play for one round. Characters entering or ending their turns in the AOE suffer an unboostable POW 12 fire damage roll.

	COST	RNG	AOE	POW	UP	OFF
INFLUENCE	1	10	—	—	NO	YES

The spellcaster makes a contested Willpower roll against target living enemy hit by this spell. If the spellcaster loses, nothing happens. If the spellcaster wins, his player takes control of the character hit. The character immediately makes one normal melee attack, then Influence expires.

	COST	RNG	AOE	POW	UP	OFF
INHOSPITABLE GROUND	3	SELF	CTRL	—	NO	NO

While in the spellcaster's control area, other characters treat open terrain as rough terrain. Inhospitable Ground lasts for one round.

	COST	RNG	AOE	POW	UP	OFF
IRON AGGRESSION	3	6	—	—	YES	NO

Target steamjack can run, charge, or make slam or trample power attacks without spending focus or being driven and gains boosted melee attack rolls.

	COST	RNG	AOE	POW	UP	OFF
JACKHAMMER	1	6	—	—	NO	NO

The targeted friendly steamjack can immediately make one melee attack.

	COST	RNG	AOE	POW	UP	OFF
JUMP START	1	SELF	CTRL	—	NO	NO

The spellcaster and steamjacks under the spellcaster's control in his control area can immediately turn to face any direction. Affected steamjacks that are stationary or knocked down are no longer stationary and stand up.

	COST	RNG	AOE	POW	UP	OFF
LAMENTATION	3	SELF	CTRL	—	YES	NO

While in this character's control area, enemies pay double the fatigue, focus, or fury point cost to cast or upkeep spells.

	COST	RNG	AOE	POW	UP	OFF
LIGHT IN THE DARKNESS	1	SELF	CTRL	—	YES	NO

The area around the spellcaster glows with enough light for anyone in his control area to see in darkness (p. 225).

	COST	RNG	AOE	POW	UP	OFF
LIGHTNING TENDRILS	3	6	—	—	YES	NO

The targeted friendly character gains Immunity: Electricity, and the character's melee weapons gain Reach and Electro Leap. (When a character is hit by a weapon with Electro Leap, you can have lightning arc to the nearest character within 4″ of the character hit, ignoring the attacker. The character the lightning arcs to suffers an unboostable POW 10 electrical damage roll.)

	COST	RNG	AOE	POW	UP	OFF
LOCOMOTION	1+	6	—	—	NO	NO

The spellcaster spends up to 3 focus points to cast Locomotion. Target steamjack immediately advances up to 1″ for each focus point spent. A steamjack can be targeted by Locomotion only once per round.

	COST	RNG	AOE	POW	UP	OFF
MIRAGE	3	6	—	—	YES	NO

During the spellcaster's Control Phase after upkeep has been paid, the targeted friendly character's controller can place him anywhere completely within 2″ of his current location.

	COST	RNG	AOE	POW	UP	OFF
OBLITERATION	4	10	4	15	NO	YES

The force of this attack blasts apart the earth itself.

	COST	RNG	AOE	POW	UP	OFF
OCCULTATION	2	6	—	—	YES	NO

Target character gains stealth and +3 on his Sneak rolls.

	COST	RNG	AOE	POW	UP	OFF
OVERMIND	4	SELF	CTRL	—	NO	NO

The spellcaster immediately makes a contested Willpower roll against all living enemies in his control area. Roll once for the spellcaster. If the spellcaster beats an enemy's Willpower roll, he can cause that that character to advance up to 3″ and perform one non-spell, non-feat quick action. If the enemy beats or ties the spellcaster's roll, he is not affected. This spell can be cast only once per round.

	COST	RNG	AOE	POW	UP	OFF
POLARITY SHIELD	2	6	—	—	YES	NO

Target character cannot be targeted by a charge made by a character in his front arc.

	COST	RNG	AOE	POW	UP	OFF
POSITIVE CHARGE	2	6	—	—	NO	NO

Target steamjack gains +2 on melee attack and melee damage rolls. While within 3″ of the affected steamjack, friendly characters gain +2 on melee attack and melee damage rolls. Positive Charge lasts for one round.

	COST	RNG	AOE	POW	UP	OFF
POWER BOOSTER	1	5	—	—	NO	NO

If the target steamjack the spellcaster controls has no focus points, it gains 1 focus point. If the steamjack is Disrupted, it is no longer Disrupted.

	COST	RNG	AOE	POW	UP	OFF
PRAYER FOR GUIDANCE	3	6	—	—	NO	NO

Target character gains two additional dice on his next skill roll. Discard the lowest two dice in the roll. Prayer for Guidance can be cast only once per day.

	COST	RNG	AOE	POW	UP	OFF
PROTECTION FROM COLD	1	6	—	—	YES	NO

Target character gains Immunity: Cold.

	COST	RNG	AOE	POW	UP	OFF
PROTECTION FROM CORROSION	1	6	—	—	YES	NO

Target character gains Immunity: Corrosion.

	COST	RNG	AOE	POW	UP	OFF
PROTECTION FROM ELECTRICITY	1	6	—	—	YES	NO

Target character gains Immunity: Electricity and cannot be disrupted.

	COST	RNG	AOE	POW	UP	OFF
PROTECTION FROM FIRE	1	6	—	—	YES	NO

Target character gains Immunity: Fire.

	COST	RNG	AOE	POW	UP	OFF
PURIFICATION	3	SELF	CTRL	—	NO	NO

Continuous effects, animi, and upkeep spells in the spellcaster's control area immediately expire.

	COST	RNG	AOE	POW	UP	OFF
RAGING WINDS	4	SELF	CTRL	—	NO	NO

While in the spellcaster's control area, enemies suffer –2 DEF. Enemies beginning their turn in the spellcaster's control area cannot run or charge. Raging Winds lasts for one round.

	COST	RNG	AOE	POW	UP	OFF
RAZOR WIND	2	10	—	12	NO	YES

A blade of wind slices through the target.

	COST	RNG	AOE	POW	UP	OFF
REDLINE	2	6	—	—	YES	NO

The targeted friendly steamjack gains +2 STR and SPD and can run, charge, or make power attack slams or tramples without spending focus or being driven. When the steamjack ends its turn, it suffers d3 damage points.

	COST	RNG	AOE	POW	UP	OFF
REFUGE	2	6	—	—	YES	NO

When target character directly hits another character with an attack during his turn, immediately after his turn ends the character affected by this spell can make a full advance. The character cannot be targeted by free strikes during this movement.

	COST	RNG	AOE	POW	UP	OFF
RETURN FIRE	1	6	—	—	NO	NO

When target character is targeted by an enemy ranged attack, after the attack is resolved the affected character can make one normal melee or ranged attack, then Return Fire expires. Return Fire lasts for one round.

	COST	RNG	AOE	POW	UP	OFF
RIFT	3	8	4	13	NO	YES

The AOE is rough terrain and remains in play for one round.

	COST	RNG	AOE	POW	UP	OFF
RIGHTEOUS FLAMES	2	6	—	—	NO	NO

Target character gains Immunity: Fire. When a character without Immunity: Fire ends his turn within 2″ of the affected character, the character without Immunity: Fire suffers the Fire continuous effect. Righteous Flames lasts for one round.

	COST	RNG	AOE	POW	UP	OFF
RIME	2	6	—	—	NO	NO

Target character gains Immunity: Cold. When a character without Immunity: Cold ends his turn within 2″ of the affected character, the character without Immunity: Cold becomes stationary until the end of his next turn. Rime lasts for one round.

	COST	RNG	AOE	POW	UP	OFF
ROCK HAMMER	3	10	3	14	NO	YES

On a critical hit, characters hit are knocked down.

	COST	RNG	AOE	POW	UP	OFF
ROCK WALL	2	CTRL	WALL	—	YES	NO

Place a wall template (p. 352) anywhere completely in the spellcaster's control area where it does not touch a character's base, an obstruction, or an obstacle. The wall is a linear obstacle that provides cover.

	COST	RNG	AOE	POW	UP	OFF
RUNE SHOT: ACCURACY	1	SELF	—	—	NO	NO

The spellcaster's next rune shot ranged attack roll this turn is boosted.

	COST	RNG	AOE	POW	UP	OFF
RUNE SHOT: BLACK PENNY	1	SELF	—	—	NO	NO

The spellcaster's next rune shot ranged attack roll this turn ignores the firing into melee penalty.

	COST	RNG	AOE	POW	UP	OFF
RUNE SHOT: BRUTAL	1	SELF	—	—	NO	NO

The spellcaster's next rune shot ranged attack gains a boosted ranged attack damage roll against the target directly hit.

	COST	RNG	AOE	POW	UP	OFF
RUNE SHOT: DETONATOR	3	SELF	*	—	NO	NO

If the spellcaster directly hits a target with its next rune shot ranged attack this turn, center a 4″ AOE on the target. Characters other than the original target within the AOE suffer an unboostable damage roll with a POW equal to the POW of the ranged weapon.

	COST	RNG	AOE	POW	UP	OFF
RUNE SHOT: EARTH SHAKER	3	SELF	*	—	NO	NO

If this character directly hits a target with its next rune shot ranged attack this turn, the attack becomes AOE 5 and POW 0. Characters hit by the AOE suffer no damage but are knocked down.

	COST	RNG	AOE	POW	UP	OFF
RUNE SHOT: FIRE BEACON	2	SELF	*	—	NO	NO

The spellcaster's next rune shot ranged attack this turn becomes AOE 5 and POW —. While a character is within the AOE, he loses Camouflage and stealth, and other characters can ignore cloud effects when determining LOS to him. The AOE lasts for one round.

	COST	RNG	AOE	POW	UP	OFF
RUNE SHOT: FREEZE FIRE	4	SELF	—	—	NO	NO

If the spellcaster's next rune shot ranged attack this turn hits, the target directly hit becomes stationary for one round.

	COST	RNG	AOE	POW	UP	OFF
RUNE SHOT: HEART STOPPER	4	SELF	—	—	NO	NO

Damage exceeding the ARM of the character hit by spellcaster's next rune shot ranged attack this turn is doubled. A character disabled by this attack cannot make a Tough roll.

	COST	RNG	AOE	POW	UP	OFF
RUNE SHOT: IRON ROT	1	SELF	—	—	NO	NO

If the spellcaster's next rune shot ranged attack this turn directly hits a steamjack, in addition to any other damage and effects from the attack, the steamjack also suffers d3 damage points.

	COST	RNG	AOE	POW	UP	OFF
RUNE SHOT: MOLTEN SHOT	1	SELF	—	—	NO	NO

If the spellcaster's next rune shot ranged attack this turn hits, the target directly hit suffers the Fire continuous effect.

	COST	RNG	AOE	POW	UP	OFF
RUNE SHOT: MOMENTUM	4	SELF	—	—	NO	NO

If the spellcaster hits with his next rune shot ranged attack this turn, the character directly hit is slammed d6″ directly away from the spellcaster regardless of his base size and suffers a damage roll with a POW equal to the ranged weapon. Collateral damage from this slam is equal to the POW of the ranged weapon.

	COST	RNG	AOE	POW	UP	OFF
RUNE SHOT: PHANTOM SEEKER	3	SELF	—	—	NO	NO

The spellcaster's next rune shot ranged attack this turn ignores LOS when making ranged attacks. The attack also ignores concealment and cover.

	COST	RNG	AOE	POW	UP	OFF
RUNE SHOT: SHADOW FIRE	2	SELF	—	—	NO	NO

If the spellcaster hits a target with his next rune shot ranged attack this turn, friendly characters can ignore the target when determining LOS and making ranged or magic attacks for one round.

	COST	RNG	AOE	POW	UP	OFF
RUNE SHOT: SILENCER	1	SELF	—	—	NO	NO

The spellcaster's next rune shot ranged attack is completely silent, and gives no sign of being fired. Neither the firing of the weapon, nor the impact of its ammunition causes a sound. Any immediate sound from a target that is hit, such as a scream, shout, or the fall of a body, is silenced.

	COST	RNG	AOE	POW	UP	OFF
RUNE SHOT: SPELL CRACKER	3	SELF	—	—	NO	NO

If the spellcaster directly hits a target with his next rune shot ranged attack this turn, upkeep spells and animi on the target hit immediately expire.

	COST	RNG	AOE	POW	UP	OFF
RUNE SHOT: SPONTANEOUS COMBUSTION	1	SELF	•	—	NO	NO

If the spellcaster destroys a living character with his next rune shot ranged attack, center a 3″ AOE cloud effect on the destroyed character, then remove the destroyed character from the table. The AOE remains in play for one round.

	COST	RNG	AOE	POW	UP	OFF
RUNE SHOT: THUNDERBOLT	1	SELF	—	—	NO	NO

If the spellcaster directly hits a target with his next rune shot ranged attack this turn, the target is pushed d3″ directly away from this character. On a critical hit, the target is knocked down after being pushed.

	COST	RNG	AOE	POW	UP	OFF
RUNE SHOT: TRICK SHOT	2	SELF	—	—	NO	NO

If the spellcaster directly hits a target with its rune shot next ranged attack this turn, choose a character within 4″ of the target that was hit. After the attack is resolved, the spellcaster immediately makes a ranged attack roll against the chosen character. If the chosen character is hit, it suffers a magical damage roll with a POW equal to that of his ranged weapon but does not suffer any effects of other Rune Shot spells cast on the original attack. The point of origin for this damage is the character originally hit.

	COST	RNG	AOE	POW	UP	OFF
SANGUINE BLESSING	3	SELF	CTRL	—	YES	NO

When a friendly character in the spellcaster's control area would suffer a damage roll, the spellcaster can suffer the damage roll instead. Decide whether the spellcaster suffers the damage before the roll is made.

	COST	RNG	AOE	POW	UP	OFF
SEA OF FIRE	4	SELF	•	—	NO	NO

Enemy characters without Immunity: Fire within 5″ of the spellcaster suffer the Fire continuous effect.

	COST	RNG	AOE	POW	UP	OFF
SHATTER STORM	2	6	—	—	YES	NO

When target character directly hits and destroys an enemy with a ranged or melee attack, center a 3″ AOE on the destroyed character, then remove that character from the table. Characters in the AOE are hit and suffer an unboostable POW 8 blast damage roll.

	COST	RNG	AOE	POW	UP	OFF
SHIELD OF FAITH	2	6	—	—	YES	NO

Target character gains +2 ARM against magic attacks and attacks made by Infernal or Undead characters.

	COST	RNG	AOE	POW	UP	OFF
SHOCK WAVE	4	SELF	•	13	NO	NO

Characters with 5″ of the spellcaster suffer a POW 13 damage roll. Each enemy damaged by Shock Wave is pushed d6″ directly away the spellcaster in the order you choose.

	COST	RNG	AOE	POW	UP	OFF
SHORT OUT	1	8	—	—	NO	YES

Mechanika devices in the possession of target character hit immediately deactivate. Short Out has no effect on steamjacks or mechanika armor.

	COST	RNG	AOE	POW	UP	OFF
SNIPE	2	6	—	—	YES	NO

Target character's ranged weapons gain +4 RNG.

	COST	RNG	AOE	POW	UP	OFF
SOLID GROUND	2	SELF	CTRL	—	YES	NO

While in the spellcaster's control area, friendly characters cannot be knocked down and do not suffer blast damage.

	COST	RNG	AOE	POW	UP	OFF
SOLOVIN'S BOON	1	SELF	—	—	YES	NO

The spellcaster can reroll failed Medicine skill rolls. Each failed roll can be rerolled only once as a result of Solovin's Boon.

	COST	RNG	AOE	POW	UP	OFF
STAR FIRE	4	SELF	CTRL	—	NO	NO

Enemies that move and end their movement closer to the spellcaster than they began suffer an unboostable POW 12 damage roll. Star Fire lasts for one round.

	COST	RNG	AOE	POW	UP	OFF
STAYING WINTER'S HAND	2	SELF	CTRL	—	YES	NO

While in the spellcaster's control area, friendly characters gain +2 ARM against cold damage. Additionally, while affected by this spell, characters never suffer the effects of exposure to cold weather and are kept warm.

	COST	RNG	AOE	POW	UP	OFF
STONE STANCE	1	6	—	—	NO	NO

Target character cannot be knocked down, pushed, or slammed for one round.

	COST	RNG	AOE	POW	UP	OFF
STONE STRENGTH	2	6	—	—	YES	NO

Target character gains +1 STR and ARM.

	COST	RNG	AOE	POW	UP	OFF
STORM TOSSED	1	8	—	—	NO	YES

When an enemy character is hit by Storm Tossed, he is pushed 3″ directly away from the spell's point of origin.

	COST	RNG	AOE	POW	UP	OFF
SUNBURST	3	10	3	13	NO	YES

Blast damage from this spell only affects enemies.

	COST	RNG	AOE	POW	UP	OFF
SUPERIORITY	3	6	—	—	YES	NO

The targeted friendly steamjack gains +2 SPD, MAT, and DEF and cannot be knocked down.

	COST	RNG	AOE	POW	UP	OFF

TELEKINESIS — COST 2, RNG 8, AOE —, POW —, UP YES, OFF •

Place target character completely within 2″ of its current location. When Telekinesis targets an enemy character, it is an offensive spell and requires a magic attack roll. A character can be affected by Telekinesis only once per round.

TEMPER METAL — COST 2, RNG 6, AOE —, POW —, UP YES, OFF NO

The targeted friendly steamjack gains +2 ARM and is immune to continuous effects.

TEMPEST — COST 4, RNG 8, AOE 4, POW 12, UP NO, OFF YES

Characters hit by Tempest are knocked down and suffer a POW 12 damage roll.

TIDE OF STEEL — COST 4, RNG SELF, AOE CTRL, POW —, UP NO, OFF NO

The spellcaster and steamjacks under his control currently in his control area can immediately advance up to 3″.

TORNADO — COST 4, RNG 10, AOE —, POW 13, UP NO, OFF YES

Instead of suffering a normal damage roll, a non-incorporeal character hit by Tornado is thrown d6″ directly away from the spell's point of origin regardless of its base size and suffers a POW 13 damage roll. Collateral damage from this throw is POW 13.

TRANSFERENCE — COST 2, RNG SELF, AOE CTRL, POW —, UP YES, OFF NO

The spellcaster can allow other friendly living characters in his control area to spend focus points on him to boost melee attack or melee damage rolls during their turns at a rate of 1 focus point per boost.

TRIAGE — COST 2, RNG B2B, AOE —, POW —, UP NO, OFF NO

The spellcaster must be B2B with an incapacitated character who needs to be stabilized to cast this spell. When this spell is cast the incapacitated character is immediately stabilized.

TRUE PATH — COST 3, RNG SELF, AOE CTRL, POW —, UP NO, OFF NO

Friendly characters beginning their turns in the spellcaster's control area gain +2″ movement and Pathfinder during their turns. True Path lasts for one round.

TRUE SIGHT — COST 2, RNG SELF, AOE —, POW —, UP YES, OFF NO

This character ignores concealment, Camouflage, and stealth. The character can also see in complete darkness.

VISION — COST 2, RNG 6, AOE —, POW —, UP YES, OFF NO

The next time target character is directly hit by an attack, he suffers no damage roll from the attack, then Vision expires.

VOLTAIC LOCK — COST 4, RNG 10, AOE •, POW —, UP NO, OFF YES

Target steamjack hit cannot advance and suffers –4 DEF. A steamjack beginning an advance within 3″ of the steamjack hit cannot run or charge and can only advance directly toward it. Voltaic Lock lasts for one round.

WALL OF FIRE — COST 2, RNG CTRL, AOE WALL, POW —, UP YES, OFF NO

Place the wall template anywhere completely in the spellcaster's control area where it does not touch a character's base, an obstruction, or an obstacle. When a character enters or ends his turn in the wall area, he suffers an unboostable POW 12 fire damage roll and the Fire continuous effect. Characters within the wall template gain concealment.

WHITE OUT — COST 4, RNG SELF, AOE CTRL, POW —, UP YES, OFF NO

While in the spellcaster's control area, enemies have their LOS reduced to 5″.

WIND BLAST — COST 2, RNG CTRL, AOE 5, POW —, UP NO, OFF NO

Place a 5″ AOE anywhere completely in the spellcaster's control area. Cloud effects overlapping the AOE expire. Characters suffer –3 RAT while within the AOE. The AOE remains in play for one round.

WIND STRIKE — COST 1, RNG 6, AOE —, POW —, UP NO, OFF YES

This spell does not inflict damage. An enemy hit by this spell can be pushed 1″ directly away from the spellcaster. After the enemy is pushed, the spellcaster can advance up to 1″ toward the pushed enemy.

WINGS OF AIR — COST 2, RNG SELF, AOE —, POW —, UP NO, OFF NO

Place the spellcaster anywhere completely within 5″ of his current location. Wings of Air can be cast only once per turn.

WINTER STORM — COST 3, RNG SELF, AOE CTRL, POW —, UP NO, OFF NO

Enemies that begin their turns in the spellcaster's control range lose Eyeless Sight, Flight, and Pathfinder during their turns. Winter Storm lasts for one round.

ZEPHYR — COST 3, RNG 6, AOE —, POW —, UP NO, OFF NO

Target character can immediately advance up to 5″. A character can be affected by Zephyr only once per round.

GEAR, MECHANIKA, AND ALCHEMY

Both enterprise and the promise of adventure in the Iron Kingdoms are fraught with all sorts of peril. For that reason, any self-respecting fortune hunter or campaigner always has some sort of implement of destruction close at hand. For those who travel the byways of Immoren, battle is inevitable whether one is a soldier, scholar, rogue, or priest.

This chapter explores the weapons, armor, and gear commonly carried throughout the Iron Kingdoms as well as the wonders of mechanika and alchemy. The costs of items listed in this section are given in the equivalent of Cygnaran gold crowns (gc).

PRICE LISTS

Light Armor

Alchemist's leather	50 gc
Armored great coat	25 gc
Custom battle armor	60 gc
Leather armor	30 gc

Medium Armor

Chain mail	75 gc
Infantry armor	85 gc
Tailored plate	130 gc

Heavy Armor

Full plate	100 gc
Storm Knight armor	225 gc

Melee Weapons

Assassin's blade	10 gc
Axe	8 gc
Axe, great	25 gc
Axe, horseman's	20 gc
Bayonet	5 gc
Blasting pike	50 gc
Blasting pike explosive head charge	1 gc
Blasting pike spearhead, non-explosive	1 gc
Caspian battle blade	20 gc
Club	3 gc
Club, banded	6 gc
Cutlass	15 gc
Dagger	5 gc
Flail	15 gc
Flail, two-handed	25 gc
Halberd	25 gc
Knuckledusters	5 gc

AVAILABILITY OF GOODS

This chapter covers an expansive list of goods that can be found across western Immoren. It does not cover complications such as scarcity or supply and demand. We encourage Game Masters to be as liberal or as strict with the items and prices found below as they prefer to meet the themes of their campaigns.

Not all items are readily available everywhere. It can be hard to find a winter hat for sale in the deserts of the Protectorate at any price. Rare mechanika can seldom be found in a remote village unless said village boasts an arms firm or a retired arcane mechanik. Even in times of peace, the nations of the Iron Kingdoms engage in all manner of trade wars and embargoes against one another's goods. Under such circumstances, characters need to get creative or travel far for what they want.

Kopis	15 gc
Lance	15 gc
Mace	15 gc
Maul	20 gc
Nyss claymore	30 gc
Ogrun warcleaver	30 gc
Pickaxe	15 gc
Rapier	15 gc
Shield	20 gc
Shield, combat	35 gc
Spear	15 gc
Springblade	12 gc
Staff	5 gc
Staff, battle	12 gc
Sword	12 gc
Sword cane	15 gc
Sword, great	20 gc
Trench knife	10 gc
Trench sword	15 gc
War hammer	20 gc

Ranged Weapons

Axe, throwing	12 gc
Blunderbuss	30 gc
Bola	5 gc

Bow	20 gc
Bow, great	45 gc
Bow, Nyss	35 gc
Cannon-shield	45 gc
Carbine	60 gc
Crossbow	20 gc
Crossbow, repeating	30 gc
Grenade, concussion	20 gc
Grenade, explosive	10 gc
Grenade, smoke	5 gc
Grenade, strangle gas	20 gc
Gun axe	80 gc
Hand cannon	100 gc
Hand cannon, dual	250 gc
Harpoon gun	35 gc
Javelin	5 gc
Knife, throwing	8 gc
Ogrun battle cannon	85 gc
Pistol	20 gc
Pistol, holdout	15 gc
Pistol, magelock	150 gc
Pistol, repeating	35 gc
Quad-iron	200 gc
Radcliffe carbine	250 gc
Rifle, long	50 gc
Rifle, heavy	120 gc
Rifle, magelock	200 gc
Rifle, military	45 gc
Rifle, repeating	80 gc
Rynnish walking stick	40 gc
Scattergun	40 gc
Sling	5 gc
Slug gun	40 gc
Sword-cannon, repeating	100 gc
Sword-cannon, heavy	150 gc

Ammunition and Ranged Weapon Accessories

Ammo wheel	15
Arrows or bolts, standard: ten shots	1 gc
Arrows or bolts, explosive: one shot	20 gc
Arrows or bolts, grappler with rope: one shot	1 gc
Arrows, great bow: five shots	1 gc
Bandolier, ammo	5 gc
Bandolier, grenadier's	5 gc
Bipod	10 gc
Crossbow, repeating: magazine	10 gc
Firearm ammunition, heavy: blasting powder, bullets, and paper casings for five rounds	3 gc
Firearm ammunition, heavy: blasting powder, bullets, and metal casings for five rounds	4 gc

Firearm ammunition, light: blasting powder, bullets, and paper casings for five rounds	2 gc
Firearm ammunition, light: blasting powder, bullets, and metal casings for five rounds	3 gc
Firearm ammunition, shot: one round	1 gc
Firearm ammunition, slug: blasting powder, slug, and casings for one round	1 gc
Firearm ammunition, metal-cased	+1 gc
Gun brace	15 gc
Gunsmith's kit	20 gc
Harpoon gun: blasting powder and five charges	1 gc
Harpoon gun: additional grapple	1 gc
Harpoon gun: additional harpoon	1 gc
Holster	5 gc
Holster, wrist-spring	15 gc
Magelock pistol or rifle: one metal-cased round of rune shot ammunition	5 gc
Ogrun battle cannon: one shell	3 gc
Quiver	5 gc
Scope, pistol or rifle	20 gc
Sling: twenty sling bullets	1 gc

Clothing

Characters start with a selection of clothing matching their profession and social station. The following prices are for goods of standard quality. A character can purchase shabby goods at half the listed price or very fine garments starting at double the listed price.

Belt, leather	2 gc
Belt, pouch	5 gc
Boots, dress	25 gc
Boots, mechanik's	20 gc
Boots, work	10 gc
Cloak	5 gc
Cloak, waterproof	10 gc
Cloak, winter	20 gc
Coat, great	25 gc
Coat, military dress	40 gc
Dress	8 gc
Eye patch, leather and brass	2 gc
Glasses, reading	10 gc
Glasses, tinted	10 gc
Gown	30 gc
Gloves, dress	10 gc
Gloves, leather work	10 gc
Hat, dress	10 gc
Hat, leather traveling	10 gc
Hat, simple	2 gc
Hat, winter fur	20 gc
Officer's uniform	80 gc
Pants, dress	15 gc
Pants, work	10 gc

Robe	8 gc
Shirt, dress	10 gc
Shirt, work	5 gc
Suspenders	4 gc
Traveling clothes, cloth	12 gc
Traveling clothes, leather	20 gc
Work clothes	15 gc

Equipment

'Jack wrench	10 gc
Alchemical lab	500 gc
Alchemist's apron	15 gc
Alchemist's kit, traveling	50 gc
Anvil	40 gc
Backpack	15 gc
Bedroll	5 gc
Book	5+ gc
Canteen	3 gc
Chalk or charcoal: pack of five sticks	1 gc
Coal: one pound	5 gc
Compass	2 gc
Deck of cards	2 gc
Entrenching spade	10 gc
Flint striker	3 gc

Fountain pen and inkwell	5 gc
Gas mask	20 gc
Gas mask replacement filter	5 gc
Goggles	5 gc
Lantern	10 gc
Magnifying glass	5 gc
Manacles	10 gc
Manacles, ogrun	15 gc
Map, local terrain	3 gc
Map, nautical	10 gc
Map case	5 gc
Mechanik's tool kit	100 gc
Mechanik's workshop	500+ gc
Paper: ten sheets	1 gc
Piton and hammer: ten pitons	5 gc
Pocket watch	25 gc
Portable steam engine	500 gc
Rope and grappling hook: twenty feet	5 gc
Rivet gun	30 gc
Rivet gun rivets: ten rivets and powder	1 gc
Rope, hemp: twenty feet	2 gc
Rune etching kit	150 gc
Rune shot casting kit	50 gc
Sack, waterproof, sixteen-gallon capacity	2 gc
Sewing kit	2 gc
Spyglass	15 gc
Surgical kit	30 gc
Symbol of faith	10 gc
Tarp, waterproof, 6' x 6'	4 gc
Thief's tools	10 gc
Water skin	2 gc

Mounts and Riding Equipment

Horse, draft	60 gc
Horse, riding	80 gc
Horse, war	120 gc
Horse feed: one-day supply	1 gc
Barding, light	90 gc
Barding, medium	150 gc
Barding, heavy	300 gc
Gas mask, equestrian	45 gc
Tack	50 gc

Food, Drink, and Lodging

Dry rations: one-day supply	1 gc
Military rations: one-day supply	1 gc
Meal, basic	1 gc
Meal, quality	5 gc
Meal, luxurious feast	25 gc
Beer, bottle	1 gc

Beer, pint	1 gc
Wine, bottle	5 gc+
Wine, glass	1 gc+
Distilled spirits, bottle	5+ gc
Distilled spirits, shot	1+ gc
Lodging, basic: one night	1 gc
Lodging, standard: one night	5 gc
Lodging, standard: one month	50 gc
Lodging, exquisite: one night	25+ gc

Mechanika

Mechanika housing costs ten times the normal cost of a non-mechanikal version of the item being housed.

Alchemical capacitor	10 gc
Arcane turbine	500 gc
Arcanodynamic accumulator	50 gc
Clockwork capacitor	80 gc
Runeplate, blank	10 gc
Storm chamber	250 gc

Mechanika Runes

Accuracy (melee or ranged weapon)	150 gc
Aegis (armor)	150 gc
Arcane Force (melee weapon)	450 gc
Balefire (melee weapon)	150 gc
Blast (ranged weapon – firearm)	300 gc
Blessed (melee or ranged weapon)	300 gc
Bond Plate (melee or ranged weapon)	300 gc
Cold (melee weapon)	300 gc
Compensator (armor)	150 gc
Corruption (melee or ranged weapon)	150 gc
Disbinder (melee weapon)	300 gc
Electrocutioner (melee weapon)	450 gc
Flame (melee weapon)	300 gc
Fleet (armor)	450 gc
Grievous Wounds (melee weapon)	300 gc
Halo of Fire (armor or melee weapon – shield)	300 gc
Heightened Strength (armor)	300 gc
Light (armor, melee, or ranged weapon)	150 gc
Mechanikal Seizure (melee weapon)	300 gc
Quicken (armor)	300 gc
Repulsor (melee weapon – shield)	300 gc
Silencer (ranged weapon – firearm)	150 gc
Spell Ward (armor)	450 gc
Stall (melee weapon)	450 gc
Steady (armor)	150 gc

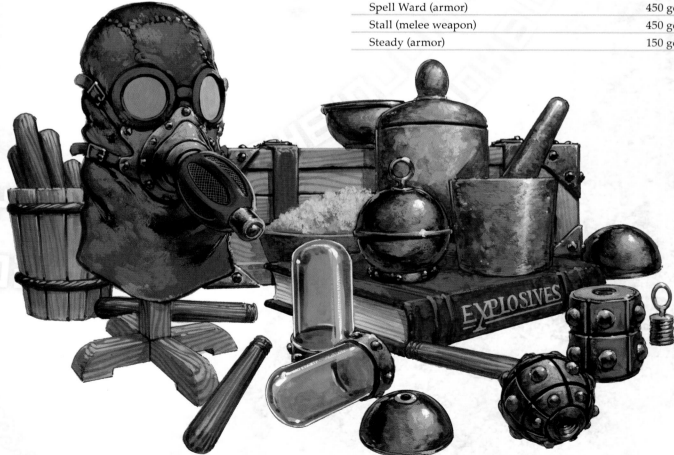

Mechanikal Devices

Arcantrik scope	590 gc
Farsight goggles	790 gc
Mechanikal prosthetic, arm	1,040 gc
Mechanikal prosthetic, eye	790 gc
Mechanikal prosthetic, hand	590 gc
Mechanikal prosthetic, leg	890 gc
Storm glaive	1,560 gc
Warcaster armor, light	2,010 gc
Warcaster armor, medium	2,360 gc
Warcaster armor, heavy	2,760 gc

Alchemical Ingredients (per unit)

Alchemist's stone	1 gc
Alchemical waste, crystal	1 gc
Alchemical waste, liquid	1 gc
Arcane extract	5 gc
Arcane minerals	7 gc
Bioluminescent extract	2 gc
Burrow mawg adrenal gland	5 gc
Ectoplasm	10 gc
Heavy metals	2 gc
Menoth's Fury	3 gc
Mineral acid	2 gc
Mineral crystals	3 gc
Mutagenic extract	8 gc
Organic acid	3 gc
Organic oil	1 gc
Organic toxin	5 gc

Alchemical Compounds

Alchemical acid: one vial	30 gc
Alchemical restorative	33 gc
Antitoxin: one dose	42 gc
Ashes of Urcaen: one application	54 gc
Bottled light (+5 gc for a liquid lantern)	27 gc
Fortemorphic elixir: one dose	42 gc
Healing liniment: one dose	27 gc
Rust agent: one two-part dose	18 gc
Somnolence elixir	36 gc
Spirit salts: one jar	54 gc
Vitriolic fire: one vial	21 gc

Alchemical Weapons

Alchemical grenade, acid bomb	40 gc
Alchemical grenade, Ashes of Urcaen	75 gc
Alchemical grenade, cinder bomb	30 gc
Alchemical grenade, knockout bomb	45 gc
Alchemical grenade, rust bomb	30 gc
Blast arrow version of alchemical grenade	+10 gc
Rifle grenade version of alchemical grenade	+10 gc
Alchemical grenade, empty	5 gc
Blast arrow, empty	10 gc
Rifle grenade, empty	10 gc

ARMOR

Though the armor worn by the standing armies of the Iron Kingdoms consists of identical battle dress, the mercenaries and adventurers of western Immoren mix and match the elements of armor they wear to their personal preferences and needs. Mercenaries commonly wear scavenged hodge-podges of armored elements that afford as much protection as they can secure. For this reason, the armor below is described in terms of how much protection it offers rather than in terms of its primary components.

The following attributes define how armor functions in the game.

Cost: This is the cost of the armor in Cygnaran gold crowns.

SPD Modifier: Some armor affects the SPD stat of the character wearing it.

DEF Modifier: Some armor affects the DEF stat of the character wearing it.

ARM Modifier: This is the degree to which the armor improves the character's ARM stat.

Description: This is a description of the armor.

Special Rules: This section describes any special rules of the armor.

LIGHT ARMOR

Light armor represents either armor that covers parts of the body without offering uniform protection, or armor made from lightweight materials that do not offer the same protection as heavier armors. It is typically favored by those individuals who prefer unencumbered movement to the weight of heavier, more protective armor, or those who cannot afford heavier armor.

ALCHEMIST'S LEATHER

Cost: 50 gc
SPD Modifier: 0
DEF Modifier: –1
ARM Modifier: +5

Description: This is a loose-fitting suit of leather armor that includes a heavy leather cloak and a gas mask (p. 274). Typical of the armor worn by the Iron Kingdom's battle alchemists, this armor is treated to provide maximum protection against blasts and alchemical agents.

Special Rules: A character wearing this armor gains an additional +3 ARM against blast, cold, corrosion, and fire damage.

Because this armor integrates a gas mask, a character wearing it is also immune to gas effects but suffers –1 on sight or hearing-based PER rolls.

ARMORED GREAT COAT

Cost: 25 gc
SPD Modifier: 0
DEF Modifier: –1
ARM Modifier: +5

Description: The armored great coat is popular among combatants and adventurers across western Immoren. Made up of layers of leather, chain, and plate, it provides protection as well as a barrier against inclement weather.

Special Rules: None.

CUSTOM BATTLE ARMOR

Cost: 60 gc
SPD Modifier: 0
DEF Modifier: –1
ARM Modifier: +6

Description: On the heavy side for light armor, battle armor is made up of light or limited plate elements over layers of chain and leather. Battle armor is often custom fit and manufactured to its owner's specifications. Though this armor is expensive, it offers improved protection and serves as a mark of distinction.

Special Rules: A character wearing battle armor tailored to the body of another character suffers a –2 DEF penalty.

LEATHER ARMOR

Cost: 30 gc
SPD Modifier: 0
DEF Modifier: –1
ARM Modifier: +5

Description: This is a suit of armor made primarily of hardened or boiled leatherwork. Metal plates, studs, and elements of chain mail are often added for additional reinforcement.

Leather armor produced using modern manufacturing methods is commonly available throughout the major cities of the Iron Kingdoms. The Nyss produce particularly well-made studded leather armor in dark and somber colorations. Less refined versions are produced by hand throughout Immoren. Though not as strong as metal armor, leather provides a surprising amount of protection.

Special Rules: None.

MEDIUM ARMOR

Medium armor is made up of protective layers of chain, metal plate, and leather armor. Though heavier than light armor, medium armor provides good protection with little impact on mobility. The infantry forces of the Iron Kingdoms are typically outfitted with medium armor.

CHAIN MAIL

Cost: 75 gc
SPD Modifier: 0
DEF Modifier: –2
ARM Modifier: +7

Description: This is a full suit of armor primarily made up of chain mail. Though elements of plate or leather can be worn as well, most of the body is covered in chain mail.

Special Rules: None.

INFANTRY ARMOR

Cost: 85 gc
SPD Modifier: 0
DEF Modifier: –2
ARM Modifier: +7

Description: Though infantry armor exists in infinite variations throughout the various kingdom and mercenary armies, it is essentially made up of an armored chest plate, shoulder pads, and armored leggings over layers of leather and sometimes chain. Cygnar's Trenchers and Long Gunners, Khador's Winter Guard, and Rhul's Gun Corps all wear variations of this armor.

Special Rules: None.

TAILORED PLATE

Cost: 130 gc
SPD Modifier: 0
DEF Modifier: –1
ARM Modifier: +7

Description: This is a suit of light plate armor that usually includes full torso protection along with armored leggings and gauntlets over layers of more form-fitting chain mail and leather. Sometimes this armor includes a fitted armored coat as well. This armor is typically quite expensive because it is tailored to the wearer. Such armor is a status symbol among successful mercenaries, duelists, and aristocrats.

Special Rules: A character wearing tailored plate customized to the body of another character suffers a –2 DEF penalty.

HEAVY ARMOR

Within the Iron Kingdoms, heavy armor has come to mean full plate, often over layers of chain mail and padded leather. This armor offers its wearer peerless protection at the cost of some mobility due to great weight and somewhat restricted freedom of motion.

FULL PLATE

Cost: 100 gc
SPD Modifier: –1
DEF Modifier: –3
ARM Modifier: +8

Description: This is a complete suit of all-encompassing plate mail. It is worn with a helmet or chain coif but could include ample neck protection for a warrior to go without those components. Plate armor often integrates shirts of additional plated layers, chain mail, or leather elements for added protection and padding. The stylized armor of the Iron Fangs is full plate.

Special Rules: None.

STORM KNIGHT ARMOR

Cost: 225 gc
SPD Modifier: –2
DEF Modifier: –3
ARM Modifier: +9

Description: This is the heavy armor of Cygnar's renowned Storm Knights. Extremely heavy plate armor is layered over padded insulation that protects the wearer from the electrical fury of his own weapons.

Special Rules: A character wearing Storm Knight armor gains the Immunity: Electricity ability.

MELEE WEAPONS

The following section describes melee weapons common throughout the Iron Kingdoms. Melee weapons have the following attributes that define how they function in the game.

Cost: This is the cost of the weapon in Cygnaran gold crowns.

Skill: This is the skill used when making an attack with the weapon.

Attack Modifier: Some weapons affect attack rolls made with them.

POW: When making a melee attack damage roll, add the POW of the weapon and the STR of the attacker to the damage roll.

Description: This is a description of the weapon.

Special Rules: This section describes any special rules of the weapon.

ASSASSIN'S BLADE

Cost: 10 gc
Skill: Hand Weapon
Attack Modifier: –1
POW: 4

Description: The assassin's blade is a thick-bladed short sword designed for thrusting. Due to its high damage output and relative ease of concealment, such weapons are favored by assassins and murderers. Though capable of dealing mortal injuries, the assassin's blade is a clumsy weapon and best plunged into an unsuspecting victim's back.

Special Rules: Add +2 to back strike damage rolls with this weapon.

AXE

Cost: 8 gc
Skill: Hand Weapon
Attack Modifier: 0
POW: 3

Description: Hand axes are simple weapons capable of inflicting severe wounds. They are commonly used by hunters, trackers, and rangers. The Khadoran Army equips most of their soldiers with axes due to the ease of training and the weapon's utility as a tool.

Special Rules: None.

AXE, GREAT

Cost: 25 gc
Skill: Great Weapon
Attack Modifier: 0
POW: 6

Description: These massive two-handed axes are intimidating and deadly. With hafts as long as a man is tall and bearing enormous blades, these weapons are favored by trollkin, ogrun, and humans possessed of exceptional strength.

Special Rules: On a critical hit, this weapon inflicts an additional die of damage.

A character must have at least STR 5 to use this weapon and can only use this weapon two-handed.

AXE, HORSEMAN'S

Cost: 20 gc
Skill: Hand Weapon
Attack Modifier: –1 (on foot), 0 (mounted)
POW: 3 (on foot), 5 (mounted)

Description: A horseman's axe is an axe blade on an extended haft intended for cleaving downward while in battle from horseback.

Special Rules: This weapon has Reach.

While wielded by a mounted combatant, add +2 to charge attack damage rolls with this weapon.

BAYONET

Cost: 5 gc
Skill: Hand Weapon (used as a dagger or affixed to a weapon smaller than a rifle), Great Weapon (affixed to a rifle)
Attack Modifier: –1
POW: 2 (used as a dagger or affixed to a weapon smaller than a rifle), 3 (affixed to a rifle)

Description: Bayonets are small, dagger-like blades that can be affixed to the barrel of a firearm. Bayonets are most often affixed to military rifles used by soldiers in the close quarters of trench warfare. Some specialized bayonets have been crafted for use with multi-barreled firearms as well as crossbows.

Special Rules: A bayonet used as a dagger or affixed to a weapon smaller than a rifle uses the Hand Weapon skill.

A bayonet affixed to a rifle has Reach, must be used two-handed, and uses the Great Weapon skill.

A character gains +2 to his charge attack rolls with a bayonet affixed to a rifle.

BLASTING PIKE

Cost: 50 gc
Skill: Great Weapon
Attack Modifier: –2
POW: 7

Description: The Iron Fang blasting pike is among the most devastating polearms ever developed. It is tipped with a powerful explosive charge with a directional blast that obliterates common foes or rips gaping holes in warjacks. The explosion also has the potential to knock foes to the ground should they survive.

Special Rules: Blasting Pikes are Reach weapons.

On a critical hit, the target is knocked down.

Explosive blasting pike heads must be replaced after every attack.

The blasting pike can also be set with a spearhead that reduces the weapon's POW to 4 when used one-handed or to 5 when used two-handed. The spearhead does not need to be replaced after every use. When used with a spearhead, however, the weapon loses the critical knockdown effect.

It takes a quick action to replace the blasting pike's head. Explosive Blasting Pike heads and non-explosive spearhead replacements each cost 1 gc.

A character must have at least STR 6 to use this weapon in one hand.

CASPIAN BATTLEBLADE

Cost: 20 gc
Skill: Great Weapon
Attack Modifier: –1 (one-handed), 0 (two-handed)
POW: 4 (one-handed), 6 (two-handed)

Description: A descendant of the cleaving swords used by the Caspians ages ago, the battleblade is a wide, hefty double-edged blade suitable for cleaving and heavy cuts. The tip of the battleblade is never sharpened; the weapon is used solely as a cleaving weapon. Some battleblades are rounded off at the end while others come to a short, purely ornamental point, and a rare few flare out at the tip in a heart or spade-like shape. Most favored by the nobility and knightly orders of Cygnar, the overall design of the blade is utilized by swordsmen across western Immoren.

Special Rules: A character must have at least STR 5 to use this weapon in one hand.

CLUB

Cost: 3 gc
Skill: Hand Weapon
Attack Modifier: 0
POW: 2

Description: A club is a wooden implement for delivering blunt trauma. These weapons take many forms, from the polished and tooled truncheons carried by the city watches across the Iron Kingdoms, to brutish weapons carried by the uncivilized races of the wilds.

Special Rules: On a critical hit, a living target hit has a chance to be knocked out (p. 219) by the attack. If the target suffers damage from the attack, he must make a Willpower roll against a target number equal to the attacking character's STR + 9. If the target succeeds, he stays conscious. If he fails, he is knocked out.

CLUB, BANDED

Cost: 6 gc
Skill: Great Weapon
Attack Modifier: –1
POW: 4

Description: The banded club is a weapon crafted specifically for war. It is a stout wooden club that has been banded in steel or iron for added weight and reinforcement.

Special Rules: A character must have at least STR 5 to use this weapon.

On a critical hit, a living target hit has a chance to be knocked out (p. 219) by the attack. If the target suffers damage from the attack, he must make a Willpower roll against a target number equal to the attacking character's STR + 11. If the target succeeds, he stays conscious. If he fails, he is knocked out.

CUTLASS

Cost: 15 gc
Skill: Hand Weapon
Attack Modifier: –1
POW: 4

Description: A cutlass is a short and broad slashing sword, with a slightly curved blade sharpened on the cutting edge. The hilt of the cutlass features a solid cupped or basket-shaped guard. The weapon is used extensively by both pirates and the navies of the Iron Kingdoms.

Special Rules: None.

DAGGER

Cost: 5 gc
Skill: Hand Weapon
Attack Modifier: +1
POW: 1

Description: Daggers are short, double-edged fighting knives. They are made in countless shapes and sizes and are popular hold-out weapons with adventurers and soldiers alike.

Special Rules: None.

FLAIL

Cost: 15 gc
Skill: Hand Weapon
Attack Modifier: –1
POW: 4

Description: Originally created as an agricultural tool, the flail is made up of one or more spiked balls or iron bars separated from a long handle by lengths of chain. These clumsy but brutal weapons are capable of circumventing an opponent's shield to deliver staggering blows. Some flails are small enough to be wielded in one hand, making them particularly useful to combatants on horseback.

Special Rules: Attacks from flails ignore ARM bonuses from bucklers and shields.

FLAIL, TWO-HANDED

Cost: 25 gc
Skill: Great Weapon
Attack Modifier: –2
POW: 6

Description: Akin to their smaller counterparts, the largest flails are massive weapons with handles over a yard long. Because they require both hands to carry, they are generally wielded only by warriors on foot. The damage a two-handed flail can inflict is even more severe than that of a standard flail, and they are just as capable of circumventing an opponent's shield.

Special Rules: Two-handed flails are Reach weapons. Two-handed flails must be used two-handed.

Attacks from flails ignore ARM bonuses from bucklers and shields.

On a critical hit with this weapon, a character can spend 1 feat point to push the target 1″ away from the attacking character and knock the target down. After the enemy is pushed, the attacking character can advance up to 1″.

HALBERD

Cost: 25 gc
Skill: Great Weapon
Attack Modifier: –1 (one-handed), 0 (two-handed)
POW: 4 (one-handed), 5 (two-handed)

Description: Halberds and other polearms are common weapons of massed infantry. They are versatile weapons that allow the wielder to stay a considerable distance from his opponents while delivering deadly offensives or withstanding the crush of a cavalry charge.

Special Rules: Halberds are Reach weapons.

This weapon can be used with one or two hands.

A character fighting two-handed with a halberd gains +2 to his charge attack damage rolls with this weapon.

KNUCKLEDUSTERS

Cost: 5 gc
Skill: Unarmed Combat
Attack Modifier: 0
POW: 1

Description: Knuckledusters are metal braces made to fit over the hand to increase damage made by punches and strikes with the hand.

Special Rules: If a character wearing knuckledusters damages his target with a knockout strike (p. 210), add +2 to the target number to avoid knockout.

KOPIS

Cost: 15 gc
Skill: Hand Weapon
Attack Modifier: −1
POW: 3

Description: The kopis is the traditional heavy cleaving sword of the Idrian tribes.

Special Rules: A character gains +2 to his charge attack rolls with this weapon.

On a critical hit with this weapon, a character can spend 1 feat point to gain an additional die on the damage roll.

LANCE

Cost: 15 gc
Skill: Lance
Attack Modifier: 0
POW: 8

Description: The lance is a long, heavy spear designed for use on horseback. The lance is longer and heavier than similar weapons used by infantrymen. It is utterly unsuited for throwing or for rapid thrusting.

Special Rules: Lances are Reach weapons.

A character must have at least STR 5 to use this weapon.

Lances can only be used to make charge attacks and then only while mounted.

MACE

Cost: 15 gc
Skill: Hand Weapon
Attack Modifier: −1
POW: 4

Description: A mace is essentially a club topped with a metal head capable of delivering brutal strikes. Some maces are spiked to inflict further injury. They are common weapons among the battle chaplains and knights of the Morrowan Church.

Special Rules: On a critical hit, a living target hit has a chance to be knocked out (p. 219) by the attack. If the target suffers damage from the attack, he must make a Willpower roll against a target number equal to the attacking character's STR + 9. If the target succeeds, he stays conscious. If he fails, he is knocked out.

MAUL

Cost: 20 gc
Skill: Great Weapon
Attack Modifier: 0
POW: 6

Description: The maul is a military sledgehammer of wood and banded steel. The massive pulverizing head is affixed to a long, two-handed shaft.

Special Rules: A character must have at least STR 5 to use this weapon and can only use this weapon two-handed.

On a critical hit with this weapon, a character can spend 1 feat point to slam the target d3″ away. The POW of the slam damage roll is equal to the Strength of the attacking character plus the POW of this weapon. The POW of collateral damage is equal to the Strength of the attacking character.

NYSS CLAYMORE

Cost: 30 gc
Skill: Great Weapon
Attack Modifier: 0
POW: 6

Description: The favored weapon of the Nyss, this claymore is an elegant and unusual weapon of remarkable quality. The blades of these swords are typically etched with Aeric runes. The hilts are wrapped in fine leathers and feature a small circular guard. So widely respected are these weapons that common lore has it that they never dull or suffer the ravages of time.

Though once these weapons were exceedingly rare, many have entered the hands of outsiders following the widespread destruction of the Nyss. The hefty price for these weapons reflects the scarcity of those with the skills to create them and the high demand for these exquisite works.

Special Rules: Nyss claymores must be used two-handed.

A character can spend 1 feat point to boost an attack roll with this weapon.

OGRUN WARCLEAVER

Cost: 30 gc
Skill: Great Weapon
Attack Modifier: −1
POW: 6

Description: Created to take full advantage of an ogrun's massive strength and size, the warcleaver is a sturdy polearm so large and heavy that even ogrun must wield it with both hands. A three-foot-long, one-foot-wide cleaver-like blade is affixed to a stout twelve-foot pole, and the back of the cleaver blade is studded with spikes, allowing the warcleaver to perform devastating chopping or piercing blows.

Special Rules: The warcleaver is a Reach weapon.

A character must have at least STR 6 to use this weapon. This weapon must be used two-handed.

A character with the Huge Stature characteristic gains +2 to his charge attack rolls with this weapon.

PICKAXE

Cost: 15 gc
Skill: Hand Weapon
Attack Modifier: −1
POW: 4

Description: A pickaxe is a sapping tool as well as a weapon of war favored by the armies of Rhul. The head is a spike ending in a sharp point, which curves slightly and has a counterweight to improve ease of use. The stronger the spike, the more effectively the tool can pierce the surface. The counterweight is nearly always a second spike, often with a flat end for prying. The efficient momentum of a pickaxe, combined with the small contact area, makes it very effective for punching through armor. Rocking an embedded spike aids in removing it, whether from hard-packed earth or the armor and bone of a felled enemy.

Special Rules: On a hit with this weapon against a knocked down target, a character can spend 1 feat point to gain an additional die on the damage roll.

RAPIER

Cost: 15 gc
Skill: Hand Weapon
Attack Modifier: 0
POW: 2

Description: A rapier is a slender, sharply pointed dueling sword, ideally used for thrusting attacks. It features a complex hilt constructed to provide protection for the hand wielding it. This weapon is seldom seen on the battlefields of western Immoren and is considered a weapon of the aristocracy and upper classes.

Special Rules: A character can spend 1 feat point to boost both his attack and damage roll with this weapon.

SHIELD

Cost: 20 gc
Skill: Shield
Attack Modifier: 0
POW: 0

Description: Shields are large metal plates designed to protect their wielder from harm. Though primarily intended to augment the armor worn by their wielder, shields are also weapons in their own right and can inflict crushing blows with the proper strength behind them.

Special Rules: A character armed with a shield gains +1 ARM for each level of the Shield skill he has against attacks originating in his front arc. This bonus is not cumulative with additional shields.

SHIELD, COMBAT

Cost: 35 gc
Skill: Shield
Attack Modifier: –1
POW: 3

Description: Combat shields are designed with additional reinforcement and spikes, making them useful for offense as well as defense.

Special Rules: A character armed with a shield gains +1 ARM for each level of the Shield skill he has against attacks originating in his front arc. This bonus is not cumulative with additional shields.

SPEAR

Cost: 15 gc
Skill: Great Weapon
Attack Modifier: –1
POW: 4 (one-handed), 5 (two-handed)

Description: The simplest of pole weapons, spears are among the most ancient weapons still utilized by the warriors of the Iron Kingdoms.

Special Rules: When wielded two-handed, spears are Reach weapons.

A character wielding a spear two-handed gains +2 to his charge attack rolls.

SPRINGBLADE

Cost: 12 gc
Skill: Hand Weapon
Attack Modifier: 0
POW: 1

Description: Springblades are daggers with retractable blades that slide back into their handles when not in use. With the touch to the button of the internal release mechanism, a powerful spring forces the blade outward into fighting position. This weapon is favored by assassins and street fighters.

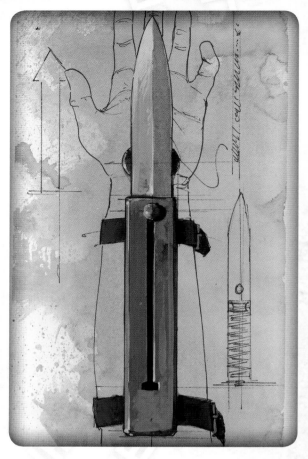

Special Rules: A character can draw a springblade without using a quick action.

STAFF

Cost: 5 gc
Skill: Great Weapon
Attack Modifier: 0
POW: 3

Description: This is a six-foot length of polished hardwood. It is favored by travelers, wanderers, and anyone seeking an unassuming weapon.

Special Rules: Staffs are Reach weapons.

Staffs must be used two-handed.

A character can spend 1 feat point to make a trip attack instead of a normal attack with his staff. If the attack hits, the target is knocked down instead of suffering damage.

STAFF, BATTLE

Cost: 12 gc
Skill: Great Weapon
Attack Modifier: 0
POW: 4

Description: Battle staffs are weapons of steel or banded hard wood set with a heavy head and one tip used for delivering crushing blows. The clergy of Menoth favor battle staffs as their primary armament and symbols of office.

Special Rules: Battle staffs are Reach weapons.

Battle staffs must be used two-handed.

A character can spend 1 feat point to make a trip attack instead of a normal attack with his staff. If the attack hits, the target is knocked down instead of suffering damage.

On a critical hit, a living target hit has a chance to be knocked out (p. 219) by the attack. If the target suffers damage from the attack, he must make a Willpower roll against a target number equal to the attacking character's STR + 9. If the target succeeds, he stays conscious. If he fails, he is knocked out.

SWORD

Cost: 12 gc
Skill: Hand Weapon
Attack Modifier: 0
POW: 3

Description: Though each nation favors its own style and means of manufacture, swords have been among the most common weapons in use across Immoren since antiquity.

Special Rules: None.

SWORD CANE

Cost: 15 gc
Skill: Hand Weapon
Attack Modifier: 0
POW: 0 (when wielded as a cane) or 2 (when drawn)

Description: Effectively a short sword concealed within the haft of a heavy walking stick, the sword cane is a favored weapon of aristocrats, assassins, and duelists.

Special Rules: An observant character can discern a sword cane from a normal cane without handling it with a successful PER + Detection roll against a target number of 14.

SWORD, GREAT

Cost: 20 gc
Skill: Great Weapon
Attack Modifier: 0
POW: 6

Description: Great swords are heavy, double-edged blades wielded with both hands. Two-handed swords have been favored by swordsmen for centuries, particularly those who regularly fight heavily armored foes or steamjacks.

Special Rules: Great swords must be used two-handed.

Great swords have Reach.

TRENCH KNIFE

Cost: 10 gc
Skill: Hand Weapon, Unarmed Combat
Attack Modifier: 0 (Hand), –1 (Unarmed Combat)
POW: 2

Description: Trench knives are long, heavy bladed daggers favored by fighting men across western Immoren. The weapon features a studded or spiked "skull crusher" hand guard that be used to deliver bone snapping blows with the fist.

Special Rules: Trench knives' skull crusher hilts can be used to make Unarmed Combat attack rolls. If a character using the skull crusher as a melee weapon makes a knockout strike (p. 210) that damages his target, add +2 to the target number to avoid knockout.

TRENCH SWORD

Cost: 15 gc
Skill: Hand Weapon, Unarmed Combat
Attack Modifier: –1
POW: 4 (Sword), 2 (skull crusher)

Description: Modeled after the trench knife, the trench sword is a stout and heavy sword blade affixed to a studded or spiked "skull crusher" hilt.

Special Rules: Trench swords' skull crusher hilts can be used to make Unarmed Combat attack rolls. On a critical hit with a skull crusher, the target is knocked down. If a character using the skull crusher as a melee weapon makes a knockout strike (p. 210) that damages his target, add +2 to the target number to avoid knockout.

WAR HAMMER

Cost: 20 gc
Skill: Great Weapon
Attack Modifier: –1
POW: 5

Description: Military hammers are oversized versions of the common tool, typically forged from iron or steel and used by individuals possessed of great strength.

Special Rules: A character must have at least STR 6 to use this weapon in one hand.

On a critical hit, a living target hit has a chance to be knocked out (p. 219) by the attack. If the target suffers damage from the attack, he must make a Willpower roll against a target number equal to the attacking character's STR + 12. If the target succeeds, he stays conscious. If he fails, he is knocked out.

RANGED WEAPONS

The majority of firearms in the Iron Kingdoms are breech loading, meaning that to reload a firearm, a trap door on the rear of the firearm is opened, the round is placed within the firearm, and then the trap door is closed. Then the firearm is ready to be fired. The cartridge sits snugly in the chamber until the trigger is pulled. By pulling the trigger, the shooter releases a pin that drives itself into the rear of the round, through two silk pouches. This causes the two components of the blasting powder within the pouches to mix, inciting a chemical reaction that explodes, driving the bullet that sits ahead of the pouches forward out of the weapon's muzzle.

In the beginning, the first firearms manufactured by the Order of the Golden Crucible utilized a multi-part loading process that included dropping two silk pouches, each with a different component of the two part blasting powder down the muzzle of the firearm, followed by a bullet tucked inside a bit of wadding and tamped down with a rod before being fired. Once fired, the bullet and wadding would be ejected from the muzzle of the weapon and the silk pouches would burn up, leaving the barrel empty and waiting for another load.

A major development of the firearm was moving to a breech loading system, where the bullet and silk pouches containing the blasting powder could be placed into the chamber through the rear of the firearm. A minor but cost saving development was to place the bullet and the powder into one paper cartridge. This paper is thin to leave as little fouling in the chamber as possible. Though these paper cartridges can withstand normal handling on a battlefield, should they become wet or receive any significant trauma, the paper falls apart. The components can still be useful if loaded individually, but the gunman's reload is slowed. Paper cartridges were seen as an improvement over the multipart loading process of the past, but the extra paper has two detriments on the internal workings of the firearm. First, more fouling is caused, which can lead to more malfunctions if the weapon is not properly cleaned after significant use. Second, the firing pin has more material that it needs to drive through to puncture the silk pouches within. This extra stress on the firing pin can cause the sharp firing pins to be dulled or bent and rendered useless. Thus, for a firearm that uses paper cartridges to remain reliable, the weapon needs to be regularly maintained following any extended use.

Around the same time the breech loading firearm was developed, the muzzle loading pepper box mechanisms were developed and a while thereafter, the ammo wheel was developed. The ammo wheel allowed the shooter to reload the wheel's chambers through the rear of the weapon using paper cartridges. In addition to being easier to reload, the pin that holds the ammo wheel in place can be pulled, allowing the ammo wheel to be removed and replaced with another preloaded ammo wheel This simple feature meant that in the time it took an average shooter to reload one round in a breech loading rifle, the ammo wheel of a weapon could be replaced and the weapon fully reloaded.

The pepper box and ammo wheel actions contain multiple preloaded chambers. The first pepper box actions were advanced by hand, but later developments possessed clockwork mechanics that advanced the chamber with the pull of a trigger before striking the cartridge with the firing pin. This made the idea of rapid firing firearms a reality.

Gunsmiths changed the battlefields of western Immoren again with the development of the metal cartridge. By placing the two silk pouches inside of a metal cartridge capped with a bullet, the gunsmiths created a cartridge which would leave less fouling and that could guide the firing pin into the round through a small well without causing the firing pin a lot of damage or dulling. By capping the rear of the cartridge where the pin enters with a small drop of wax, the gunsmiths also created a water-resistant cartridge. The rounds with metal cartridges are easily dumped out of their breech loading actions with a flick of the wrist to clear the chamber for the next round, but the paper cartridge remains the favored cartridge of gunfighters, since the weapon is left with an empty chamber following the round being fired. Further, paper cartridges are more easily acquired and loaded in the field. It was not until the introduction of the ejector that the metal cartridge's greatest contribution would come to be known in automatic weapons.

Now that gunsmiths had metal cartridges that slid with less resistance when compared to paper cartridges and ejectors to remove the spent cartridges, firearms in western Immoren could take their next major leap in advancement: the belt fed automatic gun. The lack of friction from the metal cartridges allowed for gravity fed magazines that could drop rounds into a cycling action somewhat reliably. But it was the belt feed action that allowed for battlefield reliability and consistency. These new weapons recycle the energy being blown out of the weapon to power the cycling of the automatic action, which ejects the previous cartridge while reloading a new cartridge into the chamber and recharging and releasing the firing pin. This results in one man being able to fire so many shots with one pull of the trigger that he could outperform the capabilities of the barrel of the weapon, necessitating the development of water-cooled barrels.

Ranged weapons have the following attributes that define how they function in the game.

Cost: This is the cost of the weapon in Cygnaran gold crowns (gc).

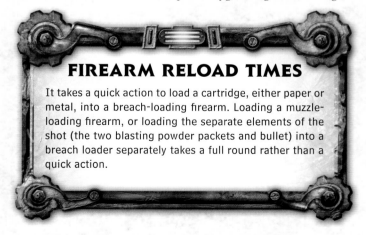

FIREARM RELOAD TIMES

It takes a quick action to load a cartridge, either paper or metal, into a breach-loading firearm. Loading a muzzle-loading firearm, or loading the separate elements of the shot (the two blasting powder packets and bullet) into a breach loader separately takes a full round rather than a quick action.

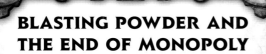

BLASTING POWDER AND THE END OF MONOPOLY

Though blasting powder was once an expensive and carefully regulated commodity of the Order of the Golden Crucible, their virtual monopoly on its manufacture has long since ended. Every kingdom has developed its own supply and methods of manufacture. The dissolution of the Golden Crucible following the Khadoran invasion of Llael saw the secrets of its creation spread to hundreds of independent chapterhouses and alchemical shops throughout the Iron Kingdoms.

Blasting powder is now available throughout the Iron Kingdoms in great supply. The quality of ammunition varies, and certain groups such as the Free Order of the Golden Crucible have a reputation for higher quality and consistency of product, and can charge a premium accordingly.

Ammo: This is the amount of ammunition the weapon holds. Once its ammunition has been expended, the weapon must be reloaded before it can fire again. Reloading one round of ammunition (or nocking a bow) requires one quick action, so fully loading a repeating firearm in the heat of battle can take some time.

Effective Range: This is the practical range of the weapon in combat. A ranged weapon can hit targets and deal damage up to its extreme range, but attacks against a target past the effective range of the weapon suffer –5 to the attack roll. The effective range of the weapon is listed in feet, with its tabletop range in inches in parentheses.

Remember that one inch on the tabletop is equal to six feet.

Extreme Range: This is the extreme range of the weapon, given in feet. Thrown weapons do not have an extreme range.

Skill: This is the skill used when making an attack with the weapon.

Attack Modifier: Some weapons affect attack rolls made with them.

POW: When making a ranged attack damage roll, add the POW of the weapon to the damage roll.

AOE: This is the size of the weapon's area of effect.

Description: This is a description of the weapon.

Special Rules: This section describes any special rules of the weapon.

AXE, THROWING

Cost: 12 gc
Ammo: —
Effective Range: 36 feet (6″)
Extreme Range: —
Skill: Thrown
Attack Modifier: 0
POW: 3
AOE: —

Description: This is a hand axe that has been balanced for throwing.

Special Rules: Add the thrower's STR to the POW of the damage roll. It can be used as a melee weapon as well as a ranged weapon.

BLUNDERBUSS

Cost: 30 gc
Ammo: 1 (heavy round)
Effective Range: 48 feet (8″)
Extreme Range: 240 feet
Skill: Rifle
Attack Modifier: –2 (one-handed), –1 (two-handed)
POW: 12
AOE: —

Description: The blunderbuss is a short, stubby breach-loading rifle with a large bore. An unrefined weapon that has changed little since the Rebellion, the blunderbuss typically fires a powerful, short-range round. The blunderbuss is the standard-issue weapon of the Khadoran Winter Guard.

Special Rules: It costs 3 gc for blasting powder, bullets, and casings for five heavy rounds.

BOLA

Cost: 5 gc
Ammo: —
Effective Range: 48 feet (8″)
Extreme Range: —
Skill: Thrown
Attack Modifier: –2
POW: 0 + Thrower's STR
AOE: —

Description: A bola is a simple throwing weapon made of lengths of rope and chain affixed together and ending in heavy weights. The weapon causes little damage, as its true purpose is to entangle and trip its target.

Special Rules: A character hit with a bola must succeed in a STR + PRW roll against a target number of 15 or be knocked down. If the character succeeds, he manages to get free of the bola before becoming entangled by it.

Once knocked down, the character must either spend a quick action and succeed in an AGL + Rope Use skill roll against a target number of 10 to untie himself or spend a quick action and succeed in a STR roll against a target number of 10 to break free. If the attempt fails, the character can spend additional quick actions repeat the attempt but can take no other action until freed.

BOW

Cost: 20 gc
Ammo: 1
Effective Range: 60 feet (10")
Extreme Range: 300 feet
Skill: Archery
Attack Modifier: 0
POW: 10
AOE: —

Description: Though bows are used less frequently in the modern age of firearms, a bow is still a deadly weapon in the hands of an expert. A bow's height is roughly equal to that of its wielder.

Special Rules: It costs 1 gc for ten arrows.

This weapon requires two hands.

BOW, GREAT

Cost: 45 gc
Ammo: 1
Effective Range: 60 feet (10")
Extreme Range: 300 feet
Skill: Archery
Attack Modifier: 0
POW: 12
AOE: —

Description: This is a large, stout bow with an extremely heavy draw.

Special Rules: It costs 1 gc for five arrows.

This weapon requires two hands.

A character must have at least STR 6 to use this weapon.

BOW, NYSS

Cost: 35 gc
Ammo: 1
Effective Range: 72 feet (12")
Extreme Range: 360 feet
Skill: Archery
Attack Modifier: 0
POW: 10
AOE: —

Description: The Nyss are known for the power of their fine composite bows. These weapons are strong enough to withstand the freezing climates of the far north where a lesser bow would shatter from use. Their ingenious design also redoubles the archer's strength, greatly increasing the range of the weapon.

Special Rules: It costs 1 gc for ten arrows.

This weapon requires two hands.

A character must have at least STR 5 to use this weapon.

CANNON-SHIELD

Cost: 45 gc
Ammo: 1 (heavy round)
Effective Range: 48 feet (8")
Extreme Range: 240 feet
Skill: Rifle
Attack Modifier: –2
POW: 12
AOE: —

Description: This is a heavy, short-range rifle mounted in the center of a shield. The weapon can be used as shield and as a ranged weapon.

Special Rules: This weapon is also a shield (p. 258).

It costs 3 gc for blasting powder, bullets, and casings for five heavy rounds.

As part of a charge, after moving but before making the charge attack, a character can spend 1 feat point to make one ranged attack with this weapon targeting the enemy charged unless the character was in melee with the enemy at the start of his turn. When resolving the ranged attack, the attacking character does not suffer the target in melee penalty. If the target is not in melee range after moving, the character can make the ranged attack before his turn ends.

CARBINE

Cost: 60 gc
Ammo: 5 (metal-cased light round)
Effective Range: 60 feet (10")
Extreme Range: 300 feet
Skill: Rifle
Attack Modifier: 0
POW: 10
AOE: —

Description: The carbine is primarily a military weapon, bridging the gap between the pistol and rifle. The weapon utilizes a five-chambered ammo wheel that can be replaced in the heat of combat instead of reloading each chamber separately. A relatively advanced weapon, it is rare to see a carbine for sale on the open market.

Special Rules: Replacing this weapon's ammo wheel requires a quick action. Reloading each chamber of the ammo wheel takes one quick action.

It costs 3 gc for blasting powder, bullets, and metal casings for five light rounds.

An extra ammo wheels cost 15 gc.

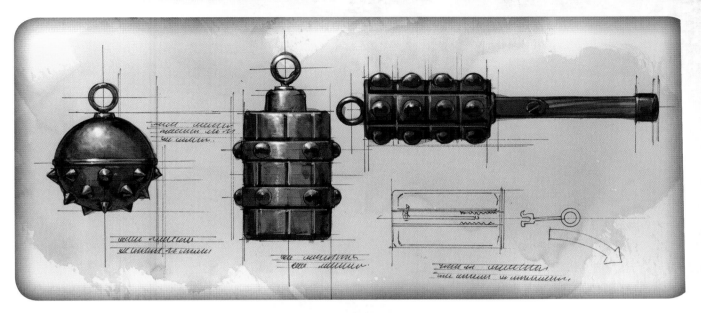

CROSSBOW

Cost: 20 gc
Ammo: 1
Effective Range: 60 feet (10")
Extreme Range: 300 feet
Skill: Crossbow
Attack Modifier: –2 (one-handed), 0 (two-handed)
POW: 12
AOE: —

Description: Numerous nations and races developed the crossbow independently, and they are widespread, if not common, weapons across western Immoren. Crossbows are popular weapons among assassins and hunters alike.

Special Rules: It costs 1 gc for ten bolts. A crossbow takes a full action to reload.

CROSSBOW, REPEATING

Cost: 30 gc
Ammo: 6
Effective Range: 60 feet (10")
Extreme Range: 300 feet
Skill: Crossbow
Attack Modifier: –1
POW: 10
AOE: —

Description: The repeating, or mechanical, crossbow is a magazine fed crossbow that reloads itself each time the bow string is locked back in place. The weapon's magazine must be removed for it to be reloaded and can be replaced in the heat of combat instead of reloading each bolt by hand.

Special Rules: Replacing this weapon's magazine requires a quick action. Loading each bolt into the magazine takes one quick action.

This weapon requires two hands.

It costs 1 gc for ten bolts. Additional magazines cost 10 gc each.

GRENADE, CONCUSSION

Cost: 20 gc
Ammo: —
Effective Range: 48 feet (8")
Extreme Range: —
Skill: Thrown
Attack Modifier: 0
POW: —
AOE: 3

Description: A concussion grenade utilizes a volume of "true air," an alchemical gas known for its expansive qualities. True air is captured, liquefied through a treatment process, then cooled and stored within the grenade. When the bomb is detonated, the true air is heated and released.

Special Rules: Once it is in hand, using a grenade requires both a quick action and an attack. The quick action is spent pulling the pin, and the attack is to actually throw the grenade.

The concussion grenade causes no damage. Characters caught in the AOE are knocked down. Cloud effects overlapping the AOE expire.

GRENADE, EXPLOSIVE

Cost: 10 gc
Ammo: —
Effective Range: 48 feet (8″)
Extreme Range: —
Skill: Thrown
Attack Modifier: 0
POW: 12
AOE: 3

Description: Explosive grenades come in many shapes and sizes. They are most often round metal objects a little smaller than a man's fist. They can also be cylindrical, integrate a stick or grip at the base for throwing, contain studs to aid in the holding of the device, or incorporate any of a countless number of other variations.

Grenades typically have a handle locked in place by a removable safety pin. Once the pin is pulled, the grenade is primed but still does not explode until the handle is released, such as by being thrown. As long as the grenade is held in the hand, the handle remains in place. Upon the handle's release, either a fuse ignites or a clockwork mechanism is thrown into motion, depending on the nature of the grenade. After a few seconds the grenade explodes.

Special Rules: Once it is in hand, using a grenade requires both a quick action and an attack. The quick action is spent pulling the pin, and the attack is to actually throw the grenade.

GRENADE, SMOKE

Cost: 5 gc
Ammo: —
Effective Range: 48 feet (8″)
Extreme Range: —
Skill: Thrown
Attack Modifier: 0
POW: —
AOE: 3

Description: Smoke grenades contain an alchemical compound that when set off produces a thick, billowing cloud of smoke. Smoke grenades come in an assortment of colors used by the militaries of the Iron Kingdoms to signal various conditions on the battlefield. These grenades are produced cheaply and in large numbers by the militaries of the Iron Kingdoms.

Special Rules: Once it is in hand, using a grenade requires both a quick action and an attack. The quick action is spent pulling the pin, and the attack is to actually throw the grenade.

Smoke grenades cause no damage. The weapon's AOE is a cloud effect that remains in play for one round.

GRENADE, STRANGLE GAS

Cost: 20 gc
Ammo: —
Effective Range: 48 feet (8″)
Extreme Range: —
Skill: Thrown
Attack Modifier: 0
POW: —
AOE: 3

Description: These grenades unleash gouts of choking, fuming gas. They are produced cheaply and in large numbers by the militaries of the Iron Kingdoms.

Special Rules: Once it is in hand, using a grenade requires both a quick action and an attack. The quick action is spent pulling the pin, and the attack is to actually throw the grenade.

Strangle gas grenades cause no damage. The weapon's AOE is a cloud effect, gas effect that remains in play for one round. While in the AOE, living characters suffer –2 DEF and –2 on attack rolls.

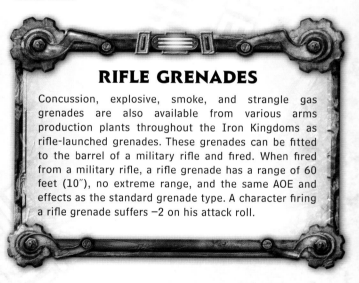

RIFLE GRENADES

Concussion, explosive, smoke, and strangle gas grenades are also available from various arms production plants throughout the Iron Kingdoms as rifle-launched grenades. These grenades can be fitted to the barrel of a military rifle and fired. When fired from a military rifle, a rifle grenade has a range of 60 feet (10″), no extreme range, and the same AOE and effects as the standard grenade type. A character firing a rifle grenade suffers –2 on his attack roll.

GUN AXE

Cost: 80 gc
Ammo: 1 (heavy round)
Effective Range: 48 feet (8″)
Extreme Range: 240 feet
Skill: Rifle
Attack Modifier: –1
POW: 12
AOE: —

Description: This weapon integrates a heavy, short-range rifle into the handle of an axe.

Special Rules: When used as a melee weapon, this weapon has an attack modifier of –1, is POW 3, and uses the One-Handed Weapon skill.

It costs 3 gc for blasting powder, bullets, and casings for five heavy rounds.

As part of a charge, after moving but before making the charge attack a character can spend 1 feat point to make a ranged attack with this weapon targeting the enemy charged unless he was in melee with the enemy at the start of his turn. When resolving the ranged attack, the attacking character does not suffer the target in melee penalty. If the target is not in melee range after moving, the character can make the ranged attack before his turn ends.

HAND CANNON

Cost: 100 gc
Ammo: 1 (heavy round)
Effective Range: 72 feet (12")
Extreme Range: 360 feet
Skill: Pistol
Attack Modifier: 0
POW: 12
AOE: —

Description: Extremely heavy and well-made pistols, hand cannons are expensive firearms most commonly found in the possession of ranking military officers. These enormous handguns pack a significant punch and are accurate to a range far beyond that of most other pistols.

Special Rules: It costs 3 gc for blasting powder, bullets, and casings for five heavy rounds.

HAND CANNON, DUAL

Cost: 250 gc
Ammo: 2 (heavy round)
Effective Range: 72 feet (12")
Extreme Range: 360 feet
Skill: Pistol
Attack Modifier: 0
POW: 12
AOE: —

Description: This is a hand cannon with two barrels. Each barrel can be fired independently, or they can be discharged together for a single massive blast.

Special Rules: Discharging both barrels together is treated as a single attack, and the weapon suffers –2 on the attack roll. If the attack hits, add +3 to the damage roll.

Reloading each barrel takes one quick action.

It costs 3 gc for blasting powder, bullets, and casings for five heavy rounds.

HARPOON GUN

Cost: 35 gc
Ammo: 1 (harpoon or grapple)
Effective Range: 60 feet (10")
Extreme Range: 120 feet
Skill: Rifle
Attack Modifier: –2
POW: 12
AOE: —

Description: The harpoon gun is a specially designed firearm made to propel a harpoon over long distances. Harpoon guns typically have short, stout barrels and are fitted with iron rings that can be used to tie off the harpoon line and to anchor the harpoon gun into secured mounting, such as on a ship. The true range of the harpoon gun is limited by the rope or cable attached to the harpoon.

The harpoon gun can also be used to fire a grappling hook and line.

Special Rules: If this weapon damages a target with an equal or smaller base, immediately after the attack is resolved the damaged character can be pushed any distance directly toward the character armed with the harpoon.

A grappling hook has a –4 attack modifier instead of –2 and has POW 8.

It costs 1 gc for blasting powder and casings for five charges. Additional harpoons or grapples cost 1 gc each.

JAVELIN

Cost: 5 gc
Ammo: —
Effective Range: 48 feet (8")
Extreme Range: —
Skill: Thrown
Attack Modifier: 0
POW: 3 + the thrower's STR
AOE: —

Description: A javelin is a light spear designed for throwing.

Special Rules: Add the thrower's STR to the POW of the damage roll.

KNIFE, THROWING

Cost: 8 gc
Ammo: —
Effective Range: 36 feet (6")
Extreme Range: —
Skill: Thrown
Attack Modifier: 0
POW: 2 + the thrower's STR
AOE: —

Description: This is a heavy knife balanced for throwing.

Special Rules: Add the thrower's STR to the POW of the damage roll. A throwing knife can be used as a melee weapon as well as a ranged weapon.

OGRUN BATTLE CANNON

Cost: 85 gc
Ammo: 1 (shell)
Effective Range: 72 feet (12")
Extreme Range: 360 feet
Skill: Rifle
Attack Modifier: –2 (one-handed), –1 (two-handed)
POW: 12
AOE: 3

Description: A small cannon designed to be fired by an ogrun from the hip, the battle cannon is a weapon of Rhulic manufacture.

Special Rules: This weapon can be wielded only by characters with the proportions of an ogrun and with STR 6 or greater.

It cost 3 gc for one ogrun battle cannon shell.

PISTOL

Cost: 20 gc
Ammo: 1 (light round)
Effective Range: 48 feet (8")
Extreme Range: 240 feet
Skill: Pistol
Attack Modifier: 0
POW: 10
AOE: —

Description: Handguns are commonly found among military officers, adventurers, and even private citizens seeking weapons of self-defense.

Special Rules: It costs 2 gc for blasting powder, bullets, and casings for five light rounds.

PISTOL, HOLDOUT

Cost: 15 gc
Ammo: 1 (light round)
Effective Range: 24 feet (4")
Extreme Range: —
Skill: Pistol
Attack Modifier: +1
POW: 8
AOE: —

Description: Concealable and easy to control, the holdout pistol fires a small-caliber ball that, though accurate, is effective only at extremely close range. Despite its shortcomings, the holdout pistol is favored as a weapon of last resort by those with little skill in firearms.

Special Rules: It costs 2 gc for blasting powder, bullets, and casings for five light rounds.

PISTOL, MAGELOCK

Cost: 150 gc
Ammo: 1 (metal-cased rune shot)
Effective Range: 60 feet (10")
Extreme Range: 300 feet
Skill: Pistol
Attack Modifier: 0
POW: 10
AOE: —

Description: The signature weapon of the gun mage, each magelock pistol is the hand-crafted product of a master gunsmith. Only rare and difficult to manufacture steel alloys can withstand the arcane stresses caused by rune shots, so magelock pistols are treasured by their owners. A magelock fires metal-cased rune shot rounds in which both the bullet and its casing have been inscribed with runes.

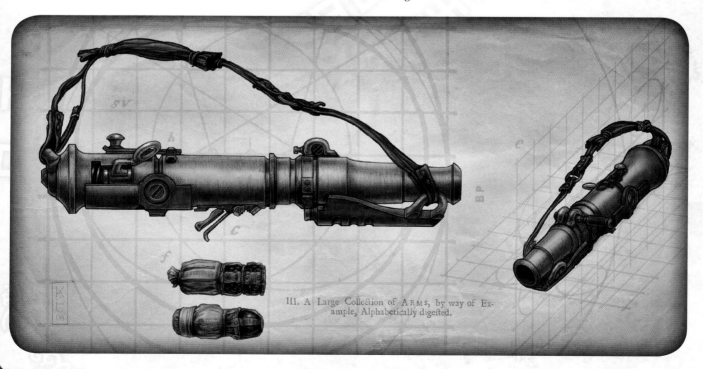

III. A Large Collection of ARMS, by way of Example, Alphabetically digested.

Special Rules: Magelock weapons can only fire rune shot ammunition.

It costs 5 gc for blasting powder, rune-scribed bullet, and metal casing for one round of rune shot ammunition. Due to the high cost of ammunition, most gun mages pour their own rune shots (see "Craft Rune Shot," p. 160).

When fired by a gun mage, this weapon is a magical weapon.

PISTOL, REPEATING

Cost: 35 gc
Ammo: 5 (light round)
Effective Range: 48 feet (8″)
Extreme Range: 240 feet
Skill: Pistol
Attack Modifier: 0
POW: 10
AOE: —

Description: The repeating pistol utilizes a five-chambered ammo wheel that can be replaced in the heat of combat instead of reloading each cylinder separately.

Special Rules: Replacing this weapon's ammo wheel requires a quick action. Reloading each cylinder of the ammo wheel takes one quick action.

It costs 2 gc for blasting powder, bullets, and casings for five light rounds. Additional ammo wheels cost 15 gc each.

QUAD-IRON

Cost: 200 gc
Ammo: 4 (light round)
Effective Range: 60 feet (10″)
Extreme Range: 300 feet
Skill: Pistol
Attack Modifier: –1
POW: 10
AOE: —

Description: A truly massive pistol, the quad-iron is a heavy, four-barreled pistol capable of firing all of its barrels in rapid succession. Expensive and rare, quad-irons are highly valued by pistoleers despite their weight and punishing recoil.

Special Rules: After a hit with this weapon, once the attack has been resolved the attacker can immediately make one additional attack with this weapon targeting the last character hit or another character within 2″ of that character. This attack is in addition to the attacker's other actions.

Reloading each barrel takes one quick action.

It costs 2 gc for blasting powder, bullets, and casings for five light rounds.

RADCLIFFE CARBINE

Cost: 250 gc
Ammo: 5 (metal-cased heavy round)
Effective Range: 78 feet (13″)
Extreme Range: 390 feet
Skill: Rifle
Attack Modifier: –2 (one-handed), 0 (two-handed)
POW: 11
AOE: —

Description: The Radcliffe Gunwerks heavy carbine is among the finest firearms ever made. Packing the punch of a military rifle and nearly the range of a long gun, this weapon is treasured by the military officers who can afford them. The weapon

utilizes a five-chambered ammo wheel that can be replaced in the heat of combat instead of reloading each cylinder separately.

Special Rules: Replacing this weapon's ammo wheel requires a quick action. Reloading each cylinder of the ammo wheel takes one quick action.

It costs 4 gc for blasting powder, bullets, and metal casings for five heavy rounds.

Additional ammo wheels cost 15 gc each.

RIFLE, LONG

Cost: 50 gc
Ammo: 1 (light round)
Effective Range: 84 feet (14″)
Extreme Range: 420 feet
Skill: Rifle
Attack Modifier: 0
POW: 10
AOE: —

Description: Popular among hunters, riflemen, and snipers, long rifles are cumbersome weapons but are extremely effective at long range.

Special Rules: It costs 2 gc for blasting powder, bullets, and casings for five light rounds.

This weapon requires two hands.

RIFLE, HEAVY

Cost: 120 gc
Ammo: 1 (heavy round)
Effective Range: 84 feet (14″)
Extreme Range: 420 feet
Skill: Rifle
Attack Modifier: 0
POW: 12
AOE: —

Description: Heavy rifles are devastating weapons found only in the hands of successful monster hunters and the most senior of the kingdoms' riflemen. The Vanar Liberator is just one example of this extremely heavy and accurate category of rifle.

Special Rules: It costs 3 gc for blasting powder, bullets, and casings for five heavy rounds.

This weapon requires two hands.

RIFLE, MAGELOCK

Cost: 200 gc
Ammo: 1 (rune shot)
Effective Range: 84 feet (14″)
Extreme Range: 420 feet
Skill: Rifle
Attack Modifier: –2 (one-handed), 0 (two-handed)
POW: 10
AOE: —

Description: Exceedingly rare, the magelock rifle is a long rifle especially constructed to fire rune shots. A magelock fires metal-cased rounds in which both the bullet and cartridge have been inscribed with runes.

Special Rules: Magelock weapons can only fire rune shot ammunition.

It costs 5 gc for blasting powder, rune-scribed bullet, and metal casing for each round of rune shot ammunition. Due to the high cost of ammunition, most gun mages pour their own rune shots (see "Craft Rune Shot," p. 160).

This weapon requires two hands. When fired by a gun mage, this weapon is a magical weapon.

RIFLE, MILITARY

Cost: 45 gc
Ammo: 1 (heavy round)
Effective Range: 60 feet (10″)
Extreme Range: 300 feet
Skill: Rifle
Attack Modifier: 0
POW: 11
AOE: —

Description: The military rifle is a stout, heavy rifle. Though it lacks the range of the long rifle, the military rifle packs more punch.

Special Rules: It costs 3 gc for blasting powder, bullets, and casings for five heavy rounds.

This weapon requires two hands.

RIFLE, REPEATING

Cost: 80 gc
Ammo: 5 (light round)
Effective Range: 84 feet (14″)
Extreme Range: 420 feet
Skill: Rifle
Attack Modifier: 0
POW: 10
AOE: —

Description: The repeating rifle is primarily a military weapon. The weapon utilizes a five-chambered ammo wheel that can be replaced in the heat of combat instead of reloading each cylinder separately.

Special Rules: Replacing this weapon's ammo wheel requires a quick action. Reloading each cylinder of the ammo wheel takes one quick action.

It costs 2 gc for blasting powder, bullets, and casings for five light rounds. Additional ammo wheels cost 15 gc each.

This weapon requires two hands.

RYNNISH WALKING STICK

Cost: 40 gc
Ammo: 1 (light round)
Effective Range: 48 feet (8″)
Extreme Range: 240 feet
Skill: Rifle
Attack Modifier: –2 (one-handed), 0 (two-handed)
POW: 10
AOE: —

Description: The Rynnish walking stick is a small firearm concealed within the haft of a cane. The weapon can be fired like a short-ranged rifle.

Special Rules: An observant character can discern a Rynnish walking stick from a normal walking stick without handling it with a successful PER + Detection roll against a target number of 14.

It costs 2 gc for blasting powder, bullets, and casings for five light rounds.

SCATTERGUN

Cost: 40 gc
Ammo: 1 (shot round)
Effective Range: 48 feet (SP 8)
Extreme Range: —
Skill: Rifle
Attack Modifier: –2 (one-handed), 0 (two-handed)
POW: 12
AOE: —

Description: Scatterguns are heavy, oversized rifles designed to fire a spray of grapeshot. Scatterguns are devastating in close quarters.

Special Rules: It costs 1 gc for blasting powder, shot, and casing for one shot round.

SLING

Cost: 5 gc
Ammo: 1
Effective Range: 60 feet (10″)
Extreme Range: —
Skill: Thrown
Attack Modifier: –2
POW: 8
AOE: —

Description: The sling is a simple and ancient weapon that still sees some use on the streets of the Iron Kingdoms. It has become an invaluable tool in the arsenal of combat alchemists who use the weapon to deliver their explosive alchemical concoctions.

Special Rules: These weapons typically are used to pitch stones, grenades, or sling bullets.

If the attacker is throwing sling bullets instead of stones or other ammunition, there is no attack modifier.

Sling bullets cost 1 gc for twenty rounds. Stones can be amassed from the ground free of cost.

SLUG GUN

Cost: 40 gc
Ammo: 1 (slug round)
Effective Range: 24 feet (4″)
Extreme Range: —
Skill: Pistol
Attack Modifier: –2 (one-handed), –1 (two-handed)
POW: 14
AOE: —

Description: Slug guns are highly specialized weapons designed specifically to crack the armor of steamjacks and other heavily armored targets. The guns fire enormous slugs at an incredible velocity but are highly inaccurate.

Special Rules: It costs 1 gc for blasting powder, slug, and casing for each slug round.

SWORD-CANNON, REPEATING

Cost: 100 gc
Ammo: 5 (metal-cased light round)
Effective Range: 60 feet (10″)
Extreme Range: 300 feet
Skill: Rifle
Attack Modifier: –1
POW: 10
AOE: —

Description: This weapon is a sword that integrates a rifle barrel with a five-chambered ammo wheel. The ammo wheel can be replaced in the heat of combat instead of reloading each cylinder separately.

Special Rules: When used as a melee weapon, this weapon has an attack modifier of –1, is POW 3, and uses the One-Handed Weapon skill.

Replacing this weapon's ammo wheel requires a quick action. Reloading each cylinder of the ammo wheel takes one quick action.

It costs 3 gc for blasting powder, bullets, and metal casings for five light rounds. Additional ammo wheels cost 15 gc each.

As part of a charge, after moving but before making the charge attack, a character can spend 1 feat point to make one ranged attack with this weapon targeting the enemy charged unless the character was in melee with the enemy at the start of his turn. When resolving the ranged attack, the attacking character does not suffer the target in melee penalty. If the target is not in melee range after the attacking character moves, the character can make the ranged attack before his turn ends.

SWORD-CANNON, HEAVY

Cost: 150 gc
Ammo: 1 (heavy round)
Effective Range: 60 feet (10″)
Extreme Range: 300 feet
Skill: Rifle
Attack Modifier: –1
POW: 12
AOE: —

Description: This weapon integrates a heavy, single-shot rifle with the blade of a sword.

Special Rules: When used as a melee weapon, this weapon has an attack modifier of –1, is POW 3, and uses the One-Handed Weapon skill.

It costs 3 gc for blasting powder, bullets, and casings for five heavy rounds.

As part of a charge, after moving but before making the charge attack, a character can spend 1 feat point to make one ranged attack with this weapon targeting the enemy charged unless the character was in melee with the enemy at the start of his turn. When resolving the ranged attack, the attacking character does not suffer the target in melee penalty. If the target is not in melee range the attacking character moves, the character can make the ranged attack before his turn ends.

AMMUNITION AND RANGED WEAPON ACCESSORIES

Although there are small variances in bullet calibers and the amount of powder grain used in the cartridges of western Immoren, most weapons accept one of the three standard sizes of cartridges: light, heavy, and slug rounds. Light rounds are those used in most pistols and rifles; the circumference of a light round is less than half of an inch. Heavy rounds are found in heavy rifles, hand cannons, and mounted antipersonnel weapons. The circumference of a heavy round is over half an inch and creates a great amount of trauma as it travels through a target. Slug rounds are about fifty percent larger than a heavy round and transfer a tremendous amount of energy to the target upon impact.

Some weapons are also armed with shot. Shot is a collection of bullets that sits on top of a charge and is driven forward when the charge is ignited. The shot usually disperses, creating a larger diameter of impact in the target along with multiple entry wounds. This delivers a lot of trauma to the target in multiple places. The average shot round is the same size as a slug round.

Firearm ammunition in the Iron Kingdoms is either paper-wrapped or metal-cased. Both types of ammunition include a bullet, casing, and silk-wrapped packets of the two components of blasting powder. Paper cartridges are more fragile than metal-cased rounds but have the advantage that they can be assembled by hand on the battlefield and do not require any special equipment to press.

A character with the required materials and either the Pistol or the Rifle military skill can hand-wrap his own ammunition at the rate of five rounds per hour. A character who chooses to wrap his own ammunition gets enough materials to make twice as many rounds as he can purchase ready-made for the same cost. For instance, a character who spends 2 gc for the materials to make light ammunition rounds gains enough materials to make ten rounds of ammo, whereas he could purchase only five ready-made rounds for the same amount.

ARROWS OR BOLTS, EXPLOSIVE

Cost: 20 gc each

Special Rules: A character making an attack roll with an explosive arrow or bolt suffers –2 on his attack roll. The attack's POW becomes 10, and the attack gains a 3″ AOE.

ARROWS OR BOLTS, GRAPPLING

Cost: 1 gc each

Special Rules: The grappling arrow has a hooked grappling head and is attached to strong, lightweight cord. A character making an attack roll with grapple arrow or bolt suffers –2 on his attack roll. Attacks made with these arrows and bolts suffer –2 POW.

SALVAGING AMMUNITION

Many a desperate soldier on the field has found himself looting the dead bodies of his fallen comrades and enemies looking for a few more rounds for his weapon. Not all rounds are compatible, but most paper rounds can be converted from one type of round to another. Slug rounds (the largest of the three types) can be converted to a heavy round or light round by recasting the lead bullet into a smaller bullet, cutting down the paper that makes the cartridge, and then repacking the paper cartridge with a reduced amount of blasting powder. Recasting lead requires a gunsmith's kit. Likewise, a heavy round can be recast and reloaded into a light round. When moving up in size, multiple smaller rounds are required in order to create each larger round. Because of the variables involved in repacking ammunition, the conversions are not exact, but in general it takes three heavy rounds to make two slug rounds and four light rounds to make three heavy rounds; thus, you need two light rounds to make one slug round. This works the other way around as well, so that two slug rounds can produce four light rounds. Additionally, one slug round can be converted into one shot round, and one shot round can be converted into two light rounds.

AMMUNITION CONVERSION TABLE

LIGHT	HEAVY	SLUG	SHOT
	3	2	
4	3		
2		1	1

BANDOLIER, AMMO

Cost: 5 gc

Description: This simple leather cross-belt features ten to twelve leather loops suitable for holding firearm charges, enabling easy access to them. These bandoliers are usually issued to military units as well as pistol-armed forces like the Corvis Watch.

A character with an ammo bandolier can draw and reload a round into a firearm as part of the same quick action.

BANDOLIER, GRENADIER'S

Cost: 5 gc

Description: This heavy leather cross-body belt can hold up to six grenades. These bandoliers are favored by combat alchemists on the battlefields of western Immoren.

A character with a grenadier's bandolier can draw grenades without spending a quick action.

BIPOD

Cost: 10 gc

Description: A bipod is a lightweight brace for a rifle. When a character with a bipod forfeits his movement to aim during his turn, the character gains +2 to his first ranged attack with a rifle that turn. It requires a quick action to setup or take down a bipod.

FIREARM AMMUNITION

Cost: 2 gc for five light rounds of ammunition, 3 gc for five heavy rounds of ammunition, 1 gc for one slug round of ammunition. Add +1 gc to the cost for metal-cased ammunition.

GUN BRACE

Cost: 15 gc

Description: A gun brace is effectively a heavy leather bandolier for pistols. A gun brace has enough sleeves to hold three or four pistols. Some gunfighters and pirates are even known to wear two full braces of loaded pistols. Rather than reloading, a character with a gun brace simply pulls another pistol each time he wants to make an attack.

A character wearing a gun brace can draw two pistols as a single quick action. He can also replace his pistols without spending a quick action.

A cheap alternative to the gun brace favored by some pirates is to simply tie a length of rope between two pistols and hang them around the neck. Any character wishing to begin the game with a rope gun brace of this kind can do so for free.

GUNSMITH'S KIT

Cost: 20 gc

Description: In addition to the specialized tools of the gunsmith's trade, this kit includes a number of tools useful for cleaning, disassembling, and reassembling firearms. It also includes a scale for measuring blast powder, lead and molds for pouring shot, and a secure area for storing completed cartridges and charges.

A character with the Craft (gunsmithing) skill can press his own metal cartridges at a fraction of the cost of buying ammunition and can convert heavier cartridges to lighter cartridges with no loss of material and lighter cartridges to heavier cartridges with a minimal loss of material.

A character with the required materials and either the Pistol or the Rifle military skill can press his own metal cartridge ammunition. A character can press up to ten rounds of ammunition in an hour. A character who chooses to press his own ammunition rather than purchasing ready-made ammunition can make twice as many rounds as if he purchased them ready made. The character must pay an additional 1 gc for metal casings unless he recycles used brass casings and makes ammunition of that size. Thus, a character who purchases the materials to make light ammunition rounds at the cost of 3 gc gains enough materials to make ten rounds instead of five at the ready-made price.

ARTILLERY ROUNDS

As can be expected, larger weapons utilize larger-caliber rounds than small arms do. Such artillery pieces, sometimes manned by a crew or equipped on a steamjack, can fire any of three basic sizes of munitions: light, standard, and heavy. The shells of these munitions vary greatly, including specialized rounds that can be explosive or are just solid shells. Some munitions are metal-cased cartridges that are fed into the chamber via a magazine, while others still rely on a multi-step loading process that places them directly into the muzzle.

HARPOON GUN BLASTING POWDER

Cost: 1 gc for five charges of blasting powder

Additional harpoons or grapples cost 1 gc each.

HOLSTER, WRIST-SPRING

Cost: 15 gc

Description: Wrist-spring holsters are leather bracers fitted with a spring-arm mechanism that holds a dagger or pistol in place and can project it immediately into the wearer's hand when triggered. This allows the wearer to draw the weapon without spending a quick action. The nature of this device enables it to be easily concealed beneath a loose, billowy sleeve.

Wrist-spring holsters work with daggers, holdout pistols, and throwing knives.

QUIVER

Cost: 5 gc

Description: A quiver is a leather or wooden container for arrows or crossbow bolts. Archers carry their quivers on the back or the hip. Crossbowmen typically mount theirs on the belt.

A character with a quiver can draw and nock an arrow or load a crossbow as part of the same quick action.

SCOPE, RIFLE OR PISTOL

Cost: 20 gc

Special Rules: Adding a scope to a rifle or pistol adds eighteen feet (3″) to the weapon's effective range and ninety feet (15″) to its extreme range when a character armed with the weapon aims during his turn. A character aiming with a weapon with a scope only gains the aiming bonus with that weapon during his turn.

CLOTHING

Unusual or specialized items are discussed below.

BOOTS, MECHANIK'S

Cost: 20 gc

Description: These sturdy leather boots buckle or lace to provide a tight fit and have hobnail soles for long-lasting grip and wear. Most important, they are fitted with steel toecaps to protect the front of the feet from damage. These tough boots have proven exceptionally popular, not just with mechaniks, but with those from a great variety of professions.

COAT, GREAT

Cost: 25 gc

Description: A new and fashionable garment, the greatcoat provides good protection against the cold and the rain, making it particularly popular with port dwellers and travelers of all varieties. These long, heavy button-up coats are usually made of leather or heavy wool and feature several inner and outer pockets. Particularly fine greatcoats usually have a silk lining.

A character wearing a greatcoat gains +1 ARM against cold damage.

EQUIPMENT

Unusual or specialized items are discussed below.

'JACK WRENCH

Cost: 10 gc

Description: This is a massive steel wrench in common use among those who maintain and repair steamjacks in the field. The wrench is at least three feet long and bears an impressive weight.

In addition to being a ubiquitous tool in the hands of skilled field mechanik's across western Immoren, the 'jack wrench can also be used as a melee weapon in its own right. Anyone attacking with a 'jack wrench uses the Hand Weapon skill for the attack. Due to the wrench's slightly clumsy weight, the attack roll suffers a –2 penalty. When used as a weapon, the 'jack wrench has POW 3.

On a critical hit with a 'jack wrench, a living target hit has a chance to be knocked out (p. 219). If the target suffers damage from the attack, he must make a Willpower roll against a target number equal to the attacking character's STR + 9. If the target succeeds, he remains conscious. If he fails, he is knocked out.

ALCHEMICAL LAB

Cost: 500 gc

Description: This is a complete alchemical lab containing all the tools of the alchemist's trade. The instruments, common compounds, glassware, crucibles, and ovens necessary for the pursuit of alchemical experimentation are seemingly endless, and only in his laboratory does an alchemist have ready access these crucial items. Likely, the alchemist's entire life is tied up in this facility and it is here that he is most at home. Some alchemists organize their labs with rigorous exactitude, whereas others prefer sprawling messes where only they know where to find a specific beaker or phial of rare chemicals.

A character who works undisturbed in an alchemical lab gains +2 on Alchemy rolls.

ALCHEMIST'S APRON

Cost: 15 gc

Description: This is a heavy cloth apron that has been extensively treated to resist heat, cold, and alchemical corrosives. Alchemist's aprons are often worn by those working with volatile chemicals or who handle crucibles full of molten metal. Alchemist's aprons have become a common sight in the foundries of the Iron Kingdoms.

A character wearing an alchemist's apron gains +3 ARM against cold, corrosion, and fire damage originating in his front arc. An alchemist's apron cannot be worn with armor.

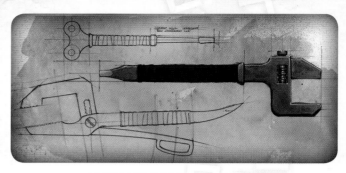

ALCHEMIST'S KIT, TRAVELING

Cost: 50 gc

Description: This kit is a carefully packed case that includes several small and durable glass beakers and tubes, a ceramic pestle, miniature burners and fuel, mixing rods of various materials, and cork stoppers. It is intended for mixing potions while in the field.

A character requires an alchemy kit or lab to create alchemical solutions.

ENTRENCHING SPADE

Cost: 10 gc

Description: This heavy-duty spade is standard issue to all Cygnaran Trenchers. It is used to dig trenches and improvised dugouts in the field.

GAS MASK

Cost: 20 gc

Description: Once unique to the workshops of the Golden Crucible, gas masks have become a rare but not-unobtainable piece of gear. The device is a face mask that affixes tightly to the head with adjustable buckles and straps to create an impermeable seal around the mouth and nose of the wearer. The "breather" of the mask is a large oblong leather sack affixed to the mask with a metal screw cap. Alchemically treated fibers in the filter allow clean air in but prevent particles and alchemical substances from permeating the filter's membranes. This allows a man to breathe air in even the most caustic and dangerous of environs without fear of damaging his lungs or windpipe.

It takes a quick action to put on or take off a gas mask.

A character wearing a gas mask gains +1 ARM against corrosion damage and is immune to gas effects. A character wearing a gas mask suffers –1 on sight- or hearing- based PER rolls. A gas mask can be worn with a specially designed helmet.

Replacement filters for a gas mask cost 5 gc each and provide enough protection for one full hour of exposure to caustic gasses and other undesirable particles the wearer might breathe.

GOGGLES

Cost: 5 gc

Description: Originally created for use by mechaniks, alchemists, and others working in hazardous professions, goggles have entered widespread use. Made of thick glass with adjustable leather straps, they provide protection from flying fragments of metal and other such dangers.

MANACLES

Cost: 10 gc

Description: Manacles are iron and steel restraints made to close over the wrists to restrain the movement of a prisoner. A character restrained by manacles can attempt to break out with a successful STR roll or slip the manacles with a successful AGL + Escape Artist against a target number of 15. Failure to break out with a STR roll inflicts 1 damage point on the restrained character. Slipping out takes ten minutes per attempt.

Manacles can also be picked by a character with the Pick Locking skill. A character attempting to pick the lock makes an AGL + Lock Picking against a target number of 15. Each attempt takes five minutes. A character attempting to pick the manacles restraining him suffers –2 to this roll.

Standard manacles are too small for ogrun. Ogrun restraining manacles cost 15 gc and cannot be used to restrain anything smaller than a trollkin. Breaking out of these reinforced manacles requires a successful STR roll against a target number of 20.

MECHANIK'S TOOL KIT

Cost: 100 gc

Description: This is a heavy wooden box or leather pouch belt stuffed with the tools of the mechanik's trade. As a matter of course a mechanik usually has three standard types of tools—the wrench, the hammer, and the boltdriver. These are easily recognizable by any casual observer, and they are practical tools in the hands of even an untrained mechanik's assistant.

The kit includes an array of other tools: in addition to several varieties of ratchets, there are usually pliers, tongs, and spanners for holding parts in place as well as calipers and dividers for measuring and spacing mountings. A mechanik who works on steamjacks has bores, chisels, reamers, and scrapers; injectors for priming pneumatic chambers; expanders for piston cylinders; and a number of hammers with heads of various shapes and sizes for shaping metal, pounding parts into place without damaging them, and smashing others out of place to allow for new parts.

MECHANIK'S WORKSHOP

Cost: 500+ gc

Description: The assortment of implements required by a mechanik in his simple day-to-day craft ranges from the rudimentary to the exotic. In addition to the myriad tools described in the mechanik's tool kit above, a full shop also includes torches, drills, pneumatic saws, steam shears, and piston rams designed to shape metal plates.

A character working out of a mechanik's workshop gains +2 to his Mechanikal Engineering rolls to repair or manufacture steamjacks and equipment.

POCKET WATCH

Cost: 25 gc

Description: With long-perfected mundane clockwork available to the populace, pocket watches have become relatively common luxury items throughout the Iron Kingdoms. They are especially fashionable among military officers and middle-class clerks, though fine silver and gold watches are preferred among the wealthier classes. Pocket watches are typically attached to fine chains to keep them well secured. Most watch faces have an hour hand only and are protected by a cover that snaps open and shut on a tiny hinge. Minute hands are rare, since they require more complex mechanics than hour hands. Pocket watches run on spring technology, which employs a coiled spring and notched wheels for the automated hand movement. Most require winding twice a day by means of a small key, though more advanced watches need to be wound only once a day.

PORTABLE STEAM ENGINE

Cost: 500 gc

Description: Compressed steam is the main motivating force of almost every technology in western Immoren. Coal-fed fires boil water to create steam, which is fed into a pressurized vent and funneled through a pipe into a piston chamber that uses variable pressure to drive the piston from both sides. With several pistons, each working in concert in larger engines, the result is an incredibly powerful engine that can power everything from foundry tools to locomotives.

Portable steam engines are used to power heavy mechanik's tools in the field and can be strapped to a man's back. Pneumatic conduits funnel steam and compressed air to the tools, allowing them to operate. Although the steam engines are quite heavy, especially with a full load of coal and water, their power and the benefits they provide to the use of powered tools often outweigh any encumbering factors.

Most steam tools attach to larger steam engines while in foundry use so that refueling is less of an issue. In the field of battle or in the dank confines of a lost ruin, the portable steam engine is king. A portable steam engine can provide sufficient power to a steam tool for one hour of operation at full steam before it requires refueling. An idling engine can burn for six hours continuously.

Running the steam engine requires 1 gc of coal for every four hours of continuous operation.

RIVET GUN

Cost: 30 gc

Description: This stubby tool can be the field mechanik's best friend for securing repairs and locking armor back down in place. It is well suited for use in combat conditions, being light and easy to load yet durable and reliable. The rivet gun doubles as a holdout weapon at close range. Although it doesn't have much stopping power against heavily armored targets, in the right hands it can prove an effective deterrent for enemy troopers or at least buy a mechanik enough time to retreat from making repairs.

The gun uses rivets, each with a paper-wrapped explosive charge in the rivet head. This mixture of blast powder is packed the same way as a cartridge. The charge is much smaller, designed to give just enough punch to pierce metal at extremely close ranges. The barrel design requires placement directly on armor plate or metal while the mechanik pulls the trigger, and

the blast charge allows the rivet to penetrate moderately thick metal and pin it in place. The gravity-fed firing mechanism does not jam easily, although water can creep into the rivet bin and waterlog the rivets so they won't fire.

The gun holds ten rivets. It takes a quick action to reload each rivet in combat.

As a weapon, the rivet gun is inaccurate and has an effective range of only twenty-four feet (4″) with no extreme range. A character making an attack with a rivet gun uses the Pistol skill and suffers a –2 penalty on his attack roll. A character hit by a rivet gun suffers a POW 10 damage roll.

Rivets and powder for a rivet gun cost 1 gc for ten rounds.

RUNE ETCHING KIT

Cost: 150 gc

Description: The arcane mechanik's rune etching kit includes the tools for creating arcane mechanika—conductance awls, etcher tubs, rune scrivers, conduit grips, glyph irons, and a variety of pristine measuring devices such as precision calipers, arcanometric slide rulers, warding sticks, incredibly accurate aligning devices, and jeweler's tools for handling fine mechanikal components. Socket mounting wrenches, arcano-conduction contact primers, and other obscure tools are included as well.

RUNE SHOT CASTING KIT

Cost: 50 gc

Description: This portable kit contains all the tools needed to craft the specialized ammunition known as rune shot (see p. 160). The kit can be used to produce mundane shot as well as rune shot.

SPYGLASS

Cost: 15 gc

Description: The spyglass is an eighteen-inch long hollow wooden or metal tube containing two glass lenses. Objects viewed through a spyglass are magnified to twice their normal size. Collapsing spyglasses that telescope down to ten inches long are also available.

A character using a spyglass gains +2 to PER rolls related to spotting at distances.

SURGICAL KIT

Cost: 30 gc

Description: The most essential instruments, salves, bandages, and sutures are stored within this portable surgical kit. In the hands of a skilled medical practitioner, the kit contains everything necessary for field surgery and even the treatment of life-threatening wounds.

A character with a surgical kit gains +1 to his Medicine skill rolls.

SYMBOL OF FAITH

Cost: 10 gc

Description: This is a finely made symbol of faith. It could be a Menofix, a holy symbol of Morrow, an ascendant talisman, a small mask of Cyriss, a Dhunian charm, or just about any other faith symbol. These symbols are generally plated with gold or silver, though trollkin Dhunian charms are often made from finely shaped stone.

THIEF'S TOOLS

Cost: 10 gc

Description: This concealable pouch of tools contains all of the tricks of the trade for the would-be thief. Inside are picks for locks, a miniature listening cone for hearing tumblers in safes, a vial of metal-eating acid for particularly tough locks, a metal wire saw, a small razor or two for the cutting of purses, and other tools that make the thief's job easier.

A character with a set of thief's tools gains +1 to Lock Picking and Pickpocket rolls.

MOUNTS AND RIDING EQUIPMENT

HORSE, DRAFT

PHY	12	SPD	7	STR	12

Cost: 60 gc

Description: A draft horse is a stocky, powerfully built workhorse. Though a draft horses can be ridden, they are most often put to work pulling a plow.

A draft horse has ARM 12 and 12 vitality points. Unmounted, a draft horse has DEF 11. A character riding a draft horse suffers an additional –2 DEF.

A perturbed draft horse without a rider can kick with MAT 5. Anyone hit suffers a damage roll with a POW equal to the draft horse's STR. Draft horses do not attack while mounted.

HORSE, RIDING

PHY	12	SPD	9	STR	8

Cost: 80 gc

Description: This is a fast horse bred for speed and riding. A riding horse is not trained for war and is not stout enough to pull a plow.

A riding horse has ARM 12 and 12 vitality points. Unmounted, a riding horse has DEF 14.

A perturbed riding horse without a rider can kick with MAT 5. Anyone hit suffers a damage roll with a POW equal to the riding horse's STR. Riding horses do not attack while mounted.

HORSE, WAR

PHY	12	SPD	8	STR	10

Cost: 120 gc

Description: A warhorse is a strong and powerful animal bred and trained for battle. A steed designated as a warhorse can make cavalry charges when ridden by a skilled rider.

A warhorse has ARM 12 and 12 vitality points. Unmounted, a warhorse has DEF 12.

A perturbed warhorse without a rider can kick with MAT 5. The animal can also make impact attacks. Anyone hit by a warhorse attack suffers a damage roll with a POW equal to the warhorse's STR.

BARDING, LIGHT

Cost: 90 gc

Description: Light barding consists of a few armored plates covering the horse's head, neck, and chest.

Light barding adds +4 to a horse's ARM.

BARDING, MEDIUM

Cost: 150 gc

Description: Medium barding consists of either light armored plates or a coat of chain mail and padding.

Medium barding adds +6 to a horse's ARM.

BARDING, HEAVY

Cost: 300 gc

Description: This is the heaviest class of equestrian armor. It consists of heavy plates over chain mail and padding that protect the horse's neck, chest, sides, flanks, legs, and head.

Heavy barding cannot be worn by riding horses.

Heavy barding adds +8 to a horse's ARM.

GAS MASK, EQUESTRIAN

Cost: 45 gc

Description: This is a large gas mask designed to fit over the head of a horse.

It takes a full action to put on or take a gas mask off a horse.

A horse wearing a gas mask gains +1 ARM against corrosion damage and is immune to gas effects. A horse wearing a gas mask suffers –1 on sight- or hearing-based PER rolls.

It costs 5 gc tor replacement filters for an equestrian gas mask. These filters provide enough protection for one full hour of exposure to caustic gasses and other undesirable particles the wearer might breathe.

TACK

Cost: 50 gc

Description: Tack includes all the equipment and accessories necessary to keep a rider on a horse. Tack includes the saddle, stirrups, reins, bit, and bridle. In addition to keeping the rider on the horse, tack also greatly enhances the rider's control over his mount.

A character riding a mount without tack suffers –3 to his Riding skill rolls.

FOOD, DRINK, AND LODGING

Western Immoren comprises a vast array of races and cultural traditions, from the nomadic Idrians in the sweltering eastern deserts to the trollkin of the Thornwood to the scattered Nyss, and each of these cultures includes foods and drink unique to its people. Because it would take the length of this entire book to catalog all the various foods and beverages within each of these cultures, the options here are generalized. A Game Master is encouraged to tailor his description of what the players purchase to the cultural situation.

DRY RATIONS

Cost: 1 gc per day

Description: Dry rations are the barest essential foodstuff for the traveling adventurer. Their form changes dramatically depending on where they are purchased, but they always offer enough sustenance for one day. In more civilized areas, dry rations appear in the form of hardtack and aged cheeses, while in the wilds they tend to be dried and salted meats. Typically, these supplies rot if they get wet or are exposed to the elements for too long.

MILITARY RATIONS

Cost: 1 gc per day

Description: The prolific nature of warfare in the Iron Kingdoms brought a boon in the form of food preservation technology. A fairly recent development has been the creation of sealed tin canisters that hold prepared meats, fruits, and vegetables and keep them fresh for months, making the contents more palatable than typical dry rations. The canister keeps the food from the elements and can resist the rough treatment typically seen on a battlefield. As a new convention, military rations can be found in most civilized areas and military posts, though they are somewhat rare in the countryside.

MEAL, BASIC

Cost: 1 gc

Description: Dished out at every tavern, inn, and homestead, this type of meal is the staple on which most of the citizens of western Immoren survive. The contents of the meal vary as dramatically as the peoples of the Iron Kingdoms. It might not be the tastiest food on Caen, but it's hot and filling.

MEAL, QUALITY

Cost: 5 gc per day

Description: Served at superior inns, restaurants, and taverns, this type of meal is made up of multiple courses including fresh fruits and vegetables, rich soups and broths, well prepared meats and fish, and a regional dessert. This is the best most establishments have to offer.

MEAL, LUXURIOUS FEAST

Cost: 25 gc

Description: This type of meal is offered in only the most expensive restaurants, inns, and royal estates and is the stuff of culinary dreams. Adorning this table would be delicacies such as spices and smoked meats procured from the distant continent of Zu, the finest Khadoran caviar, and exotic fruits from the mysterious nation of Ios, all prepared by the best chefs western Immoren has to offer. Contraband foods can be purchased in this price range.

BEER

Cost: 1 gc per bottle or per pint in a saloon

Description: Beer is typically an unfiltered, grainy, barely alcoholic beverage. Brewed all over western Immoren, this staple of commoner life is essential in places where the water might not be safe to drink. The smart traveler knows to drink this off-putting liquid rather than trust the local stream. Ciders, meads, and ales fall into the same range of pricing.

WINE

Cost: 1+ gc (glass), 5+ gc (bottle)

Description: Typically created from the fermentation of a wide variety of fruits, wine has existed in the Iron Kingdoms for as long as civilization itself. The value of wine is based on availability, region of origination, vintage, and quality. Truly rare vintages can sell for vast sums of money.

DISTILLED SPIRITS

Cost: 1+ gc (shot), 5+ gc (bottle)

Description: Brandy, rum, whiskey, gin, and all other distilled beverages fall within this category. A variety of factors go into determining the values of these beverages, the most expensive coming from long-established distilleries with a history of creating quality product.

LODGING, BASIC

Cost: 1 gc per night

Description: This class of accommodation offers little more than four walls and a roof over one's head. Stables, wind-riddled sheds, crowded shared boarding house rooms, and sleeping on the dirty floor of a tavern all qualify as boarding at this level. Your character is off the street, but just barely.

LODGING, STANDARD

Cost: 5 gc (per night), 50 gc (per month)

Description: The standard lodging is a typical private room for let found throughout the Iron Kingdoms. It is reasonably clean and a stay usually includes breakfast. Rooms of this sort are often available for rent by the month. Prices increase dramatically during the high season, religious festivals, and at harvest time.

LODGING, EXQUISITE

Cost: 25+ gc per night

Description: These rooms are found in the most civilized cities of western Immoren. Rooms are kept in immaculate condition by a staff that waits hand and foot upon the character. Beds and furnishings are of the highest quality, and tasteful art can be found wherever the eye might fall. These rooms commonly have private bathing areas with attendants to massage exotic oils into a traveler's worn muscles. An establishment with this quality of lodging goes out of its way to cater to characters who choose to purchase this option.

MECHANIKA

Science and progress move swiftly. Through innovation and study, magic in the form of mechanika has become commonplace throughout western Immoren. Steam-powered constructs and other advanced technologies have existed in one form or another since the first colossal strode the fields of battle, crushing the Orgoth beneath its immense, metal fists. This science has proven as potent as the Gift of magic.

Mechanika is the application of magic to augment physical science. Steam pistons and hydraulics work in concert to provide power to magical conduits. Mechanika runes enable arcane mechaniks to create devices that function consistently and are easy to use despite their extraordinary workings.

MECHANIKAL ITEMS

A mechanikal item has three components: **housing**, **capacitor**, and **runeplate.** The housing is the shell that contains the mechanikal components. In the case of a mechanikal weapon, this is the weapon itself. The capacitor is the arcane power source that powers the mechanika. The runeplate is the special plate inscribed with the arcane glyphs that give the item its magical effects. The runes inscribed on the runeplate determine the mechanikal item's particular magical properties.

Some items require specialized runes and runeplates that function only with that item. Other devices can work with a host of different runes, and switching between runeplates gives the item different arcane effects. For example, a mechanikal sword can function with either a Fire runeplate or an Overkill runeplate, with different arcane effects. A mechanikal sword cannot be made to function with the Fleet rune from a suit of mechanikal armor.

Some runes provide a constant benefit while the item is powered, while others are activated only briefly for a short-term

MAGICAL WEAPONS AND ITEMS

In addition to the mechanikal wonders of the modern age, truly magical devices and weapons do exist. Some are relics of bygone eras, such as the dreaded Witchfire, a weapon so ancient its origins are lost to time. Others are fearsome remnants of formerly great or fallen civilizations, such as the Fellblades left behind by the Orgoth when they departed western Immoren centuries ago. More recently created magical items include the tools and weapons devised by the mysterious Circle Orboros and the Skorne Empire and the holy blades sanctified by powerful priests.

effect. For example, some mechanikal weapons are set with force triggers and activate only upon striking a blow in combat.

All mechanikal weapon and armor runeplates integrate glyphs that compensate for the added weight of mechanikal augmentation. These glyphs are constantly active but draw only a minute amount of power from the device's capacitor.

MECHANIKAL WEAPONS

While charged, a mechanikal weapon is considered a magical weapon.

If a mechanikal weapon's capacitor completely loses its charge, the weapon suffers –1 on attack rolls until the capacitor has been recharged or replaced.

MECHANIKAL ARMOR

The housing for mechanikal armor is based on rigid plate mail. Chain and leather armor tend to be useless for mechanikal housing, but mechanikal armor can integrate elements of chain and leather armor into its design.

If the capacitor in a suit of mechanikal armor completely loses its charge, the wearer suffers –2 DEF until the capacitor has been recharged or replaced.

ACTIVATING A MECHANIKAL ITEM

Depending on the nature of its runes, a mechanikal device must either be activated in advance by spending a quick action or be on constantly. Some mechanikal weapons have triggers that activate when the weapon strikes a blow.

FABRICATION AND ASSEMBLY

These rules are an extrapolation of the building process. Players need not be concerned with the specifics of every length of conduit, trickle switch, or arcantrik divining gauge.

The key components of any mechanikal device are the housing, capacitor, and the runeplate. A player wishing to fabricate or assemble a mechanikal device must first assemble the necessary parts. He can build the device from scratch, build some parts and purchase others, or collect the component parts separately.

SOME ASSEMBLY REQUIRED

Once a character has gathered the three necessary components for constructing a mechanikal device, he must spend time assembling the device. A character must have the Mechanikal Engineering skill to assemble a mechanikal device. Assembling a handheld device takes approximately two hours. Assembling larger devices can take much longer. Assembly requires a mechaniks tool kit.

Once the character has spent the allotted time assembling the device, his player makes an INT + Mechanikal Engineering skill roll against a target number of 13 to determine his success. If the roll succeeds, the character has correctly assembled the device. If the roll fails, the device does not function. The player can make another roll after his character spends an hour making corrections to his work.

DISMANTLING

Just as a character can assemble a mechanikal device, he can also dismantle it. Dismantling a handheld mechanikal device takes thirty minutes and a successful INT + Mechanikal Engineering roll against a target number of 13. If the roll fails, the character can try again after an additional fifteen minutes of labor. Dismantling larger devices can take longer at the Game Master's discretion.

Note that although the nature of the other components of the mechanikal object is obvious, unless the character has the Inscribe Formulae ability he has no way to identify the device's runeplate by sight.

CHANGING A CAPACITOR

Mechanikal devices require constant power, and the creation of alchemical and mechanikal power supplies is a growing industry throughout the Iron Kingdoms. Changing the capacitor in a mechanikal device requires five minutes but does not require a die roll or any specialized skills.

CHANGING A RUNEPLATE

One of the strengths of mechanika is the ease with which runeplates can be exchanged to give the item a different arcane effect. Not all mechanikal devices can have their runeplates switched in this way. Many have dedicated plates that do not function without a very specific set of runes empowering the device.

Changing a runeplate involves opening the housing, carefully extracting the plate currently set into the housing, and replacing it with a new plate before bolting the housing back together. With the proper tools, it takes five minutes to fully change the runeplate of a handheld device, a weapon, or mechanikal armor. Successfully changing a runeplate does not require a die roll.

HOUSING

A device's housing is the shell or body that houses the capacitor, runeplate, triggers, conduits, venting, and other parts required to create a functioning piece of mechanika. The time and cost required to fabricate the housing for a mechanikal device depends on the size and complexity of the object being constructed. All mechanika housings must be painstakingly crafted, so the creation of these objects should be attempted only by the most skilled engineers and craftsmen.

Purchasing the housing for a mechanikal device costs ten times the cost of a normal, non-mechanikal version of the item. For example, a character wishing to purchase a mechanikal axe housing would pay 80 gc for the axe (8 gc for the cost of a normal axe x 10). Purchasing the materials to fabricate a mechanikal device housing costs three times the cost of a normal, non-mechanikal version of the item. The raw materials to create a mechanikal spear housing cost 45 gc (15 gc for the cost of a normal spear x 3).

Mechanikal weapon and armor housings have the same stats as the weapons they are based on.

MECHANIKA HOUSING

Cost: 10 x the cost of a non-mechanikal version of the item being housed

Description: The mechanika housing is the shell of the mechanikal object. It houses the runeplate, capacitor, and other components.

Special Rules: None.

Fabrication Requirements: Applicable Craft skill and Mechanikal Engineering. For example, if the character is trying to create a mechanikal pistol housing, the pertinent Craft skill is Craft (gunsmithing).

ARCANE DISJUNCTION

Retrofitting a magical weapon with mechanikal fittings results in a thaumaturgic dissonance that destroys both the magic weapon and the runeplate. Don't try this at home.

Material Costs to Fabricate: 3 x the cost of a non-mechanikal version of the item.

Fabrication Rules: Fabrication of a mechanikal object's housing requires access to a mechanik's workshop.

Once a character has the raw materials to construct the housing, he must spend time preparing and assembling the components. The amount of time required is equal to the amount of time a mundane version of the item would take to craft plus an additional week to create the mechanikal interface conduits, capacitor seating, and reflect triggers.

Once the character has spent the required amount of time fabricating his device housing, the player makes a roll using his character's INT + either his Mechanikal Engineering skill or his pertinent Craft skill, whichever is lower, against a target number of 15. If the roll succeeds, the character has successfully crafted the device housing. If the roll fails, the character can spend another week working on the housing and then roll again.

EXAMPLE: *A character wishing to purchase a mechanikal axe housing would pay 80 gc for the axe (8 gc for the cost of a normal axe x 10). Alternatively, a character with the right skills could craft the same mechanikal axe housing using raw materials with a cost of 24 gc (8 gc for the cost of a normal axe x 3).*

RETROFITTING

Instead of constructing or buying the housing for a mechanikal device, it is also possible to retrofit an existing item, such as a pistol or shield, to serve as mechanikal housing.

A character attempting to retrofit an existing item must first purchase the raw mechanikal components for the retrofit. These components cost the same as the original price of the item. Once a character has the necessary parts, it takes a week to modify the retrofitted object. After this time the player makes a roll using his character's INT + either his Mechanikal Engineering skill or his pertinent Craft skill, whichever is lower, against a target number of 15. If the roll succeeds, the character has successfully retrofitted the object. If the roll fails, the character can spend another week working on the housing and then roll again.

A character can also purchase a retrofitted housing, which can save substantial coin. The cost of a retrofitted housing is five times the original cost of the non-mechanikal version of the item.

Though retrofitting is a less expensive alternative to buying or constructing a custom-built mechanikal housing, it does have its drawbacks. Retrofit items have a cobbled-together appearance, and even the finest work is at least moderately unbalanced.

A character armed with a retrofitted weapon suffers –1 on his attack rolls with the weapon as a result of the weapon's unbalance.

CAPACITORS

Every mechanikal device requires a power source to fuel its runeplate. Though capacitors technically function very differently, each is designed to provide energy to the item it powers.

The amount of energy a capacitor stores depends on the capacitor. The rate the energy is consumed depends on the item's runeplate and how it is used.

MAKING IT ALL FIT

The capacitor descriptions below are written in broad strokes and do not take into account the specific sizes and shapes of capacitors required to fit into a given housing. Unless it was created in a military arms factory that takes care to standardize its production, each piece of mechanika is unique, a device of art as much as science. There are no general stores selling ready-to-fit-all capacitors. Instead, each capacitor is crafted to fit the housing of the device it was designed to power. As a result, unless a character purchases a capacitor at the same time he buys the device's housing, he has to have the capacitor custom-fit to his housing. The same is true of buying replacement capacitors. Custom-fitting a capacitor does not cost anything additional but is simply rolled into the cost of doing business. Custom-fitting a capacitor can take considerable time.

That said, a skilled mechanik can bodge together almost any piece of mechanika with a capacitor of any size with a little time, some coupling tubing, and a successful Mechanikal Engineering roll (target number 14). If the roll succeeds, the ill-fitting capacitor powers the device but it is unbalanced and haphazard in appearance. Any rolls to use the device, such as attacks made with an unbalanced mechanikal weapon, are made at –1.

The following attributes define capacitors in the game.

Cost: This is the cost of the capacitor in Cygnaran gold crowns (gc).

Power Output: This is an abstract measure of the number of rune points (p. 284) the capacitor can power at a time. If a mechanikal device's runes require more power than the available capacitor, the device does not function.

Lifespan: This is the length of time the capacitor can be expected to continue reliably providing its power output.

Description: This is a description of the capacitor.

Special Rules: This section describes any special rules of the capacitor.

Fabrication Requirements: These are skills and abilities required to fabricate the capacitor. A character without all the skills listed automatically fails in his attempt to fabricate the capacitor.

Material Cost: This is the cost for the materials required to fabricate the capacitor.

Fabrication Rules: These are rules for building the capacitor once the character has the materials at hand.

ALCHEMICAL CAPACITOR

Cost: 10 gc
Power Output: 3
Lifespan: 1 week

Description: This is a small alchemical battery that can be used to power most handheld devices. The capacitor functions by creating an alchemical reaction that generates power.

Special Rules: Though alchemical capacitors are the least expensive mechanikal power sources available, they lose efficacy rapidly over time whether used or not.

Alchemical capacitors cannot be recharged.

Fabrication Requirements: Alchemy and Mechanikal Engineering

Material Costs: 3 gc

Fabrication Rules: Construction requires both an alchemist's lab and a mechanik's workshop.

Once a character has the raw materials to construct the alchemical capacitor, he must spend four hours preparing and assembling the components. At the end of this time, his player makes an INT + Alchemy or Mechanikal Engineering roll, whichever is lower, against a target number of 13. If the roll succeeds, the character creates a functional capacitor. If the roll fails, the character can make another attempt once he has spent an additional hour reworking the capacitor.

ARCANE TURBINE

Cost: 500 gc

Power Output: 8

Lifespan: 6 hours at a time, with a steady supply of coal and water

Description: The arcane turbine is a highly efficient and advanced generator that transforms energy from a steam engine into arcane energy. The heart of the turbine is a complex series of wire-coiled wheels spinning inside a thinly layered metal lattice of arcane-sensitive alloys. This creates energy that is carried through arcane conduits to power various mechanikal functions, most notably the power field of warcaster armor and peripheral steamjack systems such as sensory equipment and reflex triggers.

While there is variance in arcane turbines used for warcaster armor, most include a highly efficient integrated steam engine that provides a steady charge for up to twelve hours of operation on a full load of coal and water. These turbines can be set to minimal power, deactivating the power field but maintaining range of movement, to double the operation time and reduce smoke output. Warcaster arcane turbines integrate cooling systems to protect the wearer from the steam engine's heat. The arcane turbines on a steamjack are powered by steam vents from its main steam engine and do not require separate coal or water.

Special Rules: An arcane turbine is typically housed in a suit of mechanikal armor, but it is not limited to powering that suit of armor. Weapons and shields can be connected to the turbine using arcane conduits at a cost of 10 gc per item. Changing out an attached weapon requires ten minutes of labor and a successful INT + Mechanikal Engineering roll against a target number of 11.

An arcane turbine requires 1 gc of coal per day for twelve hours of continuous operation.

Fabrication Requirements: Mechanikal Engineering, Inscribe Formulae

Material Costs: 160 gc

Fabrication Rules: Construction requires a mechanik's workshop.

Once a character has the raw materials to construct the arcane turbine, he must spend a week crafting and assembling the components. At the end of this time, his player makes an INT + Mechanikal Engineering roll against a target number of 17. If the roll succeeds, the character creates a functional arcane turbine. If the roll fails, the character can make another attempt once he has spent an additional day reworking the turbine.

ARCANODYNAMIC ACCUMULATOR

Cost: 50 gc
Power Output: 4
Lifespan: 1 month

Description: Arcanodynamic accumulators are capacitors constructed with glass cylinders or spheres that contain steel and gold scrolls etched with complex runes to generate an arcane charge. They are very slow to produce but pack a great deal of energy into a single capacitor. Accumulators can be used to power most handheld devices. The capacitor functions by creating an alchemical reaction that generates power.

Special Rules: The complex mechanika of an arcanodynamic accumulator allows it to keep its charge much longer than the alchemical capacitor.

Arcanodynamic accumulators cannot be recharged.

Fabrication Requirements: Craft (glasswork), Mechanikal Engineering, Inscribe Formulae

Material Costs: 15 gc

Fabrication Rules: Construction requires both a mechanik's workshop and a glassworker's workshop.

Once a character has the raw materials to construct the accumulator, he must spend one day preparing and assembling the components. At the end of this time, his player makes an INT + Craft (glasswork) or Mechanikal Engineering roll, whichever is lower, against a target number of 13. If the roll succeeds, the character creates a functional capacitor. If the roll fails, the character can make another attempt once he has spent an additional hour reworking the capacitor.

CLOCKWORK CAPACITOR

Cost: 80 gc
Power Output: 3
Lifespan: 1 day, with the ability to be recharged as described below

Description: The clockwork capacitor is an ingenious mechanikal device that can be recharged through winding. The Cult of Cyriss produces a vast array of these devices that can be much more sophisticated than those commonly available throughout the markets of the Iron Kingdoms. A clockwork capacitor can be built in any size but has the same general attributes regardless of size.

Special Rules: Completely recharging this capacitor requires fifteen minutes of winding.

Fabrication Requirements: Mechanikal Engineering, Inscribe Formulae

Material Costs: 20 gc

Fabrication Rules: Construction requires a mechanik's workshop.

Once a character has the raw materials to construct the arcane turbine, he must spend three days crafting and assembling the components. At the end of this time, his player makes an INT + Mechanikal Engineering roll against a target number of 15. If the roll succeeds, the character creates a functional clockwork capacitor. If the roll fails, the character can make another attempt once he has spent an additional four hours reworking the capacitor.

STORM CHAMBER

Cost: 250 gc
Power Output: 5
Lifespan: 1 year

Description: The storm chamber is a revolutionary accumulator developed and used widely by the Cygnaran military. The accumulator is powered by lightning generated and harnessed within the chamber itself.

Special Rules: Any character handling an activated storm chamber suffers a POW 12 electrical damage roll. Such power sources are either designed to be used by individuals with galvanic shields or integrated into the housing of mechanika where no one can contact the accumulator.

Storm chambers cannot be recharged.

Fabrication Requirements: Mechanikal Engineering, Inscribe Formulae

Material Costs: 80 gc

Fabrication Rules: Construction requires a mechanik's workshop.

Once a character has the raw materials to construct the storm chamber, he must spend a week crafting and assembling the components. At the end of this time, his player makes an INT + Mechanikal Engineering roll against a target number of 16. If the roll succeeds, the character creates a functional storm chamber. If the roll fails, the character can make another attempt once he has spent an additional day reworking the generator.

RUNEPLATES

Runeplates are the surfaces on which magical runic formulae are inscribed. They are created from rare magically attuned materials that can harness powerful arcane energy. Mechanika runes are the magical formulae inscribed onto runeplates. These runes transform the magical energy charging the runeplate into arcane effects. Each rune is a true expression of the arcane mechanik's craft, and the inscription of different runes upon powerful runeplates allows for almost unlimited combinations of arcane effects.

RUNE POINTS

Each mechanika rune has an associated **rune point value** that describes its complexity. The more complex the rune, the higher its rune point value. Each runeplate can have up to five points of runes. Rune points are also a measure of the amount of power output required from the device's capacitor to power the runeplate. Take care to make sure that the power source can in fact power the plate. Few power sources can accommodate five points of power.

PURCHASING A RUNEPLATE

A character purchasing a runeplate can buy it with runes already inscribed, or he can inscribe it himself. The cost of a blank runeplate is 10 gc. The cost of each rune is described below. Remember that all runes on a single runeplate must be of the same type.

INSCRIBING A RUNEPLATE

A runeplate can be inscribed with any number of runes with a total rune point value of five. All the runes inscribed on the plate must be of the same type (melee weapon, armor, and so on) A runeplate inscribed with a mix of rune types does not function and is a waste of time and resources. For example, a runeplate that is inscribed with a mix of both armor and melee weapon runes will not function.

To inscribe a runeplate, a character must have the Mechanikal Engineering skill and the Inscribe Formulae ability.

Inscribing a rune takes one week per rune point. Once this time has passed, the player makes an INT + Mechanikal Engineering roll to determine success. The difficulty number for this roll is equal to 12 + the rune's point value. A character who takes his time and spends an additional week inscribing his plate gains +2 to his roll. If the roll succeeds, the character has inscribed the rune on the plate. If the roll fails, the character must carefully and painstakingly correct his inscription. After a week of laborious refinement, the character can attempt this roll again.

If a runeplate has not reached its rune point allowance in runes, it can have additional runes inscribed on it.

The following attributes define runeplates in the game.

Type: A runeplate inscribed with runes of more than one type does not function.

Cost: This is the cost of the rune already inscribed on a runeplate, in Cygnaran gold crowns (gc). This cost is in addition to the cost of the plate itself.

Rune Points: This is the number of rune points the rune takes up on a runeplate.

Effect: This is the effect of the rune in the game.

ACCURACY

Type: Melee or Ranged Weapon
Cost: 150 gc
Rune Points: 1

Effect: While the weapon has power, the character wielding it gains +1 on his attack rolls with it.

AEGIS

Type: Armor
Cost: 150 gc
Rune Points: 1

Effect: While the armor has power, the character wearing it is immune to continuous effects.

ARCANE FORCE

Type: Melee Weapon
Cost: 450 gc
Rune Points: 3

Effect: While the weapon has power, it gains +2 POW. On a critical hit, the attacking character can slam the character hit instead of rolling damage normally. The character hit is slammed d6″ directly away from the attacker and suffers a damage roll with POW equal to the attacker's STR plus the POW of this weapon. The POW of collateral damage is equal to the attacker's STR.

BALEFIRE

Type: Melee Weapon
Cost: 150 gc
Rune Points: 1

Effect: While the weapon has power, it gains boosted damage against undead characters.

BLAST

Type: Ranged Weapon (firearm)
Cost: 300 gc
Rune Points: 2

Effect: While the weapon has power, the character wielding it can attack with the weapon normally or can give the weapon AOE 3.

BLESSED

Type: Melee or Ranged Weapon
Cost: 300 gc
Rune Points: 2

Effect: While the weapon has power, attacks with it ignore spell effects that add to the target's DEF and ARM.

BOND PLATE

Type: Melee Weapon, Ranged Weapon
Cost: 300 gc
Rune Points: 2

Effect: This is a runeplate specially designed to enable a warcaster to bond with a mechanikal weapon. While a weapon the warcaster is bonded to has power, the warcaster can boost attack and damage rolls with the weapon.

COLD

Type: Melee Weapon
Cost: 300 gc
Rune Points: 2

Effect: While the weapon has power, it gains +1 POW. On a critical hit, a target without Immunity: Cold becomes stationary for one round.

COMPENSATOR

Type: Armor
Cost: 150 gc
Rune Points: 1

Effect: While the armor has power, reduce the DEF penalty of the armor by 1.

CORRUPTION

Type: Melee or Ranged Weapon
Cost: 150 gc
Rune Points: 1

Effect: While the weapon has power, characters it hits suffer the Corrosion continuous effect.

DISBINDER

Type: Melee Weapon
Cost: 300 gc
Rune Points: 2

Effect: While the weapon has power, upkeep spells on characters it hits immediately expire.

ELECTROCUTIONER

Type: Melee Weapon
Cost: 450 gc
Rune Points: 3

Effect: While the weapon has power, it gains +1 POW and steamjacks it hits suffer Disruption. (A steamjack suffering Disruption loses its focus points and cannot be allocated focus or channel spells for one round)

FLAME

Type: Melee Weapon
Cost: 300 gc
Rune Points: 2

Effect: While the weapon has power, it gains +1 POW. On a critical hit, the target suffers the Fire continuous effect.

FLEET

Type: Armor
Cost: 450 gc
Rune Points: 3

Effect: While the armor has power, the character wearing it gains +1 SPD and DEF.

GRIEVOUS WOUNDS

Type: Melee Weapon
Cost: 300 gc
Rune Points: 2

Effect: While the weapon has power, characters it hits lose Tough, cannot heal or be healed, and cannot transfer damage for one round.

HALO OF FIRE

Type: Armor or Melee Weapon (Shield)
Cost: 300 gc
Rune Points: 2

Effect: While the armor or shield has power, the character carrying the shield or wearing the armor gains Immunity: Fire.

While the runeplate is active, the character can make a quick action to unleash a burning field around himself. For one round, any character hitting him with a melee attack suffers the Fire continuous effect. If this runeplate is set into a shield, only attackers in the character's front arc suffer the damage roll and continuous effect.

HEIGHTENED STRENGTH

Type: Armor
Cost: 300 gc
Rune Points: 2

Effect: While the armor has power, the character wearing it gains +1 STR.

LIGHT

Type: Melee Weapon, Ranged Weapon, or Armor
Cost: 150 gc
Rune Points: 1

Effect: While the item has power, it can provide light (p. 225) in a large area around the character carrying the weapon or wearing the armor. The light can be turned on or off as a quick action.

MECHANIKAL SEIZURE

Type: Melee Weapon
Cost: 300 gc
Rune Points: 2

Effect: While the weapon has power, steamjacks it hits become stationary for one round.

QUICKEN

Type: Armor
Cost: 300 gc
Rune Points: 2

Effect: While the armor has power, once per turn the character wearing it can immediately advance up to twelve feet (2″) as a quick action.

REPULSOR

Type: Melee Weapon (Shield)
Cost: 300 gc
Rune Points: 2

Effect: While the shield has power, a character hit by it is pushed 1″ directly away from the attacker. While the shield has power, when the character wielding the shield is hit with a melee attack made by a character in his front arc, after the attack is resolved the attacker is pushed 1″ directly away from him.

SILENCER

Type: Ranged Weapon (Firearm)
Cost: 150 gc
Rune Points: 1

Effect: While the weapon has power, attacks made with the weapon make no sound.

SPELL WARD

Type: Armor
Cost: 450 gc
Rune Points: 3

Effect: While the armor has power, the character wearing it cannot be targeted by spells.

STALL

Type: Melee Weapon
Cost: 450 gc
Rune Points: 3

Effect: While the weapon has power, it gains +1 POW. Steamjacks hit by this weapon suffer the Stall continuous effect. (While a steamjack is suffering Stall, its base DEF becomes 7 and it cannot run or charge.)

STEADY

Type: Armor
Cost: 150 gc
Rune Points: 1

Effect: While the armor has power, the character wearing it cannot be knocked down.

DEDICATED MECHANIKAL DEVICES

There are many mechanikal devices with a dedicated form and function that work only when empowered with a very specific set of runes. The makeup of these devices can change only slightly and still remain functional. The power source and specific look of the housing can change, but the runeplates themselves cannot be altered in any way.

A character fabricating such a device uses the rules above to determine the cost of materials and length of time required to construct the device's housing and capacitor. Each device then requires a specific runeplate described in the text of each item below.

The following attributes define how mechanikal devices function in the game.

Cost: This is the cost of purchasing the finished device in Cygnaran gold crowns.

Description: This is a description of the device.

Rune Points: This is the number of rune points inscribed on the device's runeplate.

Special Rules: This section describes any special rules of the armor.

Fabrication: These are the rules for fabricating the device.

ARCANTRIK SCOPE

Cost: 590 gc

Description: This is a mechanikal scope that enables its user to pierce the most obscuring magic. The scope includes a housing, a clockwork capacitor, and a dedicated runeplate.

Rune Points: 2

Special Rules: The scope functions as a normal rifle scope (see p. 273). While the scope has power, when a character armed with a weapon with an arcantrik scope forfeits his movement to aim with the weapon, the character ignores stealth that turn.

Fabrication: The material cost of the scope's housing is 60 gc. It takes one week to construct the device. The pertinent Craft skill for construction is Craft (gunsmithing).

The scope's runeplates require two weeks to inscribe and requires a successful INT + Mechanikal Engineering roll against a target number of 14.

FARSIGHT GOGGLES

Cost: 790 gc

Description: Farsight goggles are a complex piece of optical mechanika. Originally developed for forward observers to monitor troop movements, the high cost of the goggles has dramatically restricted their use. Notably, they have found a place among the agents of the Cygnaran Reconnaissance Service who use the goggles on desperate missions when they must navigate hostile terrain in the dead of night. The goggles appear as a pair of heavy, three-lensed goggles with glowing green lenses, attached to a heavy belt with a low-slung alchemical capacitor supplying power to the device.

Rune Points: 3

Special Rules: While the goggles' mechanika has power, the wearer can see in night conditions as if it were day. The goggles can be set for normal vision or can function as a normal spyglass (p. 277).

Farsight goggles cannot be worn with a helmet.

Fabrication: The material cost of the goggles' housing is 75 gc. It takes two week to construct the device. The pertinent Craft skill for construction is Craft (glassworking).

The goggles' runeplates require three weeks to inscribe and requires a successful INT + Mechanikal Engineering roll against a target number of 15.

MECHANIKAL PROSTHETIC, ARM

Cost: 1,040 gc

Description: This is a mechanikal arm that can be grafted to the body to restore most of the function of a lost limb. Though cumbersome and ugly, these ingenious devices are a godsend to those in need. The device integrates an alchemical capacitor and a dedicated runeplate sensitive to the body's natural motion. When powered it acts like a natural limb, albeit with a slightly slowed reaction time.

Rune Points: 3

Special Rules: A character with a mechanikal prosthetic arm suffers –1 to AGL and POI rolls (including attacks) when resolving actions taken with a prosthetic arm. This penalty extends to attacks made with two-handed weapons.

The arm has STR 7. When resolving the damage of an attack made with the arm, the damage roll is made at STR 7. When resolving the damage of a two-handed attack, use the character's natural STR or the arm's STR 7, whichever is higher.

If the arm runs out of power, it becomes completely unresponsive and cannot be used to take any action. Additionally, the character suffers –1 DEF while is arm is not functional.

Successfully grafting this prosthetic to a character's body requires two hours of labor and an INT + Medicine skill roll against a target number of 15. If the character succeeds, the operation works. If the roll fails, the patient suffers d6 damage points. The operation can be attempted again after another ten minutes of labor.

Fabrication: The material cost of the arm's housing is 150 gc. It takes three week to construct the device. The pertinent Craft skill for construction is Craft (metalworking).

The arm's runeplates require three weeks to inscribe and requires a successful INT + Mechanikal Engineering roll against a target number of 15.

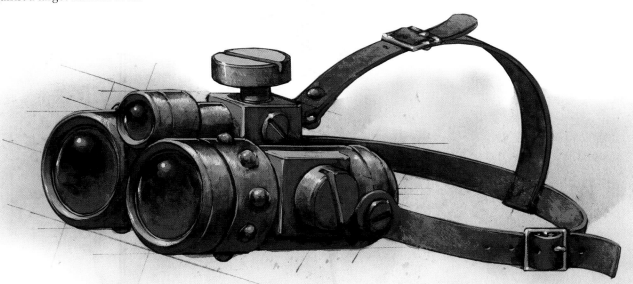

MECHANIKAL PROSTHETIC, EYE

Cost: 790 gc

Description: This is a device of extraordinary complexity, a brass and glass orb capable of flawlessly mimicking the function of a natural eye.

The device comprises an anchor set into the eye socket and the eye itself. The eye is powered by a miniature clockwork capacitor that can be removed from the socket anchor to be wound.

Rune Points: 3

Special Rules: While the eye has power, the character wearing it does not suffer the effects of a lost eye (p. 217).

Successfully grafting this prosthetic to a character's body requires two hours of labor and an INT + Medicine skill roll against a target number of 15. If the character succeeds, the operation works. If the roll fails, the operation can be attempted again after another thirty minutes of labor.

Fabrication: The material cost of the eye's housing is 75 gc. It takes three weeks to construct the device. The pertinent Craft skill for construction is Craft (metalworking).

The eye's runeplate requires three weeks to scribe and requires a successful INT + Mechanikal Engineering roll against a target number of 14.

MECHANIKAL PROSTHETIC, HAND

Cost: 590 gc

Description: This is a mechanikal hand that can be grafted to the arm to restore most of the function of a lost hand. The device integrates a clockwork capacitor and a dedicated runeplate sensitive to the body's natural motion. When powered it acts like a natural hand, albeit with a slightly slowed reaction time and reduced dexterity.

Rune Points: 2

Special Rules: A character with a mechanikal prosthetic hand suffers –1 to AGL and POI rolls (including attacks) when resolving actions taken with the hand. This penalty does not extend to attacks made with two-handed weapons unless both the character's hands are prosthetics.

If the hand runs out of power, it becomes completely unresponsive and cannot be used to take any action.

Successfully grafting this prosthetic to a character's body requires two hours of labor and an INT + Medicine skill roll against a target number of 15. If the character succeeds, the operation works. If the roll fails, the patient suffers d6 damage points. The operation can be attempted again after another ten minutes of labor.

Fabrication: The material cost of the hand's housing is 60 gc. It takes three weeks to construct the device. The pertinent Craft skill for construction is Craft (metalworking).

The arm's runeplates require two weeks to scribe, and a successful INT + Mechanikal Engineering roll against a target number of 14.

MECHANIKAL PROSTHETIC, LEG

Cost: 890 gc

Description: This is a mechanikal leg designed to be grafted to the body to replace the function of a missing leg. When powered it acts like a natural leg, albeit with a slightly slowed reaction time and little reduced agility.

Rune Points: 2

Special Rules: A character with a functional mechanikal leg suffers only –1 SPD instead of the normal –2 for a missing leg.

If the leg runs out of power, it becomes completely unresponsive. The character suffers –2 SPD while the leg is not functional.

Fabrication: The material cost of the leg's housing is 150 gc. It takes three weeks to construct the device. The pertinent Craft skill for construction is Craft (metalworking).

The arm's runeplates require two weeks to scribe, and a successful INT + Mechanikal Engineering roll against a target number of 14.

STORM GLAIVE

Cost: 1,560 gc

Skill: Great Weapon

Attack Modifier: –2 (one-handed), –1 (two-handed)

POW: 5 (one-handed), 7 (two-handed)

Description: The Storm Glaive is the fearsome mechanikal weapon of the Stormblade. It is powered by a dedicated storm chamber.

Rune Points: 4

Special Rules: A character armed with a Storm Glaive can use it to make electrical blast ranged attacks. Storm Glaive blasts are RNG 4, AOE –, POW 12 ranged attacks that cause electrical damage. When making a Storm Glaive ranged attack, the character makes the attack roll using his POI.

Each time a character makes an attack with this weapon he suffers a POW 12 electrical damage roll. For this reason it is advised that a character wielding a Storm Glaive wears electricity resistant Storm Knight armor (p. 253).

Fabrication: The material cost of the Storm Glaive housing is 210 gc. It takes three weeks to construct the device. The pertinent Craft skill for construction is Craft (metalworking).

The Storm Glaive's runeplates require four weeks to inscribe and require a successful INT + Mechanikal Engineering roll against a target number of 16.

WARCASTER ARMOR

The militaries of the Iron Kingdoms equip their warcasters with mechanikal armor so advanced that only the most skilled armorers and arcane mechaniks understand the techniques behind its construction. All warcaster armor is custom-fitted to the individual. Plate armor is used as the basis for warcaster armor, but a wide variety of types can be modified to suit the needs of the 'caster, some sacrificing greater protection for augmented mobility. Every suit of warcaster armor is unique, and the cost, look, and specific materials vary considerably. The most expensive and refined suits are built from the finest alloys by wealthy kingdom militaries and include small, precisely tooled components. Those built by mercenary companies or poorer nations are usually more cumbersome and employ heavier metals and thicker pipes and gauges. Even these are marvels of modern mechanika, employing scores of dedicated runeplates connected by an intricate lattice of arcane conduits.

Most important, all warcaster armor is integrated with an arcane turbine, a highly efficient and advanced type of steam engine worn on the back and fueled by coal. The steam engine in an arcane turbine powers small internal mechanisms, the negligible weight of which allows the turbine to run for many hours on a small quantity of coal. A turbine should be refueled once a day, although if its wearer has not been in active combat it can sustain itself at its lowest setting over several days of use. Warcaster armor includes exhaust pipes for venting smoke and excess steam pressure. These expel thick plumes when running at full power but only a trickle when dampened. Warcasters must be wary of running turbines at full power in enclosed spaces, such as aboard a passenger train, where emissions quickly become a breathing hazard.

The heart of the turbine is a complex series of wire-coiled wheels spinning inside a thinly layered metal lattice, all constructed of arcane-sensitive alloys. When worn by a focuser who has bonded to the armor, the turbine powers a protective power field around the warcaster that also helps negate the encumbrance of the armor and ensures heat generated by its boiler is safely dispersed. This field absorbs damage that would otherwise be sustained by the focuser. The focuser can enhance the field's protective qualities by overboosting the field, which can allow a warcaster to walk unscathed through explosions and direct fire that would otherwise be instantly fatal.

Military warcasters are usually aided in the process of donning armor and priming its turbine by an assisting adjutant, but practiced mercenaries can don their own armor with a bit of hassle and additional time. The turbine requires only a couple of minutes to be stoked and quickly reaches peak efficiency.

POWER FIELD RULES

While its boiler is fueled and its arcane turbine is in operation, a bonded suit of warcaster armor generates a power field that absorbs damage. This acts as a buffer against incoming damage in two different ways. Note that non-bonded warcaster armor cannot generate a power field.

POWER FIELD DAMAGE BOXES

Warcaster armor has six power field damage boxes. When a warcaster takes damage, mark his power field boxes before marking his life spiral. The warcaster can spend focus points during his turn to regenerate lost power field boxes at a rate of 1 focus point for each power field box restored.

OVERBOOSTING THE POWER FIELD

Unspent focus points on a warcaster wearing bonded warcaster armor increases his ARM by 1 for each unspent focus point.

WARCASTER ARMOR, LIGHT

Cost: 2,010 gc
DEF Modifier: 0
ARM Modifier: +5

Description: This warcaster armor is made of very light plate including a breastplate to support the turbine and boiler. This armor primarily relies on the power field for protection as much of the body is left unarmored.

Rune Points: 5

Special Rules: Light warcaster armor incorporates an arcane turbine that provides 8 rune points of power. It has a power draw of 5 rune points for the bond plate and the power field's mechanikal devices. Additional devices can be connected to the turbine as described in the arcane turbine rules.

If this armor does not have power, its wearer suffers –2 DEF.

Fabrication: The material cost of light warcaster housing is 225 gc. It takes one month to construct the armor. The pertinent Craft skill for construction is Craft (metalworking).

Light warcaster armor runeplates require five weeks to scribe, and a successful INT + Mechanikal Engineering roll against a target number of 17. Note that warcaster armor runeplates integrate bond runes into their makeup.

WARCASTER ARMOR, MEDIUM

Cost: 2,360 gc
DEF Modifier: –1
ARM Modifier: +7

Description: This warcaster armor is based on infantry armor used throughout the Iron Kingdoms. Though it invariably includes a fitted breastplate that houses the arcane turbine, other elements vary from nearly full suits of plate armor to armored shoulder and leg elements along with an armored greatcoat.

Rune Points: 5

Special Rules: Medium warcaster armor incorporates an arcane turbine that provides 8 rune points of power. It has a power draw of 5 rune points for the bond plate and the power field's mechanikal devices. Additional devices can be connected to the turbine as described in the arcane turbine rules.

If this armor does not have power, its wearer suffers –4 DEF and –1 SPD.

Fabrication: The material cost of light warcaster housing is 330 gc. It takes one month to construct the armor. The pertinent Craft skill for construction is Craft (metalworking).

Medium warcaster armor runeplates require five weeks to scribe, and a successful INT + Mechanikal Engineering roll against a target number of 17. Note that warcaster armor runeplates integrate bond runes into their makeup.

WARCASTER ARMOR, HEAVY

Cost: 2,760 gc
DEF Modifier: –2
ARM Modifier: +8

Description: The warcaster armor is based on extremely heavy full plate mail armor and fitted with a huge boiler and arcane turbine. Though the armor is effectively weightless, its sheer bulk somewhat restricts its wearer's movement.

Rune Points: 5

Special Rules: Heavy warcaster armor incorporates an arcane turbine that provides 8 rune points of power. It has a power draw of 5 rune points for the bond plate and the power field's mechanikal devices. Additional devices can be connected to the turbine as described in the arcane turbine rules.

If this armor does not have power, its wearer suffers –6 DEF and –2 SPD.

Fabrication: The material cost of heavy warcaster housing is 450 gc. It takes one month to construct the armor. The pertinent Craft skill for construction is Craft (metalworking).

Heavy warcaster armor runeplates require five weeks to scribe and require a successful INT + Mechanikal Engineering roll against a target number of 17. Note that warcaster armor runeplates integrate bond runes into their makeup.

ALCHEMY

Alchemy is arguably the oldest arcane art in the Iron Kingdoms. Its roots and practices predate the Gift of sorcery by centuries. Alchemical formulae and discoveries have become an essential element in mechanikal invention. Like most sciences, it also has applications in war. Alchemists crafted the first firearms, using them to equip the Army of Thunder against the Orgoth. Over the centuries keen minds have continued to enact new and deadly uses of these principles. Only recently have such weapons become available for individual use. Today mercenaries, rebels, and rogues find alchemical weapons excellent tools for achieving their goals both on and off the battlefield.

True alchemy is the synergy of natural ingredients and arcane lore. What began as a simple study of herbs and their properties has evolved into a vast field of study. Alchemy includes everything from the brewing of love potions and the mixing of healing salves to the careful creation of blasting powder.

Though many alchemical concoctions can be derived from simple plant, animal, and mineral components carefully extracted by a trained practitioner, in the hands of an alchemist these mixtures can be enhanced with magic to give them greater potency and duration. This results in safer elixirs and balms as well. In some cases, magical techniques are necessary to isolate the key ingredients from their original source.

Early alchemy was simply the process of deriving potent concoctions directly from plant and animal mixtures, but modern alchemy is as firmly enmeshed with arcane magic as is the study of mechanika. The early forms of alchemy are still practiced by modern apothecaries, while true alchemists have moved on to perfecting magically enhanced alchemicals.

The rigorous science that evolved as part and parcel of alchemy was incredibly important to the later development of the Gift of magic. Without this precise scientific approach, the folk of western Immoren would have had a very difficult time embracing and understanding the difficult rituals and formulaic castings necessary to wield the Gift.

ORIGINS OF ALCHEMY IN WESTERN IMMOREN

Herbalists and healers were responsible for the initial study of alchemy two and a half millennia ago. These individuals began to record the herbs and plants they used to treat a variety of conditions and illnesses and began to examine the processes by which potent poultices and herbal elixirs were prepared. Early alchemists systematically observed these processes to determine how and why they worked. Some of the earliest recorded alchemical experiments appear in the rare tome *Crucibilus Synthetatus,* penned by the scholar Copolius in 753 BR. Many of his notes have been lost or destroyed over the years, but the surviving fragments indicate Copolius understood the founding principles of modern alchemy.

The science of alchemy began as simple dabbling with herbal concoctions, and it was not until quite some time later that real progress was made in advancing that understanding. Roughly 600 years ago, while the seeds of rebellion against the Orgoth were just taking root, a small group of alchemists began the first experiments in the development of simple mechanika. Working closely with a small group of arcanists and engineers, they discovered some of the basic principles of joining magic with mechanical devices.

A group of alchemists secretly banded together for mutual protection against the Orgoth in Leryn to form the original Order of the Golden Crucible in 25 BR. They vowed to share all their knowledge in an effort to preserve the secrets of alchemy and to find a means to help rid themselves of their oppressors. This consolidation and sharing of knowledge led to some of the most drastic advancements in alchemy in the past 1,300 years. Out of this effort emerged destructive alchemicals such as alchemist's fire, acids, incendiary arrows, and crude grenades.

Ultimately, this led to the first firearms and the early development of the hybrid science of mechanika as alchemists and engineers began to envision huge mechanikal war machines. The Orgoth butchered members of the Order when they could find them, but surviving members remained true to their purpose and continued on, pushing forward the science

known as rip lung—a disease that had resisted all other techniques and had led to the deaths of thousands. This selfless act, along with a life filled with good works, led to Corben's ascension on his death in 102 AR, and he is now seen as a paragon of the benevolent applications of alchemy and arcane science.

THE ART AND SCIENCE OF ALCHEMY

The key components of any alchemical creation are its ingredients. A character wishing to create an alchemical item must first gather all the ingredients listed in the formula. In a location where the ingredients can be readily purchased, the character can simply pay the material costs listed in the item description. If the character is creating the item in the field where ingredients are not available for purchase, he must use ingredients from his inventory. Without access to all the proper ingredients, an alchemical formula cannot be brewed.

Once a character has gathered the necessary ingredients for an alchemical formula, he must spend time brewing the formula by combining, cooking, and stabilizing the ingredients using an alchemy lab. A character must have the Alchemy skill to brew an alchemical formula. Ingredients and alchemical formulae are listed in the entry for each item that can be created using alchemy.

Once the character has spent the allotted time brewing the formula, he must make an INT + Alchemy skill roll against a target number. If the roll succeeds, he has successfully created the item. Each formula produces a different result if the roll fails. Target numbers, success results, and failure results are listed in the entry for each item that can be created using alchemy.

DISTILLATION

Just as a character can brew alchemical formulae, he can also distil ingredients from existing alchemical substances. Distillation of an alchemically created item requires a character to spend half the time it requires to brew the item processing the alchemical materials with an alchemy lab. At the end of the process, the player makes an INT + Alchemy skill roll against a target number equal to the target number required to brew the formula. If he succeeds, the alchemical substances are destroyed, but the character can extract one unit of a single ingredient listed to create that substance and one unit of alchemical waste (crystal or liquid).

of alchemy and helping find the means of ending the Orgoth Occupation once and for all. The contributions of alchemists to this task are well documented, and those who gave their lives to the cause are remembered and honored.

One of the most astounding events in the history of modern alchemy was the ascension of Corben to the ranks of Morrow's ascendants. Corben, an extremely pious arcanist and member of the Order of the Golden Crucible, was single-handedly responsible for finding an alchemical cure to the great plague

PRIMARY ALCHEMICAL INGREDIENTS

Alchemical items are created from a formula of ingredients and processes. Although complex formulae can include unique and rare ingredients, nearly all formulae contain ingredients from this list of core alchemical ingredients. Ingredients valued at less than 5 gc are readily available in most mid-sized cities. Core ingredients that cost 5 gc and over can be more difficult to procure, at the Game Master's discretion.

GATHERING INGREDIENTS

Many alchemical reagents can be rendered from the flora and fauna found in the wilds of Immoren. When he has access to a region of uncivilized land, a character with the Alchemy skill can gather the proper plants and minerals needed to create alchemical stone, heavy metals, mineral acid, and mineral crystals. A character who has the Alchemy skill and the Survival skill can gather the proper plants and animals to create bioluminescent extract, organic acid, organic oil, and organic toxin.

An alchemist can gather the materials equating to 1 gc of these materials per hour per level of his Alchemy skill. In particularly sparse or plentiful regions, the Game Master might rule that gathering is easier, harder, or altogether impossible.

Alchemical reagents not listed are harder to come by and require specific plants, animals, or minerals to procure. Some monster descriptions also include alchemical loot items, and an alchemist will want to stock up on ingredients when the right monsters cross his path.

ALCHEMICAL STONE

Cost: 1 gc per unit

Alchemical stone is a dense but easily ground white stone that serves as a foundation for allowing other alchemical ingredients to bond together more strongly than is otherwise achievable.

ALCHEMICAL WASTE, CRYSTAL

Cost: 1 gc per unit

This crystalline byproduct of the alchemical brewing process is often left behind when more valuable alchemical compounds have been distilled during brewing.

ALCHEMICAL WASTE, LIQUID

Cost: 1 gc per unit

Liquid waste is often drained off or filtered out during the alchemical brewing process to achieve the desired mixture of alchemical effects.

ARCANE EXTRACT

Cost: 5 gc per unit

This mildly luminescent liquid is infused with residual arcane energies. Its sources are as varied as the tint of its faint glow and include plants and creatures with arcane powers or long-term exposure to arcane energies.

ARCANE MINERALS

Cost: 7 gc per unit

Sacred geological sites and arcane constructs are the most common source of arcane minerals. Usually the substance is sandlike and granular, although it can sometimes be procured in solid pieces the size of a marble.

BIOLUMINESCENT EXTRACT

Cost: 2 gc per unit

This ingredient is usually a liquid or a paste and is collected from a variety of fungus, insects, and aquatic creatures. The substance gives off a faint glow that can be manipulated with a variety of alchemical processes.

BURROW MAWG ADRENAL GLAND

Cost: 5 gc per gland

A powerful alchemical ingredient, this pea-sized gland rests at the base of the brain of a burrow mawg in a small, bony cavity covered by a dural fold. Burrow mawg adrenal glands need to be fresh for inclusion in most alchemical compounds, though some call for dried glands. Upon removal from the burrow mawg's skull, the gland must be alchemically preserved, so only characters with the Alchemy skill can perform the procedure.

ECTOPLASM

Cost: 10 gc per unit

This dense, gray, translucent ooze is left behind when an incorporeal undead creature moves through a solid object. The ooze rapidly dissipates, so it must be collected quickly and stored in an airtight jar. A living creature coming into direct contact with ectoplasm feels a sickly cold sensation moving rapidly through his body as long as contact persists.

HEAVY METALS

Cost: 2 gc per unit

Toxic metals such as iron, copper, and mercury are common in most industrialized areas of the Iron Kingdoms. Most alchemical formulae that require them use only trace amounts.

MENOTH'S FURY

Cost: 3 gc per unit

Derived from crudely refined and treated oil, Menoth's Fury is a highly flammable alchemical agent that ignites on contact with air and burns with incredible intensity.

MINERAL ACID

Cost: 2 gc per unit

This caustic liquid can be found in nature at the bottom of deep cave pools or pushed through to the surface in geysers. It is most commonly acquired as a by-product of metal smelting.

MINERAL CRYSTALS

Cost: 3 gc per unit

Various salts and other rock crystals are a common element in alchemical brewing, as their nature allows the bonding and retention of various energies desired by alchemists. Occasionally a formula calls for more valuable gems, which are not part of this category.

MUTAGENIC EXTRACT

Cost: 8 gc per unit

This highly prized liquid can be gathered only from creatures that undergo physical transformations.

ORGANIC ACID

Cost: 3 gc per unit

Corrosive bile and caustic natural weaponry are harvested to create this alchemical ingredient. It can also be refined from some plant extracts, although the process to do so is lengthy and expensive.

ORGANIC OIL

Cost: 1 gc per unit

Whale oil is one of the most common animal-based organic oil in the Iron Kingdoms due to the creatures' high concentration of blubber. Organic oil can also be harvested from a variety of other animals, nuts, seeds, and fruits.

ORGANIC TOXIN

Cost: 5 gc per unit

Venomous creatures of all shapes and sizes sting, spit, and bite with a variety of deadly toxins. Alchemists harvest and use the venom of such creatures to create dangerous poisons or brew anti-venom to halt the effects of life-threatening toxins.

ALCHEMICAL ITEMS

The following attributes define alchemical items in the game.

Cost: This is the cost of the alchemical item Cygnaran gold crowns (gc).

Description: This is a description of the alchemical item.

Special Rules: This section describes any special rules of the alchemical item.

Brewing Requirements: These are skills and abilities required to brew the alchemical item. A character without all the skills listed automatically fails in his attempt to brew the item.

Ingredients: This lists the ingredients required to brew the alchemical item and their individual associated costs.

Total Material Cost: This lists the total cost of all the ingredients required to brew the alchemical item.

Alchemical Formula: These are rules for brewing the alchemical item once the character has the required ingredients in hand. The character can double or even triple the ingredients described for a single batch to produce two or three doses at the same time without adding any additional manufacturing time.

ALCHEMICAL ACID

Cost: 30 gc per vial

Description: Alchemical acid is a potent corrosive alchemical compound.

Special Rules: Vials of alchemical acid can be used as improvised thrown weapons, but due to the inaccuracy of thrown glassware and the low cost of reliable grenade housings, acid bombs (p. 297) are the preferred delivery method for the substance.

Brewing Requirements: Alchemy

Ingredients: 2 units of alchemist's stone, 1 unit of mineral acid, 2 units of organic acid

Total Material Cost: 10 gc

Alchemical Formula: Brewing an alchemical acid requires an alchemy lab and two hours of labor spent combining, cooking, and stabilizing the ingredients. At the end of this time, the alchemist makes an INT + Alchemy roll against a target number of 14. If the roll succeeds, the character creates one dose of alchemical acid. If the roll fails, he creates one unit of alchemical waste (liquid).

ALCHEMICAL RESTORATIVE

Cost: 33 gc per vial

Description: This is a fast acting alchemical pharmaceutical that promotes rapid blood clotting and regeneration.

Special Rules: A grievously injured character who drinks or is fed a dose of this substance is immediately stabilized (p. 216).

Brewing Requirements: Alchemy

Ingredients: 2 units of alchemist's stone, 1 unit of mutagenic extract, 1 unit of organic oil

Total Material Cost: 11 gc

Alchemical Formula: Brewing an alchemical restorative requires an alchemy lab and two hours of labor spent combining, cooking, and stabilizing the ingredients. At the end of this time, the alchemist makes an INT + Alchemy roll against a target number of 14. If the roll succeeds, the character creates one dose of alchemical restorative. If the roll fails, he creates one unit of alchemical waste (liquid).

ANTITOXIN

Cost: 42 gc per dose

Description: This pungent elixir can be ingested to help counteract many natural and alchemical poisons.

Special Rules: A living creature suffering the effects of an alchemical poison can consume antitoxin to counteract an alchemical poison. After ingestion it takes 6 +d6 minutes for the substance to take effect. When the antitoxin takes effect, the character immediately makes a PHY roll +5 against the toxin rating of the poison. If the roll succeeds, the alchemical poison is counteracted and the character does not make any addition toxin rolls. If the roll fails, the alchemical poison continues its course, but the character gains +3 on additional PHY rolls to resist its effect.

Brewing Requirements: Alchemy, Medicine

Ingredients: 1 unit alchemist stone, 1 unit organic acid, 2 units organic toxin

Total Material Cost: 14 gc

Alchemical Formula: Brewing an antitoxin requires an alchemy lab and one hour of labor spent combining, cooking, and stabilizing the ingredients. At the end of this time, the alchemist makes an INT + Alchemy skill roll against a target number of 14. If the roll succeeds, the character creates one dose of anti-toxin. If the roll fails, he creates one unit of alchemical waste (liquid).

ASHES OF URCAEN

Cost: 54 gc per application

Description: This ashen powder has the faint smell of sulfur and is laced with energy from beyond the living world. When cast into the air, the powder binds with disembodied spirits and drags them into the physical world.

Special Rules: A character can use a quick action to throw the powder into the air. When he does so, place a 3″ AOE anywhere in base contact with him. An incorporeal creature within the AOE loses the Incorporeal ability for d3 rounds.

Brewing Requirements: Alchemy

Ingredients: 1 unit of alchemist's stone, 1 unit of arcane minerals, 1 unit of ectoplasm

Total Material Cost: 18 gc

Alchemical Formula: Creating Ashes of Urcaen requires an alchemy lab and two hours of labor spent cooking the ingredients and grinding them to ash. At the end of this time, the alchemist makes an INT + Alchemy roll against a target number of 16. If the roll succeeds, the character creates one application of Ashes of Urcaen. If the roll fails, he creates one unit of alchemical waste (crystal).

BOTTLED LIGHT

Cost: 27 gc per jar, 5 gc for a liquid lantern

Description: This is a two-part oil tightly sealed in a liquid-filled lantern or jar. One part is a thick, viscous oil. The other is a sickly yellow grease that floats atop the oil. When shaken, the two oils mix to give off light.

Special Rules: Bottled light can be shaken as a quick action. Once shaken, the substance gives off alchemical torchlight (p. 225) for d6+3 rounds. After it goes dark, the bottle can be reshaken to activate the light once more.

After two weeks, bottled light loses efficacy and no longer reacts when shaken.

Brewing Requirements: Alchemy

Ingredients: 1 unit arcane extract, 2 units bioluminescent extract

Total Material Cost: 9 gc

Alchemical Formula: Brewing bottled light requires an alchemy lab and one hour of labor spent combining, cooking, and stabilizing the ingredients. At the end of this time, the alchemist makes an INT + Alchemy skill roll against a target number of 14. If the roll succeeds, the character creates enough bottled light to simulate a torch. The fluid components of bottled light must be poured into a jar or airtight liquid lantern for storage. If the roll fails, the character creates one unit of alchemical waste (liquid).

FORTEMORPHIC ELIXIR

Cost: 42 gc per dose

Description: This clear, red solution is a strength-enhancement serum intended for injection. The side effects can outweigh the benefits with periodic usage.

Special Rules: Administering a dose of this substance requires a syringe.

A living character injected with fortemorphic elixir gains +2 STR at the start of his turn two turns after being injected. This bonus lasts for a number of rounds equal to the character's PHY stat. Immediately after the STR bonus wears off, the character suffers a –2 penalty to AGL, POI, and PER rolls for a number of rounds equal to the character's PHY.

Brewing Requirements: Alchemy

Ingredients: 1 unit of alchemist stone, 1 burrow mawg adrenal gland, 1 unit mutagenic extract

Total Material Cost: 14 gc

Alchemical Formula: Brewing fortemorphic elixir requires an alchemy lab and two hours of labor spent combining, cooking, and stabilizing the ingredients. At the end of this time, the alchemist makes INT + Alchemy roll against a target number of 15. If the roll succeeds, the character creates one dose of fortemorphic elixir. If the roll fails, he creates one unit of organic toxin.

HEALING LINIMENT

Cost: 27 gc per dose

Description: This divinely infused alchemical salve is applied to grievous wounds and wrapped with clean bandages to accelerate healing.

Special Rules: When applied, the user heals 1 additional vitality point per hour for a number of hours equal to d3+ the Medicine skill level of the character applying the salve.

Brewing Requirements: Alchemy

Ingredients: 1 unit alchemist stone, 1 unit arcane minerals, 1 unit organic oil

Total Material Cost: 9 gc

Alchemical Formula: Brewing a healing liniment requires an alchemy lab and two hours of labor spent combining, cooking, and stabilizing the ingredients. At the end of this time, the alchemist makes an INT + Alchemy roll against a target number of 14. At the beginning of the process the equipment and ingredients must be blessed by a priest of Veteran level or higher. If the roll succeeds, the character creates one dose of healing liniment. If the roll fails, he creates one unit of alchemical waste (liquid).

RUST AGENT

Cost: 18 gc for a two-part dose

Description: Rust agent is a fast-acting alchemical compound that temporarily softens and rapidly corrodes metals. The agent is made up of two reactive substances that must be mixed to take effect.

Special Rules: Mixing the two parts of rust agent requires a quick action. Once mixed, the substance must be immediately applied or thrown as an attack. A thrown gout of rust agent has a RNG of thirty-six feet (6˝).

Steamjacks and characters wearing primarily metal armor that are hit by rust agent suffer –2 ARM for one round. Characters and steamjacks with Immunity: Corrosion are not affected.

Brewing Requirements: Alchemy

Ingredients: 1 unit alchemist stone, 1 unit alchemical waste (crystal), 1 unit heavy metals, 1 unit mineral acid

Total Material Cost: 6 gc

Alchemical Formula: Brewing the two parts of rust agent requires an alchemy lab and two hours of labor spent combining, cooking, and stabilizing the ingredients. At the end of this time, the alchemist makes an INT + Alchemy roll against a target number of 14. If the roll succeeds, the character creates the two parts of a single dose of rust agent. If the roll fails, the ingredients are wasted.

SOMNOLENCE ELIXIR

Cost: 36 gc per dose

Description: Imbibing just a few drops of this opalescent liquid quickly dulls one's senses and helps him to have a peaceful night's sleep. A larger dose can knock out a grown man almost immediately.

Special Rules: When a dose of somnolence elixir is ingested, the character must make a PHY roll against a target number of 16. If the character succeeds, he remains conscious but his INT and PER are reduced to 1 for the next hour. If he fails, he immediately falls unconscious.

Brewing Requirements: Alchemy

Ingredients: 1 unit arcane minerals, 1 unit organic acid, 2 units organic oil

Total Material Cost: 12 gc

Alchemical Formula: Brewing a somnolence elixir requires an alchemy lab and two hours of labor spent combining, cooking, and stabilizing the ingredients. At the end of this time, the alchemist makes an INT + Alchemy roll against a target number of 14. If the roll succeeds, the character creates one dose of somnolence elixir. If the roll fails, he creates one unit of alchemical waste (liquid).

SPIRIT SALTS

Cost: 54 gc per jar

Description: The homes in many Cygnaran coastal towns have a tradition of keeping lines of salt in front of their doors to keep evil spirits from entering their homes. When the minerals that this symbolic defense originated from are properly prepared and poured in a line upon the ground, the alchemically treated salt forms a barrier that undead creatures and infernals cannot cross.

Special Rules: A character can spend a quick action to pour out the spirit salts. When he does so, place a wall template in base contact with the character. Undead creatures and infernals cannot cross that wall. The wall remains effective for d3+1 rounds and expires at the start of this character's turn on the round determined. (The Game Master should keep the duration a secret).

Brewing Requirements: Alchemy

Ingredients: 2 units of alchemist's stone, 1 unit of ectoplasm, 2 units of mineral crystals

Total Material Cost: 18 gc

Alchemical Formula: Brewing spirit salts requires an alchemy lab and two hours of labor spent combining, cooking, and stabilizing the ingredients. At the end of this time, the alchemist makes an INT + Alchemy roll against a target number of 14. If the roll succeeds, the character creates one jar of spirit salts. If the roll fails, he creates one unit of alchemical waste (crystal).

VITRIOLIC FIRE

Cost: 21 gc per vial

Description: Vitriolic fire is dangerous alchemical oil that bursts into superheated flame upon exposure to the air. Some alchemical arms producers make huge batches of this substance for use in cinder bombs (see "Alchemical Grenades," below).

Special Rules: Vials of vitriolic fire can be used as improvised thrown weapons, but due to the inaccuracy of thrown glassware and the low cost of reliable grenade housings, cinder bombs (next page) are the preferred delivery method for the substance.

Brewing Requirements: Alchemy

Ingredients: 2 units of alchemist's stone, 1 unit of heavy metals, 1 unit of Menoth's Fury

Total Material Cost: 7 gc

Alchemical Formula: Brewing vitriolic fire requires an alchemy lab and two hours of labor spent combining, cooking, and stabilizing the ingredients. At the end of this time, the alchemist makes an INT + Alchemy roll against a target number of 14. If the roll succeeds, the character creates one dose of vitriolic fire. If the roll fails, he creates one unit of alchemical waste (liquid).

FIELD ALCHEMY

Not all alchemy takes place in the lab. Alchemists can also use field alchemy to create quick effects in the field.

SIMPLE ACID

Description: This unstable acid can be made quickly, but its potency is very short-lived. Alchemists can brew simple acid at a moment's notice for immediate use.

Special Rules: A vial of simple acid can be used as a thrown weapon with a RNG of thirty-six feet (6˝). A creature hit by a vial of simple acid suffers d3 points of damage. Inanimate stone and metal take d3 points of damage per round and have their ARM reduced by d3 per round in a six-foot (1˝) area when simple acid is poured or thrown on them. Simple acid lasts d3 rounds, expiring at the start of the alchemist's turn.

Brewing Requirements: Alchemy

Ingredients: 1 unit alchemical waste (crystal) and 1 unit mineral acid

Total Material Cost: 3 gc

Alchemical Formula: Creating simple acid can be done without an alchemy lab and requires a character to dissolve crystallized alchemical waste in a vial of mineral acid with a bit of vigorous shaking. A character must spend a quick action to combine the ingredients and then makes an INT + Alchemy roll against a target number of 11. If the roll succeeds, the character creates one unit of simple acid. If the roll fails, the ingredients are lost and the character takes d3 points of corrosion damage as the brew boils over. The substance can be thrown as quickly as it is mixed.

Throwing the acid is a thrown ranged attack.

SIMPLE STIMULANT

Description: A quick combination of alchemical ingredients gives a wounded character a burst of energy.

Special Rules: The moment the ingredients are combined, select a friendly character in base contact with the alchemist.

The character ignores the wound penalties of lost aspects for one round.

Brewing Requirements: Alchemy

Ingredients: 1 unit alchemical waste (crystal) and 1 unit alchemical waste (liquid)

Total Material Cost: 2 gc

Alchemical Formula: Creating a simple stimulant can be done without the use of an alchemy lab and requires a character to dissolve crystallized alchemical waste into liquid alchemical waste, releasing a foul-smelling gas. A character must spend a quick action to combine the ingredients and then makes an INT + Alchemy roll against a target number of 11. If the roll succeeds, the character creates the stimulant effect listed under Special Rules. If the roll fails, the ingredients are lost.

SIMPLE STINK GAS

Description: A quick combination of alchemical ingredients creates a noxious cloud of invisible gas.

Special Rules: The moment the ingredients are combined, place a 3˝ AOE gas effect anywhere in base contact with the alchemist. While in the AOE, living creatures suffer –2 on their attack rolls. The AOE remains in play for one round.

Brewing Requirements: Alchemy

Ingredients: 1 unit alchemical waste (liquid), 1 unit organic acid

Total Material Cost: 4 gc

Alchemical Formula: Creating simple stink gas can be done without an alchemy lab and requires a character to vaporize liquid alchemical waste with organic acid. A character must spend a quick action to combine the ingredients and then makes an INT + Alchemy roll against a target number of 12. If the roll succeeds, the character creates the smoke effect listed under Special Rules. If the roll fails, the ingredients are lost.

SIMPLE SMOKE

Description: A quick combination of alchemical ingredients creates a cloud of smoke.

Special Rules: The moment the ingredients are combined, place a 3˝ AOE cloud effect centered on the character creating the simple smoke. The AOE remains in play for one round.

Brewing Requirements: Alchemy

Ingredients: 1 unit mineral acid and 1 unit mineral crystals

Total Material Cost: 5 gc

Alchemical Formula: Creating simple smoke can be done without an alchemy lab and requires a character to dissolve volatile crystals in an open vial of mineral solvent. A character must spend a quick action to combine the ingredients and then makes an INT + Alchemy roll against a target number of 10. If the roll succeeds, the character creates the smoke effect listed under Special Rules. If the roll fails, the ingredients are lost.

GRENADES

The standard for a grenade in the Iron Kingdoms is a small clockwork or fuse-triggered bomb that relies on blasting powder, heat, the mixture of reactive agents, or spring-released venting to disperse noxious or explosive alchemical compounds. More exotic, complex, and expensive compounds are typically found only in the hands of mercenary specialists, combat alchemists, and adventurers.

ALCHEMICAL GRENADE

Cost: See Special Rules.
Ammo: —
Effective Range: 48 feet (8″)
Extreme Range: —
Skill: Thrown
Attack Modifier: 0
POW: —
AOE: 3

Description: Alchemical grenades are specially treated clockwork vessels for containing and detonating alchemical compounds. Each grenade holds one application of an alchemical substance. Pulling the grenade's pin starts the clock's very short timer, which detonates the grenade soon after. The grenade's effects depend on the alchemical compound used.

Special Rules: Once it is in hand, using a grenade requires both a quick action and an attack. The quick action is for pulling the pin, and the attack is for throwing the grenade.

Empty clockwork grenade vessels that can be armed with an alchemist's chosen alchemical compound are available on the open market for 5 gc, far less than the cost of materials for an artisan clocksmith to build the same. This is because the militaries of the Iron Kingdoms have developed industrial production methods for manufacturing grenades that have greatly driven down their cost, even for the unaffiliated combat alchemist. Once an alchemist has an empty clockwork grenade vessel, he can carefully fill and arm it in ten minutes without a skill roll.

The types of alchemical grenades include:

- **Acid Bomb –** The acid bomb is a grenade filled with alchemical acid (p. 293). Characters hit by an acid bomb AOE suffer a POW 12 corrosion damage roll and the Corrosion continuous effect. Acid bombs cost 40 gc each.

- **Ashes of Urcaen –** This grenade is filled with Ashes of Urcaen (p. 294). The grenade causes no damage, but incorporeal creatures hit by the AOE lose the Incorporeal ability for d3+1 rounds. Additionally, the AOE is a cloud effect that remains in play for one round. An incorporeal creature entering the AOE immediately loses the Incorporeal ability for one round. Though alchemical grenades filled with Ashes of Urcaen are not for sale on the open market, they can be special ordered for 75 gc each.

- **Cinder Bomb –** The cinder bomb is a grenade filled with vitriolic fire (p. 295). Characters hit by a cinder bomb AOE suffer a POW 12 fire damage roll. The weapon's AOE is a cloud effect that remains in play for one round. A character who ends his turn in the AOE suffers the Fire continuous effect. Cinder bombs cost 30 gc each.

- **Knockout Bomb –** The knockout bomb is a grenade filled with somnolence elixir (p. 295). All characters hit by a knockout bomb AOE must make a Willpower roll against a target number of 16. If the character succeeds, he shakes off the effects. If he fails, he is knocked down and falls unconscious. The character awakens when he suffers damage or is roused as a quick action by a character B2B with him. The knockout bomb is a gas effect. Knockout bombs cost 45 gc each.

- **Rust Bomb –** The rust bomb is a grenade filled with both parts of rust agent (p. 295). Its detonation mixes the parts and unleashes a vaporized gout of fast-acting rust agent. The rust bomb causes no damage. Steamjacks and characters wearing metal armor hit by the AOE suffer –2 ARM for one round unless they are immune to corrosion. Rust bombs cost 30 gc each.

ALTERNATIVE METHODS OF DELIVERY

In addition to the clockwork grenades, the armories of the Iron Kingdoms have developed a number of devious methods for delivering weaponized alchemical compounds.

Rifle grenades can be fired from a military rifle. Rifle grenades do not have to be primed, though loading one onto the end of rifle takes a quick action. The rifle grenade uses the military rifle's RNG, has a 3″ AOE, and has a −1 modifier to its attack roll. Otherwise its effect depends on the type of grenade fired. An empty rifle grenade vessel costs 10 gc. Readily armed rifle grenades can be purchased for 10 gc more than alchemical grenade equivalent, so a Cinder Bomb rifle grenade would cost 40 gc.

Blast arrows are made up of a heavy arrow with an alchemical warhead. The weapon can either be primed as it is nocked, meaning it must be immediately fired, or it can be primed while nocked with a second quick action. The blast arrow uses the bow's RNG, has a 3″ AOE, and has a −1 modifier to its attack roll. Otherwise its effect depends on the type of grenade fired. An empty blast arrow vessel costs 10 gc. Readily armed blast arrows can be purchased for 10 gc more than their alchemical grenade equivalent, so a rust bomb blast arrow would cost 40 gc.

STEAMJACKS

A steamjack is a mechanikal construct given the ability to reason by a magical brain, known as a cortex. A steamjack does not possess high cognitive powers, but it can execute simple commands and make logical decisions to complete its assigned tasks. Throughout the Iron Kingdoms, steamjacks perform a variety of heavy or dangerous tasks that would be impossible for a human.

Steamjacks fall under one of two classifications: laborjacks and warjacks. Laborjacks are relatively simple machines built for physical labor, whereas warjacks are sophisticated weapons of war bristling with state-of-the-art arms and armor. With the realities of the modern world in which clapped-out military 'jacks find themselves pulling plows after decades of service and laborjacks are armored and retrofitted with military-grade hardware by desperate mercenary outfits, these distinctions can blur.

Laborjacks are strong and rugged workers used primarily for physical labor, such as hauling cargo off ships or construction work, where their great strength is a huge asset. These machines have simple mechanika minds geared toward following careful instructions and carrying out simple tasks. They are not quick thinking and are ill suited for complex roles on the battlefield.

Warjacks, on the other hand, are dedicated fighting machines with the reflexes and cognitive capacity to recognize friend from foe easily and operate a battery of complex weapon systems. Warjacks are built with strength as well as speed and intelligence in mind; they are capable of limited autonomy in combat and select their own targets to engage. Warjacks are protective of their controllers and dedicated to the destruction of their enemies.

ANATOMY OF A STEAMJACK

For the purposes of the IKRPG, a steamjack is comprised of a **chassis**, a **cortex**, and **weaponry**. The steamjacks produced by the human nations of the Iron Kingdoms and most of those produced by Rhul are bipedal with two arms. Additional gear and modifications can be added to the machine to enhance its performance or to give it special capabilities.

The technology of Cryx and Ios is proprietary and operates on fundamentally different principles than the steamjack technology and mechanika of the human and dwarven nations. Though the technology shares surface similarities, the steamjacks of these nations are not compatible, in some cases using completely different power sources. As a result, parts from human steamjacks cannot be integrated into myrmidons, helljacks, or bonejacks.

Rhulic mechanika is based on the same principles used by humans, but their engineering and design has departed significantly and many parts are not easily interchangeable. The same is true for specialized kingdom military hardware; warjacks built in one kingdom cannot readily use parts from a different kingdom. Mercenary 'jacks are designed with flexibility in mind and can sometimes be repaired with local salvage.

CHASSIS

Made of a skeleton of steel and a musculature of pneumatic pipes, the chassis holds the components of the steamjack on a frame of metal armatures and joints. The 'jack's reflex triggers lie along the primary chassis, running the length of the spine and across the various pneumatic connections for the limbs. Conduits that lead back to the cortex housing connect all the triggers into a system allowing the cortex to control the 'jack's every movement.

STEAMJACK LOGISTICS

Running steamjacks over an extended period of time requires occasionally burdensome logistics, since coal runs out and water for steam boilers must be replaced. On long journeys it is common for steamjacks to be hauled by trains or wagons as close to their destination as possible, to save on coal. Most steamjacks can run without refueling for most of a day if involved only in travel or light activity, but active combat burns fuel far more quickly. A steamjack should be refueled every day that it is functional, whether or not it is in combat.

Players and the Game Master should discuss and agree on how to handle these details at the outset. Steamjacks are an important part of the Iron Kingdoms and logistics should not interfere with the fun of playing a warcaster or 'jack marshal. Specific plots might make these difficulties part of the narrative, or force a warcaster out of his comfort zone. This should be the exception, not the rule. Refueling can be handled along with ordinary rest cycles between active adventuring and kept largely unmentioned except when required as an obstacle during play.

There are times and places, such as entering narrow subterranean caves, when a heavy steamjack would be inappropriate and should be left behind. In general, campaigns should allow a warcaster or 'jack marshal to include his machines as a vital element of the adventure.

The limbs of the steamjack are extremely formidable. With arms and legs made of steel and iron, held together with valves of brass and copper, the strength of a 'jack rests in its appendages. Most are designed with modular tools or weapons in mind; replacing the limbs can drastically change the capabilities of the machine.

Focal lenses and clockwork devices carefully connected to the cortex by conduits allow the steamjack to perceive and interpret its surroundings. These complex apparatuses are all, of course, mechanikal in nature.

The chassis determines the shape, strength, and structural integrity of the steamjack. It also impacts the steamjack's agility, power output, and potential speed. As a rule, the heavier the chassis, the larger the engine and steam boiler driving the machine. Though most laborjacks are built with little more than sheer strength in mind, warjacks are built to traverse all manner of hostile terrain in the midst of battle. Warjack chassis have greater articulation and heavier boilers designed with speed and power in mind.

Chassis come in two weight classes, heavy and light. Heavy steamjacks are rugged machines built for strength and the capacity to endure tremendous punishment. Heavy steamjacks stand over twice the height of a man. Light steamjacks are smaller and more maneuverable but lack the physical power of heavy steamjacks. They tend to be faster and more nimble.

The following attributes define different steamjack chassis in the game.

Cost: This is the cost of the chassis in Cygnaran gold crowns.

Description: This is a description of the chassis.

Height/Weight: The chassis' technical specs.

Fuel Load/Burn Usage: This describes the chassis standard fuel load and burn rate.

Initial Service Date: This is the date the chassis first entered service.

Original Chassis Design: This is the original manufacturer or designer of the chassis.

Stock Cortex: This is the cortex that comes stock with the steamjack chassis. The cost of this cortex is included in the cost of the chassis. The cortex can be replaced, but the original personality of the steamjack is lost as a result. For cortex descriptions, see p. 303.

Stats: These are the chassis' stats. The steamjack's INT and PER are determined by its cortex. The stats listed below assume a stock cortex.

Special Rules: These are the special rules that apply to the chassis.

Damage Grid: This is the chassis' damage grid. See p. 314 for a description of damage grids.

The following chassis are among the most commonly available on the open market throughout Iron Kingdoms. Most often the steamjack chassis up for sale are older models that have been refurbished or else painstakingly maintained for decades. A steamjack chassis purchased at the going rate is in good repair and in full operating condition.

A stock cortex is included in the price of the chassis. It is assumed that the cortex has been wiped and has no lingering personality at the time of purchase.

STEAM ENGINE

If the chassis is the skeleton of a 'jack, the engine is its heart. On the back of all steamjacks sits a powerful steam engine, comprised of a coal-burning firebox, a boiler, and an arcane steam turbine. Most steamjacks can run for hours on a full bin of coal. Light 'jacks burn through a full hopper of coal and a full tank of water in five to ten hours depending on the model, while heavy 'jacks burn through their coal and water in four to eight hours. When pushed, coal consumption increases dramatically. Under the intense action and mechanical strain of combat, light 'jacks burn through their reserves in fifty to one hundred minutes, while heavy 'jacks run out of steam in forty to eighty minutes. Fully loaded with coal and water, a steamjack gains anywhere between 400 to 650 pounds, depending on the size of its coal hopper and boiler.

The burning coal heats the water in the boiler, turning it to steam, and the steam fires pistons, providing power to pneumatic valves in the steamjack's chassis—converting heat and pressure into motive force. Steam vents allow for the release of excess pressure, and the steam also turns the 'jack's arcane turbines. These turbines generate a field of arcane energy that runs along a primary cortex conduit, similar to the accumulator conduit lines in a piece of mechanika. Additional conduits connect the 'jack's sensory equipment and reflex triggers to the cortex and provide power to these peripheral systems.

Warjacks have more demanding energy requirements, and typically have a larger coal hopper to allow for longer periods of activity. During intense activity, a complex clockwork mechanism inside the 'jack stokes the engine to meet the increased demands for energy. If a steamjack runs low on coal it starts to brown out, losing strength, mobility, and perception. It becomes less responsive and eventually shuts down completely.

DOCKER HEAVY LABORJACK CHASSIS

COST: 3500 GC (WITH STOCK FERRUM-GRADE CORTEX), 2500 GC (CHASSIS ONLY)

DESCRIPTION: THE DOCKER IS TYPICAL OF A HEAVY LABORJACK USED FOR HAULING CARGO ON AND OFF SHIPS THROUGHOUT THE IRON KINGDOMS.

HEIGHT/WEIGHT: 12′ / 6 TONS

FUEL BURN/LOAD USAGE: 600 LBS / 6 HRS GENERAL, 55 MINS COMBAT

INITIAL SERVICE DATE: 563 AR

ORIGINAL CHASSIS DESIGN: ENGINES EAST

STOCK CORTEX: FERRUM-GRADE

PHY	10
STR	10
SPD	4
AGL	3
PRW	3
POI	2
INT	1
PER	1
Initiative	8
MAT	3
RAT	2
DEF	8
ARM	16

DAMAGE GRID

Special Rules: Initiative is rolled only in the case of an uncontrolled steamjack. Otherwise, the 'jack activates on its controller's initiative.

Initiative MAT, RAT, DEF, and ARM assume a stock ferrum-grade cortex.

FORAGER LIGHT LABORJACK CHASSIS

COST: 2500 GC (WITH STOCK FERRUM-GRADE CORTEX), 1500 GC (CHASSIS ONLY)

DESCRIPTION: THE FORAGER IS A TYPICAL LIGHT LABORJACK. HEAVY TOOLS ARE OFTEN INTEGRATED INTO THE CHASSIS FOR SPECIALIZED WORK.

HEIGHT/WEIGHT: 8′9″ / 2.8 TONS

FUEL BURN/LOAD USAGE: 300 LBS / 7 HRS GENERAL, 1 HR COMBAT

INITIAL SERVICE DATE: 540 AR

ORIGINAL CHASSIS DESIGN: ENGINES EAST

STOCK CORTEX: FERRUM-GRADE

PHY	7
STR	7
SPD	5
AGL	4
PRW	4
POI	2
INT	1
PER	1
Initiative	10
MAT	4
RAT	2
DEF	10
ARM	14

DAMAGE GRID

Special Rules: Initiative is rolled only in the case of an uncontrolled steamjack. Otherwise, the 'jack activates on its controller's initiative.

Initiative MAT, RAT, DEF, and ARM assume a stock ferrum-grade cortex.

NOMAD HEAVY WARJACK CHASSIS

Cost: 8000 GC (WITH STOCK AURUM-GRADE CORTEX), 5500 GC (CHASSIS ONLY)

Description: THE NOMAD IS A SIMPLE BUT EFFECTIVE MONSTER OF BOLTED IRON AND REINFORCED STEEL. AMONG THE FIRST WARJACKS TO ENTER WIDESPREAD PRODUCTION, THE NOMAD SERVED AS CYGNAR'S PREMIERE HEAVY WARJACK FOR DECADES. SINCE IT WAS DECOMMISSIONED, THE NOMAD HAS BECOME A MAINSTAY FOR MERCENARY COMPANIES THROUGHOUT WESTERN IMMOREN.

Height/Weight: 12′1″ / 7.5 TONS

Fuel Burn/Load Usage: 660 LBS / 5 HRS GENERAL, 50 MINS COMBAT

Initial Service Date: 455 AR, DECOMMISSIONED 563 AR

Original Chassis Design: FRATERNAL ORDER OF WIZARDRY

Stock Cortex: AURUM-GRADE

PHY	11
STR	11
SPD	5
AGL	3
PRW	5
POI	4
INT	2
PER	2
Initiative	12
MAT	6
RAT	5
DEF	10
ARM	18

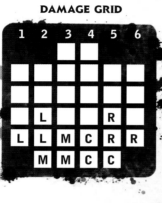

DAMAGE GRID

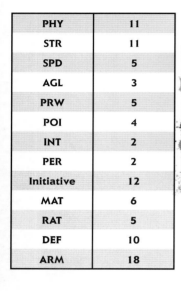

Special Rules: Initiative is rolled only in the case of an uncontrolled steamjack. Otherwise, the 'jack activates on its controller's initiative.

Initiative MAT, RAT, DEF, and ARM assume a stock aurum-grade cortex.

TALON LIGHT WARJACK CHASSIS

Cost: 6000 GC (WITH STOCK AURUM-GRADE CORTEX), 3500 GC (CHASSIS ONLY)

Description: ORIGINALLY DEVELOPED AS A FRONTLINE CYGNARAN WARJACK, THE TALON IS A COMMON SIGHT IN TODAY'S MERCENARY MARKETS AND SALVAGE YARDS. AFTER DECADES OF SERVICE, THE CYGNARAN ROYAL ARMORY DECOMMISSIONED THE CHASSIS IN FAVOR OF MORE MODERN DESIGNS. DESPITE THEIR RETIREMENT, TALONS HAVE REMAINED A FAVORITE AMONG MERCENARIES WITH THE GOLD OR INFLUENCE TO ACQUIRE THEM.

Height/Weight: 9′ / 3.25 TONS

Fuel Burn/Load Usage: 330 LBS / 5.5 HRS GENERAL, 1 HR COMBAT

Initial Service Date: 522 AR, DECOMMISSIONED 579 AR

Original Chassis Design: FRATERNAL ORDER OF WIZARDRY

Stock Cortex: AURUM-GRADE

PHY	8
STR	8
SPD	6
AGL	4
PRW	5
POI	3
INT	2
PER	2
Initiative	13
MAT	6
RAT	4
DEF	12
ARM	16

DAMAGE GRID

Special Rules: Initiative is rolled only in the case of an uncontrolled steamjack. Otherwise, the 'jack activates on its controller's initiative.

Initiative MAT, RAT, DEF, and ARM assume a stock aurum-grade cortex.

CORTEX

The cortex is the mechanikal brain of the steamjack. Cortexes come in a variety of grades, representing their sophistication as well as their cost and difficulty to produce. Warjack-grade cortexes are capable of rapidly interpreting new information and making tactical decisions, whereas laborjack-grade cortexes are designed to respond to simple commands and are not intended for combat. Nearly all modern cortex architecture allows for some degree of learning and adaptation.

The cortex is a complicated matrix of arcane patterns, developed from the technology of mechanika runes. Though it can be rightly said that a cortex is similar to the runeplates in mechanikal devices, such a comparison is an injustice to the highly complex art of cortex construction. Cortexes contain glimmers of actual sentience. The intelligence of a steamjack makes it capable of following complicated orders and performing complex tasks. Over time, some 'jacks gain some modicum of a personality, with the most ancient universally displaying quirky behavior and odd eccentricities, as well as limited self-directed initiative.

The cortex is a sphere constructed from various metals, crystals, and rare trace minerals, wrapped in a series of carefully etched, flexible plates. Each cortex has multiple layers, often containing twenty to thirty alchemically treated copper, silver, or gold foil spheres. Metal spines interconnect these layers, acting as arcane meridians. The primary focus, a crystal orb, sits in the center of the sphere. Along the three primary axes of the cortex are connection sockets: one that hooks up to the turbine conduits, another that connects to the reflex trigger conduit, and a third that connects the cortex to the 'jack's sensory equipment. A variety of baffles and tightly wound springs protect the cortex from shock and provide stability.

Cortex construction is an art. In theory the cortex is essentially blank at creation, allowing behaviors and response patterns to be learned. Steamjacks that have been around for a long time tend to be smarter and know more, but they don't take well to new handlers or new orders. The more advanced the cortex, the more readily it learns and can adapt.

'Jack marshals all know that a new steamjack is as naïve and loyal as a newborn puppy, and the massive constructs loyally follow their handler everywhere if not ordered to "sit" or "stay." 'Jack marshals have to train their steamjacks to tread softly, not step on anyone, and behave. This process takes time. Even at early stages of cognitive development some steamjacks show uncanny signs of sentience, often taking the initiative to protect their handlers or anticipate reactions.

The rules for removing and replacing cortexes can be found on p. 320.

A steamjack's cortex grade indicates the general level of decision-making and intellect that it possesses. Cupernum- and ferrum-grade cortexess are most simple, relegated to laborjacks. Aurum and arcanum are the most sophisticated cortexes and are considered to be warjack-grade.

The following attributes define different steamjack cortexes in the game.

Cost: This is the cost of the cost of the cortex in Cygnaran gold crowns.

Description: This is a description of the cortex.

Special Rules: These are the cortex's special rules.

Stats: These are the cortex's stats.

CUPERNUM-GRADE CORTEX

Cost: 100 gc

Description: A steamjack with a cupernum-grade cortex is capable of following only the simplest instructions. These 'jacks require a great deal of handling and a watchful eye.

Special Rules: A steamjack with a cupernum-grade cortex possesses a limited intellect. It enjoys pleasing its controller and can be trained to follow simple commands. Over time it develops habits and limited personality traits, but it cannot gain an imprint or learn to enhance its fighting skills.

A steamjack with a cupernum-grade cortex can be allocated up to 1 focus point. Furthermore, a steamjack with a cupernum-grade cortex can be affected by only one 'jack marshal drive (p. 323) each turn.

INT	1
PER	1

FERRUM-GRADE CORTEX

Cost: 1000 gc

Description: Ferrum-grade cortexes are mostly relegated to laborjacks. A steamjack with a ferrum-grade cortex can carry out the following simple commands without supervision: move, fetch, follow, seek, stay, and work. More complicated orders require careful guidance from a 'jack marshal.

Special Rules: A steamjack with a ferrum-grade cortex learns to follow instruction fairly quickly. Over time it improves its ability to execute simple tasks and develops a limited personality. The steamjack can develop an imprint. It cannot improve its fighting skills.

The steamjack can be allocated focus and 'jack marshaled normally.

INT	1
PER	1

AURUM-GRADE CORTEX

Cost: 2500 gc

Description: Steamjacks designed to perform tasks requiring intelligence and problem solving are normally equipped with aurum-grade cortexes. Though some sophisticated laborjacks are outfitted with an aurum-grade cortex, for the most part these cortexes are reserved for warjacks.

Special Rules: A steamjack with an aurum-grade cortex gains +1 MAT, +1 RAT, the Two-Weapon Fighting ability, and the Ambidextrous Skilled benefit.

The steamjack can be allocated focus and 'jack marshaled normally.

INT	2
PER	2

ARCANUM-GRADE CORTEX

Cost: 4500 gc

Description: This military-grade cortex is always chosen for high performance warjack designs.

Special Rules: A steamjack with an arcanum-grade cortex is instinctively protective of its controller. The steamjack quickly develops a personality, usually drawing on traits from its controller. The steamjack can learn and form an imprint.

A steamjack with an arcanum-grade cortex gains +2 MAT, +2 RAT, the Two-Weapon Fighting ability, and the Ambidextrous Skilled benefit.

'JACK PERSONALITY AND CORTEX WIPES

Cortexes are sophisticated mechanikal devices that use complex arcane techniques to simulate a living mind. Over time cortexes learn and pick up a variety of information from the environment. An experienced 'jack becomes steadily better at its tasks, but also eventually develops unexpected quirks and habits. Over decades, these traits give rise to distinct personalities that in extreme cases can interfere with a jack's work or even transform a formerly useful machine into a lethal hazard. When a 'jack develops quirks that threaten to make it a liability, its cortex can be wiped to eliminate the problem.

Cortex wiping is an involved process requiring the cortex to be entirely extracted from a 'jack chassis and placed within a special sealed iron enclosure. A properly trained arcane mechanik can employ accumulators to subject the cortex to a barrage of disruptive energies over several hours. This wipe resets the cortex to its original manufactured state. This process erases a 'jack's personality as well as skills developed over its service lifetime, so cortexes are wiped only when absolutely necessary. Most warcasters have a strong aversion to cortex wipes for warjacks since actual combat experience is invaluable and difficult to replicate. Warcasters are willing to endure extreme quirks from a favored warjack as long as it proves able to fight effectively. Labor 'jacks are more likely to have cortexes wiped on a periodic basis, such as every twenty or thirty years of active service. That said, this procedure is cost prohibitive and it is common for older warjacks to be sold at a discount, allowing for extreme personalities and an accumulation of peculiar habits.

Cortexes are also wiped if the cortex needs to be installed in a different chassis, such as if the cortex and 'jack are intended to perform an entirely different role, or if a military warjack needs to have its cortex locks reset and rebuilt. The same ability to learn and become skilled at certain tasks can make it difficult for an experienced cortex to master an unfamiliar chassis, weapons, or tasks. The degree to which this is necessary varies, particularly with cortex grades. The highest grade military cortexes have no issues adjusting to a change in weapons, for example. And in the case of a chassis that has been destroyed, if the cortex is salvaged, it can be placed into a similar new chassis and maintain its accumulated skills, personality, and quirks.

The steamjack can be allocated focus and 'jack marshaled normally.

INT	3
PER	3

WEAPONRY

The governments of the Iron Kingdoms spend vast amounts researching and developing new and ever-more terrifying armaments in a perpetual escalating race. Over the years, as new weapons are developed and older ones become obsolete, they pass into the hands of mercenary and irregular forces that greedily snap them up. Polished and refurbished, surplus weaponry can either augment or replace the arms of existing warjacks, or be retrofitted to laborjacks to create low-cost alternatives to dedicated combat machines. Though armed laborjacks are seldom able to truly compete with warjacks in battle, they can bring an edge to the force that fields them.

Steamjacks are ready platforms for a wide variety of weapon systems. Even a technically unarmed steamjack can still be an incredibly destructive combatant, its fists capable of striking with the force of a locomotive. Warjacks are typically armed and armored with some of the most advanced weaponry ever developed. The cortexes of these great machines are adaptable enough to utilize a wide-variety of weapon systems and most dedicated warjack chassis support a number of different weapon configurations.

Even laborjacks that have not been retrofit for war may be equipped with heavy tools with some combat applications, such as crushing cargo claws, welding torches, or an industrial bolt driver.

Steamjack weapons have the following attributes that define how they function in the game.

Cost: This is the cost of the weapon in Cygnaran gold crowns.

Type: This is the weapon's type, either melee or ranged.

Location: This is the location on the steamjack that the weapon can be mounted.

Ammo: This is the amount of ammunition that a steamjack ranged weapon can hold. Once its ammunition has been expended, the weapon must be reloaded before it can be used to attack again. Reloading steamjack weaponry is an involved task not suitable for the heat of combat.

Effective Range: This is the practical range of a ranged weapon in combat. A ranged weapon can hit targets and do damage up to its extreme range, but attacks against a target past the effective range of the weapon suffer −5 on the attack roll. The effective range of the weapon is listed in feet with its tabletop range in inches in parenthesis.

Remember that one inch on the tabletop is equal to six feet.

HANDHELD WEAPONS

Even the most rudimentary steamjack fists are capable of picking up and wielding handheld melee weapons. Most weapons designed for use by living creatures and smaller constructs are far too delicate to be used by steamjacks. Steamjacks can only wield weapons designed and specially reinforced for their use. Furthermore, due to the specifics of steamjack engineering and anatomy, these iron behemoths also never fight with two-handed weapons.

Extreme Range: This is the extreme range of a steamjack ranged weapon given in feet.

Attack Modifier: This is the modifier to attack rolls made with the weapon. Remember that a steamjack also rolls one fewer die on attack rolls when attacking with a weapon in a crippled location (p. 315).

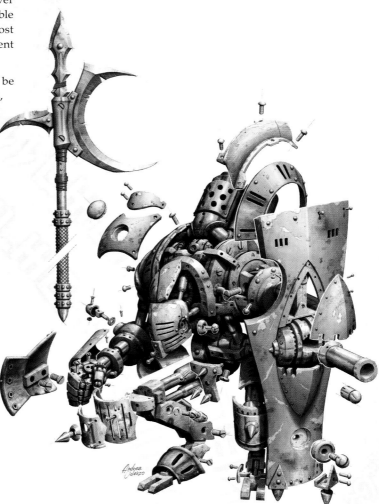

POW: This is the POW of the weapon. When making a melee attack damage roll, add the POW of the weapon and the STR of the attacker to the damage roll. Remember that a steamjack also rolls one fewer die on damage rolls when attacking with a weapon in a crippled location (p. 315).

AOE: This is the size of a ranged weapon's area of effect.

Description: This is a description of the weapon.

Special Rules: This section describes any special rules of the weapon.

MELEE WEAPONS

STEAMJACK FIST (HEAVY STEAMJACK)

Cost: None (part of the steamjack's arm)
Type: Melee
Location: Arm
Attack Modifier: 0
POW: 3

Description: The fists of a steamjack can be used as weapons.

Special Rules: A steamjack fist has the Open Fist rule and can be used to make Headlock/Weapon Lock, Push, Throw, and Two-Handed Throw power attacks (p. 312). It can also be used to pick up other weapons.

STEAMJACK FIST (LIGHT STEAMJACK)

Cost: None (part of the steamjack's arm)
Type: Melee
Location: Arm
Attack Modifier: 0
POW: 2

Description: The fists of a steamjack can be used as weapons.

Special Rules: A steamjack fist has the Open Fist rule and can used to make Headlock/Weapon Lock, Push, Throw, and Two-Handed Throw power attacks (p. 312). It can also be used to pick up other weapons.

BATTLE BLADE (HEAVY STEAMJACK ONLY)

Cost: 275 gc
Type: Melee
Location: Arm
Attack Modifier: 0
POW: 6

Description: The venerable weapon of the Nomad, this is a steamjack-sized great sword based on the design of the Caspian battle blade.

Special Rules: The battle blade can be wielded only by heavy steamjacks. A steamjack must have a non-crippled arm system with an Open Fist to pick it up. While wielding the battle blade, the steamjack cannot make attacks with the fist in which it holds it.

The battle blade has Reach.

BATTLE MACE (HEAVY STEAMJACK ONLY)

Cost: 180 gc
Type: Melee
Location: Arm
Attack Modifier: 0
POW: 5

Description: Designed for the Mule configuration of the Nomad chassis (decommissioned 582 AR), the battle mace is a heavy spiked ball atop a long, reinforced steel rod.

Special Rules: The battle mace can be wielded only by heavy steamjacks. A steamjack must have a non-crippled arm system

with an Open Fist to pick it up. While wielding the battle mace, the steamjack cannot make attacks with the fist in which it holds it.

The battle mace has Reach.

CARGO CLAW (HEAVY STEAMJACK ONLY)

Cost: 260 gc
Type: Melee
Location: Arm
Attack Modifier: –1
POW: 3 (and +2 STR)

Description: The cargo claw is a heavily reinforced limb that replaces one of the heavy steamjack's existing arms. Light steamjacks cannot be outfitted with cargo claws because their chassis are not strong enough to support the claw system and the weight of the cargo it is designed to lift.

Special Rules: When resolving actions taken with the cargo claw, the steamjack gains +2 STR, including damage rolls from claw attacks.

The cargo claw has Open Fist and Reach. A steamjack with a cargo claw cannot make Two-Handed Throw power attacks. A steamjack cannot fight with a weapon held in its cargo claw.

Mounting a cargo claw on steamjack chassis requires the mechanik to first remove the steamjack's old arm and replace it with the cargo claw (see "Removing or Replacing Arms," pp. 319-320).

Paying to have an arm system removed and a cargo claw mounted on a steamjack in place costs an additional 60 gc unless the character does the job himself.

DRILL RIG

Cost: 150 gc (light steamjack), 225 gc (heavy steamjack)
Type: Melee
Location: Arm
Attack Modifier: –1
POW: 3 (light steamjack), 5 (heavy steamjack)

Description: The heavy industrial drill replaces one of the steamjack's existing arms.

Special Rules: On a critical hit with the drill on a steamjack or warbeast, fill in the unmarked damage boxes or circles on the last column or branch damaged.

Mounting a drill rig on steamjack chassis requires the mechanik to first remove the steamjack's old arm and replace it with the drill (see "Removing or Replacing Arms," pp. 319-320).

Paying to have an arm system removed and a drill mounted on a steamjack in place costs an additional 60 gc unless the character does the job himself.

FLAIL

Cost: 100 gc (light steamjack), 175 (heavy steamjack)
Type: Melee
Location: Arm
Attack Modifier: 0
POW: 3 (light steamjack), 5 (heavy steamjack)

Description: The steamjack fail is a weapon consisting of one or more heavy, spiked iron balls suspended by a chain.

Special Rules: A steamjack must have a non-crippled arm system with an Open Fist to pick up a flail. While armed with a flail, the steamjack cannot make attacks with the fist in which it holds the weapon.

Attacks from flails ignore ARM bonuses from bucklers and shields.

HALBERD

Cost: 200 gc (light steamjack), 300 gc (heavy steamjack)
Type: Melee
Location: Arm
Attack Modifier: 0
POW: 4 (light steamjack), 6 (heavy steamjack)

Description: The steamjack halberd is a heavy, reinforced cleaving implement at the end of a long steel pole.

Special Rules: A steamjack must have a non-crippled arm system with an Open Fist to pick up a halberd. While armed with a halberd, the steamjack cannot make attacks with the fist in which it holds the weapon. If the arm system holding the halberd is crippled, the steamjack can continue fighting with the halberd, but suffers the penalties for the crippled system (p. 315).

The halberd has Reach.

A steamjack gains +2 to its charge attack rolls with this weapon.

HAND-WEAPON

Cost: 80 gc (light steamjack), 120 (heavy steamjack)
Type: Melee
Location: Arm
Attack Modifier: 0
POW: 3 (light steamjack), 5 (heavy steamjack)

Description: This covers a broad category of steamjack sized steel axes, maces, and cleaving blades.

Special Rules: A steamjack must have a non-crippled arm system with an Open Fist to pick up the hand-weapon. While wielding the hand-weapon, the steamjack cannot make attacks with the fist in which it holds the weapon. If the arm system holding the hand-weapon is crippled, the steamjack can continue fighting with the weapon, but suffers the penalties for the crippled system (p. 315).

PUNCHING SPIKE

Cost: 50 gc
Type: Melee
Location: Arm
Attack Modifier: 0
POW: +1

Description: This is a heavy steel spike grafted to the steamjack's fist or forearm to increase the damage of its punches.

Special Rules: When a steamjack with a punching spike makes an attack with its fist, the POW of the fist is increased by 1. The steamjack suffers –2 on non-attack AGL rolls made with the arm the spike is grafted to.

Grafting a punching spike to a steamjack's arm requires the proper tools, two hours of labor, and a successful INT + Mechanikal Engineering roll against a target number of 14. If the roll fails, it can be repeated after another hour of labor. Until the failure is corrected, the steamjack suffers –2 on attack rolls with the arm and does not gain the damage bonus for the spike.

Paying to have a punching spike grafted to a steamjack costs an additional 50 gc.

SHIELD

Cost: 350 gc
Type: Melee
Location: Arm
Attack Modifier: 0
POW: 1

Description: Steamjack shields can be used as weapons in addition to offering protection.

Special Rules: A steamjack must have a non-crippled arm system with an Open Fist to pick up a shield. While armed with a shield, the steamjack cannot make attacks with the fist in which it holds the shield.

A steamjack armed with a shield gains +2 ARM against attacks originating in its front arc.

SPEAR

Cost: 140 gc (light steamjack), 210 gc (heavy steamjack)
Type: Melee
Location: Arm
Attack Modifier: 0
POW: 4 (light steamjack), 5 (heavy steamjack)

Description: This is a heavy spear of reinforced steel.

Special Rules: A steamjack must have a non-crippled arm system with an Open Fist to pick up a spear. While armed with a spear, the steamjack cannot make attacks with the fist in which it holds the weapon.

The spear has Reach.

A character in the front arc of a steamjack armed with a spear suffers –2 on charge, slam power attack, and impact rolls against the steamjack.

STUN LANCE (LIGHT STEAMJACK ONLY)

Cost: 2470 gc (2000 gc for the light steamjack halberd housing, 10 gc for the alchemical capacitor, 460 gc for a runeplate inscribed with the Stall rune)
Type: Melee
Location: Arm
Attack Modifier: 0
POW: 4

Description: The stun lance is the venerable stock weapon of the Talon (not included with the chassis). The weapon relies on a negatively tuned apparatus in the lance to send conflicting signals into the cortex of steamjacks it strikes. The weapon is designed to be used with an integral alchemical capacitor.

The weapon can only be used by light steamjacks.

Special Rules: A steamjack must have a non-crippled arm system with an Open Fist to pick up the lance. While armed with the lance, a steamjack cannot make attacks with the fist in which it holds the weapon.

The stun lance has Reach.

A steamjack gains +2 to its charge attack rolls with this weapon.

For the rules for the Stall rune, see p. 286.

RANGED WEAPONS

CANNON (HEAVY STEAMJACK ONLY)

Cost: 450 gc
Type: Ranged
Location: Arm
Ammo: 8
Effective Range: 78 feet (13″)
Extreme Range: 390 feet
Attack Modifier: 0
POW: 14
AOE: 3

Description: This heavy, self-loading cannon is mounted in place of one of the steamjack's arms.

Special Rules: Due to the slow rate of its auto-loading mechanism, this weapon can be fired only once per round.

Reloading the cannon outside of combat takes twenty minutes and can be accomplished by any character with the Mechanikal Engineering skill without a die roll. The cannon fires standard artillery rounds in metal casings. Standard artillery rounds cost 15 gc each.

Mounting a cannon on steamjack chassis requires the mechanik to first remove the steamjack's old arm and replace it with the cannon (see "Removing or Replacing Arms," pp. 319-320).

Paying to have an arm system removed and a cannon mounted on a steamjack in place costs an additional 60 gc unless the character does the job himself.

FLAMETHROWER

Cost: 300 gc (light steamjack), 450 gc (heavy steamjack)
Type: Ranged
Location: Arm
Ammo: 6 (light steamjack), 10 (heavy steamjack)
Effective Range: SP 8 (light steamjack), SP 10 (heavy steamjack)
Extreme Range: —
Attack Modifier: 0
POW: 12
AOE: ––

Description: Based on weapons technology that originated in the Protectorate of Menoth, flamethrowers are horrific weapons that spray burning fuel over their targets.

Special Rules: Due to the slow rate of its fuel-pump mechanism, this weapon can be fired only once per round.

Flamethrowers cause fire damage. A character hit by a flamethrower suffers the Fire continuous effect.

The steamjack can spray out heavy or sustained gouts of firing, effectively increasing the POW of the flamethrower to POW 14. Increasing the POW expends an additional point of ammo, and the flamethrower cannot be used during the next round as fuel pressure rebuilds in the chamber.

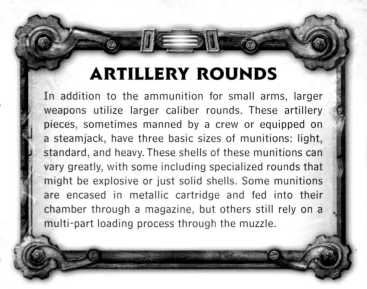

ARTILLERY ROUNDS

In addition to the ammunition for small arms, larger weapons utilize larger caliber rounds. These artillery pieces, sometimes manned by a crew or equipped on a steamjack, have three basic sizes of munitions: light, standard, and heavy. These shells of these munitions can vary greatly, with some including specialized rounds that might be explosive or just solid shells. Some munitions are encased in metallic cartridge and fed into their chamber through a magazine, but others still rely on a multi-part loading process through the muzzle.

Reloading the flamethrower outside of combat takes thirty minutes and can be accomplished by any character with the Mechanikal Engineering skill without a die roll. It costs 10 gc for each gout of flamethrower fuel.

Mounting a flamethrower on steamjack chassis requires the mechanik first to remove the steamjack's old arm and replace it with the flamethrower (see "Removing or Replacing Arms," pp. 319-320).

Paying to have an arm system removed and a flamethrower mounted on a steamjack in place costs an additional 60 gc unless the character does the job himself.

HARPOON

Cost: 200 gc (light steamjack), 300 gc (heavy steamjack)
Type: Ranged
Location: Arm
Ammo: 4
Effective Range: 48 feet (8″)
Extreme Range: —
Attack Modifier: –1
POW: 10 (light steamjack), 12 (heavy steamjack)
AOE: —

Description: This is a self-loading, blasting powder-driven harpoon launcher mounted in place of one of the steamjack's arms.

Special Rules: Due to the rate at which the harpoon's winch mechanism retracts the harpoon, this weapon can be fired only once per round.

If this weapon damages an enemy with an equal or smaller base, immediately after the attack is resolved the damaged character can be pushed any distance directly toward this steamjack. After the damaged character is moved, this steamjack can make one normal melee attack against the character pushed. After resolving this melee attack, this steamjack can make additional melee attacks during its activation.

Reloading the harpoon cannon outside of combat takes twenty minutes and can be accomplished by any character with the Mechanikal Engineering skill without a die roll.

It costs 10 gc for blasting powder and casings for one charge. Extra harpoons cost 10 gc.

Mounting the harpoon gun on steamjack chassis requires the mechanik to first remove the steamjack's old arm and replace it with the gun (see "Removing or Replacing Arms," pp. 319-320).

Paying to have an arm system removed and a harpoon mounted on a steamjack in place costs an additional 60 gc unless the character does the job himself.

LIGHT GUN (LIGHT STEAMJACK ONLY)

Cost: 200 gc
Type: Ranged
Location: Arm
Ammo: 10
Effective Range: 72 feet (12")
Extreme Range: 360 feet
Attack Modifier: 0
POW: 12
AOE: —

Description: This is a light, self-loading cannon mounted in place of one of the steamjack's arms.

Special Rules: This weapon can be fired only once per round. A bonded steamjack with this weapon can spend a focus point to make one additional attack with this weapon during its activation, or a 'jack marshal with the Drive: Ancillary Attack ability can use the drive to make one immediate attack in addition to the steamjack being able to use the cannon once per round.

Reloading the cannon outside of combat takes twenty minutes and can be accomplished by any character with the Mechanikal Engineering skill without a die roll.

The light gun fires light artillery rounds in metal casings. Light artillery rounds cost 5 gc each.

Mounting the gun on steamjack chassis requires the mechanik to first remove the steamjack's old arm and replace it with the gun (see "Removing or Replacing Arms," pp. 319-320).

Paying to have an arm system removed and a light gun mounted on a steamjack in place costs an additional 60 gc unless the character does the job himself.

SCATTERSHOT CANNON

Cost: 150 gc (light steamjack), 275 (heavy steamjack)
Type: Ranged
Location: Arm
Ammo: 8
Effective Range: SP6 (light steamjack), SP8 (heavy steamjack)
Extreme Range: —
Attack Modifier: 0
POW: 12
AOE: —

Description: This is a short, broad-barreled cannon designed to disperse grape shot into masses of enemy troops.

Special Rules: Due to the slow rate of its auto-loading mechanism, this weapon can be fired only once per round.

Reloading the cannon outside of combat takes twenty minutes and can be accomplished by any character with the Mechanikal Engineering skill without a die roll.

The scattershot cannon uses paper-wrapped shot rounds. It costs 5 gc for blasting powder, shot, and casings for one scattershot cannon round.

Mounting a cannon on steamjack chassis requires the mechanik to first remove the steamjack's old arm and replace it with the cannon (see "Removing or Replacing Arms," pp. 319-320).

Paying to have an arm system removed and a cannon mounted on a steamjack in place costs an additional 60 gc unless the character does the job himself.

STEAM LOBBER (HEAVY STEAMJACK ONLY)

Cost: 550 gc
Type: Ranged
Location: Arm
Ammo: 6
Effective Range: 48 feet (8")
Extreme Range: 240+ feet
Attack Modifier: –1
POW: 15
AOE: 4

Description: Developed for the Mule warjack, the steam lobber relies on pressure from the steamjack's boiler to hurl powerful explosive projectiles. A simple cutoff valve between the steamjack's movement system and the lobber allow it to route the full yield of its boiler's pressure into the cannon to maximize its range.

Special Rules: Due to the slow rate of its auto-loading mechanism, this weapon can be fired only once per round.

The steamjack can forfeit its movement to give this weapon +4 RNG this activation and gain the aiming bonus.

When attacking with this weapon, a steamjack can ignore intervening characters except those within 1" of the target.

On a critical hit, instead of suffering a normal damage roll, each character in the AOE is thrown d6" directly away from the steamjack regardless of their base sizes. Move characters farthest from the steamjack first. The character directly hit by the attack suffers a POW 15 damage roll. Other characters hit by the attack suffer a POW 8 damage roll. The POW of collateral damage is equal to the POW of the damage roll suffered by the thrown characters.

Reloading the cannon outside of combat takes twenty minutes and can be accomplished by any character with the Mechanikal Engineering skill without a die roll.

The steamlobber uses ammunition unique to its design. Each lobber round costs 15 gc.

Mounting a lobber on steamjack chassis requires the mechanik to first remove the steamjack's old arm and replace it with the lobber (see "Removing or Replacing Arms," pp. 319-320). Once the lobber has been mounted, a character with the proper tools must then spend four hours affixing the lobber to the steamjack's boiler and hydraulic systems and succeed in an INT + Mechanikal Engineering roll against a target number of 16. If the roll fails, the character can attempt it again after an additional two hours of labor.

Paying to have a steam lobber mounted on a steamjack costs a total of 110, gc including labor for the additional hassle of connecting the steam lobber to the steamjack's boiler and hydraulic systems.

GEAR AND UPGRADES

Steamjacks offer dedicated mechaniks virtually endless opportunities for customization. Though the military and labor sectors prefer to use stock machines, mercenary companies and freelance warcasters have developed numerous methods to customize and personalize their steamjacks. One favorite modification is to integrate a heavier boiler into a smaller-sized chassis, providing the steamjack with an extra burst of speed when it needs it most.

Steamjack gear has the following attributes that define how it functions in the game.

Cost: This is the cost of the gear in Cygnaran gold crowns.

Description: This is a description of the gear.

Special Rules: This section describes any special rules of the gear.

ARC NODE

Cost: 500 gc

Description: The arc node is an incredibly advanced mechanikal relay that enables a focuser to channel spells

through a steamjack bound to him. The arc node must be linked directly to the steamjack's arcane steam turbine to draw power.

Special Rules: The steamjack outfitted with the arc node is a channeler (p. 234).

A steamjack outfitted with an arc node gains two additional damage boxes on its damage grid. Additionally, the lowest boxes in columns 3 and 4 that do not already contain letters for systems become "A" boxes representing the arc node system.

Arc nodes must be mounted on the steamjack's chassis and joined to its arcane steam turbine (see "Installing an Arc Node," p. 319).

Paying to have an arc node mounted on a steamjack costs an additional 30 gc.

BUCKLER

Cost: 100 gc

Description: The buckler is a small shield mounted on the arm of a steamjack.

Special Rules: A steamjack armed with a buckler gains +1 ARM against attacks originating in its front arc. A steamjack cannot gain the benefit from both a buckler and a shield on the same arm.

Mounting a buckler on a steamjack's arm requires the proper tools, two hours of labor, and a successful INT + Mechanikal Engineering roll against a target number of 12. If the roll fails, it can be repeated after another hour of labor.

Paying to have a buckler mounted on a steamjack's arm costs an additional 30 gc.

HEAVY BOILER

Cost: 400 gc (light steamjack), 700 gc (heavy steamjack)

Description: This modification replaces the steamjack's standard boiler with a heavier boiler that enables it to build greater steam pressure. The extra pressure is routed directly to its movement systems, which grants it the ability to run greater distances.

Special Rules: A steamjack with a heavy boiler can run without spending a focus point or being marshaled. It burns fuel twenty percent faster than a steamjack with a stock boiler for its chassis.

The boiler is part of the movement system. Replacing a boiler requires a mechanik to first remove the old boiler and replace it with the new one (see "Removing or Replacing the Boiler," p. 320).

Paying to have a boiler replaced costs an additional 50 gc.

HYDRAULIC CRANE

Cost: 120 gc

Description: This is a steam-powered mechanical crane. The crane can easily lift several hundred pounds and can be a great asset when attempting to assemble other steamjacks while outside of a shop.

Special Rules: Mounting a crane on a on a steamjack requires the proper tools, three hours of labor, and a successful INT + Mechanikal Engineering roll against a target number of 14. If the roll fails, it can be repeated after another hour of labor.

When a steamjack with a hydraulic crane is used to assist with steamjack production, with mounting an item to another steamjack, or with salvaging parts from a steamjack, the character making the Mechanikal Engineering roll gains a +2 bonus on his roll.

Paying to have a crane mounted costs an additional 40 gc.

STEAMJACK RULES

Steamjacks are classified according to base size on the tabletop: a light steamjack has a medium base (40 mm), and a heavy steamjack has a large base (50 mm).

Steamjacks are **constructs** rather than living characters. A construct is not a living character and never suffers the effects of fear.

A steamjack generally has a **controller**. This is the 'jack marshal or warcaster commanding the steamjack.

COMBAT

The differences between warjacks and laborjacks become apparent in combat. A warjack's cortex is sophisticated enough to allow for some degree of true autonomy in combat, but a laborjack lacks significant friend-or-foe recognition capabilities and must be controlled by a 'jack marshal or warcaster to take part in a battle.

WEAPON LOCATIONS

A steamjack's weapon stat bars should be noted to indicate where its weapons are located: left arm (L), right arm (R), or head (H). When all the system boxes for a location have been damaged, the system is crippled (see "Crippling Systems," p. 315). These weapon locations are also used when resolving headlocks and weapon locks (see below). A weapon not in one of these locations is marked with "—."

TURN ORDER

A steamjack activates during its controller's turn during the Activation Phase. The steamjack can move and take its action either before or after its controller moves and takes his action. If a 'jack's controller is destroyed or otherwise leaves combat and the 'jacks that he controlled remain in the battle and do not become inert, they continue to take their turns in the established initiative order.

Autonomous or otherwise uncontrolled steamjacks taking part in a battle roll their initiative normally.

MOVEMENT

A steamjack cannot run or charge during its turn unless it has a special rule that enables it to do so, is affected by a drive enabling it to run or charge by its controlling 'jack marshal, or spends a focus point .

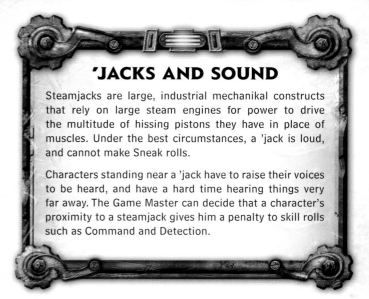

'JACKS AND SOUND

Steamjacks are large, industrial mechanikal constructs that rely on large steam engines for power to drive the multitude of hissing pistons they have in place of muscles. Under the best circumstances, a 'jack is loud, and cannot make Sneak rolls.

Characters standing near a 'jack have to raise their voices to be heard, and have a hard time hearing things very far away. The Game Master can decide that a character's proximity to a steamjack gives him a penalty to skill rolls such as Command and Detection.

POWER ATTACKS

Power attacks are special attacks that can be made by steamjacks. To make a power attack, a steamjack must have a special rule enabling it to do so, be affected by a drive enabling it to make a power attack, or spend a focus point.

Power attacks include knockout strikes, grapples, head and weapon locks, head-butts, pushes, slams, throws, and trample. Knockout strikes and grapples are described on p. 210.

HEADLOCK/WEAPON LOCK

A steamjack making a headlock/weapon lock power attack can lock a steamjack or warbeast's weapon or head and prevent its use. A steamjack must have at least one non-crippled Open Fist to make a headlock/weapon lock power attack. When a steamjack attempts a headlock/weapon lock power attack, its controller should declare what the steamjack is attempting to lock before making the attack roll.

When a steamjack makes a headlock/weapon lock, its controller should also declare which weapon with Open Fist the steamjack is using to make the attack before making a melee attack roll. A knocked down character cannot be locked. If the attack hits, then the specified head/weapon is locked. Headlock/weapon lock attacks do not cause damage.

A target cannot make attacks with a locked weapon or any other weapons in the same location. Locking a weapon with a location of "—" has no effect on other weapons. A steamjack or warbeast held in a headlock cannot make attacks with any weapons located in its head (H). A steamjack or warbeast held in a headlock/weapon lock cannot make power attacks.

While involved in a lock, the attacker cannot make power attacks or attack with the weapon with which it made the lock attempt, nor can it use any other weapon in the same location. The attacker and the defender are free to attack with any of their other melee weapons.

During its turn, a steamjack or warbeast held in a headlock/weapon lock must attempt to break the lock. For each weapon lock and headlock, both characters involved in the lock roll a d6 and add their STR. If the locked character's total exceeds that of the steamjack holding the lock, the lock is broken. The locked character can make its initial attacks with any melee weapons not located in a locked system as normal. After resolving these attacks and attempts to break free, a steamjack can spend focus points to make more attempts to break a lock or to make additional attacks with usable weapons, at 1 focus point per break attempt or additional attack. Once a lock is broken, the steamjack can use the weapon that was locked. A steamjack can voluntarily release a lock it is maintaining at any time during its activation.

Neither character can advance or be pushed while involved in a lock. A lock is broken automatically if:

- An effect causes either character to move or be placed;
- An effect knocks down either character;
- An effect causes either character to become incorporeal;
- An effect causes the attacker to become stationary;
- The weapon system maintaining the lock is crippled;
- Either character is destroyed.

HEAD-BUTT

A steamjack making a head-butt power attack smashes its head into a character to drive it to the ground. The steamjack makes a melee attack roll against its target. If the attack hits, the target is knocked down and suffers a damage roll with a POW equal to the steamjack's current STR.

A steamjack cannot head-butt while held in a headlock. A steamjack cannot head-butt power attack a character with a larger base.

PUSH

A steamjack making a push power attack uses its bulk and strength to shove another character. A push power attack automatically hits and deals no damage. Both characters roll a d6 and add their STR. If the defender's total is greater, it resists being pushed. If the steamjack's total equals or exceeds the defender's, the defending character is pushed 1" directly away from the steamjack.

After a character is pushed by a push power attack, the steamjack can immediately advance directly toward the pushed character up to the distance the pushed character was moved.

SLAM

A steamjack making a slam power attack rams a model with the full force of its body to send the target model flying backward and knock it to the ground. Any effects that prevent a character from charging, such as a penalty to its SPD or movement for any reason other than for being in rough terrain, also prevent the steamjack from making a slam power attack. A steamjack must have both its movement and action available during its turn in order to make a slam power attack.

During its activation, a steamjack can attempt to slam any character who is in its line of sight at the beginning of its normal movement. A knocked down character cannot be moved by a slam.

Declare the slam attempt and its target before moving the steamjack.

To make a slam attack, declare the slam attempt and its target, then turn the slamming steamjack to face the slam target directly. The slamming steamjack then advances its full SPD plus 3" directly toward its target. The slamming steamjack cannot voluntarily stop its movement unless its target is in its melee range, but it can end this movement at any point with its slam target in its 0.5" melee range. It must stop if it contacts a character, an obstacle, or an obstruction. The slamming steamjack cannot change its facing during or after this movement.

A slamming steamjack that ends its slam movement with its slam target in its 0.5" melee range has made a successful slam. If it advanced at least 3" it makes a melee attack roll against its target. A steamjack that power attack slams a character with a larger base suffers –2 on its attack roll. If the attack hits, the target is slammed directly away from the steamjack (see "Slammed" p. 204).

If a slamming steamjack makes a successful slam but moved less than 3" it has not moved fast enough to get its full weight and power into the blow. The steamjack makes an attack roll against its target. If the target is hit, it suffers a damage roll with a POW equal to the steamjack's current STR but is not slammed. These are still considered slam attack rolls and slam damage rolls.

A steamjack that does not end its slam movement within 0.5" of the target has failed its slam power attack. If a steamjack fails its slam power attack during its activation, its activation ends.

The POW of the slam damage roll and any resulting collateral damage rolls is equal to the Strength of the steamjack.

THROW

A steamjack making a throw power attack picks up and throws another character. A steamjack cannot throw a character with a larger base. A steamjack must have at least one non-crippled Open Fist to make a throw power attack.

The attacking steamjack makes a melee attack roll against its target. If the attack hits, both characters roll a d6 and add their current STR. If the target's total is greater, it breaks free without taking any damage and avoids being thrown. If the attacking steamjack's total equals or exceeds the target's, the target character is thrown.

When a steamjack throws another character, it chooses a direction for the thrown character to be moved. This direction must be away from the steamjack. Measure a distance from the character thrown equal to half the steamjack's current STR in inches along the chosen direction to a point on the table. This point is the thrown character's intended point of impact. A heavy steamjack throwing a small-based character adds 1" to this distance.

The POW of the throw damage roll and any resulting collateral damage rolls is equal to the Strength of the steamjack.

DOUBLE-HAND THROW

A steamjack making a double-hand throw power attack uses both its arms to pick up and throw another character. A steamjack cannot throw a character with a larger base. A steamjack must have two non-crippled Open Fists to make a double-hand throw power attack.

The attacking steamjack makes a melee attack roll against its target. If the attack hits, the target rolls a d6 and adds its current STR. The attacking steamjack rolls 2d6 and adds its current STR. If the target's total is greater, it breaks free without taking any damage and avoids being thrown. If the steamjack's total equals or exceeds the target's, the target model gets thrown.

To determine the direction of the double-hand throw, the steamjack can either follow the steps for determining the direction of a regular throw (see "Throw," above) or simply throw the character at another target within the steamjack's line of sight. Ignore the character being thrown when determining line of sight to the other target. The throw distance is equal to half the steamjack's current STR in inches. A heavy steamjack throwing a small-based character adds 1″ to this distance. If the target is within range, the steamjack makes a melee attack roll against it. If it is outside this range, resolve the throw using the rules in "Throw," above, as if the thrown character were thrown directly toward the target. On a hit, move the thrown character from its current location directly toward the target's base until it contacts the target. This throw does not deviate. A double-hand throw at another character is not an attack against that character.

If the attack roll misses, determine the thrown character's point of impact by rolling deviation from the center of the target's base. Referencing the deviation rules (p. 212), roll a d6 for direction and a d3 for distance in inches. If the target is beyond the throw distance, determine deviation from a point on the line to it equal to the throw distance. The thrown character moves directly from its current location in a straight line to the determined point of impact.

The POW of the slam damage roll and any resulting collateral damage rolls is equal to the Strength of the steamjack.

TRAMPLE

A steamjack making a trample power attack crashes its way through small-based characters in its path. Any effects that prevent a model from charging, such as a penalty to its SPD or movement for any reason other than for being in rough terrain, also prevent the steamjack from making a trample power attack. A steamjack must have both its normal movement and action available in order to make a trample power attack. Light steamjacks cannot make trample power attacks.

Declare a trample power attack at the beginning of the steamjack's turn. The steamjack then turns to face any direction. The steamjack advances up to its current SPD plus 3″ in a straight line in that direction. It moves through any small-based characters in its path, but there must be room for the trampling steamjack's base at the end of the movement. It

stops if it contacts a character with a medium or larger base, an obstacle, or an obstruction. The trampling steamjack cannot change its facing during or after this movement. Do not resolve free strikes against the trampling steamjack during this movement.

After the steamjack has finished its trample movement, it makes a melee attack roll against each small-based character it contacted. Characters hit by a trample attack roll suffer a damage roll with a POW equal to the steamjack's current STR. Trample damage can be boosted.

Resolve free strikes against the trampling steamjack after resolving all trample attacks. Characters contacted cannot make free strikes against the trampling steamjack. Ignore the distance between characters when resolving free strikes against the trampling steamjack; if a character was eligible to make a free strike against the trampling steamjack during the trampling steamjack's movement, it can do so whether or not the trampling steamjack ended its movement in the eligible character's melee range.

DAMAGING A STEAMJACK

Steamjacks can take a tremendous amount of damage before they fall in combat. What might be an incapacitating or mortal wound to a mere mortal just dents a steamjack's hull.

DAMAGE GRIDS

Steamjacks have damage grids consisting of six columns of damage boxes labeled with the numbers 1 through 6. When a steamjack suffers damage, roll a d6 to determine which column takes the damage. Starting with the uppermost unmarked box in that column and working down, mark one damage box per damage point taken. Once a column is full, continue recording damage in the next column to the right that contains an unmarked damage box. If all the damage boxes in column 6 are marked, continue recording damage in column 1 or the next column that contains an unmarked damage box. Continue filling columns as required until every damage point taken has been recorded.

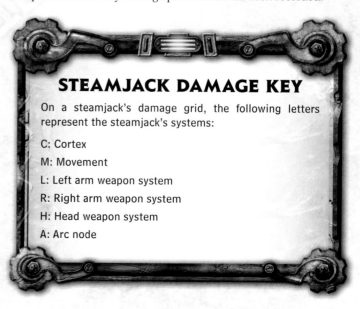

STEAMJACK DAMAGE KEY

On a steamjack's damage grid, the following letters represent the steamjack's systems:

C: Cortex

M: Movement

L: Left arm weapon system

R: Right arm weapon system

H: Head weapon system

A: Arc node

When a rule specifically states a steamjack suffers damage to the "first" box of a given type, find the lowest numbered column on the steamjack's damage grid that has an unmarked damage box of that type. Within that column, mark the topmost unmarked damage box of that type.

CRIPPLING SYSTEMS

When a steamjack suffers damage, individual systems critical to its combat performance can be damaged and crippled. Blank damage boxes on the steamjack's damage grid represent its hull. The hull is not a system. Beneath the hull are the steamjack's vital systems, represented by system boxes. Each of these boxes is labeled with a letter designating the system it supports. System boxes are still damage boxes; when recording damage, mark both blank boxes and those containing system labels to record the correct amount of damage. While all its system boxes are marked, a system is crippled. Mark the appropriate system status box below the damage boxes to show this. The effects of crippled systems are as follows.

- Crippled Arc Node: The steamjack cannot be used to channel spells.

- Crippled Cortex: The steamjack loses any focus points it has been allotted and cannot be allocated focus points. It cannot spend focus points for any reason.

- Crippled Movement: The steamjack has its base DEF changed to 7. It cannot run or charge. A steamjack that has its movement system crippled while advancing as part of a charge, slam, or trample immediately stops advancing, and its activation ends.

- Crippled Arm or Head Weapon System: The steamjack rolls one fewer die on the attack and damage rolls with weapons in the crippled location. Additionally, a steamjack cannot use weapons in a crippled location to make power attacks. If a weapon in the crippled location has the Buckler or Shield weapon quality, the steamjack loses the ARM bonus for that quality while the location is crippled.

If 1 or more damage points are removed from a crippled system, the system is no longer crippled.

CRIPPLED SYSTEMS AND CATASTROPHIC DAMAGE

Though most of the damage sustained by a steamjack can be repaired by a mechanik given enough time, should the steamjack sustain severe enough damage it could require replacement parts or even whole limbs to return to complete functionality.

After a battle, for each system that was crippled during the battle, roll once on the appropriate Catastrophic Damage table. This roll is made even if the crippled system was repaired during the battle. Roll once for each system even if was crippled multiple times during the same battle. Remember, this roll is made after the battle so it does not further impair the functionality of the steamjack during the battle the damage was sustained.

CATASTROPHIC DAMAGE TABLE, ARC NODE

If an arc node suffers the same effect on a subsequent catastrophic damage roll (a roll of 3–11) before the previous effect has been repaired, the arc node suffers no additional catastrophic effect. See the rules and costs associated with repairing or replacing a catastrophically damaged arc node, p. 319.

2D6	RESULT
2	**Destroyed** – The arc node was destroyed as a result of the damage the steamjack endured in combat. Though the arc node might have been bodged back together during the battle, by the time the dust clears it is broken beyond all repair and requires replacement.
3–4	**Power Leak** – As a result of the damage the damage inflicted on the arc node, it has developed a power leak. Until it is repaired, a warcaster channeling a spell through the arc node must spend one additional focus point to cast the spell.
5–6	**Receptor Lag** – The damaged arc node has a slight delay in its relay time that makes targeting offensive spells channeled through it exceptionally difficult. Until it is repaired, offensive spells channeled through the arc node suffer −2 to their attack rolls.
7	**Feedback** – The arc node's relays were badly damaged. Until it is repaired, any time the steamjack's controller channels a spell through it, immediately after the spell has been resolved the warcaster suffers d3 damage points from psychic feedback. This damage is applied to the warcaster's life spiral (bypassing his warcaster armor power field if applicable).
8–9	**Damaged Locus** – The mechanisms that focus the arcane energies of spells channeled through the arc node have become damaged. Until it is repaired, offensive spells channeled through the arc node suffer −2 to their damage rolls.
10–11	**Misalignment** – The arc node has become badly misaligned. Until it is repaired, spells channeled through the arc node suffer −2 RNG.
12	**Wear and Tear** – Though it suffers no immediate effects from the catastrophic damage it has endured, the arc node is starting to show its age. Each time this result is rolled, the target number for all future rolls to repair the arc node is increased by a cumulative +2. An arc node's Wear and Tear cannot be repaired; it can only be tolerated until the arc node is replaced.

CATASTROPHIC DAMAGE TABLE, CORTEX

If a cortex suffers the same effect on a subsequent catastrophic damage roll (a roll of 3–11) before the previous effect has been repaired, the cortex suffers no additional catastrophic effect. See the rules and costs associated with repairing or replacing a catastrophically damaged cortex, p. 320.

2D6	RESULT
2	**Destroyed** – The cortex was destroyed as a result of the damage the steamjack endured in combat. Though the cortex might have been bodged back together during the battle, by the time the dust clears it is ruined beyond all repair.
3–4	**Slow Processing** – The steamjack's cortex has been slowed tremendously due to the damage it sustained. Until repaired, the steamjack must forfeit its movement or action each turn.
5–6	**Targeting System Misaligned** – The steamjack's optical relays have been knocked out of alignment with the cortex. Until repaired, the steamjack suffers –2 to its PER rolls and loses one die on its ranged attack rolls.
7	**Reduced Power** – The integrity of the steamjack's cortex has been badly compromised. Until repaired, the maximum number of focus points the steamjack can be allocated is reduced by 1. The steamjack can benefit from up to one drive each turn.
8–9	**Brain Damage** – Extensive damage to the steamjack's cortex has caused a glitch in its delicate machinery. As a result, the steamjack suffers –2 on INT rolls and cannot benefit from drives.
10–11	**Unstable** – Extensive damage to the steamjack's cortex has weakened its integrity. Until repaired, at the end of any activation in which the steamjack spent 1 or more focus points, roll a d6. If the roll is equal to or less than the number of focus points spent, the steamjack explodes and characters within 3″ of it suffer an unboostable POW 14 blast damage roll. The steamjack is completely destroyed in the explosion.
12	**Wear and Tear** – Though it suffers no immediate effects from the catastrophic damage it has endured, the cortex is starting to show its age. Each time this result is rolled, the target number for all future rolls to repair the cortex is increased by a cumulative +2. A cortex's Wear and Tear cannot be repaired; it can only be tolerated until the cortex is replaced.

CATASTROPHIC DAMAGE TABLE, HEAD

If a head suffers the same effect on a subsequent catastrophic damage roll (a roll of 3–11) before the previous effect has been repaired, the head suffers no additional catastrophic effect. See the rules and costs associated with repairing or replacing a catastrophically damaged head, p. 320.

2D6	RESULT
2	**Destroyed Head** – The steamjack's head system has been destroyed as a result of the damage it sustained. Though the steamjack might have been bodged back together during the battle, its head systems and weaponry are now completely ruined.
3–4	**Blind** – Due to the damage it sustained, the steamjack has been completely blinded. Until repaired, the steamjack suffers –4 MAT and –4 DEF, cannot run or charge, and must forfeit either its movement or action during its turn.
5–6	**Weapon System Damage** – The steamjack's weapon systems integrated into its head have been badly damaged. Until repaired, the steamjack loses one die on damage rolls with weapons located on its head.
7	**Damaged Optics** – The steamjack's optical systems have been badly damaged. Until repaired, all the steamjack's non-spray weapons suffer –4 RNG.
8–9	**Partially Blinded** – The steamjack's optical systems have been crippled by the damage it sustained. Until repaired, the steamjack's LOS is reduced to forty-eight feet (8″).
10–11	**Weak Spot** – Due to the heavy damage the steamjack sustained, the armor protecting its head and central torso has been severely compromised. Until repaired, the steamjack suffers –1 ARM.
12	**Wear and Tear** – Though it suffers no immediate effects from the catastrophic damage it has endured, the steamjack's head and internal systems are starting to show their age. Each time this result is rolled, the target number for all future rolls to repair the head system is increased by a cumulative +2. A head's Wear and Tear cannot be repaired; it can only be tolerated until the head is replaced.

CATASTROPHIC DAMAGE TABLE, MOVEMENT

If movement system suffers the same effect on a subsequent catastrophic damage roll (a roll of 3–11) before the previous effect has been repaired, the movement system suffers no additional catastrophic effect. See the rules and costs associated with repairing or replacing a catastrophically damaged portion of the steamjack's movement system, p. 320.

2D6	RESULT
2	**Destroyed Chassis** – The steamjack's chassis has buckled under the damage it sustained and can no longer sustain the weight of the machine. Though the steamjack might have been bodged back together during the battle, it now stands with its back broken, fit only for salvage.
3–4	**Pressure Leaks** – The steamjack's boiler has numerous leaks preventing it from building a steady amount of pressure. Until repaired, roll a die at the start of the steamjack's activation. If a 6 is rolled, it must forfeit its movement or action for the turn.
5–6	**Damaged Boiler** – The steamjack's boiler has been badly damaged. Until repaired, the steamjack cannot run or charge and suffers –2 STR.
7	**Damaged Drive Shaft** – The steamjack's movement systems have been severely damaged. Until repaired, the steamjack suffers –1 SPD and DEF.
8–9	**Gears Stripped** – The gears in the steamjack's movement systems are badly damaged. Until repaired, each time the steamjack runs, charges, or performs a slam or trample power attack, the steamjack suffers 1 point of damage to its movement system.
10–11	**Weakened Joints** – The steamjack's legs are badly damaged. Until repaired, whenever it takes five or more points of damage from an attack, it must make a PRW roll against a target number of 10. If it succeeds, nothing happens. If it fails it is knocked down.
12	**Wear and Tear** – Though it suffers no immediate effects from the catastrophic damage it has endured, the steamjack's movement system is starting to show its age. Each time this result is rolled, the target number for all future rolls to repair the movement system is increased by a cumulative +2. A movement system's Wear and Tear cannot be repaired; it can only be tolerated until the movement system is replaced.

CATASTROPHIC DAMAGE TABLE, ARM (RIGHT OR LEFT)

If an arm suffers the same effect on a subsequent catastrophic damage roll (a roll of 3–11) before the previous effect has been repaired, the arm suffers no additional catastrophic effect. See the rules and costs associated with repairing or replacing a catastrophically damaged arm, pp. 319-320.

2D6	RESULT
2	**Destroyed Arm** – The steamjack's arm system has been completely destroyed as a result of the damage it sustained. Though the steamjack might have been bodged back together during the battle, its arm system and weaponry are now completely ruined.
3–4	**Seizing Gears** – Due to the damage the steamjack's arm system sustained, its gears have a tendency to seize up. Until repaired, the steamjack can make only a single attack with each of its melee weapons integrated into the arm each round.
5–6	**Damaged Weapon** – The arm weapon system has been damaged. Until the arm has been repaired, weapons that are part of that system, including handheld weapons, suffer –1 POW.
7	**Weakness** – The steamjack's arm has been severely weakened by the damage it sustained. Until repaired, the steamjack suffers –2 STR on actions performed with the arm, including melee attack damage roll resolutions.
8–9	**Slowed Reaction Speed** – The steamjack's arm has been miscalibrated by the damage it sustained. Until repaired, the steamjack suffers –1 on its attack rolls made with that arm.
10–11	**Jam-prone** – Due to the damage the steamjack's arm system sustained, ranged weapon auto-loaders integrated into the arm system are prone to jamming. Until repaired, the steamjack can make only a single attack with each of its ranged weapons integrated into the arm each combat. The weapons then have to be painstakingly cleaned and reloaded by hand.
12	**Wear and Tear** – Though it suffers no immediate effects from the catastrophic damage it has endured, the steamjack's arm system is starting to show its age. Each time this result is rolled, the target number for all future rolls to repair the movement system is increased by a cumulative +2. A movement system's Wear and Tear cannot be repaired; it can only be tolerated until the movement system is replaced.

317

WRECKING A STEAMJACK

A steamjack is considered wrecked once all of its damage boxes have been filled. When a steamjack is wrecked, remove it from the table and replace it with a wreck marker (see p. 353) corresponding to its base size. A wreck marker is not a character. After the battle it is possible to repair the wrecked steamjack, although if the catastrophic damage results are bad enough, it might be preferable to salvage parts from the wrecked steamjack instead.

A wreck marker is rough terrain and can provide cover to characters within 1″ whose bases are partially obscured from the attacker by the wreck. Characters at least partially within the area of the wreck can also use it for cover.

Any effects on a steamjack expire when it is wrecked.

SALVAGE

Wrecked, inert, and simply inactive steamjacks can be salvaged for their component parts. Dismantling a steamjack for salvage requires an hour of labor followed by a successful INT + Mechanikal Engineering roll against a difficulty of 14. If the roll fails, the character can try again after another 30 minutes of work. If the mechanik has access to a full mechanik's shop, he gains +2 to his roll.

A successful salvage roll enables the mechanik to separate out all the functional parts and weapons from the steamjack. If a salvaged steamjack had crippled systems, the Game Master should roll on the appropriate Catastrophic Damage tables to determine the condition of the damaged parts.

Salvaged parts and weapons can be kept to refit onto steamjacks at a later date or else sold as used parts. Damaged parts sell for a fraction of their original costs. Parts in good condition could be sold for up to half of their original value.

EVALUATING DAMAGED PARTS

A character with the Mechanikal Engineering skills can identify damaged parts and their condition with a successful INT + Mechanikal Engineering skill roll against a target number of 14. If the roll fails, the character evaluates the parts as functional and cannot discern their true condition until given a reason to reevaluate the parts.

REPAIRING A STEAMJACK IN THE FIELD

Most of the damage that a steamjack sustains in battle can be repaired by a skilled mechanik. If the steamjack loses a system, the damage is more extensive and requires additional labor and potentially replacement parts to fix completely. A steamjack can be truly ruined beyond repair only if its cortex is destroyed. Even then, the steamjack's wreck yields parts that can be salvaged to get another machine up and running.

BODGING

When time is of the essence, such as in the heat of battle, a character with the Bodge ability can attempt to patch a steamjack back together temporarily. Bodging is a tactic of last recourse and at best it only enables a heavily damaged steamjack to limp through the battle until more extensive repairs can be made.

A character must have the Bodge ability to attempt any repairs on a steamjack in combat. Bodging is a full action. The mechanik then makes an INT + Mechanikal Engineering roll against a target number of 14. If the roll fails, nothing happens and the mechanik can attempt to repair the steamjack again next turn. If the roll succeeds, the steamjack regains 1 damage box in each of its crippled systems.

A character must have the proper tools to attempt to bodge a steamjack.

Bodging has no effect on wrecked steamjacks.

COMMON REPAIRS

The following rules cover the requirements and costs of steamjack repairs and services. Whether your character needs to replace the arm of a steamjack because of battle damage or he wants to replace the arm with a new cannon, the rules are same.

REPAIRING DAMAGE

Repairs more extensive than bodging cannot be conducted on the battlefield and require access to sheet metal, scrap, and a full mechanic's tool kit.

Every hour a mechanik labors over a damaged steamjack, he can remove a number of damage points from anywhere on its damage grid equal to his Mechanikal Engineering skill level. If the character has access to a full mechanik's shop and/or a ready supply of replacement parts, he can remove an additional d3 damage points each hour.

ASSISTED REPAIRS

A mechanik assisted in his repairs by additional characters with the Mechanikal Engineering skill can remove one additional damage point from the steamjack for each other character assisting him.

PAYING FOR REPAIRS

A character paying for the repair of non-catastrophic damage to a steamjack can expect to pay 10 gc per hour per mechanik working on his 'jack until the job is done.

ARC NODE REPAIRS

REPAIRING A CATASTROPHICALLY DAMAGED ARC NODE (A)

Repairing catastrophic damage to an arc node requires the arc node to be removed from the steamjack, four hours of labor with the proper tools, and a successful INT + Mechanikal Engineering skill roll against a target number of 16. If the roll fails, the character can attempt it again after another hour of labor. A successful repair removes the effects of one catastrophic damage roll. Results of Destroyed and Wear and Tear cannot be repaired.

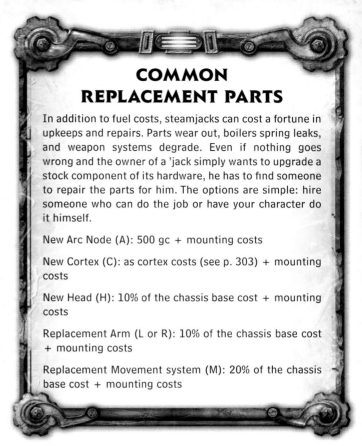

COMMON REPLACEMENT PARTS

In addition to fuel costs, steamjacks can cost a fortune in upkeeps and repairs. Parts wear out, boilers spring leaks, and weapon systems degrade. Even if nothing goes wrong and the owner of a 'jack simply wants to upgrade a stock component of its hardware, he has to find someone to repair the parts for him. The options are simple: hire someone who can do the job or have your character do it himself.

New Arc Node (A): 500 gc + mounting costs

New Cortex (C): as cortex costs (see p. 303) + mounting costs

New Head (H): 10% of the chassis base cost + mounting costs

Replacement Arm (L or R): 10% of the chassis base cost + mounting costs

Replacement Movement system (M): 20% of the chassis base cost + mounting costs

Paying to have catastrophic arc node damage repaired costs 100 gc (including the cost of having the arc node removed and reinstalled).

INSTALLING AN ARC NODE

Adding an arc node to a steamjack requires mechanik's tools and two hours of labor. After the time has passed, the mechanik must make an INT + Mechanikal Engineering roll against a target number of 16. If the roll succeeds, the character has successfully removed or installed the arc node. If the roll fails, the arc node does not function. The character must spend an additional hour of labor before attempting the roll again.

Paying to have an arc node installed on a steamjack costs an additional 30 gc.

ARM REPAIRS

REPAIRING A CATASTROPHICALLY DAMAGED ARM (L OR R)

Repairing catastrophic damage to an arm requires the arm to be removed from the steamjack, three hours of labor with the proper tools, and a successful INT + Mechanikal Engineering skill roll against a target number of 14. If the roll fails, the character can attempt it again after another hour of labor. A successful repair removes the effects of one catastrophic damage roll. Results of Destroyed and Wear and Tear cannot be repaired.

Paying to have catastrophic arm damage repaired costs 100 gc.

REMOVING OR REPLACING ARMS

Removing or replacing an arm or an arm-mounted weapon system requires access to a crane, a mechanik's tool kit, and two hours of labor. After the time has passed, the mechanik must make an INT + Mechanikal Engineering roll against a target number of 14. If the roll succeeds, the character has successfully removed or installed the arm or weapon system. If the roll fails, the arm either cannot be removed without additional labor or was improperly installed and does not function. Either way, the character must spend an additional hour of labor before attempting the roll again.

A character who wishes to pay to have an arm installed or removed can expect to pay 30 gc in labor.

CORTEX REPAIRS

REPAIRING A CATASTROPHICALLY DAMAGED CORTEX (C)

Repairing catastrophic damage to a cortex requires the cortex to be removed from the steamjack, four hours of labor with the proper tools, and a successful INT + Mechanikal Engineering skill roll against a target number of 18. If the roll fails, the character can attempt it again after another hour of labor. A successful repair removes the effects of one catastrophic damage roll. Results of Destroyed and Wear and Tear cannot be repaired.

Paying to have catastrophic cortex damage repaired costs 100 gc (including the cost of having the cortex removed and reinstalled).

REMOVING OR REPLACING THE CORTEX

Removing or replacing the cortex requires access to a crane, a mechanik's tool kit, and one hour of labor. After the time has passed, the mechanik must make an INT + Mechanikal Engineering roll against a target number of 14. If the roll succeeds, the character has successfully removed or installed the cortex. If the roll fails, the cortex either cannot be removed without additional labor or was improperly installed and the steamjack does not function. Either way, the character must spend an additional thirty minutes of labor before attempting the roll again.

A character who wishes to pay to have a cortex installed or removed can expect to pay 20 gc in labor.

HEAD REPAIRS

REPAIRING A CATASTROPHICALLY DAMAGED HEAD (H)

Repairing catastrophic damage to a steamjack's head requires the head to be removed from the steamjack, three hours of labor with the proper tools, and a successful INT + Mechanikal Engineering skill roll against a target number of 16. If the roll fails, the character can attempt it again after another hour of labor. A successful repair removes the effects of one catastrophic damage roll. Results of Destroyed and Wear and Tear cannot be repaired.

Paying to have catastrophic head damage repaired costs 100 gc.

REMOVING OR REPLACING THE HEAD

Removing or replacing a steamjack's head requires access to a crane, a mechanik's tool kit, and one hour of labor. After the time has passed, the mechanik must make an INT + Mechanikal Engineering roll against a target number of 14. If the roll succeeds, the character has successfully removed or installed the head. If the roll fails, the head either cannot be removed without additional labor or was improperly installed and the steamjack does not function. Either way, the character must spend an additional thirty minutes of labor before attempting the roll again.

A character who wishes to pay to have a head installed or removed can expect to pay 20 gc in labor.

MOVEMENT SYSTEM REPAIRS

REPAIRING A CATASTROPHICALLY DAMAGED MOVEMENT SYSTEM (M)

Repairing catastrophic damage to a steamjack's movement system requires three hours of labor with the proper tools and a successful INT + Mechanikal Engineering skill roll against a target number of 16. If the roll fails, the character can attempt it again after another hour of labor. A successful repair removes the effects of one catastrophic damage roll. Results of Destroyed and Wear and Tear cannot be repaired.

Paying to have catastrophic movement system damage repaired costs 100 gc.

REMOVING OR REPLACING THE BOILER

Removing or replacing the boiler requires access to a crane, a mechanik's tool kit, and four hours of labor. After the time has passed, the mechanik must make an INT + Mechanikal Engineering roll against a target number of 14. If the roll succeeds, the character has successfully removed or installed the boiler. If the roll fails, the boiler either cannot be removed without additional labor or was improperly installed and the steamjack does not function. Either way, the character must spend an additional hour of labor before attempting the roll again.

A character who wishes to pay to have a boiler installed or removed can expect to pay 50 gc in labor.

REMOVING OR REPLACING A LEG

Removing or replacing a steamjack's leg requires access to two or more cranes, a mechanik's tool kit, and three hour of labor. After the time has passed, the mechanik must make an INT + Mechanikal Engineering roll against a target number of 14. If the roll succeeds, the character has successfully removed or installed the leg. If the roll fails, the leg either cannot be removed without additional labor or was improperly installed and the steamjack does not function. Either way, the character must spend an additional hour of labor before attempting the roll again.

A character who wishes to pay to have a leg installed or removed can expect to pay 40 gc in labor.

COMMAND PROTOCOLS: CONTROLLING A STEAMJACK

Steamjacks come in a wide variety of chassis types, configurations, ages, and functions, and characters with the training and ability to control them to perform these tasks smoothly are highly valued. One of the wonders of modern steamjacks is they are somewhat autonomous and can be trusted to work without constant supervision. Once set to a task they are well equipped to make small adjustments to see it done. A controller is needed to ensure they are where they are needed, set to the proper tasks, and to prioritize choices when obstacles arise. In all respects a controlled and directed 'jack is more efficient than one left to its own initiative, whether it is offloading a ship or fighting in a chaotic melee alongside soldiers.

Most commonly a steamjack is controlled by verbal instructions, a task referred to as 'jack marshaling. A variety of security measures (described below) ensure a steamjack obeys only the commands of an authorized handler, and it ignores words spoken by anyone else. A steamjack has sensory apparatus to remain aware of its environment, to avoid accidentally stepping on or running into passers-by or striking allied soldiers, but the words of its marshal always take priority. A 'jack marshal knows precisely the best way to get a 'jack's attention and to provide it tasks amid even chaotic environments. This requires a protocol of precisely delineated sentence construction combined with gestures to convey its immediate priorities to a 'jack.

To outsiders it might seem as though a 'jack marshal orders a 'jack the way one might instruct an intelligent animal or a young child. In practice, this is an advanced and nuanced skill requiring an understanding of how cortexes interpret their environment and the vocabulary a 'jack can comprehend. Cortex grade has a major impact on how a 'jack interprets complicated instructions, as well as how many tasks can be set in motion without requiring subsequent orders. The most advanced military-grade cortexes adapt well to changing circumstances and can be given a chain of long-reaching commands.

Warcasters can command steamjacks mentally, which allows for much more precise and constant supervision, as well as eliminating environmental distractions such as loud noises. There are two types of command exerted by a warcaster, depending on circumstances: mental orders and direct control. A warcaster can deliver sequences of commands to a 'jack just like a 'jack marshal, if he wishes to afford the 'jack autonomy and not govern its every movement. Alternatively, a warcaster can take direct control over a 'jack and perform its functions as if he were moving his own limbs or looking through its eyes. By directly controlling a steamjack, a warcaster can execute fine control such as aiming a ranged weapon for a small and specific target, or performing complex motions that would be difficult to describe, such as gently lifting a fallen beam off a person who has been trapped beneath without risking additional injury.

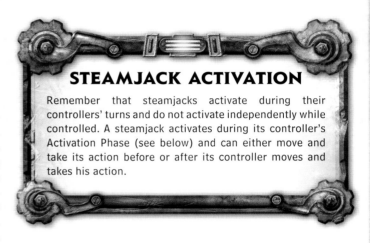

STEAMJACK ACTIVATION

Remember that steamjacks activate during their controllers' turns and do not activate independently while controlled. A steamjack activates during its controller's Activation Phase (see below) and can either move and take its action before or after its controller moves and takes his action.

STEAMJACK SECURITY

All steamjacks have some degree of security in place to prevent unauthorized use. These measures vary based on cortex grade and the intended use of the machine, but even the simplest laborjack has basic security. For simplicity, two degrees of security are described here, one for laborjacks, and one for warjacks. Former laborjacks modified for battle by mercenary companies are usually augmented to include cortex locks and are therefore treated as warjacks.

The fundamental security measure for all steamjack cortexes is a series of code phrases used to unlock command and allow the 'jack to recognize a specific handler. Controlling the steamjack requires knowledge of these phrases, which are in the language of the cortex's country of origin. A 'jack can be put in a "receptive" state to receive its cortex lock phrase by throwing a switch or lever—which might be conveniently placed for laborjacks requiring frequent changes in 'jack marshals, or more securely inside the locked cortex access panel on the top of the chassis for those that do not. While the steamjack is receptive, a person standing adjacent to the 'jack and speaking this phrase is recognized from that point forward as an authorized 'jack marshal, and their verbal commands are heeded.

'JACK MARSHALING

Although even the simplest laborjack can understand the language of its country of origin, actually deriving useful work from a 'jack requires the 'Jack Marshal ability. Trying to control a 'jack without this skill is unpredictable and potentially dangerous. A 'jack is receptive to only a single authorized handler at a time.

LABORJACK SECURITY

Laborjacks are primarily intended to be controlled by 'jack marshals. As a result, these 'jacks are secure only against unauthorized verbal commands and are typically unprotected against warcasters, who can slip past the crude security associated with verbal commands to deliver instructions directly to the cortex. A warcaster that can speak the cortex's native language can bond to an unbonded laborjack by touching its chassis and spending a full action.

WARJACK SECURITY AND BONDS

Bonding with a warjack is more difficult. Warjacks and any 'jack with the appropriate cortex augmentation are protected with additional security measures, known as cortex locks, which require a separate and more complex projected mental code to access the cortex. The codes used to unlock unbonded warjack cortexes are long and include specific mental images which must be remembered in proper sequence. Understanding these phrases requires specific instruction including focus on the visual elements required (often patterns or specific illustrations). Militaries of the Iron Kingdoms also take pains to update their cortex locks frequently as further protection against tampering. It is for this reason that Cygnar's warjacks cannot be controlled by Khadoran warcasters, for example, even if captured and handled extensively and even if spies have a written transcription of the lock phrase. The cortex must be

entirely wiped and reconfigured before it can be converted to a different military cortex lock.

When a warcaster has mentally delivered the appropriate cortex lock code to an unbonded steamjack, he establishes his own bond, as long as he has free slots to do so. In the process, a warcaster creates a personal layer of mental code by which the steamjack recognizes him, effectively adding an additional cortex lock that creates a far more robust connection between the steamjack and its warcaster. A warcaster can actively relinquish control of the steamjack and break his bond with it at will.

Should a warcaster be killed or suddenly lose consciousness, the separation between the mind of the caster and the cortex creates a psychic backlash that resets the 'jack's cortex. This backlash effectively breaks the bond, removes added cortex locks, and renders the steamjack inert. This connection is maintained while the warcaster sleeps; only sudden and violent separation between the mind of the warcaster and the steamjack resets the cortex.

An inert steamjack is shut down. It enters a temporary stasis in which it awaits a new controller to reactivate it and assume control. Most warjacks include a reset switch in an accessible location known to qualified mechaniks or 'jack marshals, which can be triggered if a controlling warcaster is knocked unconscious or killed in action. When a warjack without an active bond is reactivated, it waits for spoken commands and can be marshaled by any character who knows how to bypass its verbal locks.

'JACK MARSHALS

Since the first steamjacks were built there has been a need for those who can control them, whether tasking them to the labor of lifting massive cargo crates or charging into battle swinging an axe. The 'jack marshals have the training and the knack for verbally commanding and instructing steamjacks in a wide variety of tasks. A skilled 'jack marshal can always squeeze greater efficiency and performance out of a 'jack, accomplishing tasks in a fraction of the time and sometimes making the difference between victory and defeat in times of war.

ESTABLISHING CONTROL

To marshal a 'jack, a character must know the native language of its cortex and know the verbal security codes to take control of the 'jack.

A steamjack can be commanded by only a single 'jack marshal at a time. Unless control of the steamjack is handed over by its current 'jack marshal to another marshal, it does not accept verbal pass codes or instructions from another character while in the company of its current marshal. A warcaster who knows his cortex's native language can still bond to the steamjack and usurp control from its marshal.

Bonded steamjacks cannot be marshaled and ignore verbal pass codes.

SEEING THROUGH THE EYES OF A 'JACK

A warcaster can utilize the bonds he shares with the steamjacks in his battlegroup to literally see through their eyes all the while still maintaining his own vision. This can be invaluable for warcasters on patrol or in potentially hostile circumstances. Trying to take in the world through multiple points of view can be confusing for junior warcasters and takes practice to fully master. More experienced warcasters are comfortable integrating the vision of multiple steamjacks to gain a comprehensive perspective on the battlefield.

As long as a bonded 'jack is in the control area of a warcaster, the warcaster can use a quick action to see through the 'jack's visual apparatus, and this vision can be maintained indefinitely. A warcaster can perceive anything his bonded 'jacks would see, although any spell augmenting a warcaster's own vision does not augment vision through a 'jack unless the spell specifically states otherwise. While a warcaster is maintaining the ability to see through the eyes of one or more steamjacks, all social skill rolls suffer a −2 penalty due to his divided attention.

MARSHALING A STEAMJACK

A 'jack marshal can give simple verbal instructions to any steamjack he controls that is in his command range. Once the steamjack receives its instructions it follows them to the best of its abilities until it receives new instruction.

DRIVES

In addition to simply instructing the steamjacks he controls, a 'jack marshal can also drive them into action. A drive is a quick, verbal command that guides a steamjack in the execution of a specific action. A 'jack marshal can spend a quick action to drive any steamjack he controls that is currently in his command range. A steamjack can be affected by any number of drives simultaneously. A steamjack can be affected by the same drive only once per turn. All drives expire at the end of the turn.

Steamjacks that are bonded to a warcaster are not affected by drives.

Every 'jack marshal has the following drives:

- Boost Attack Roll – The steamjack can boost one attack roll during its turn this round.

- Boost Damage Roll – The steamjack can boost one damage roll during its turn this round.

- Charge – The steamjack can charge without spending a focus point this turn.

- Run – The steamjack can run without spending a focus point this turn.

There are a number of other drives available to 'jack marshals as separate abilities.

WARCASTERS, BONDS, AND THE BATTLEGROUP

A warcaster and the steamjacks he controls are collectively referred to as a battlegroup. The steamjacks in a battlegroup are mentally commanded by the warcaster. A warcaster can allocate focus points to steamjacks in his battlegroup and can channel spells through any steamjack with an arc node in his battlegroup. Steamjacks activate independently of the warcaster and take their turns in initiative order.

STEAMJACK BONDS

To add a steamjack to his battlegroup, a warcaster must mentally bond to it. Bonding requires a warcaster with an available bond slot (see the Bond ability, p. 158) to physically touch the steamjack and spend a full action bonding to it. The warcaster must also know the cortex's native language and the pass codes for its cortex locks.

A warcaster cannot bond to a steamjack bonded to another character.

While a 'jack is bonded to a warcaster, the warcaster is its only recognized controller; it ignores 'jack marshaled verbal commands. When the warcaster surrenders control of the 'jack by abandoning

PERSONALITY TRAITS

All steamjacks, whether bonded or not, develop unique quirks, affectations, and character traits over time. Steamjacks with higher grade cortexes develop positive personality traits faster than those with lower grades, and steamjacks with a lot of contact with 'jack marshals and warcasters develop even faster. Lower grade cortexes are more likely to develop quirks that interfere with their functions or at least require small efforts to compensate by their controller.

Example of personality quirks include: a 'jack that simmers with anger and takes a threatening posture with approaching strangers; an overprotective 'jack that is eager to leap to the defense of its controller or other allies; an easily distracted 'jack that pays too much attention to small shiny things or sudden movements despite more important things going on; an imitative 'jack that regularly picks up small bodily mannerisms from those around it, even those it just meets; a twitchy 'jack that eagerly points its ranged weapon or raises its melee weapon against otherwise innocuous individuals that happen to be nearby. Such quirks do not impact the steamjack's rules but can come up in play, particularly during social interactions.

Players controlling characters with steamjacks should discuss potential quirks with their Game Masters. Ideally every steamjack should have at least a relatively entertaining and interesting, if simple, personality. This can sometimes be defined in a single word or sentence such as: overly protective, sullen, clumsy when handling fragile things, or easily angered.

'Jacks manifest personality through non-verbal communications such as body movements, posture, and the use of certain primitive sounds such as venting steam from engines, clanks from fired pistons, and other signals. Other ways personality can manifest have to do with unusual requirements for obeying commands, such as a preference for unusually constructed sentences, orders needing to be shouted since the 'jack's hearing apparatus is faulty, or a 'jack that has trouble realizing when it has actually completed a given task. Personality traits should be used to add to a scene, to make the 'jack seem individual and distinct, rather than sabotaging players or the 'jack's controller in an important situation.

his bond, a 'jack marshal needs to reestablish command of it by presenting its verbal command codes as normal.

Bonded steamjacks are not affected by drives.

A warcaster can break his bond with a steamjack at will.

BACKLASH

When a warcaster dies or is knocked unconscious, the resulting psychic backlash has the effect of overloading and shutting down the cortexes of the steamjacks in his battlegroup. The steamjacks become inert and must be reactivated and have control established over them again before they can take any action.

Backlash also severs any bonds the warcaster had with the warjacks in his battlegroup.

ALLOCATING FOCUS POINTS

A warcaster can allocate focus points to steamjacks bonded to him during the Control Phase of his turn. A steamjack must be in the warcaster's control area (p. 231) to be allocated focus. It does not need to be in his line of sight. Based on its cortex, a steamjack can be allocated up to 3 focus points but can have no more than 3 focus points at any given time as a result of allocation. A steamjack can gain focus by means other than allocation without this limit, however.

A steamjack controlled by a focuser can spend focus points to perform the following:

- Boost Attack and Damage Rolls – A steamjack can spend focus points to boost attack and damage rolls. Each time a steamjack boosts an attack or damage roll, it must spend 1 focus point. Boosting must be declared before rolling any dice for the roll.

- Make an Additional Attack – A steamjack can spend focus to make additional melee or ranged attacks during its turn. The steamjack can make one additional attack for each focus point it spends.

- Make a Power Attack – A steamjack must spend 1 focus point to make a power attack. All steamjacks can make slam, head-butt, knockout strikes, grapples, and push power attacks. Heavy steamjacks can make trample power attacks. Steamjacks with at least one non-crippled weapon with the Open Fist weapon quality can make headlock/weapon lock and throw power attacks. Steamjacks with two non-crippled weapons with the Open Fist weapon quality can make double-hand throw power attacks.

- Shake – A steamjack can spend focus points to shake knockdown or stationary status. During the Control Phase after being allocated focus, if a steamjack is knocked down it can spend 1 focus point to stand up. During the Control Phase after being allocated focus, if a steamjack is stationary it can spend 1 focus point to cause the stationary status to expire.

Unless otherwise noted, a steamjack can spend focus points only during its controller's turn (or during its own turn if it is autonomous).

STEAMJACK DEVELOPMENT

Steamjacks are capable of learning and developing over time. Even those with the simplest cortexes eventually develop personality traits and can be trained like particularly smart animals. Steamjacks with more advanced cortexes begin developing personalities as soon as they are first activated, and pick up certain body posture habits from their handlers. Personality can also develop around certain hardware issues or a faulty part that is not immediately repaired as the 'jack learns to compensate. The process of personality development is accelerated for steamjacks that share a bond with a warcaster. These 'jacks are not only capable of learning, but their very cortexes are shaped by their connection to their warcaster in the form of imprints.

Each time a warcaster reaches a multiple of 25 experience points (at 25, 50, 75, 100, 125, and 150), the steamjacks that are currently bonded to him that possess either aurum- or arcanum-grade cortexes also experience advancement. The player can choose to have each steamjack either improve a combat skill or gain an imprint.

A steamjack that increases its combat skills or develops an imprint retains the improvement even if its bond to its warcaster is severed. These advancements are lost if the steamjack's cortex is ever wiped.

If a steamjack with an aurum- or arcanum-grade cortex has already gained an imprint and has advanced its combat skills as far as possible based on its cortex grade, the benefits of further advancement are lost.

IMPROVING COMBAT SKILLS

When a warcaster reaches a multiple of 25 experience points, he can choose to have each of the steamjacks currently bonded to him with aurum- or arcanum-grade cortexes improve their combat skills. When a steamjack gains this advancement, its controller can choose to have it improve its MAT or RAT by 1.

How far a steamjack can improve its combat skills depends on its cortex grade. A steamjack with an aurum-grade cortex can improve its MAT and RAT by 1 through advancement. A steamjack with an arcanum-grade cortex can improve its MAT and RAT by 2 through advancement.

IMPRINTS

When a warcaster reaches a multiple of 25 experience points, he can choose to have the steamjacks bonded to him with aurum- or arcanum-grade cortexes gain an imprint. The imprint represents a strengthening of the bond shared between the warcaster and his steamjack evolving over time, further shaping and developing the personality of the machine. This process awakens a steamjack's cortex, opens it more fully to its controlling warcaster, and imbues it with heightened self-awareness. As this connection grows stronger, the steamjack's nascent personality begins to take on traits acquired from its warcaster. In essence, the personality of the warcaster is imprinted on the steamjack's cortex.

A steamjack can gain an imprint only once and have only one imprint at any given time. If it loses its imprint, such as through having its cortex wiped, it can then gain another.

By the time a steamjack's cortex has been imprinted, its connection to its warcaster has grown so strong that the imprinted steamjack can now be allocated up to 4 focus points.

Imprinting affects each steamjack in a unique way. When an imprint is established, roll 2d6 and add the warcaster's ARC. Consult the Imprint Table below to determine the effects of the imprint. The warcaster's controller can choose to modify the result of the die roll by 1 (adding or subtracting) if he wishes.

IMPRINT TABLE

2D6 + ARC	RESULT
7 or less	**Dominator** – The steamjack lives for contests of strength against the greatest possible opponents so that it can continually prove its value to its warcaster. The steamjack can make power attacks without spending a focus point. Additionally, the steamjack gains +2 on melee damage rolls against other steamjacks and warbeasts.
8	**Highly Aggressive** – The steamjack is an aggressive, foul tempered machine that lives for battle. It stomps and snorts when kept from battle, and charges into combat at the slightest provocation. The steamjack gains Counter Charge. (When an enemy advances and ends its movement within 6″ of this steamjack and in its LOS, the steamjack can immediately charge it. If it does, it cannot make another counter charge that round. The steamjack cannot Counter Charge while engaged.)
9	**Berserker** – Its imprint forged in the heat of battle, the steamjack is a peerless killing machine. In combat the steamjack is a blur of motion, striking at anything that gets in its path, whether friend or foe. The steamjack's warcaster is the only potential target spared its berserk frenzy. When the steamjack destroys one or more models with a melee attack during its warcaster's turn, immediately after the attack is resolved it must make one additional melee attack against another model in its melee range other than its warcaster. During an activation that the steamjack charged, it cannot gain additional attacks from this imprint until its charge attack has been resolved.
10	**Enduring** – The steamjack has a determination that transcends its mechanical body. Refusing to fail its master under any circumstances, the defiant machine can hold itself together through sheer force of will. The steamjack does not suffer the effects of crippled systems. It still suffers the effects of catastrophic damage rolls and is still wrecked when all its damage boxes are marked.
11	**Frenetic** – The steamjack possesses inexhaustible reserves of energy and is constantly on the move. Seemingly unable to stand still, it follows its warcaster everywhere or else moves to investigate any interesting commotion on its own. In battle the steamjack moves constantly with a speed that belies its mechanical form. Additionally, each time the steamjack hits an enemy with a melee or ranged attack it can advance up to 2″.
12	**Hunter** – The steamjack possesses the spirit of a hunter and comes alive when stalking and destroying prey. Its arcane senses are well tuned and utterly dedicated to the hunt. Little escapes its attention and it constantly waits for the moment its warcaster unshackles its aggressive tendencies so that it can hunt down and destroy its master's enemies. As a downside, the steamjack perceives any unknown character as a potential threat that it is eager to attack until it can be convinced by its warcaster otherwise. The steamjack ignores forests, concealment, and cover when determining LOS or making a ranged attack.
13	**Vengeful** – Protective to a fault, the steamjack is prone to fits of righteous rage when those it identifies as friendly, especially its warcaster, are harmed. The steamjack is anxious and unsettled when its warcaster is not clearly safe in its field of vision. If one or more friendly characters were damaged or destroyed by enemy attacks while in the steamjack's LOS since its warcaster's last turn, at the start of the steamjack's activation it can make a full advance followed by one normal melee attack. This advance and attack are in addition to its normal movement and action during its turn.
14	**Sentinel** – The steamjack is inhumanly stoic and calm at all times. Aside from the smoke escaping its carefully stoked furnace, the steamjack could be mistaken for a statue. Beneath this façade, the steamjack is in a state of constant alert. The steamjack gains boosted PER and ranged attack rolls.
15	**Protective** – The steamjack is incredibly protective of its warcaster and is willing to get into harm's way to preserve its master. The steamjack seldom strays far from its warcaster. Once per round, when its warcaster is directly hit by a melee or ranged attack while within 2″ of the steamjack, the steamjack steps in front of the attack and can become the target of the attack and be automatically hit instead. The steamjack cannot step in front of an attack if it is incorporeal, knocked down, or stationary.
16	**Open Conduit** – The steamjack is an open vessel in constant contact with the will of the warcaster. The steamjack develops little personality of its own, but it acts in flawless concert with its master. As a result of this connection, when checking to see if the steamjack is in its warcaster's control area for focus allocation, double the area. Additionally, the warcaster can upkeep a spell on the steamjack without spending a focus point.
17+	**Battle Brothers** – The steamjack has not only adopted his warcaster's fighting style, he has learned to complement it. Additionally, the close link the warcaster and the 'jack share enable each to anticipate the moves and actions of the other. When making a melee attack targeting an enemy in the melee range of its warcaster, the steamjack gains +2 to melee attack and melee damage rolls. When making a melee attack targeting an enemy in the melee range of the steamjack, its warcaster gains +2 to melee attack and melee damage rolls.

FULL METAL FANTASY GAME MASTERING

The Iron Kingdoms are filled with dangers and mysteries that present unique opportunities and challenges for players and Game Masters alike. It falls to the Game Master to present this world and the rules of the game in a way that is entertaining and engaging to his players. Roleplaying groups are symbiotic in nature; the Game Master and players work in harmony through the game system to create a unique storytelling experience.

THE ROLE OF THE GAME MASTER

First and foremost, the Game Master's job is to tell a good story. The Game Master is the architect of the game, and whether it is filled with daring escapades and swashbuckling or skullduggery and intrigue, the Game Master directs the action. The Game Master draws the characters, settings, and rules together and forges them into a story starring the players in the group.

The Game Master chooses the locations in the Iron Kingdoms where he sets the game, and he scripts the story and populates it with characters. Throughout play, it falls upon the Game Master to describe the world and act as the eyes and ears of the players. He gives voice to all the supporting characters, and when the time comes, he guides the actions of antagonists both on and off the battlefield.

There are a few guidelines many good Game Masters follow when creating scenarios, plot hooks, non-player characters, and encounters that make up a great game. When you assume the role of Game Master, take heed of the following advice.

Do not compete against the players; play with them. At first glance, the game places you in the role of an antagonist who counters your players' every move. After all, you challenge them, set target numbers, pit villains and monsters against them, and weave all manner of machinations to keep their lives interesting. The players might even feel like you are sometimes their enemy, but you are definitely not out to get them!

If you have created a scenario, encounter, or event with the intent to "win" against the players, you are defeating the purpose of running a roleplaying game in the first place. How can you tell your story if you have wiped out all the main characters? If you make your players miserable because you're playing to beat them, they might begin to wonder why they're playing your game in the first place. On the other hand, a story without any challenges can grow dull. Nothing is sweeter for players than a victory pulled from the jaws of defeat, so provide your players with situations that challenge them but that they can overcome through teamwork and cunning.

Make the players the main characters of the story. Always keep in mind that your players are the focus of your story. The Iron Kingdoms are filled with powerful personalities that can overshadow the actions and intentions of your players. You should never make the players feel like they are irrelevant. A one-time rescue by a Cygnaran scouting party led by the famous warcaster Kara Sloan could be a thrilling encounter the players will love, but having Kara Sloan follow the characters around and eclipse their own heroics is far less endearing. Non-player characters, even those of the Game Master's own creation, should be used to highlight the player characters' actions, not the other way around.

Be fair and flexible in all things. You are not just the storyteller; you are also the arbitrator of rules disputes. You create scenarios in which the players have to think quickly—and perhaps in ways you had not considered. You need to set fair target numbers for skill rolls and come up with unique solutions for determining outcomes when the rules do not cover the player characters' actions. If those unpredictable actions help tell a great story and fits within the framework of the setting you have created, then be reasonable about letting these unique solutions succeed. Give the characters the chance to be the protagonists you want them to be. Being inflexible stifles player creativity, which is the very fuel of your ongoing story.

Be consistent. Try to be consistent when you adjudicate the rules. Sometimes you encounter a situation not easily resolved by the rules, and you need to use your own judgment in determining how best to resolve that situation. Your players appreciate it if they know you will uphold that ruling in the future. Once your players understand how you adjudicate the game they come to depend on your interpretation of the rules, so it can be frustrating for them if your rulings suddenly change.

PLAYER CHARACTERS

The Game Master should work closely with the players when they create their characters and should encourage them to discuss their characters openly. Teamwork and compatibility among the player characters in a party is essential to their survivability and success. The Game Master should not stifle players' creativity but should strive to tailor the stories to be challenging for the players by accounting for their strengths and weaknesses.

It is also a good idea to suggest the players use the rules for an adventuring company (p. 151) that suits the campaign. This gives players a little extra guidance and identity as a group as their characters take shape.

The type of campaign the Game Master intends to run and the themes he is interested in exploring can guide character creation as well. See "Campaigns," p. 336.

Starting characters in the *Iron Kingdoms Full Metal Fantasy Role Playing Game* are meant to represent individuals who have already proven themselves on the field of battle (or in the nuances of court intrigue, exploration of the wilds, in the dark back alleys of their city, and so on). Combating the threats of Cryxian raiders, duplicitous Cygnaran nobles, and treacherous sell-swords are not tasks for the meek and unprepared. Instead, player characters are intended to be confident masters of the basic tools of their trade, whether those are swords and pistols, cunning words, or alchemical reagents. They still have plenty of room to grow and new tricks to master, but they are ready for the challenging adventures that await them.

Some Game Masters prefer to run games with more experienced characters, increasing the threats, the scope of the story, and the potential rewards of success accordingly. If you are interested in such a campaign, start the player characters in your group with a number of experience points (XP). The amount of XP you allow your players to start with should be determined by the scale of the game you want to run. If you simply want to give your players some options for customization at the start of the game, start them off with 10 XP. If you want more seasoned characters in the player party, consider starting them off with 25 XP or more and up to 1,000 gold coins for extra gear and mechanika. Such options are not recommended for inexperienced players due to the increased time and complexity that goes into character creation.

On the other hand, you and your players might prefer to play with characters of even lower capability than the default character creation rules anticipate. There are a number of methods to generate greener characters. You can have characters start without any archetype abilities, gaining just the core feature of the archetype and picking up abilities later. You can have players select just one career for their characters at character creation instead of two. You can skip the "Increase Stats" step of character creation or reduce their starting gold. When building encounters, remember that the enemies presented in this book were not designed with the reduced capabilities of your player characters in mind.

As the Game Master, you challenge your players with threats and challenges appropriate to the abilities of their characters. Sometimes you want to present them with an overwhelming opponent to help drive your plot, but by and large, you should craft your campaign to assume your characters have a solid chance of success in their endeavors, provided they plan accordingly and do not rush in, quad-irons blazing, every time you offer them the chance to parley!

NON-PLAYER CHARACTERS (NPCS)

Non-player characters, or "NPCs" for short, are among the most important tools in the Game Master's toolkit. Every person or beast the player characters meet during their adventures is an NPC under the Game Master's control. From advising scholars to dangerous thugs and slavering monsters, the Game Master must approach the creation of his NPCs with an eye to how they will be used.

There are different methods of creating NPCs for your encounters, and the Game Master should choose the method best suited to the needs of that particular game or scenario. At times you want to create NPCs as fully realized and powerful as a player character, particularly when crafting archvillains or long-term allies for your scenarios. In these situations you can use **Comprehensive NPCs.** At other times, you need NPCs who use a few key abilities but not enough to justify the creation of a full character sheet. For these purposes, you should create **Single-Career NPCs.** When creating the enemies your players' characters meet in combat, you most often need **Battle NPCs.** Finally, you often need NPCs who represent the common people of the Iron Kingdoms: mechanics, merchants, and farmers. For these kinds of characters you most likely want to use **Simple NPCs.**

REWARDING FEAT POINTS

Feat points are the fuel that drives the steam engine of a combat encounter. Feat points grant player characters the edge they need to take on dangerous enemies. It is expected that, once engaged in combat, players will spend this resource rapidly to accomplish all manner of heroic feats, avoid lethal damage, and pass hard skill checks. Do not view feat points as a reward but rather as a resource that ebbs and flows with the tide of battle and should be distributed accordingly.

It is critical this supply of feat points is given out at a measured pace. Hand out too many feat points, and the battles can become trivial as player characters spend and regain their feat points too quickly for your encounter to challenge them. Offer too few opportunities to earn them, and players might not have the resources they need to deal with incoming damage or overcome their foes.

Game Masters should keep in mind the abilities and specialties of the players' characters. Though some characters have no problem surviving on the feat points earned through defeating enemies, other characters might find it difficult to earn those points despite contributing to the combat in less direct ways. Do not be afraid to offer feat points to these players for what they contribute to the team. Tactical advice or support from an Intellectual character to the frontline fighters that results in a success might generate a feat point for that character. A Wall of Fire that blocks a rampaging warbeast from slaughtering a family of innocents might be heroic enough to grant that spellcaster a feat point. Be generous with your players and give them the tools they need to be the heroes of your story and scenario.

NPCS AND FEAT POINTS

Some NPCs can gain and spend feat points like player characters. Unlike player characters, NPCs do not gain feat points based on critical successes or from incapacitating or destroying enemies. Instead, an NPC with feat points gains a set number every round, generally limited to 1 or 2. Unspent feat points should not accumulate. An NPC who gains 1 feat point each round can have only up to 1 feat point at any time. NPCs should start each combat encounter with their feat point allotment and replenish their feat points at the start of each of their turns.

NPCs can spend these points the same way player characters do.

COMPREHENSIVE NPCS

The most comprehensive way for a Game Master to construct an NPC is to follow the rules for building a player character. NPCs created in this way are starting-level heroes in the *Iron Kingdoms Full Metal Fantasy Roleplaying Game*. If a more experienced NPC is required, simply assign XP and use the advancement rules under "Player Characters," p. 155, to create a more seasoned character.

Once you have determined the NPC's starting stats, skills, abilities, and the rest, it is time to arm and equip the character. Using the NPC's careers' Starting Assets is a good jumping-off point, but you should feel free to tailor the NPC's gear to your concept of the character. If he is particularly poor or inexperienced, he has shabbier gear than if he were more successful and experienced. Truly powerful characters could have very high-end weapons and armor, possibly even mechanika devices. Keep in mind that whatever you supply your NPC with is likely to fall into the hands of your player characters, should their relationship with the NPC turn oppositional and violent.

The benefit of building comprehensive NPCs is that the Game Master knows their relevant stats, abilities, archetype benefits, careers, XP, and everything else that could possibly be needed during the adventure. The drawback of building comprehensive NPCs is the amount of time this sort of NPC generation takes.

A comprehensive NPC should be allotted at least 1 feat point each round. How many feat points the character is allotted depends on how powerful and pivotal the NPC is. Most comprehensive NPCs should be allotted only 1 feat point each round. Characters intended to be exceptionally powerful or substantial threats to the player characters could be allotted 2 or even 3 feat points each round.

Comprehensive NPCs are best used as adventuring companions who join the party for some period of time, important townsfolk with whom the player characters repeatedly interact, or recurring villains who require more detail than a handful of combat stats.

SINGLE-CAREER NPCS

A simpler way for a Game Master to construct an NPC is to follow the standard for character creation but choose just one career for the character instead of two. A Game Master can even forego giving a single-career NPC an archetype. If you want the NPC to be more skillful or experienced, feel free to issue the character some XP to advance him accordingly.

The gear possessed by a single-career NPC reflects his career's Starting Assets. As with the comprehensive NPC described above, the character's gear and weapons should reflect the concept of the character.

The benefit of building single-career NPCs is that such characters have nearly as much gameplay detail as comprehensive NPCs but require fewer choices during character creation since you choose only one direction for the character and flesh out that role. The drawback of building single-career NPCs is that they do not have the same room for growth as comprehensive NPCs.

Single-career NPCs can be allotted feat points each round, though seldom more than 1.

Single-career NPCs are best used as short-term adventuring companions who join the party, supporting role townsfolk, or villain lieutenants who need some detail but less character than their overlords.

BATTLE NPCS

Moving away from highly detailed NPC creation into more rapid-fire NPC generation techniques, battle NPCs give a Game Master a supporting cast of enemies without requiring the time commitment required to create complex characters. These NPCs are typically created to provide simple foes for the player characters to fight in combat encounters.

To make a battle NPC, select a race normally, but then abandon the standard character generation and advancement process. Battle NPCs do not have archetypes or careers. Instead, use the following chart for increasing the character's capabilities.

LEVEL	STAT ROLL CALCULATION
HERO	+ 1 to all stats (to a limit of Hero racial limits), level 2 in one military skill, and level 1 in all other military skills
VETERAN	+2 to all stats (to a limit of Veteran racial limits), level 3 in one military skill, and level 2 in all other military skills
EPIC	+3 to all stats (to a limit of Epic racial limits), level 4 in one military skill, and level 3 in all other military skills

Once the battle NPC's stats and skills are determined, select some basic arms and armor. Battle NPCs are typically used in groups, so feel free to experiment with arms and armor to lend some distinction to a band of highwaymen or mercenaries. Bear in mind that the player characters are likely to loot weapons and armor from the corpses of their defeated foes, so be sure not to equip battle NPCs with anything you do not want your players to have!

Battle NPCs are not generally allotted feat points.

The benefit of building battle NPCs is that the Game Master can quickly customize challenging enemies for his players to face. He can also pit the party against a greater number of battle

NPCs in a single encounter, since they have a naturally lower power level than other NPCs who have access to archetypes, archetype benefits, and career abilities.

The drawback of building battle NPCs is the limited scope of use they have. Battle NPCs are strictly supporting cast for combat encounters. They are best used to flesh out the numbers in an encounter with other enemies.

SIMPLE NPCS

Another way for a Game Master to construct an NPC is to apply a bare minimum of stats, skills, and abilities to accomplish a specific purpose. After all, you need to know very little about the shopkeep at the dry goods store beyond his Perception stat (to avoid thievery) and his Negotiation skill roll (to make deals). A common fisherman most likely requires little more than his Negotiation, Sailing, and Swimming skills.

Hero-level simple NPCs are of most common use to the Game Master, but even these NPCs can have Veteran or Epic status. A grizzled world-weary trencher who now sells firearms is likely to be a tougher salesman than a baker's young apprentice.

For stat rolls, use the following table:

LEVEL	STAT ROLL CALCULATION
HERO	Racial starting stat + 1
VETERAN	Racial Hero stat limit
EPIC	Racial Veteran stat limit

For skill rolls, use the following table for the most relevant skill rolls and the stat table (above) for skills that are not central to the character's role or occupation.

LEVEL	STAT ROLL CALCULATION
HERO	Racial starting stat + 2 for applicable occupational skills
VETERAN	Racial Hero stat limit + 3 for applicable occupational skills
EPIC	Racial Veteran stat limit + 4 for applicable occupational skills

Simple NPCs are not allotted feat points.

The benefit of building simple NPCs is that they can be generated extremely quickly and have all the information necessary for non-combat interaction. On the other hand, simple NPCs have minimal depth of character and are no use in combat situations. Should your players decide to engage in violence with simple NPCs, you might allow the party to be victorious automatically unless they are facing off with a crowd. Even a mob of farmers can be a deadly opponent for adventurers. In such situations the Game Master can give some impromptu combat skills to the simple NPCs, making them antagonist NPCs as described below, and improvise as best he can.

Simple NPCs are best used for the masses of non-combat characters found throughout western Immoren. Farmers, herders, craftsmen, miners, loggers, and merchants are common

throughout the land, but you do not need to build extensive NPC profiles for all of them.

MODIFIED ANTAGONIST NPCS

The final way for a Game Master to construct an NPC is to start with a pregenerated antagonist entry (see Appendix A: The Bestiary, p. 340) and make a few changes to suit the needs of his story. Altering an antagonist's weaponry or spell lists is one of the easiest changes to make, yet it can lend significant diversity to an encounter.

Creating a modified antagonist NPC is also a great way to turn a simple NPC into one with combat stats quickly. If trading with a simple NPC shopkeeper devolves into violence, just grab a roughly suitable enemy and add or subtract character abilities as needed to fit the character. It is better to keep things moving along than to take a five-minute break from the action to create an NPC shopkeeper for the player characters to shoot up.

Conversely, when an antagonist NPC is interrogated instead of killed or when players seek out a non-violent solution to an encounter, adding the skills and abilities of a simple NPC to an antagonist is a quick fix that keeps the game rolling.

ENCOUNTERS, SCENARIOS, AND CAMPAIGNS: THE BUILDING BLOCKS OF THE GAME

Before planning a game, the Game Master should consider its comprising elements. **Encounters** are like scenes in a movie and focus on combat, clandestine meetings, high-speed footraces across moving trains, or anything else the Game Master wants. A **scenario** is a story for the characters to play through, made up of a number of encounters. A scenario can be very short, encompassing a few encounters and taking a single play session to complete. Other scenarios can be quite long, requiring several sessions to play. When a number of scenarios are linked together, they become a longer, more fully realized story called a **campaign**.

ENCOUNTERS

Encounters are the lifeblood of a scenario. They are the points at which your characters interact with the story. Broadly speaking, there are two kinds of encounters: **combat encounters** and **narrative encounters**.

As you are plotting the story of your scenario, you come up with challenges for the characters to overcome. If you expect an encounter to be resolved through violence (an attack by cephalyx slavers or an opposing mercenary force, for example), that is a combat encounter. Encounters that can be resolved through diplomacy, negotiation, or investigation are narrative encounters. In some cases, an encounter could begin as a narrative encounter and end as a combat encounter, depending on the choices the characters make and the way the NPCs react to those choices.

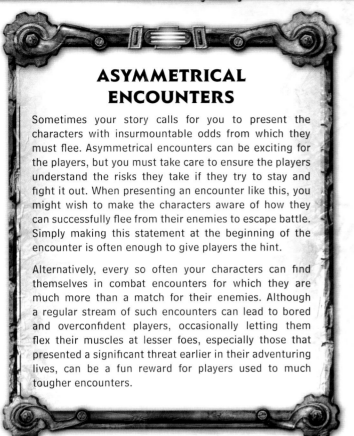

ASYMMETRICAL ENCOUNTERS

Sometimes your story calls for you to present the characters with insurmountable odds from which they must flee. Asymmetrical encounters can be exciting for the players, but you must take care to ensure the players understand the risks they take if they try to stay and fight it out. When presenting an encounter like this, you might wish to make the characters aware of how they can successfully flee from their enemies to escape battle. Simply making this statement at the beginning of the encounter is often enough to give players the hint.

Alternatively, every so often your characters can find themselves in combat encounters for which they are much more than a match for their enemies. Although a regular stream of such encounters can lead to bored and overconfident players, occasionally letting them flex their muscles at lesser foes, especially those that presented a significant threat earlier in their adventuring lives, can be a fun reward for players used to much tougher encounters.

Often you want to present combat encounters filled with adversaries that offer an equal challenge to the characters' capabilities. Every foe, monster, or antagonist in the game has an Encounter Point rating that allows you to tailor your fights accordingly (see "Combat Encounter Building," p. 333).

Be sure to pick foes that speak to the material of your scenario's story. If the story involves characters confronting a group of thugs in a dockside warehouse in Mercir, you probably shouldn't throw in a few dregg! Your players will appreciate that you're being consistent, not just with your rules but with the setting of the game. Small changes keep things interesting within the story you're telling. Instead of just sending human thugs, perhaps the gang's leaders have hired a down-on-his-luck arcanist to lend them some magical might, or one of the thugs has a caged burrow-mawg as a guard animal at his disposal.

Not every fight needs to be to the death, either. At your discretion as Game Master, some of the victims of combat might live long enough to breathe a few last words to give the characters important information, or fallen NPCs could miraculously survive the battle, having been knocked out or fallen unconscious as a result of wounds rather than actually being killed as a result of being incapacitated in battle. Situations like these allow the easy transition from a combat encounter to a narrative encounter.

Combat encounters serve to resolve situations that arise from narrative encounters. As you tell your story, be sure that your combat encounters make sense within that context and that the players are invested in the outcomes. If you can manage that, your story will be compelling and could lead into future scenarios.

NARRATIVE ENCOUNTERS

Essentially all interactions, plots, and planning the characters engage in outside of battle are narrative encounters. Narrative encounters are the heart and soul of the game, for it is here the characters meet and talk with your NPCs and give you the opportunity to describe the world of the Iron Kingdoms in detail.

Social and investigative skills, and the encounters involving them, are a crucial and integral part of the roleplaying experience. How characters interact with the world around them involves not only the skills the player characters possess but also the players' ability to articulate their characters' emotions and desires. Narrative encounters combine these two aspects to determine how successfully player characters interact with each other and NPCs to bring life to the setting.

Many, if not most, narrative encounters occur without a player ever rolling a die. Some narrative encounters ultimately hinge on the use of the characters' skills such as Negotiation or Intimidation, whereas others revolve around efforts at theft, scholarly research, or the detection of important clues. No matter the situation, as the Game Master you should not feel obligated to stick to straight die rolls every time. For example, a player who roleplays his negotiations particularly well should be rewarded with either an automatic success or a bonus on any rolls he makes related to that negotiation.

SOCIAL ENCOUNTERS

When a character uses a social skill, it is the Game Master's role to determine which stat best represents the character's use of that skill. The way the character chooses to leverage his skills in social interactions can dramatically change which stats he uses in order to achieve the desired result. For example, a character attempting a moving oratory to improve the morale of a group of locals could do so in several ways. The Game Master might decide that a character who speaks to the logic of their plan of attack rolls Intelligence when making his Oratory roll, whereas one who makes an impassioned speech using grand gestures, clasping the shoulders of his audience, and emphasizing his past victories with great confidence instead uses his Physique for the roll. Savvy and experienced players roleplay to their characters' strengths. Characters who depend on their strength of arms to intimidate their foes shouldn't expect much success making intricate threats if their Intelligence is very low.

The most important aspect of any social or narrative encounter is the act of roleplaying itself—players acting the roles of their characters believably and fulfilling their roles as the protagonists of the story.

INVESTIGATIVE ENCOUNTERS

Sometimes a scenario involves the uncovering of mysteries or other opportunities for the player characters to investigate hidden or obscure knowledge and locations. The mechanics of these encounters are largely covered by the use of skill checks, but their presentation is important, as are the results of success.

It can seem daunting to write a mystery for your characters to solve, but the basics are simple. Determine the nature of the hidden material and why the player characters are motivated to investigate it, then flesh out some possible ways they might proceed. Perhaps you wish to tell a story about a killer on the loose in the party's home city of Corvis. First, you'll need to figure out who the killer is and what his motivations are. Next, determine why he hasn't been caught yet by the city watch. Is someone in power protecting him? If so, why, and how does that NPC react to the player characters' investigations? Finally, you'll need to provide a plot hook to involve the characters. This could be anything from a cash reward posted by the city to the killer taking the life of a friend. You might wish to add an interesting twist to the killer. What if he's not just a brutal monster, but a former soldier being blackmailed by agents of a Thamarite cult (who are the real villains of your *next* scenario)? Characters investigating this kind of story might make heavy use of the Detection and Forensic Science skills, or even the Cryptography skill to break the code in the killer's journal and discover the name of his next intended victim. Player characters might find themselves embroiled in political intrigue where careful application of the Etiquette skill could grant them valuable information.

Other kinds of investigation can be more academic. Characters might find themselves investigating the bloody rites of the Tharn in preparation for a journey through territory held by those terrible cannibals. Use of the Research skill can help prepare them for that journey or even shed light on the purpose of a mysterious Tharn relic found in the course of their travels.

If player characters use skills like Lore to uncover knowledge about their foes, consider granting them and their allies bonuses in combat against those enemies. For example, if they expect to traverse the wastelands of the Bloodstone Marches and a player character uses his Lore skill to gain information about the environment and monstrous creatures of the region, it might be appropriate to grant him and his allies a +1 bonus on Survival skill checks in that region or even a bonus on damage rolls against certain creatures of that area. Naturally, some investigative encounters provide less tangible benefits. A character might need to make a successful Cryptography skill check to decipher an enemy communiqué before the party can attempt to intercept a raiding party described in that missive, for instance.

MISCELLANEOUS NARRATIVE ENCOUNTERS

Some kinds of encounters require the characters to engage in challenges that measure their physical prowess but are not related to combat. Characters might need to construct shelter via the Survival skill or attempt to avoid discovery with a Sneak roll while picking a pocket or committing burglary. These situations are highly varied but can be extremely important in designing a scenario and story. When constructing your scenario, keep in mind opportunities for the characters to become involved in their environment, whether that effort involves scaling walls or swimming across dangerous rapids.

COMBAT ENCOUNTERS

Combat encounters occur when player characters face off against their enemies. These encounters could be initiated as an ambush or a headlong attack or as the result of a standoff. In some cases, a narrative encounter evolves into a combat encounter when one character issues a threat to another or when one character simply attacks another.

Most combat encounters begin when the Game Master calls for initiative at the start of a battle. If one group of characters attempts to get the drop on another group of characters, the combat encounter begins with a surprise round (p. 201).

Generally the Game Master plans out a number of combat encounters as part of his scenarios. In preparation for running these encounters, the Game Master should draw simple maps of the area that characters typically fight on and have them ready for when fighting begins. When the shooting starts, the Game Master can pull out the map and place models on it that represent both the player characters and the NPCs taking part in the battle.

COMBAT ENCOUNTER BUILDING

As with any other element of a roleplaying game, the composition and difficulty of an adventure's encounters are up to the Game Master. Each battle can be a harrowing, life-threatening ordeal or just a minor speed bump on the road of adventure. The specific NPCs and player characters involved, as well as the type of adventure or campaign you are running, should inform the types of encounters you create and their level of difficulty. Below is a three-step process that outlines how to build balanced threats for a player character party. Each pre-generated NPC antagonist in Appendix A: Bestiary (p. 340) has an Encounter Point (EP) value assigned you will use to determine how many of a given creature type you can throw at your players. Do not hesitate to deviate from the official encounter-building process to suit your own games!

Some encounters do not require these guidelines for encounter creation. If a player character initiates an unexpected brawl with an aging stable hand, or if an entire kompany of Khadoran soldiers are camped over the next ridge, you do not need to determine Encounter Points for the battle; your player has done that for you. But when you intend the player character to go toe-to-toe with enemies in a challenging (yet not insurmountable) combat, the following guidelines can assist you in designing the encounter.

MAP DESIGN

Do not worry if your map isn't a work of art. Just make sure it has terrain, buildings, and cover drawn in a clear manner. You should be sure of where you place these features as moving them once combat begins can be confusing and unfair to the players.

Step 1: Tally the number of player characters in the party and determine their average XP. Add the number of steamjacks in the party to the number of player characters, then consult the chart below to determine the base quantity of EPs you have to build the combat encounter.

PLAYER CHARACTERS' XP	NUMBER OF CHARACTERS IN THE PARTY					
	3	4	5	6	7	8+
0–10	12	28	35	42	49	56
10–20	24	32	40	48	56	64
20–35	27	26	45	54	63	72
35–50	30	40	50	60	70	80
50–75	36	48	60	72	84	96
75–100	42	56	70	84	98	112
> 100	> 42	> 56	> 70	> 84	> 98	> 112

Step 2: Adjust the quantity of EPs based on the following factors.

When designing the encounter, consider its context. Is the encounter a brief fight intended as a prologue to your real story, a standard battle in the course of the adventure, or the climactic finish to a scenario or campaign? Warm-ups should use substantially fewer EPs (up to 40% fewer) while climactic finishes should use more (up to 40% more).

You should also consider how many encounters are included in the game session. Characters start out healthy, with intact steamjacks and plenty of feat points and ammunition, but how much of their resources will they have remaining at the start of the encounter in question? If you are planning just a single encounter for a game session, you can amp up the difficulty quite a bit without killing everyone, but if you're planning for multiple battles, each individual combat needs to be substantially less vigorous.

Next, are there environmental factors to consider? Will the party be ambushed or get the drop on their foes? Does either side have a substantial advantage in terms of cover or elevation? This factor is the most wildly variable element, since the setup for an encounter can range from being attacked by flying enemies while scaling a cliff wall to shooting unwitting thugs in a warehouse. You should feel free to alter the EPs substantially to account for environmental considerations—but take care not to go overboard.

Is the party geared toward investigation and social interaction with a just a bit of military training and equipment? If so, adjust the EP amount for the encounter to be significantly less difficult than the encounter table recommends (up to 40% fewer EPs). On the other hand, if the party is optimized for destruction, amp up the difficulty of combat encounters to better suit the game at hand (up to 40% more EPs).

Last but not least, is the party kitted out in the best equipment gold can buy, or are they barely scraping to get by and counting every last bullet? Both options have their place in the setting, but this element can greatly impact the balance of an encounter and should be factored into encounter construction as well (up to a 20% variance in EPs, based on increased or decreased equipment availability). Steamjacks should not be considered equipment, because they are added to character count and are therefore already factored into the EP quantity.

Step 3: Once you have your EP budget all sorted out, choose some antagonists for the player characters to face. Appendix A: The Beastiary (p. 340) lists the profiles of several antagonists, including their EP cost. Do not worry about sticking strictly to your EP total for encounter—a few points more or less will not have a major influence on the encounter. Simply add the enemies that fit your concept for the encounter until roughly hitting that EP amount.

NPCS AS ENEMIES

Not all encounters require hulking monsters or packs of wild animals. NPC encounters afford the Game Master a wide degree of customization in encounter building.

The rules for creating NPCs that begin on p. 328 do not include EP values for these foes. It might be tempting to simply pit four comprehensive NPCs against four player characters, but that is as likely to lead to a total party kill as it is to the players defeating their adversaries. Instead, use the chart below as a general guideline for NPC EP values.

When creating NPCs for a combat encounter, remember to consider the NPCs' equipment as potential player character loot. Repeated use of overly well-equipped NPC encounters can lead to steadily increasing player character power.

On the other hand, feel free to discount your NPCs' EP cost if they are particularly poorly equipped. A comprehensive NPC with leather armor and a club isn't a major threat to a well-equipped player character.

ENCOUNTER POINTS FOR NON-PLAYER CHARACTERS

	NPC TYPE			
NPC XP LEVEL	**COMPREHENSIVE**	**SINGLE-CAREER**	**BATTLE**	**ANTAGONIST**
STARTING	14	10	5	See profile.
HERO	18	14	5	See profile.
VETERAN	23	18	7	See profile.
EPIC	28	23	9	See profile.

SCENARIOS

A scenario is the basic story unit of gameplay. A scenario can often be completed in a single play session, which usually comprises a full afternoon or evening spent playing the game. Some scenarios can be extended over multiple game sessions. Before you plot out the specific challenges the players face within the scenario, you should consider the overall story of that scenario. What nation or city are the characters exploring? What kinds of people do they meet? Will the characters face violent combat against their enemies or will they need to take a subtler route to victory? Are they hired to complete a job for an employer, or are they caught up in a situation that explodes around them? Naturally, these kinds of questions are nearly endless, but thinking about those situations gives you some good starting points as you begin to craft your scenario.

The Iron Kingdoms provide nearly limitless opportunities for different kinds of stories, and as Game Master, you might feel overwhelmed. You do not need to touch on every aspect of the Iron Kingdoms. Focus on a few ideas or themes of interest to you and your players. You might want to set your scenario amid the cramped streets of a major city like Caspia, where your story focuses on back-alley dealings, labor unions, and the crafting of mechanika. Alternatively, you might be more interested in telling a tale of exploration far from the safety of cities, stories in which the characters must journey through the harrowing wilderness of western Immoren. Or perhaps you'd prefer to set your stories on the battlefields where the nations of the Iron Kingdoms settle their disputes. Any of these ideas could be the seed for a great scenario involving combat, subterfuge, or the logistics of supply and travel. It is up to you to choose the elements most important to your story and build the scenario around them.

Once you know the broad strokes of the kind of story you want to tell (combat, intrigue, exploration, or other theme), you can begin plotting the major points. You likely already have some ideas, but taking at least a few notes on the important plot points helps you craft a compelling tale for your players. At the very least, you should know how your story begins, how the characters become involved, and how the story might end. Knowing the beginning and climax is already half the work, but you need to consider the events that occur between those points, and possibly what happens after the story's climax.

Those events in the middle are open to a great deal of interpretation, especially if the players react to the events in an unexpected way. Be ready to move your plot points around, change the order in which they are presented, or even drop elements of the story if the players come up with a course of action you did not anticipate. Do not punish your players for going off-course or force them back on track with your story. Much of the fun of a roleplaying game comes from the unfolding of events and how the characters react to them.

When creating scenarios, it is also worth considering the characters in the party. Though some characters are more combat-focused and others are more socially oriented, you should take care to make sure every character has the chance to meaningfully take part in the story as it unfolds. This makes it as important for you to give your players insight into the style of game you want to run as it is for you to tailor the stories, scenarios, and encounters to the characters in your party.

With your story plotted, you can begin working out the details of how the scenario actually plays out.

SCENARIO SETTINGS

Western Immoren is a big place, and the Game Master is advised to read over "Life in the Iron Kingdoms" (p. 50) before beginning to design his stories and scenarios. Once you know what part of the Iron Kingdoms you wish to explore you can begin to focus on the gritty details of those places.

URBAN SETTINGS

The modern city is one of the most important and iconic elements of the Iron Kingdoms. Many scenarios can be placed within the context of a city, and stories gain a great deal of detail from that setting. Each city is a unique location influenced by its parent nation, its neighbors, its borders, and the different races that call it home. Almost any kind of scenario in the Iron Kingdoms can feature cities heavily, and the smoke-belching factories, cramped streets, and industrialized way of life there make for compelling details and backdrops for the stories you and your players tell. Many characters rely on mechanikal devices or even steamjacks, and scenarios set in urban centers allow them to easily refuel and support their treasured arms and armor. Alchemists and arcanists benefit from easy access to labs and libraries, and cities offer plentiful dubious dealings, whether criminal or political, for more social characters to tackle.

MILITARY BASE

The present day is a time of tense ceasefire and strained relations between the powers of western Immoren. Wary of the brittle peace, the different nations' military forces look at one another from border fortresses and forward-fire bases, fingers on triggers. Characters might find themselves among the forward positions of the standing armies of the Iron Kingdoms and be enlisted in service to one nation or another, perhaps as spies or saboteurs. Other characters might be mercenaries in search of contracts. Military bases are often in need of supply, and some merchant companies deem the profits worth the risks of running caravans and supply trains, many of which hire adventurers to provide an armed escort.

BATTLEFIELD

Throughout its long history, the battlefields of western Immoren have been littered with the bodies of countless inhabitants who have perished in the name of gods and nations. Though a fragile peace exists, skirmishes are regular occurrences on the borders between nations, particularly along the Black River that separates Cygnar and Khador as well as along the rugged Ordic border. Swords ring out against steel armor, and guns roar as man and warjack clash in ruthless combat.

Battlefields, recent or ancient, can provide compelling events for adventurers. Some might be enlisted on one side or another of a conflict and find themselves caught up in the unforgiving battles of the Iron Kingdoms. Others might even seek out such fights, hoping to win glory and fame—or even just simple coin, for those of more mercenary inclination. Warcasters are the peerless masters of the battlefield, and a warcaster and his supporting troops can make for compelling adventuring parties.

But there are rewards to be had even after the battle is over. Those willing to risk treacherous no-man's-lands can find a small fortune in salvage awaiting them. Others might be motivated to find their wounded comrades left behind or to find wounded enemies to take for ransom.

RUINS

Over the millennia empires have risen to greatness, building mighty works that outlasted their societies. In the course of time the priest-kings built their walls, the warlords constructed their fortresses, and the dark empires of Morrdh and the Orgoth left their mark in the ruined stones that lie long-forgotten across the face of western Immoren.

Adventurers deliberately seek out these ruins in search of rarefied lore or items of power lost to time. Others might be forced to take refuge from pursuers or the elements in obscure and ruined temples or vaults. Ancient ruins are most often left abandoned for a reason, though. In addition to housing treasures and forbidden lore, those sites might be guarded by ancient watchers, spirits, or even monstrous creatures. Some ruins contain hidden passages that connect with caves and tunnel systems, leading to darker places in the earth.

THE WILDS

There are many reasons for characters to end up the wilds. They might find themselves fleeing authorities, for example, and have little recourse but to take their chances in the hinterlands. If they are poorly prepared, the environment itself presents a challenge—to say nothing of territorial satyrs, hungering Tharn tribes, and secretive cults. Other adventurers venture into these unforgiving regions with a particular goal. An entire campaign could be built around a group of characters taming a small region and founding a safehold, for instance, either out of personal necessity or in the employ of a patron.

Some explorers might be in search of obscure items and experiences. Major universities in Cygnar and Ord regularly sponsor expeditions tasked with collecting zoological or archaeological specimens and artifacts. Although these goals are seemingly mundane, the complications encountered by irate trollkin kriels or inconveniently placed Tharn villages can make for compelling adventures. Even more so if the adventurers signed on to collect a still-living specimen of a particularly intractable species!

CAMPAIGNS

Put simply, when the story you told in one scenario is continued by the same player characters in a subsequent scenario, it has become a campaign. Campaign play can be one of the most rewarding ways to game in the Iron Kingdoms, since it allows the players to see their characters gain experience and develop over time as they confront long-term nemeses and ultimately engage them in a final conflict after many game sessions of ups and downs.

As the Game Master, the first thing you need to do is determine the sort of campaign you want to run for your players and how involved you want it to be. Your campaign could be very structured, following the rise and fall of important NPCs as you tell your overarching story in the form of linked serialized scenarios, or your campaign could be simpler and more free-form, simply tracking the lives of your players' characters as they play through stand-alone scenarios with few continuous links and little overarching structure.

However you choose to run your campaign, you should give your players a solid indication of what they can expect from the campaign so they can create characters accordingly.

Some Game Masters choose to take a more interactive approach to their campaigns by soliciting their players for feedback before getting too deep in the creation of the campaign. If a Game Master wants to tell tales of swashbuckling pirates on the Broken Coast but some of your players are more interested in a military campaign, the group might enjoy a campaign in which the player characters take on the role of privateers hunting down pirates and protect the shipping interests of the Ordic Crown. The best campaigns are ones in which the players as well as the Game Master feel invested.

Just as with a scenario, the Game Master should plot out his campaigns with a beginning, a middle, and (usually) an end. Each scenario becomes a chapter in the ongoing story and creates rising tension through the challenges the player characters confront. As the Game Master crafts each scenario, he should consider how it continues the themes and events set up in previous scenarios and how it ties into the following ones. If in one scenario the characters were ambushed aboard a train on a remote stretch of rail, the next scenario could require the characters to begin to make their way to civilization on foot. During their travel they could encounter farrow and learn a farrow warlord has set his tribe to assault another train in the coming days. This provides a hook for a third climactic scenario, in which the characters must race against time to confront the farrow before they can enact their scheme.

A Game Master might wish to present the world of the Iron Kingdoms as a "sandbox" for his players to play in, heavily improvising the events as they go. This sort of campaign is less focused, at least initially, but as the player characters take action, the consequences of those actions provide the framework of a story for the Game Master to use in shaping his campaign. A sandbox campaign requires a great deal of improvisation on the part of the Game Master, but many groups find this a very satisfying way to play.

Depending on the sort of campaign the Game Master decides to run, he might wish to guide his players through character creation to some extent. Some careers and races could clash with the envisioned campaign. For example, if a Game Master intends to run a campaign focusing on crusading knights of the Church of Morrow, a trollkin fell caller would be out of place. As the individual responsible for both running the game and ensuring its continuity, the Game Master has the right not to allow characters who clash with his concepts. He should explain his concerns to his players and work with them to create characters who fit into the Game Master's concept for the campaign and are still enjoyable to portray. It's important for this conversation to go both ways; a Game Master might even allow an oddly fitting character he initially rejected if an innovative player comes up with an intriguing pretext for the character's inclusion.

Adventuring companies (see p. 151) can be an excellent tool for a Game Master seeking to inform his players about the sort of campaign he intends to run and the sorts of characters most appropriate for the campaign.

CAMPAIGN CONCEPTS

The "Life in the Iron Kingdoms" chapter of this book contains the seeds for many kinds of stories and campaigns. The options for adventure can seem overwhelming, but the Iron Kingdoms are especially fertile ground for certain campaign concepts. In most cases, these campaign concepts focus on small, tight-knit groups of characters, since that dynamic provides more freedom and opportunity for adventure than groups of characters who answer to large organized forces such as military regiments and the like.

The Game Master should not feel limited in choosing from the following concepts; they are starting points, not hard-and-fast rules for structuring a campaign.

MERCENARY LIFE

The possibilities of a campaign themed around a mercenary company are nearly endless. Characters can begin play as members of a venerable company such as the Shields of Durant, or instead set out to found their own charter and work to have it recognized by the major powers of the Iron Kingdoms.

For the Game Master, mercenary-themed campaigns offer excellent opportunities for a variety of adventures. The characters can take contracts that become considerably more complex than they expected and create consequences with future employers. More important, the variety of missions helps keep an ongoing campaign fresh. Mercenaries are hired to achieve objectives that would be otherwise impossible for their employers and can range from supporting military units to finding personnel and equipment lost behind enemy lines. Other adventures could focus on intelligence gathering, espionage, and reconnaissance. A major benefit to a mercenary campaign is that it allows the Game Master to explore material appropriate to military efforts without forcing the characters to be permanently beholden to an official chain of command.

A group of mercenaries might compete for lucrative contracts, and a canny Game Master should consider creating a group of rival mercenaries to act as foils to the player characters. These rivals can grow in power and reputation to parallel that of the player characters, allowing the Game Master to have ongoing and power-appropriate antagonists for the duration of his campaign. An interesting climax to this sort of campaign would be to ultimately place the characters opposite from their competitors in a battle, allowing them the opportunity to settle with their rivals once and for all.

URBAN CAMPAIGNS

The exploits of criminals, the unraveling of larcenous mysteries, and the travails of life on the mean streets of cities are strong material on which to found an urban campaign. Perhaps the characters are members of the city watch. Over the course of play they must confound the schemes of the criminal underworld, beginning with the crimes of petty thugs at the start of the campaign and eventually revealing sprawling criminal conspiracies that reach into the upper levels of society. A criminal mastermind can make an excellent archvillain, since the players might not be immediately aware of who pulls the strings of their foes from scenario to scenario. The characters might even face the threat of internal corruption from compromised colleagues within the watch. Alternatively, the characters might be the criminals. Perhaps they are a lowly gang looking to make a name for themselves and they combat not only the forces of law and order, but also contend with rival gangs.

The forces of industry can also provide inspiration for interesting campaigns. The characters might represent a merchant company looking to take its place as a financial power. The machinations of trade, the demands of unions, and political considerations all conspire to present the characters with serious challenges. Depending on the nation in which your campaign is set, the particular needs of war efforts are significant factors that spur adventure and intrigue.

Of course, no major city in the Iron Kingdoms is without its own political manipulations. Feudal lords, military commanders, and private merchant concerns struggle endlessly for wealth and control, and the unwary can easily be caught up as pawns in the machinations. The intrigues of the rich and powerful result in opportunities for characters who wish to take their own places among the halls of power. A truly expansive urban campaign could easily incorporate elements of crime, politics, and industry, though the Game Master should exercise care in interweaving these themes.

WILDERNESS EXPLORATION

The wilds of western Immoren are vast, and there are trackless wastes where none have gone and returned to tell the tale. Characters might be hired to explore a specific region for a merchant interest, a military agency, or an individual with unique motives. Forgotten ruins litter the wilderness and can sometimes even be found in the hidden depths beneath modern cities. Adventurers brave enough to risk the ancient guardians of the Orgoth or the fell empire of Morrdh gain much for their peril.

Not all exploration takes place on land. The high seas of the Meredius are a wilderness larger and less explored than any region of western Immoren. Campaigns built around characters as pirates, privateers, or merchant explorers can easily be focused on lengthy sea voyages to exotic Zu or the distant subcontinent of Alchiere. Just keep in mind that extended journeys mean the characters must carefully manage their rations and ammunition.

TOMB RAIDERS

The forgotten ruins of western Immoren hold treasure and peril in equal measure. The potential for characters to spend an entire campaign exploring the remnants of lost civilizations is tremendous. An especially large complex of ruins, such as a vast city of the empire of Morrdh found in the Gnarls, could be the focus of an entire campaign. Characters begin by researching what little is known of the ruin and discovering the possibility

of priceless occult lore and ancient coin. They must next prepare for their journey, which could require exploration and nearly make up a campaign in its own right. Upon arrival, depending on the nature of the characters, they might choose to survey the ruins as part of a scholarly expedition or instead plunge into its depths with swords and magelock pistols at the ready.

As the characters explore the ruins, they could find hidden secrets that lure them deeper into the catacombs or send them on a wild chase to far-flung places in search of related secrets. The overarching plot of the campaign could revolve around an ancient evil let loose by the characters in their meddling or even place them in competition with a rival team of tomb robbers for a priceless relic.

CLOAK AND DAGGER

The intrigues of royal courts, religious power, and military espionage can make fertile ground for a campaign. This sort of game play requires players interested in playing characters who rarely raise a fist in anger, instead relying on their wits and diplomacy for success.

Characters in the employ of aristocrats or powerful merchant princes such as the Khadoran kayazy find themselves embroiled in all manner of schemes. A campaign could begin with the characters hired to spy upon a rival of their aristocratic patron, only to find themselves betrayed in the act. The characters could be forced to flee for their lives to another city and then attempt to learn why their powerful backer sold them out. Over the course of many sessions their patron's schemes become known to them through spying, intimidation, the theft of crucial documents, and perhaps even some uncouth thuggery. Eventually the characters gain enough leverage to

either confront their betrayer directly or perhaps set him up for a lethal failure of his own, assuring his ruin at court—if not his execution as a traitor.

The uncovering of military secrets can also be a powerful motivation for characters who act out of duty, patriotism, or the promise of coin. This sort of campaign likely sees the characters infiltrating the cities and facilities of an enemy nation, and certain skills are likely to be invaluable, such as Sneak, Disguise, and Forgery as they cross hostile borders and Interrogation as they seek secret information. Characters might have to endure scenarios of protracted journey and then devise a way into a heavily guarded military base. Once inside, the heist begins as the characters evade capture, acquire the mechanikal plans or devices they seek, and then make their way back to the safety of their own nation, almost certainly with the enemy in pursuit.

TOOLS OF THE TRADE

A Game Master can use a wide variety of tools to help players visualize exactly what is happening in the narrative he is describing, especially during combat. The most common are models, maps, and even three-dimensional terrain (for motivated Game Masters). These tools become critical when characters are engaged in combat or are in an encounter that requires working within a defined space in the game. The rules for combat support the use of maps and models, and many Game Masters will find using them to be a great deal easier than trying to orchestrate the action solely in the imaginations of their players.

If a Game Master uses models to represent characters during play, each character must be represented by a model with the appropriate base size. It will take a variety of models with different base sizes to represent the various NPCs in a particular adventure. Players are encouraged to choose models of appropriate likenesses to their characters. The models on the table do not need to correspond directly to the characters they stand for as long as the Game Master and players understand what they represent. Nevertheless, the more closely the models match the characters in the game, the more immersive and enjoyable the play experience will be. Privateer Press models can be found in gaming shops and online, and models from the WARMACHINE and HORDES tabletop miniatures games are well suited to the roleplaying game.

If a Game Master intends to use models to resolve combat encounters, he also needs a play surface for them. This is simply an area of the table where the actions, events, and locality being described are represented. Large white boards and maps drawn on butcher paper are the most commonly used play surfaces, but any surface with enough room for all the models representing the characters involved in the encounter will do. A Game Master who plays games like WARMACHINE and HORDES might already have access to terrain he can use to detail the play surface. We encourage Game Masters to experiment with different approaches to representing combat encounters to find a version that works best for their games.

A Game Master drawing his own maps might also consider using different colors of markers to distinguish certain map details, such as green for trees or brown for wooden buildings. Such color-coding makes the map features easier for players to identify at a glance.

When preparing the play surface, the Game Master should attempt to include all pertinent information his players might need when making decisions for their characters. For example, if there is a small river dividing the play field in half, it should be represented on the play surface. If there are tactically important interactive elements such as differences in elevation or pieces of cover, they need to appear on the play surface. The Game Master should be as detailed as he can to bring his encounters to life in the imaginations of the players. Game Masters who develop and use symbols in their mapmaking should be careful to make sure their players understand the key to the maps used in their games. Keep in mind that the map does not need to be drawn at a professional skill level or contain an exacting level of detail in order to be useful. Any map that is clear and includes the information players are most likely to need about the geography around them will serve its purpose effectively.

When utilizing models for an encounter, the Game Master places the player models and NPC models where he imagines them standing when the encounter begins. He should be prepared to work with the players to determine their position at the start of the encounter, since what they imagine could be different than what he has in mind. As characters move and act, the Game Master and players move their models on the map. When performing any actions involving distances, such as movement or firing at an opponent, use a measuring tape to ensure the distances reflect the character's capabilities. When moving, measure the distance the character intends to move and then move the model. Measure the reach of a model's melee attack if there is any question about the distance based on the positions of the attacking character and his enemy. In this way, the Game Master can use the play surface as an active display for the characters in the game as well as a tool to determine possibilities and reconcile uncertainties.

PLAYING WITHOUT MODELS

Although the *Iron Kingdoms Full Metal Fantasy Roleplaying Game* is designed to be played with models and a play surface, with a little adjustment it can be played without them. The ranges in this book are given in feet as well as tabletop-friendly inches so that players choosing to play without a play surface have an easy frame of reference when imagining the encounter. Game Masters must take great care to describe the encounter in detail and then keep that description consistent so all the players share a universal understanding of what they are supposed to be imagining.

In deciding whether to play without models and a play surface, remember that some concepts, such as AOEs and spray attacks, are much easier to represent on the tabletop than to picture mentally. These concepts require an exercise in abstract thought to resolve them in a game run without models.

APPENDIX A: BESTIARY

The Iron Kingdoms are full of marvelous and terrifying creatures. Here we present a few to set against the player characters.

ANATOMY OF AN ANTAGONIST

Antagonists are pregenerated NPC threats for player characters. They include farrow brigands, human thugs, and wild monsters. Each antagonist entry includes a brief description of the antagonist's race or species as well as a description of the varying types of that enemy.

Stat Profile: Each antagonist entry has one or more stat profiles. These profiles represent different stages of development, skill sets, or degrees of experience. Antagonist stat profiles include both stats used by player characters and a few stats used only by antagonists.

SPD, STR, MAT, RAT, DEF, ARM, Willpower, and Initiative are used by antagonists in the same way as they are used by player characters. Antagonists also have Detection and Sneak stats. These stats represent the antagonist's combined skill level and stat total.

When you need to determine an antagonist's PHY, use its STR instead. When you need to determine an antagonist's PRW, use its MAT instead.

Weapon: The antagonist's typical weaponry is listed after its stat profile. If an antagonist has both melee and ranged weapons, it must choose to attack with one or the other during the Activation Phase of its turn.

Abilities: This section lists the antagonist's abilities.

Arcane: This is the ARC stat for antagonists that can cast spells.

Vitality: Most antagonists simply have an amount of damage points they can suffer before being disabled. More powerful or important antagonists have full life spirals.

Base Size: Recommended base size this enemy should have when a Game Master uses models to resolve encounters. Small bases are 30 mm in diameter, medium bases are 40 mm, and large bases are 50 mm.

Encounter Points: This section gives the EP cost of the enemy. See "Combat Encounter Building" (p. 333) to determine how many EPs you should spend on a specific combat encounter.

Loot: This section lists any items or valuables commonly found on this enemy.

Lore: This section gives the Game Master some information about this enemy. Player characters with the appropriate Lore skill can also learn this information with a successful Lore skill.

BURROW-MAWG

Burrow-mawgs are vicious badger-sized creatures with a ravenous hunger for flesh. They have very acute hearing and a powerful sense of smell. When a member of a pack scents a potential meal, it signals with a piercing squeal. A few burrow-mawgs can easily dispatch a sheep or wild dog, but a large enough (or hungry enough) pack can slaughter deer, bulls, or even armed men.

Each pack typically has a single alpha, but multiple packs come together to hunt during particularly lean seasons. With multiple alphas leading the charge, a pack becomes truly fearsome and quickly forces nearby towns to deal with their savagery.

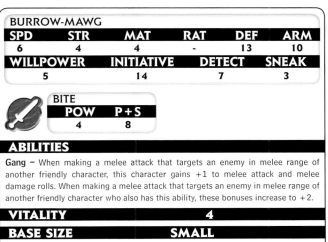

BURROW-MAWG

SPD	STR	MAT	RAT	DEF	ARM
6	4	4	-	13	10

WILLPOWER	INITIATIVE	DETECT	SNEAK
5	14	7	3

BITE

POW	P+S
4	8

ABILITIES

Gang – When making a melee attack that targets an enemy in melee range of another friendly character, this character gains +1 to melee attack and melee damage rolls. When making a melee attack that targets an enemy in melee range of another friendly character who also has this ability, these bonuses increase to +2.

VITALITY	4
BASE SIZE	SMALL
ENCOUNTER POINTS	2

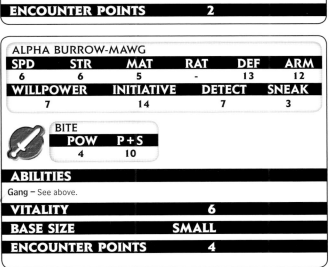

ALPHA BURROW-MAWG

SPD	STR	MAT	RAT	DEF	ARM
6	6	5	-	13	12

WILLPOWER	INITIATIVE	DETECT	SNEAK
7	14	7	3

BITE

POW	P+S
4	10

ABILITIES

Gang – See above.

VITALITY	6
BASE SIZE	SMALL
ENCOUNTER POINTS	4

Loot: Burrow-mawgs are indiscriminant when it comes to devouring their prey. There is a chance that coins or small jewelry are lodged in their digestive tracts, or can be found where the creatures make their dens.

Burrow-mawg adrenal glands are prized by alchemists. A Medicine or Alchemy skill roll with a target number of 10 is necessary to successfully remove the glands.

Lore: Burrow-mawgs have extremely sensitive noses and can smell prey over large distances. When they scent prey, they call the pack with a signal squeal.

Burrow-mawg adrenal glands are used in the creation of some alchemical compounds.

DREGG

Dregg are a wretched race of humanoids that live underground, coming out at night to raid and pillage. They are extremely sensitive to sunlight and rarely venture out of their lairs during the day. They revel in pain, even their own, fighting harder if they are wounded.

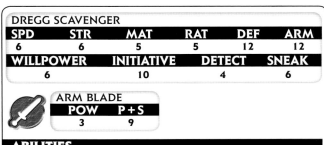

DREGG SCAVENGER

SPD	STR	MAT	RAT	DEF	ARM
6	6	5	5	12	12

WILLPOWER	INITIATIVE	DETECT	SNEAK
6	10	4	6

ARM BLADE

POW	P+S
3	9

ABILITIES

Light Sensitive – If the dregg ends its turn in bright light it suffers 1 point of damage.

Night Vision – The dregg treats darkness as dim light, and dim light as bright light.

Pain Fueled – While the dregg has one or more marked vitality points, it gains +2 on its melee attack and melee damage rolls.

Scavenged Weapons – There is a chance the dregg has stolen weapons from previous victims. When designing the encounter roll a d6.

1–2: NO WEAPON
3–5: CHOOSE A MELEE WEAPON
6: CHOOSE A PISTOL OR RIFLE

Tough – When the dregg is disabled, roll a d6. On a 5 or 6, the dregg heals 1 vitality point, is no longer disabled, and is knocked down.

VITALITY	6
BASE SIZE	SMALL
ENCOUNTER POINTS	4

DREGG PAIN MONGER

SPD	STR	MAT	RAT	DEF	ARM
6	7	6	—	11	15

WILLPOWER	INITIATIVE	DETECT	SNEAK
10	14	4	4

ARM BLADE X2

POW	P+S
3	10

ABILITIES

Light Sensitive, Night Vision, Pain Fueled, Tough: See above.

Retaliatory Strike – When the dregg is hit by a melee attack made by an enemy at any time other than during its own turn, after the attack is resolved the dregg can immediately make one normal melee attack against the enemy that hit it.

VITALITY	12
BASE SIZE	**SMALL**
ENCOUNTER POINTS	**7**

Loot: After a raid, dregg carry off anything of value they can carry with them. They keep large vaults of plundered goods in their lairs.

Lore: Dregg have an intense aversion to light, and they hate everyone. Pain makes them stronger.

DREGG RAID MASTER

SPD	STR	MAT	RAT	DEF	ARM
6	7	7	6	13	14

WILLPOWER	INITIATIVE	DETECT	SNEAK
8	10	6	8

ARM BLADE

POW	P+S
3	10

ABILITIES

Light Sensitive, Night Vision, Pain Fueled, Tough – See above.

Master Scavenger – There is a good chance the dregg has stolen weapons from previous victims. When designing the encounter roll a d6.

1: NO WEAPON
2–4: CHOOSE A MELEE WEAPON
5-6: CHOOSE A PISTOL OR RIFLE

BASE SIZE	**SMALL**
ENCOUNTER POINTS	**7**

FARROW

Farrow are brutish pig-men that live in tribal societies. They are more than capable of using human weapons and often ambush small military forces to arm themselves better.

FARROW BRIGAND

SPD	STR	MAT	RAT	DEF	ARM
5	6	6	5	12	14

WILLPOWER	INITIATIVE	DETECT	SNEAK
7	10	3	3

BANDED CLUB

POW	P+S
4	10

MILITARY RIFLE

RNG	ROF	AOE	POW
10	—	—	11

ABILITIES

Dig In – While he has a spade in hand, this character can make a quick action to dig an improvised foxhole. Until he moves, is placed, goes prone, or is engaged, the character gains cover, does not suffer blast damage, and does not block line of sight. A character cannot use the Dig In ability during a turn in which he ran.

VITALITY	6
BASE SIZE	**SMALL**
ENCOUNTER POINTS	**4**

FARROW SLAUGHTERHOUSER

SPD	STR	MAT	RAT	DEF	ARM
5	7	6	4	12	15

WILLPOWER	INITIATIVE	DETECT	SNEAK
9	10	3	2

POLE CLEAVER

POW	P+S
4	11

Powerful Charge – This character gains +2 to charge attack rolls with this weapon.

The pole cleaver is a Reach weapon.

ABILITIES

Finisher – This character gains an additional die on damage rolls against damaged models.

Tough – The character is incredibly hardy. When this character is disabled, roll a d6. On a 5 or 6, the character heals 1 vitality point, is no longer disabled, and is knocked down.

VITALITY	7
BASE SIZE	**SMALL**
ENCOUNTER POINTS	**6**

FARROW WARLORD

SPD	STR	MAT	RAT	DEF	ARM
5	6	6	5	12	14

WILLPOWER	INITIATIVE	DETECT	SNEAK
7	10	3	3

GREAT SWORD

POW	P+S
6	12

The great sword is a Reach weapon.

BLUNDERBUSS

RNG	ROF	AOE	POW
8	—	—	12

ABILITIES

Dig In – See above.

Feat Points – This character starts each encounter with 1 feat point. He is allocated 1 feat point at the start of each of his turns. He can have up to 1 feat point at a time.

Battle Plan – Hog Wild – Once a turn, this character can use a quick action to use Battle Plan: Hog Wild. When he does so, friendly characters in his command range that are under his command can make one ranged attack during their next activation before their normal movement. After the normal movement, affected characters that make attack actions can only make melee attacks.

COMMAND RANGE	5
BASE SIZE	**SMALL**
ENCOUNTER POINTS	**8**

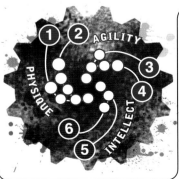

FARROW SHAMAN

SPD	STR	MAT	RAT	DEF	ARM
5	6	4	4	13	14

WILLPOWER	INITIATIVE	DETECT	SNEAK
10	12	5	5

 BATTLE STAFF

POW	P+S
4	10

This is a Reach weapon.

ARCANE	4

Will Weaver

BASE SIZE	SMALL

ENCOUNTER POINTS	7

SPELLS	COST	RNG	AOE	POW	UP	OFF
GUIDED BLADE	1	6	—	—	NO	NO

The targeted friendly character gains +1 on his melee attack rolls and his melee weapons gain Magical Weapon. Guided Blade lasts for one round.

HEX BLAST	3	10	3	13	NO	YES

Upkeep spells and animi on the character directly hit by Hex Blast immediately expire.

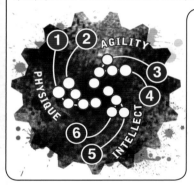

Loot: In addition to the weapons they carry into battle, many farrow have a trinket or two from a previous victory that they use as a luck charm. The more important the farrow, the more elaborate the trophy. Most of these items are simply worth a small value in gold, but some might be runeplates or similar useful items.

Lore: Farrow are pernicious scavengers and dislike allowing anything to go to waste. They can be distracted from patrols if presented with a quantity of raw or cooked meat (including fresh corpses) or broken machinery they can salvage for metal.

HUMAN

The Iron Kingdoms abound with unscrupulous thugs and criminals that a major villain can recruit for his organization, and most towns employ a few watchmen to keep the peace.

HUMAN THIEF

SPD	STR	MAT	RAT	DEF	ARM
7	3	4	4	14	10

WILLPOWER	INITIATIVE	DETECT	SNEAK
8	15	6	7

 DAGGER

POW	P+S
1	4

ABILITIES

Skills (stat already included): Climbing – 7, Pickpocket – 7, Lock Picking – 6, Escape Artist – 8

Dodger – When this character is missed by an enemy attack, he can immediately advance up to 2˝ after the attack is resolved unless he was missed while advancing. He cannot be targeted by free strikes during this movement.

Get Away – When the character is missed by an enemy attack at any time other than while advancing, instead of advancing up to 2˝, the character can immediately make a full advance.

VITALITY	5

BASE SIZE	SMALL

ENCOUNTER POINTS	1

HUMAN THUG

SPD	STR	MAT	RAT	DEF	ARM
6	5	5	5	12	12

WILLPOWER	INITIATIVE	DETECT	SNEAK
9	12	4	5

SWORD

POW	P+S
3	8

PISTOL

RNG	ROF	AOE	POW
8	—	—	10

ABILITIES

Skills (stat already included): Intimidation – 5

Anatomical Precision – When this character hits a living target with a melee attack but the damage roll fails to exceed the target's ARM, the target suffers d3 damage points instead of the damage rolled.

VITALITY	7
BASE SIZE	SMALL
ENCOUNTER POINTS	3

HUMAN WATCHMAN

SPD	STR	MAT	RAT	DEF	ARM
5	5	6	5	12	14

WILLPOWER	INITIATIVE	DETECT	SNEAK
9	12	6	3

HALBERD

POW	P+S
5	10

This is a Reach weapon.

A character fighting two-handed with a halberd gains +2 to his charge attack damage rolls with this weapon.

PISTOL

RNG	ROF	AOE	POW
8	—	—	10

ABILITIES

Set Defense – While armed with a with a weapon with reach, a character in this character's front arc suffers –2 on charge, slam power attack, and impact attack rolls against him.

Sound the Alarm – Once an encounter, as a full action, a watchman can sound the alarm. Add one new watchman to the encounter. Watchmen added to the encounter this way cannot sound the alarm.

VITALITY	7
BASE SIZE	SMALL
ENCOUNTER POINTS	5

HUMAN ARCANIST

SPD	STR	MAT	RAT	DEF	ARM
6	3	4	4	13	11

WILLPOWER	INITIATIVE	DETECT	SNEAK
10	14	5	4

STAFF

POW	P+S
3	6

This is a Reach weapon.

ARCANE	4

Will Weaver

VITALITY	5
BASE SIZE	SMALL
ENCOUNTER POINTS	2

SPELLS

	COST	RNG	AOE	POW	UP	OFF
ARCANE BOLT	2	12	—	11	NO	NO

Magical bolts of energy streak toward the target.

| **AURA OF PROTECTION** | 2 | SELF | CTRL | — | YES | NO |

While in the spellcaster's control area, friendly characters gain +2 ARM.

HUMAN WATCHMAN

SPD	STR	MAT	RAT	DEF	ARM
6	4	5	5	14	12

WILLPOWER	INITIATIVE	DETECT	SNEAK
10	14	4	5

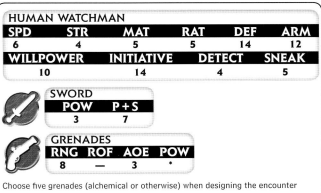

SWORD

POW	P+S
3	7

GRENADES

RNG	ROF	AOE	POW
8	—	3	•

Choose five grenades (alchemical or otherwise) when designing the encounter

ABILITIES

Grenadier – The character gains an additional quick action each turn that can be used only to pull the pin on a grenade.

Fire in the Hole – This character can make a grenade attack at the start of the Action Phase of his turn before moving or making his normal attacks. A character making a Fire in the Hole! attack must use his movement that turn to run or make a full advance.

Grenadier's Bandolier – A character with a grenadier's bandolier can draw grenades without spending a quick action.

Alchemist's Leather – A character wearing this armor gains an additional +3 ARM against blast, cold, corrosion, and fire damage.

VITALITY	6
BASE SIZE	SMALL
ENCOUNTER POINTS	5

Loot: Human criminals and thugs carry very little in the way of valuable objects. They have weapons, armor, and possibly small amounts of gold. If an encounter takes place in a gang's hideout, loot is more readily available.

Lore: Information available for Lore rolls against human antagonists depends on how the Game Master is using them. Recognizable gang affiliation indications or other similar details could be discernable by the players.

THRALL

Thralls are undead slaves created by inscribing necromantic thrall runes on a corpse. Risen are fairly simple to create in great numbers. More capable thrall warriors are more powerful but take more effort to create. They act the shock troopers for their necromantic creators.

RISEN THRALL

SPD	STR	MAT	RAT	DEF	ARM
5	5	4	-	9	11
WILLPOWER	**INITIATIVE**		**DETECT**		**SNEAK**
1	7		1		5

CLAWS		
	POW	**P + S**
	2	7

ABILITIES

Undead –This character is not a living character and never flees.

Gang – When making a melee attack that targets an enemy in melee range of another friendly character, this character gains +1 to melee attack and melee damage rolls. When making a melee attack that targets an enemy in melee range of another friendly character who also has this ability, these bonuses increase to +2.

Tough – The character is incredibly hardy. When this character is disabled, roll a d6. On a 5 or 6, the character heals 1 vitality point, is no longer disabled, and is knocked down.

VITALITY	5
BASE SIZE	SMALL
ENCOUNTER POINTS	2

Loot: The necromancer who created the thrall has already stripped it of any valuables possessed in life.

Lore: The existence of thralls in an area usually indicates there is a necromancer nearby.

THRALL WARRIOR

SPD	STR	MAT	RAT	DEF	ARM
5	6	6	-	11	15
WILLPOWER	**INITIATIVE**		**DETECT**		**SNEAK**
1	10		3		3

GREAT SWORD		
	POW	**P + S**
	6	12

This is a Reach weapon.

ABILITIES

Undead and **Tough** – See above.

VITALITY	10
BASE SIZE	SMALL
ENCOUNTER POINTS	5

THRULLG

Thrullg most commonly dwell in the sewers of urban areas, but they can be found in any dark, forbidding places in western Immoren. They feed upon the magical energies of any item or individual they can wrap their tentacles around.

THRALL WARRIOR

SPD	STR	MAT	RAT	DEF	ARM
6	9	7	-	13	16

WILLPOWER	INITIATIVE	DETECT	SNEAK
10	14	8	6

TENTACLES

POW	P+S
4	13

This is a Reach weapon.

CLAWS X2

POW	P+S
3	12

ABILITIES

Skills (stats already included): Climbing – 6

Fearless (p. XXX)

Arcane Consumption – When an enemy character casts a spell or uses an animus while in this model's command range, after the spell is cast the enemy character suffers d3 damage points and this character regains d3 vitality.

Arcane Interference – When this character hits another character with an attack, upkeep spells and animi on the character hit expire and the character hit loses the focus points on it. When this character hits a steamjack with an attack, that steamjack suffers Disruption. (A steamjack suffering Disruption loses its focus points and cannot be allocated focus or channel spells for one round.)

Blackout Pulse – This character can use a quick action to do a Blackout Pulse. Mechanika devices in the possession of enemy characters in this character's command range area immediately deactivate. If an enemy enters this character's command range, mechanika devices in his possession immediately deactivate. While in this character's command range, enemy characters cannot activate mechanika devices. Blackout Pulse has no effect on steamjacks or mechanika armor. Blackout Pulse lasts for one round.

COMMAND RANGE	7
BASE SIZE	MEDIUM
ENCOUNTER POINTS	11

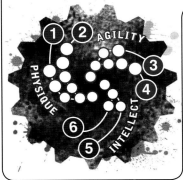

Loot: Thrullg lairs are filled with scrap metal and partially devoured bits of mechanika items that have had their accumulators drained. Virtually all of these items are damaged beyond repair.

Lore: Thrullg sensitivity to magic seems rooted in their mouth tentacles, which if removed are valuable to alchemists and bone grinders. Certain fluids extracted from these tentacles can inhibit magic or mechanika if processed properly.

STEAMJACK

STEAMJACK NAME

CHASSIS TYPE

HEIGHT _____ **WEIGHT** _____

MAX FUEL LOAD

FUEL CONSUMPTION

STATS

PHY	STR	AGI
PRW	POI	INT
	SPD	PER

RANGED WEAPONS

NAME _____ **LOC** [ ]
NOTES _____

RNG	RAT	POW
AMMO _____

NAME _____ **LOC** [ ]
NOTES _____

RNG	RAT	POW
AMMO _____

MELEE WEAPONS

NAME _____ **LOC** [ ]
NOTES _____

MAT	P + S

NAME _____ **LOC** [ ]
NOTES _____

MAT	P + S

ADDITIONAL WEAPON

NAME _____

NOTES _____

DEF

BASE DEF [ ] + MODIFIERS [ ] = TOTAL DEF [ ]

ARM

BASE ARM [ ] + MODIFIERS [ ] = TOTAL ARM [ ]

CATASTROPHIC DAMAGE

AREA DAMAGED — **DESCRIPTION/NOTES**

GEAR & UPGRADES

NAME — **DESCRIPTION/NOTES**

DAMAGE GRID

(grid rows numbered 1–6, columns 1 2 3 4 5 6)

Crippled Arc Node:
Cannot be used to channel spells.

Crippled Cortex:
Lose all focus points and cannot be allocated focus.
Cannot spend focus points for any reason.

Crippled Movement:
DEF 7. Cannot run or charge.

Crippled Arm or Head:
Roll one fewer die on attack and damage rolls with weapons in the crippled location. Cannot make power attacks with weapons in crippled location.

CORTEX

IMPRINT:

NOTES:

FIGHTING BONUS:

LANGUAGE:

GEAR & UPGRADES

NAME — **DESCRIPTION/NOTES**

WEAPON LOCK
Requirement: Open Fist
Roll: MAT
Effect: Target cannot attack with locked location
Pg Ref: 312

HEAD-BUTT
Requirement: Attack equal or smaller size base
Roll: MAT
Effect: STR damage roll + Knockdown
Pg Ref: 313

PUSH
Requirement: None
Roll: Contested Roll STR + d6
Effect: Target pushed 1" directly away
Pg Ref: 313

SLAM
Requirement: 3" + movement and charge capable
Roll: MAT (−2 vs larger base)
Effect: STR damage roll + Slammed
Pg Ref: 313

THROW
Requirement: Open Fist
Roll: MAT then contested STR + d6
Effect: STR damage roll + target thrown 1/2 STR inches
Pg Ref: 313

DOUBLE HANDED THROW
Requirement: Two Open Fists
Roll: MAT then contested: Attacker STR + 2d6, Defender STR + d6
Effect: As throw but STR inches. Targeted throw possible
Pg Ref: 314

TRAMPLE
Requirement: Heavy steamjack and charge capable
Movement: Straight line advance through small based models
Roll: MAT
Effect: Target cannot attack with locked location
Pg Ref: 314

KNOCKOUT STRIKE
Requirement: Melee attack against living target
Roll: MAT −1
Effect: POW + STR Damage Roll, Target must pass Willpower test versus STR + 7 or be knocked out.
Pg. Ref: 210

GRAPPLE
Requirement: Open Fist
Roll: MAT
Effect: Enter Grapple with Target
Pg. Ref: 210

IRON KINGDOMS ROLEPLAYING GAME CHARACTER SHEET

CHARACTER NAME

ARCHETYPE   **RACE**   **CAREERS**

SEX   **DEFINING CHARACTERISTIC(S)**

FAITH   **PLAYER NAME**

WEIGHT   **LEVEL**

HEIGHT   **TOTAL XP EARNED**

CHARACTER PORTRAIT

STATS

PHY
- MAX
- SPD   MAX
- STR   MAX

AGI
- MAX
- PRW   MAX
- POI   MAX

INT
- MAX
- ARC   MAX
- PER   MAX

WILLPOWER (PHY + INT)

RANGED WEAPONS

NAME   RNG   RAT   POW
NOTES

NAME   RNG   RAT   POW
NOTES

MELEE WEAPONS

NAME   AMMO   MAT   P+S
NOTES

NAME   AMMO   MAT   P+S
NOTES

ADDITIONAL WEAPON

NAME
NOTES

DEF

SPD + AGL + PER
STAT   STAT   STAT

+ RACIAL MODIFIER + EQUIPMENT MODIFIERS = TOTAL DEF

ARM

PHY STAT

+ SHIELD MODIFIER + ARMOR MODIFIERS + OTHER MODIFIERS = TOTAL ARM

INITIATIVE

SPD + PRW + PER
STAT   STAT   STAT

+ EQUIPMENT MODIFIERS + ADDITIONAL MODIFIERS = TOTAL INITIATIVE

COMMAND RANGE

INT STAT

+ COMMAND SKILL + ABILITY MODIFIERS = TOTAL CMD RANGE

SKILLS

	PARENT STAT SET VALUE	SKILL LEVEL	TOTAL
HAND WEAPON (PRW)		+	=
GREAT WEAPON (PRW)		+	=
PISTOL (POI)		+	=
RIFLE (POI)		+	=
DETECTION (PER)		+	=
SNEAK (AGL)		+	=
COMMAND (SOCIAL)		+	=

DAMAGE CAPACITY

PHYSIQUE
AGILITY
INTELLECT

1 2 3 4 5 6

Crippled Physique: −2 STR.
Crippled Agility: −2 to attack rolls.
Crippled Intellect: −2 DEF and cannot upkeep spells.

POWER FIELD

BENEFITS & ABILITIES

NAME   **DESCRIPTION/NOTES**   **PAGE#**

FEAT POINTS

CURRENT FEAT POINTS

Feat Points can be earned by:
- Critical success on a skill roll
- Given by the GM

Feat Points can be spent to:
- Re-roll a failed roll
- Remove a continuous effect
- Perform a relentless charge
- Destroy an enemy
- Perform a Run & Gun
- Perform a Two-Fister
- Perform a Heroic Dodge
- Boost a non-combat skill roll
- Make a quick action
- Shake
- Sprint
- Parry
- Walk it Off

IRON KINGDOMS ™

NOTES

PERMANENT INJURIES

SPOKEN LANGUAGES

RELIGIOUS BELIEFS

GOLD

MECHANIKA

HOUSING	RUNEPLATE	CAPACITOR	NOTES

RUNE PLATE	BENEFIT	CAPACITORS	CHARGES

SPELLS

ARCANE TRADITION

NAME	COST	RNG	AOE	POW	UP	OFF

GEAR

NAME	BENEFIT

WORN ARMOR

NAME	DESCRIPTION/NOTES	SPD	DEF	ARM

CONNECTIONS

NAME	DESCRIPTION/NOTES	PAGE #

IRON KINGDOMS™

IRON KINGDOMS

™

IRON KINGDOMS GAME MASTER ENCOUNTER SHEET

CAMPAIGN NAME _____

ENCOUNTER _____

INITIATIVE ORDER

NOTES

NAME: _____
NAME: _____
NAME: _____
NAME: _____
NAME: _____
NAME: _____
NAME: _____
NAME: _____
NAME: _____
NAME: _____
NAME: _____
NAME: _____
NAME: _____

NUMBER NUMBER NUMBER NUMBER NUMBER NUMBER NUMBER NUMBER NUMBER NUMBER NUMBER NUMBER

CREATURES

1.) NAME: _____
NOTES:
VITALITY | STATUS EFFECT

2.) NAME: _____
NOTES:
VITALITY | STATUS EFFECT

3.) NAME: _____
NOTES:
VITALITY | STATUS EFFECT

4.) NAME: _____
NOTES:
VITALITY | STATUS EFFECT

5.) NAME: _____
NOTES:
VITALITY | STATUS EFFECT

6.) NAME: _____
NOTES:
VITALITY | STATUS EFFECT

7.) NAME: _____
NOTES:
VITALITY | STATUS EFFECT

8.) NAME: _____
NOTES:
VITALITY | STATUS EFFECT

9.) NAME: _____
NOTES:
VITALITY | STATUS EFFECT

10.) NAME: _____
NOTES:
VITALITY | STATUS EFFECT

11.) NAME: _____
NOTES:
VITALITY | STATUS EFFECT

12.) NAME: _____
NOTES:
VITALITY | STATUS EFFECT

LIFE SPIRALS

NAME: _____
EFFECT: _____

PHYSIQUE · AGILITY · INTELLECT
1 2 3 4 5 6

NAME: _____
EFFECT: _____

NAME: _____
EFFECT: _____

NAME: _____
EFFECT: _____

NAME: _____
EFFECT: _____

NAME: _____
EFFECT: _____

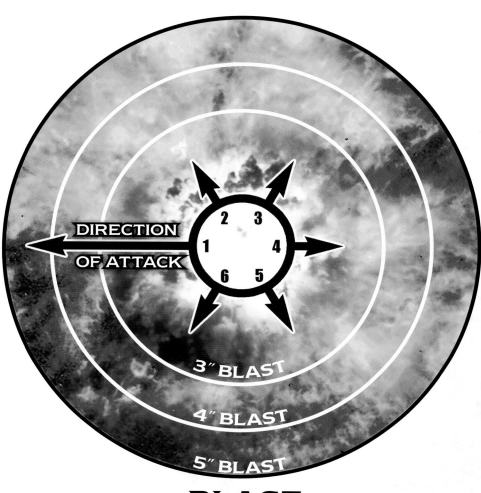

DIRECTION OF ATTACK

3" BLAST

4" BLAST

5" BLAST

BLAST

WALL

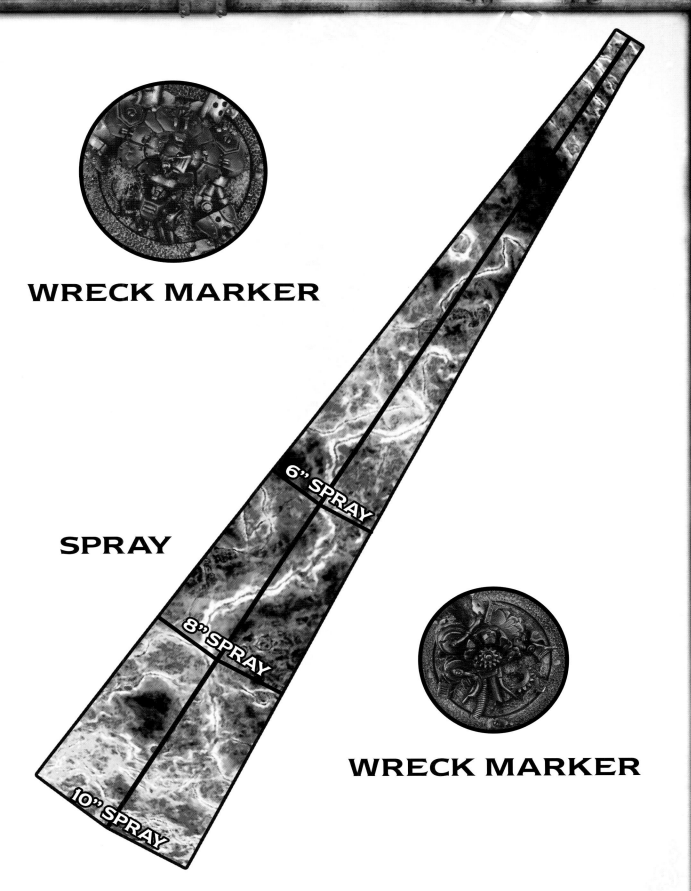

WRECK MARKER

SPRAY

6" SPRAY

8" SPRAY

10" SPRAY

WRECK MARKER

INDEX

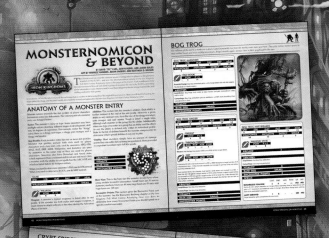
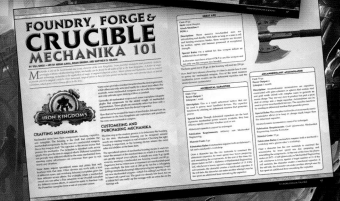